Introduction to Probability

GW00585855

Introduction to Probability

J. Laurie Snell
Dartmouth College

McGraw-Hill Book Company

New York • St. Louis • San Francisco • Auckland •
Bogotá • Hamburg • London •
Madrid • Mexico • Montreal • New Delhi •
Panama • Paris • São Paulo • Singapore • Sydney •
Tokyo • Toronto

Preface

Probability theory began in seventeenth century France when the two great French mathematicians, Blaise Pascal and Pierre de Fermat, corresponded over two problems from games of chance. Problems like those Pascal and Fermat solved continued to influence such early researchers as Huygens, Bernoulli, and DeMoivre in establishing a mathematical theory of probability. Today, probability theory is a well established branch of mathematics that finds applications in every area of scholarly activity from music to physics, and in daily experience from weather prediction to predicting the risks of new medical treatments.

This text is designed for an introductory probability course taken by sophomore or junior level students in mathematics, the physical and social sciences, engineering, and computer science. It presents a thorough treatment of probability ideas and techniques necessary for a firm understanding of the subject. The text can be used in a variety of course lengths, levels, and areas of emphasis.

For use in a standard one-term course, students should have taken as a prerequisite two terms of calculus, including an introduction to multiple integrals. If time permits, as in a two-term course, a brief introduction to matrix theory is necessary for coverage of the chapter on Markov chains.

Very little computing background is assumed or necessary in order to obtain full benefits from the use of the computing material and examples in the text. Students need only a familiarity with one of the standard computing languages such as BASIC or Pascal, and indeed, they enjoy learning some programming in the context of interesting probability simulations and computation.

The text can also be used in a discrete probability course. The material has been organized in such a way that the discrete and continuous probability discussions are presented in a separate, but parallel, manner. This organization dispels an overly rigorous or formal view of probability and offers some strong pedagogical value in that the discrete discussions can sometimes serve to motivate the more abstract continuous probability discussions. For use in a discrete probability course, students should have taken one term of calculus as a prerequisite.

TOPIC COVERAGE AND ORGANIZATION

The following is a brief outline of the chapters in the book.

Chapter 1 gives the basic definitions of probabilities as they are applied to experiments with a finite or denumerable number of outcomes. Typical problems that we study later are introduced by computer simulations. The computer experiments reinforce the intuitive frequency concept of probability, which in turn guides us in our definitions.

Chapter 2 deals with continuous probabilities. Here simulations are first introduced to motivate the concept of a density function and to show how continuous experiments can be thought of as limits of discrete experiments. Computer graphics are used to compare empirical densities with theoretical densities.

Chapter 3 deals with the combinatorial theory of permutations and combinations essential to the computation of probabilities. Computer routines for computing permutations and combinations are introduced. A typical computer exercise is to write a program to print out Pascal's triangle. The student can then print out the results mod 2 to see the kind of self-similar patterns that occur in cellular automata.

Chapter 4 introduces the concept of conditional probability and discusses its application to such fields as medical diagnosis. We discuss the computation of Bayesian probabilities both by tree measures and by the use of the computer. The famous two-armed slot machine problem is used to illustrate the variety of strategies that can sensibly be used in experiments for deciding between two different medical treatments.

Chapter 5 introduces the concept of a random variable and the concept of an independent trials process. We spend more than the usual time on this topic, since it is central to probability and mysterious to the student. In the section on continuous random variables, standard densities, such as the normal and exponential densities, are studied.

Chapter 6 introduces the important concepts of expected value and variance and develops their properties. Here the computer is used to illustrate that insurance companies and gambling casinos can be assured of quite predictable average winnings. The futility of gambling systems is easily demonstrated by computer simulations.

Chapter 7 deals with sums of independent random variables. Here the use of the computer makes it possible to fully understand and apply the concept of convolution to compute the density of the sum of independent random variables. Computer graphics of the resulting densities illustrate the smoothing properties of convolution, leading the way to the Central Limit Theorem.

Chapter 8 discusses Bernoulli's famous Law of Large Numbers and shows how it justifies the frequency concept of probability. Again, the computer simulation provides a way to understand what this fundamental theorem tells us, and indeed what it does not tell us, about repeated experiments.

Chapter 9 presents the Central Limit Theorem of DeMoivre and Laplace. Use of computer graphics strikingly illustrates this remarkable theorem. Here, indeed, a picture is worth a thousand words. After working a few problems by hand, the student is encouraged to let the computer do the transformations necessary to apply the Central Limit Theorem.

Chapter 10 discusses the concept of generating functions. Discrete generating functions are used to study branching processes and continuous generating functions are used to show how to prove the Central Limit Theorem.

Chapter 11 deals with finite Markov chains. Examples in genetics, physics, and the social sciences are used to illustrate the results of this elegant probability topic. Basic results are obtained from elementary matrix calculations. Computer programs lend themselves to calculation of basic descriptive quantities.

FEATURES

Level of rigor and emphasis: Probability is a wonderfully intuitive and applicable field of mathematics. We have tried not to spoil its beauty by presenting too much formal mathematics. Rather, we have tried to develop the key ideas in a somewhat leisurely style, to provide a variety of interesting applications to probability, and to show some of the nonintuitive examples that make probability such a lively subject.

Exercises: There are over 600 exercises in the text providing plenty of opportunity for practicing skills and developing a sound understanding of the ideas. In the exercise sets are routine exercises to be done with and without the use of a computer and more theoretical exercises to improve the understanding of basic concepts. More difficult exercises are indicated by an asterisk.

Historical remarks: Introductory probability is a subject in which the fundamental ideas are still closely tied to those of the founders of the subject. For this reason, there are numerous historical comments in the text, especially as they deal with the development of discrete probability.

Pedagogical use of computer programs: Probability theory makes predictions about experiments whose outcomes depend upon chance. Consequently, it lends itself beautifully to the use of computers as a mathematical tool to simulate and analyze chance experiments.

In the text the computer is utilized in several ways. First, it provides a laboratory where chance experiments can be simulated and the students can get a feeling for the variety of such experiments. This use of the computer in probability has been already beautifully illustrated by William Feller in the second edition of his famous text *Introduction to Probability Theory and Its Applications* (New York: Wiley, 1950). In the preface, Feller wrote about his treatment of fluctuation in coin tossing: "The results are so amazing and so at variance with common intuition that even sophisticated colleagues doubted that coins actually misbehave as theory predicts. The record of a simulated experiment is therefore included."

In addition to providing a laboratory for the student, the computer is a powerful aid in understanding basic results of probability theory. For example, the graphical illustration of the approximation of the standardized binomial densities to the normal curve is a more convincing demonstration of the Central Limit Theorem than many of the formal proofs of this fundamental result.

Finally, the computer allows the student to solve problems that do not lend themselves to closed-form formulas such as waiting times in queues. Indeed, the introduction of the computer changes the way in which we look at many problems in probability. For example, being able to calculate exact binomial probabilities for experiments up to 1000 trials changes the way we view the normal and Poisson approximations.

Computer programs: There are a number of computer programs in the text where they illustrate the algorithms or the methods of computation for important problems. A modern structured language is used for these programs (True BASIC™ developed by John Kemeny and Thomas Kurtz, the original inventors of BASIC). This language, besides being our own language of choice, can also serve effectively as a pseudolanguage for those preferring some other structure language such as Pascal or C. A brief discussion about the programs appears in Appendix D. (The programs are available to adopters on a microcomputer disk in either IBM or Macintosh versions.)

ACKNOWLEDGMENTS

Anyone writing a probability text today owes a great debt to William Feller, who taught us all how to make probability come alive as a subject matter. If you find an example, an application, or an exercise that you really like, it probably had its origin in Feller's classic text, *An Introduction to Probability Theory and Applications.*

Our book had its start with a course given jointly at Dartmouth College with Professor John Kemeny. I am indebted to Professor Kemeny for convincing me that it is both useful and fun to use the computer in the study of probability. He has continuously and generously shared his ideas on probability and computing with me. No less impressive has been the help of John Finn in making the computing an integral part of the text and in writing the programs so that they not only can be easily used, but they also can be understood and modified by the student to explore further problems. Some of the programs in the text were developed through collaborative efforts with John Kemeny and Thomas Kurtz on a Sloan Foundation project and with John Finn on a Keck Foundation project. I am grateful to both foundations for their support.

I am indebted to many other colleagues, students, and friends for valuable comments and suggestions. A few whose names stand out are: Eric and Jim Baumgartner, Tom Bickel, Bob Beck, Ed Brown, Christine Burnley, Richard Crowell, David Griffeath, John Lamperti, Beverly Nickerson, Reese Prosser, Cathy Smith, and Chris Thron.

The following individuals were kind enough to review various drafts of the manuscript. Their encouragement, criticisms, and suggestions were very helpful.

Ron Barnes	*University of Houston, Downtown College*
Thomas Fischer	*Texas A & M University*
Richard Groeneveld	*Iowa State University*
James Kuelbs	*University of Wisconsin, Madison*
Greg Lawler	*Duke University*
Sidney Resnick	*Colorado State University*
Malcom Sherman	*SUNY Albany*
Olaf Stackelberg	*Kent State University*
Murad Taqqu	*Boston University*
Abraham Wender	*University of North Carolina*

In addition, I would especially like to thank James Kuelbs, Sidney Resnick, and their students for using the manuscript in their courses and sharing their experience and invaluable suggestions with me.

The versatility of Dartmouth's mathematical word processor PREPPY, written by Professor James Baumgartner, has made it much easier to make revisions, but has made the job of typist extraordinaire Marie Slack correspondingly more challenging. Her high standards and willingness always to try the next more difficult task has made it all possible.

Finally, I must thank all the people at Random House who helped during the development and production of this project. First, among these was my editor Wayne Yuhasz, whose continued encouragement and commitment was very helpful during the development of the manuscript. The entire production team provided efficient and professional support: Margaret Pinette, project manager; Michael Weinstein, production manager, and Kate Bradford of Editing, Design, and Production, Inc.

Contents

Introduction to Probability

Introduction

You are asked what it means to say: If a fair coin is tossed, heads will turn up with probability $1/2$. You might answer: There are two possible outcomes, and so the chances are fifty-fifty that heads will turn up; the probability for heads is $1/2$. But suppose that you are asked for the probability that you will pass this course. There are again only two possible outcomes: pass or fail. Here you might not be as happy assigning probability $1/2$ for passing. You defend your coin answer by saying that there is a symmetry to the coin that is not present in the problem of passing or failing.

A second popular answer to the coin tossing question is: If we toss the coin many times, about half the time heads will turn up. But how many times do we have to toss the coin, and what do we mean by *about half?* Pressed further, you might say that, if you continue to toss the coin, the proportion of heads will get closer and closer to $1/2$. But this can't be quite right because the coin *could* come up heads every time. You say, yes, but this is very unlikely to happen. You are now using the term *unlikely* to explain what you mean by probability, and this seems to be going in circles. This second explanation, however, has the advantage that it is not tied to the idea of symmetry. A doctor could say that a drug will be effective with probability .8 and mean that, if the drug is given to a large number of patients with similar symptoms, it will most likely be effective about 80 percent of the time.

Still a third answer to our coin question is that you are willing to bet even money that heads will turn up when a coin is tossed. This interpretation is also not tied to symmetry. For example, if you are willing to give two-to-one odds that Dartmouth will beat Harvard next year, you are saying that Dartmouth is twice as likely to win as Harvard and are assigning a probability $^2/_3$ that Dartmouth will win and $^1/_3$ that Harvard will win. But suppose that your friend is willing to give three-to-one odds that Dartmouth will win. Does this change the probability to $^3/_4$?

As these simple examples show, we all assign probabilities, and we have some vague ideas about what we mean, but these ideas can be quite different and quite imprecise. The history of probability might be described as the attempt to make these ideas more precise and to develop methods for calculating new probabilities from known probabilities.

Probability had its origins in the study of gambling, and probability and gambling remain close friends today. Board games involving chance were highly developed in Egypt by 3500 B.C. and used a crude form of four dice made from bones. But it was not until the sixteenth century that the first attempts were made to develop a theory of probability. One of the first to attempt to write down a method to compute probabilities as well as a description of some of the basic probability laws was Gerolamo Cardano. Cardano was truly a renaissance man; he wrote books on mathematics, medicine, theology, cosmology and, in fact, on almost every branch of knowledge studied during his time. You can read about Cardano's colorful life and his contributions to probability in Oystein Ore's *Cardano: The Gambling Scholar* (1953).[1] This book contains a translation of Cardano's book *The Book on Games of Chance*. In this book, Cardano not only explains basic probability laws but analyzes games of chance and tells you who to gamble with and how to detect cheaters. He himself was an ardent gambler. Cardano correctly analyzes dice problems, showing that he understood the calculation of probabilities for the symmetric or *equally likely* case. In this case he defines the probability of an event to be the ratio of the number of outcomes that made the event occur to the total number of outcomes. For example, the probability of an even number occurring when a die is rolled is $^3/_6$, since there are six possible outcomes for the die and three are even numbers. Using this principle, he calculates, for example, the probability that, when three dice are thrown, a specific total will turn up. Even in this simple problem, care must be taken in assigning probabilities. A half-century later Galileo was apparently asked by gamblers to explain the fact that, when three dice are rolled, a total of 10 seemed to turn up more often than a total of 9, despite the fact that there are six combinations which add to 9: 621, 531, 522, 441, 432, 333, and six which add to 10: 631, 622, 541, 532, 442, 433. Galileo observed, as had Cardano, that it is only reasonable to assign equal probabilities to the outcomes when the order of the outcomes is also taken into account. When this is done there are $6 \cdot 6 \cdot 6 = 216$ possible outcomes of which 25 result in a total of 9, and 27 result in a total of 10, making the probabilities 25/216 and 27/216, respectively. Some historians have wondered if gamblers could really have detected such a small difference in probabilities and raised this problem with Galileo—or did Galileo just want to show that he could do it?

[1]Oystein Ore, *Cardano. The Gambling Scholar*, (Princeton N.J.: Princeton University Press, 1953).

Another important probability law that Cardano discovered was the product law for independent outcomes. If the probability that a head turns up when a coin is tossed is $^1/_2$, and the probability that a six turns up when a die is rolled is $^1/_6$, then the probability that both of these outcomes occur is the product $(^1/_2) \cdot (^1/_6) = ^1/_{12}$.

Cardano's work was a remarkable first attempt at writing down the laws of probability, but it was not the spark that started a systematic study of the subject. This came from a famous series of letters between Pascal and Fermat. This correspondence was initiated by Pascal to consult Fermat about problems he had been given by Chevalier de Méré, a well-known writer, a prominent figure at the court of Louis XIV, and an ardent gambler.

The first problem de Méré posed was a dice problem. The story goes that he had been betting that at least one six would turn up in four rolls of a die and winning too often, so he then bet that a pair of sixes would turn up in 24 rolls of a pair of dice. The probability of a six with one die is $^1/_6$ and, by the product law for independent experiments, the probability of two sixes when a pair of dice are thrown is $(^1/_6) \cdot (^1/_6) = ^1/_{36}$. Ore[2] claims that a gambling rule of the time suggested that, since four repetitions was favorable for the occurrence of an event with probability $^1/_6$, for an event six times as unlikely, $6 \cdot 4 = 24$ repetitions would be sufficient for a favorable bet. Pascal showed, by exact calculation, that 25 rolls are required for a favorable bet for a pair of sixes.

The second problem was a much harder one: it was an old problem and concerned the determination of a fair division of the stakes in a tournament when the series, for some reason, is interrupted before it is completed. The problem had been a standard problem in mathematical texts; it appeared in Fra Luca Paccioli's book, *Summa de Arithmetica, Geometria, Proportioni et Proportionalità*, printed in Venice in 1494,[3] in the form:

> A team plays ball such that a total of 60 points are required to win the game, and each inning counts 10 points. The stakes are 10 ducats. By some incident they cannot finish the game and one side has 50 points and the other 20. One wants to know what share of the prize money belongs to each side. In this case I have found that opinions differ from one to another but all seem to me insufficient in their arguments, but I shall state the truth and give the correct way.

Reasonable solutions, such as: divide the stakes according to the ratio of games won by each player, had been proposed, but no correct solution had been found at the time of the Pascal-Fermat correspondence. The letters deal mainly with the attempts of Pascal and Fermat to solve this problem. Blaise Pascal (1623–1662) was a child prodigy, having published, at age sixteen, his treatise on conic sections and, at eighteen, having invented a calculating machine. At the time of the letters, his demonstration of the weight of the atmosphere had already established his position at the forefront of contemporary

[2]Oystein Ore, "Pascal and the Invention of Probability Theory," *American Mathematics Monthly*, vol. 67 (1960), pp. 409–419.

[3]Ibid., p. 414.

physicists. Pierre de Fermat (1601–1665) was a learned jurist in Toulouse. In his spare time he studied mathematics and, as a mathematician, he has been called by some the prince of amateurs and one of the greatest pure mathematicians of all times.

The letters, translated by Maxine Merrington, appear in Florence David's fascinating historical account of probability, *Games, Gods and Gambling*.[4] In a letter dated Wednesday, 29th July, 1654, Pascal writes to Fermat:

Sir,

1. Like you, I am equally impatient, and although I am again ill in bed, I cannot help telling you that yesterday evening I received from M. de Carcavi your letter on the problem of points, which I admire more than I can possibly say. I have not the leisure to write at length, but, in a word, you have solved the two problems of points, one with dice and the other with sets of games with perfect justness; I am entirely satisfied with it for I do not doubt that I was in the wrong, seeing the admirable agreement in which I find myself with you now. . . .

2. Your method is very sound and is the one which first came to my mind in this research; but because the labour of the combination is excessive, I have found a short cut and indeed another method which is much quicker and neater, which I would like to tell you here in a few words: for henceforth I would like to open my heart to you, if I may, as I am so overjoyed with our agreement. I see that truth is the same in Toulouse as in Paris.

Here, more or less, is what I do to show the fair value of each game, when two opponents play, for example, in three games and each person has staked 32 pistoles.

Let us say that the first man had won twice and the other once; now they play another game, in which the conditions are that, if the first wins, he takes all the stakes; that is 64 pistoles; if the other wins it, then they have each won two games, and therefore, if they wish to stop playing, they must each take back their own stake, that is, 32 pistoles each.

Then consider, Sir, if the first man wins, he gets 64 pistoles; if he loses he gets 32. Thus if they do not wish to risk this last game but wish to separate without playing it, the first man must say: "I am certain to get 32 pistoles, even if I lose I still get them; but as for the other 32, perhaps I will get them, perhaps you will get them, the chances are equal. Let us then divide these 32 pistols in half and give one half to me as well as my 32 which are mine for sure." He will then have 48 pistoles and the other 16. . . .
(p. 230 ff.)

Pascal's argument produces the table illustrated in Figure 1 for the amount due player A at any quitting point.

Each entry in the table is the average of the numbers just above and to the right of the number. This fact, together with the known values when the tournament is completed, determine all the values in this table. If player A wins the first game, then he needs two games to win and B needs three games to win; and so, if the tournament is called off, A should receive 44 pistoles.

[4]F. N. David, *Games, Gods and Gambling* (London: G. Griffin, 1962). Reprinted with permission.

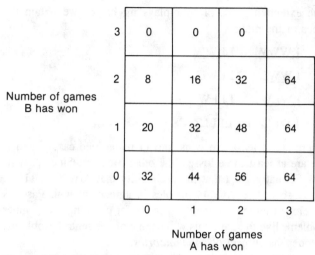

Figure 1 Payoff to A if the series is stopped.

The letter in which Fermat presented his solution has been lost; but fortunately, Pascal describes Fermat's method in a letter dated Monday, 24th August, 1654. From Pascal's letter[5]:

> This is your procedure when there are *two* players: If two players, playing several games, find themselves in that position when the first man needs *two* games and second needs *three,* then to find the fair division of stakes, you say that one must know in how many games the play will be absolutely decided.
>
> It is easy to calculate that this will be in *four* games, from which you conclude that it is necessary to see in how many ways four games can be arranged between two players, and one must see how many combinations would make the first win and how many the second and to share out the stakes in this proportion. I would have found it difficult to understand this if I had not known it myself already; in fact you had explained it with this idea in mind.

Fermat realized that the number of ways that the game might be finished may not be equally likely. For example, if A needs two more games and B needs three to win, two possible ways that the tournament might go for A to win are WLW and LWLW. These two sequences do not have the same chance of occurring. To avoid this difficulty, Fermat extended the play, adding fictitious plays, so that all the ways that the games might go have the same length, namely four. He was shrewd enough to realize that this extension would not change the winner and that he now could simply count the number of sequences favorable to each player since he had made them all equally likely. If we

[5]Ibid, p. 239ff.

list all possible ways that the extended game of four plays might go, we obtain the following 16 possible outcomes of the play:

<u>WWWW</u>	<u>WLWW</u>	<u>LWWW</u>	<u>LLWW</u>
<u>WWWL</u>	<u>WLWL</u>	<u>LWWL</u>	LLWL
<u>WWLW</u>	<u>WLLW</u>	<u>LWLW</u>	LLLW
<u>WWLL</u>	WLLL	LWLL	LLLL

A wins in the cases where there are at least two wins (the 11 underlined cases), and B wins in the cases where there are at least three losses (the other 5 cases). Since A wins in 11 of the 16 possible cases Fermat argued that the probability that A wins is 11/16. If the stakes are 64 pistoles, A should receive 44 pistoles in agreement with Pascal's result. Pascal and Fermat developed more systematic methods for counting the number of favorable outcomes for problems like this, and this will be one of our central problems. Such counting methods fall under the subject of *combinatorics*.

We see that these two mathematicians arrived at two very different ways to solve the problem of points. Pascal's method was to develop an algorithm and use it to calculate the fair division. This method is easy to implement on a computer and easy to generalize. Fermat's method, on the other hand, was to change the problem into an equivalent problem for which he could use counting or combinatorial methods. In our study of probability today we shall find that both the algorithmic approach and the combinatorial approach share equal billing, just as they did 300 years ago when probability theory got its start.

Chapter 1

Discrete Probability Densities

1.1. COMPUTER SIMULATION OF DISCRETE PROBABILITIES

Probabilities

We shall consider chance experiments with a finite number of possible outcomes $\omega_1, \omega_2, \ldots, \omega_n$. For example, we roll a die and the possible outcomes are 1,2,3,4,5,6 corresponding to the side that turns up. We toss a coin with possible outcomes H (heads) and T (tails). We shall assign probabilities to these possible outcomes. We do this by assigning to each ω_j a nonnegative number $p(\omega_j)$ in such a way that

$$p(\omega_1) + p(\omega_2) + \cdots + p(\omega_n) = 1.$$

For the case of the roll of the die we would assign equal probabilities or probabilities $\frac{1}{6}$ to each of the outcomes. Similarly, in the case of the toss of a coin, we shall assign probability $\frac{1}{2}$ to each outcome. In both of these experiments each outcome is assigned an equal probability. This would certainly not be the case in general. For example, if a drug is found to be effective 30 percent of the time it is used, we might assign a probability .3 that the drug is effective the next time it is used and .7 that it is not effective. This last example illustrates the intuitive *frequency concept of probability*. That is, if we have a probability p that an experiment will result in outcome A, then if we repeat this experiment a large number of times we should expect that the fraction of times that A will occur is about p. Before studying the theoretical way to assign probabilities and to check intuitive ideas like this, we shall find it helpful to look at some of these problems experimentally. We could, for example, toss a coin a large number of times and see if the fraction of times heads turns up is about $1/2$. Another way to carry out such experiments is by *computer simulation*.

Simulation

We want to be able to perform an experiment that corresponds to a given set of probabilities: for example $p(\omega_1) = 1/2$, $p(\omega_2) = 1/4$, and $p(\omega_3) = 1/4$.

We first describe a mechanical device for carrying out this experiment. We construct a spinner with a *unit circumference* (radius $= 1/2\pi$) and with a pointer as shown in Figure 1.

We mark off three arcs A_1, A_2, A_3 of lengths $1/2$, $1/4$, $1/4$, respectively, as shown in Figure 2.

We spin the pointer; if it stops in arc A_1 we say that outcome ω_1 occurs, if it stops in arc A_2 we say that outcome ω_2 occurs, and if it stops in arc A_3 we say that outcome ω_3 occurs. If the pointer stops on an endpoint of two arcs, we choose the arc counterclockwise from the endpoint. (This is unlikely to happen and the convention we choose is not important.) If the probability that the spinner stops in a particular interval is equal to the length of that interval, then $p(\omega_1) = 1/2$, $p(\omega_2) = 1/4$, and $p(\omega_3) = 1/4$.

For the general case $p(\omega_1)$, $p(\omega_2)$, . . . , $p(\omega_r)$, we proceed in the same way. We mark off arcs A_1, A_2, . . . , A_r with A_j having length $p(\omega_j)$. This is possible because the circle has unit circumference and the sum of the probabilities for all outcomes is 1. We say that the outcome ω_j occurs if the spinner stops in arc A_j.

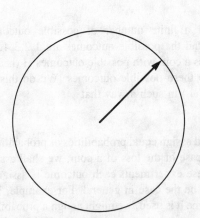

Figure 1 Spinner.

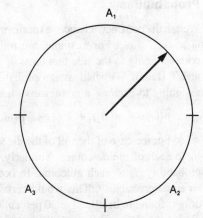

Figure 2 Three arcs.

We will be particularly interested in repeating a chance experiment a large number of times. Although the spinner would be a convenient way to carry out a few repetitions, it would be difficult to carry out a large number of experiments. Since the modern computer can do a large number of operations in a very short time, it is natural to turn to the computer for this task.

Random Numbers

We must first find a computer analog of spinning a pointer. This is done on the computer by means of a *random number generator,* with which the computer picks a number between 0 and 1 at random in such a way that the probability that the number lies in any particular subinterval of this unit interval is equal to the length of the subinterval.

Then if $\Omega = \{\omega_1, \omega_2, \omega_3\}$ with $p(\omega_1) = {}^1/_2$, $p(\omega_2) = {}^1/_4$, and $p(\omega_3) = {}^1/_4$, we divide the interval $[0,1]$ into three parts, as shown in Figure 3. We say outcome ω_1 occurs if the random number lies in I_1, ω_2 occurs if it lies in I_2, and ω_3 occurs if it lies in I_3. If it falls on the endpoint of an interval, we choose the interval to the *right* of this point.

It would take us too far afield to discuss the method by which random numbers are generated here. However, in BASIC, to obtain a random number we simply ask for *rnd*. Every time we ask for *rnd*, we get a different random number between 0 and 1. The program **Random** chooses a sequence of 20 random numbers and prints them out.

```
! Random    (RANDOM)
!
! Illustrates output from a random number generator.
! Prints 20 numbers in columns.

randomize

for i = 1 to 20          ! Twenty times ...
    print rnd,           ! get and print a random number.
next i

end
```

Running this program produced the following twenty *random numbers*.

.897361	.348143	.777036	.784251	.326503
.488932	.674219	.161927	.336582	.281764
.89888	.546613	.450411	.322555	.993371
.976563	.827341	.273281	.623127	.839876

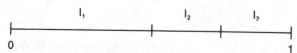

Figure 3 Three intervals.

If the instruction *randomize* were omitted, the program would produce the same outcome each time it is run. Although this is often desirable for testing a program, we will usually include the instruction *randomize* so that we obtain different experiments.

Coin Tossing

EXAMPLE 1

Let us modify this program slightly to toss a coin a sequence of times. As we have noted, our intuition suggests that the probability of obtaining a head on a single toss of a coin is $1/2$. To have the computer "toss a coin," we ask it to pick a random number and test to see if this number is less than $1/2$. If so, we shall call the outcome *heads;* if not we call it *tails*. The program **Coin 1** carries out the experiment of tossing a coin 20 times.

```
! Coin 1    (COIN1)
!
! Simulates tossing a coin 20 times.

let probability = 1/2
randomize

for toss = 1 to 20          ! for each toss

    if rnd < probability then    ! determine whether "heads"
       print "H" ;               ! if so, print "H"
    else
       print "T" ;               ! otherwise it must be "tails", so ...
    end if                       ! print "T" instaed

next toss

end
```

Running this program resulted in

```
THTTTHTTTTHTTTTTHHTT
```

Notice that in 20 tosses, we obtained 5 heads and 15 tails. Let us toss a coin 10,000 times and see if we obtain a proportion of heads closer to our intuitive guess of $1/2$. We modify the program **Coin 1** so that it no longer prints out "H" and "T" for each toss.

Instead, we use a counter *heads* to keep track of the number of heads. We call this modified program **Coin 2**.

```
! Coin 2    (COIN2)
!
! Tosses a coin a given number of times and prints the proportion of heads.

let probability = 1/2
randomize

input prompt "Number of tosses = ": tosses

let heads = 0
for toss = 1 to tosses
    if rnd > probability then let heads = heads + 1    ! count heads
next toss

print

print "In"; tosses; "tosses heads came up"; heads; "times"
print "Proportion of heads ="; heads/tosses

print

end
```

We run this program twice: first for 1000 tosses and then for 10,000 tosses.

```
Number of tosses = 1000

In 1000 tosses heads came up 494 times
Proportion of heads = .494


Number of tosses = 10000

In 10000 tosses heads came up 5039 times
Proportion of heads = .5039
```

We notice that when we toss the coin 10,000 times, the proportion of heads is close to the "true value" .5 for obtaining a head when a coin is tossed. The *Law of Large Numbers*, which we shall study later (see Chapter 8), will show that this should happen, justifying our intuitive idea of the frequency interpretation of probability.   □

In the case of coin tossing, we already knew the probability of the event occurring on each experiment. The real power of simulation comes from the ability to estimate probabilities when they are not known ahead of time. This method has been used in the recent discoveries of strategies that make the casino game of blackjack favorable to the player. We illustrate this idea in a simple situation in which we can compute the true probability and see how effective the simulation is.

Dice Rolling

EXAMPLE 2

We consider a dice game that played an important role in the historical development of probability (see Introduction). The famous letters between Pascal and Fermat, which many believe started a serious study of probability, were instigated by a request for help from a French nobleman and gambler, Chevalier de Méré. It is said that de Méré had been betting that, in four rolls of a die, at least one six would turn up. He was winning consistently and, to get more people to play, he changed the game to bet that, in 24 rolls of two dice, a pair of sixes would turn up. We are considering two bets. For each bet, the gambler is betting that, in n experiments, with probability p for success on any one experiment, there will be at least one success. A gambling rule of Pascal's time suggested that, if we have two such bets which are fair, the ratios of the probabilities for success should equal the ratios of the number of experiments. For de Méré's first bet, $p = \frac{1}{6}$ and $n = 4$, and the bet was actually slightly favorable. Thus the gambling rule would suggest that for the second bet, in which $p = \frac{1}{36}$, 24 experiments should yield a fair (in fact favorable) bet for de Méré. It is claimed that de Méré lost with 24 and felt that 25 rolls were necessary to make the game favorable. It was *un grand scandale* that mathematics was wrong.

We shall try to see if de Méré is correct by simulating his various bets. To do this, we shall want the computer to roll a die. This involves choosing an integer from 1 to 6 at random. To do so, we first choose a random number *rnd* between 0 and 1. If we then multiply it by 6, we obtain a random number between 0 and 6. If we then take the integer part of this number, int(6*rnd), and add 1, we obtain an integer from 1 to 6. (We assume that *rnd* can have the value 0 but cannot ever exactly equal 1, preventing the possible outcome of 7.)

We use this method to simulate a large number of experiments, seeing, in each one, if a six turns up in four rolls of a die. The program **de Mere** carries out this simulation.

```
! de Mere   (DEMERE)
!
! Computes the proportion of times that a six appears in a given number
! of games of four rolls of a die.

randomize

def roll = int(6*rnd) + 1                    ! rolls a die

input prompt "Number of games? ": games

for game = 1 to games

    let rolls = 0                            ! reset counter

    do
        let outcome = roll
        let rolls = rolls + 1
    loop until outcome = 6 or rolls = 4      ! is game over?

    if outcome = 6 then let sixes = sixes + 1   ! count sixes

next game
```

```
print
print "The proportion of times that a six turned up"
print "in four rolls of a die was"; sixes/games
print

end
```

Running this program for 1000 plays and then 10,000 plays gives:

```
Number of games? 1000

The proportion of times that a six turned up
in four rolls of a die was .486


Number of games? 10000

The proportion of times that a six turned up
in four rolls of a die was .5198
```

We note that the result of the second run suggests that de Méré was correct in believing that his bet with one die was favorable; however, if we had based our conclusion on the first run, we would have decided that he was wrong. *Accurate results by simulation require a large number of experiments.* □

It is a simple matter to modify the program **de Mere** to simulate de Méré's second bet that a pair of sixes will occur in n rolls of a pair of dice. We could then run this program 10,000 times for $n = 24$ and then for $n = 25$, and we would very likely conclude that de Méré was also correct in his claim that 25 are necessary for a favorable bet with two dice. However, to simulate even 10,000 plays of this game takes a significant amount of computing time. Fortunately, for this dice game, it will be easy to compute the exact probabilities. We shall show in the next section that for the first bet the probability that de Méré wins is $1 - (5/6)^4 = .518$. Similarly, for the second bet, with 24 rolls, the probability that de Méré wins is $1 - (35/36)^{24} = .491$, and for 25 rolls it is $1 - (35/36)^{25} = .506$. The difference between the probability of winning if we require 25 rolls as compared to 24 rolls is only $.518 - .491 = .017$. It is interesting to ponder whether a gambler can detect a difference as small as .017 from gambling experience. As we have seen, a large number of experiments is necessary to estimate these probabilities accurately. Some writers on the history of probability suggest that de Méré was, in fact, just interested in these problems as intriguing probability problems.

Heads or Tails

EXAMPLE 3
For our next example, we consider a problem where the exact answer is difficult to obtain but for which simulation easily gives the qualitative results. Peter and Paul play a game

called *heads or tails*. In this game, a fair coin is tossed a sequence of times—we choose 12. Each time a head comes up Peter wins 1 penny from Paul, and each time a tail comes up Peter loses 1 penny to Paul. For example, if the results of the 12 tosses are

T H T H T T H H H H T H

Peter's winnings may be graphed as in Figure 4.

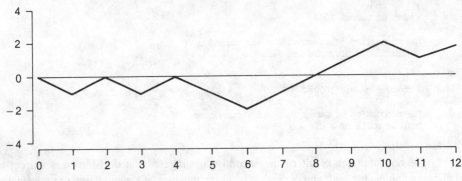

Figure 4 Peter's winnings.

Peter has won 2 pennies from this particular game. It is natural to ask for the probability that he will win j pennies: here j could be any even number from -12 to 12. Since he ends up even when the number of heads and tails are equal, it is reasonable to guess that his winnings are most likely 0; and his winnings are least likely to be -12 or $+12$ — each of the latter outcomes can occur in only one way while 0 can occur in many different ways.

A second interesting question about this game is the following: How many times in the 12 tosses will Peter be in the lead? Looking at the graph of his winnings, we see that Peter is in the lead when his winnings are positive, but we have to make some convention when his winnings are 0 if we want all tosses to contribute to the number of times in the lead. We adopt the convention that, when Peter's winnings are 0, he is in the lead if he was ahead at the previous toss and not if he was behind at the previous toss. With this convention, Peter is in the lead four times in our example. Again, our intuition might suggest that the most likely number of times to be in the lead is $1/2$ of 12, or 6, and the least likely numbers are the extreme cases of 12 or 0.

It is easy to settle this by simulating the game a large number of times and keeping track of the number of times that Peter's final winnings are j, and the number of times that Peter ends up being in the lead by k. The proportions over all games then give estimates for the corresponding probabilities. The program **HT Simulation** carries out this simulation. Note that when there is an even number of tosses of the game, it is possible to be in the lead only an even number of times.

```
! HT Simulation  (HTSIM)
!
! Simulates heads and tails and estimates win and lead probabilities.

let probability = 1/2
randomize

dim lead_count(0 to 12), win_count(-12 to 12)

input prompt "Number of games? " : games

for game = 1 to games

    let winnings, lead, last_win = 0     ! reset counters to zero

    for toss = 1 to 12

        if rnd < probability then        ! see if "heads" appears
            let winnings = winnings + 1   ! if so, Peter wins
        else                             ! else, "tails" appears
            let winnings = winnings - 1   ! so Peter loses
        end if

        if (winnings > 0) or (winnings = 0 and last_win > 0) then
            let lead = lead + 1          ! count times in lead
        end if

        let last_win = winnings          ! keep track of last winnings

    next toss

    let lead_count(lead) = lead_count(lead)+1        ! keep track of leads
    let win_count(winnings) = win_count(winnings)+1 ! ... and of winnings
next game

print
print "winnings","Proportion of games"
print
for winnings = -12 to 12 step 2
    print winnings, win_count(winnings)/games
next winnings

print
print "Times in lead","Proportion of games"
print
for times_in_lead = 0 to 12 step 2
    print times_in_lead, lead_count(times_in_lead)/games
next times_in_lead

end
```

We have run this program 10,000 times and the results are

```
Number of games? 10000

winnings        Proportion of games

-12             0
-10             .0028
-8              .0171
-6              .0542
-4              .123
-2              .1955
 0              .2254
 2              .1888
 4              .1224
 6              .0535
 8              .0138
10              .0032
12              .0003

Times in lead   Proportion of games

 0              .2284
 2              .1247
 4              .1016
 6              .0947
 8              .1036
10              .12
12              .227
```

Our intuition about Peter's final winnings was quite correct, but our intuition about the number of times Peter was in the lead was completely wrong. The simulation suggests that the least likely number of times in the lead is 6 and the most likely is 0 or 12. This is indeed correct, and the explanation for it is suggested by playing the game of heads or tails with a large number of tosses and looking at a graph of Peter's winnings. In Figure 5 we show the results of two simulations of the game, for 1000 tosses and for 10,000 tosses.

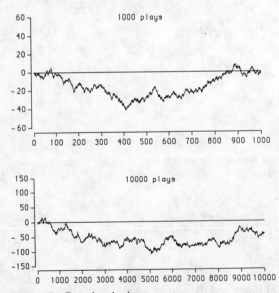

Figure 5   Peter's winnings.

16

In both examples Peter was behind most of the time. It is a remarkable fact, however, that, if play is continued long enough, Peter's winnings will continue to come back to 0, but there will be very long times between the time that this happens. □

In all of our examples so far, we have simulated equiprobable outcomes. We illustrate next an example where the outcomes are not equiprobable.

Horse Races

EXAMPLE 4

Four horses (Acorn, Balky, Chestnut, and Dolby) have raced many times. It is estimated that Acorn wins 30 percent of the time, Balky 40 percent of the time, Chestnut 20 percent of the time, and Dolby 10 percent of the time. The program **Horse Race** simulates the outcome of their next ten races.

```
! Horse Race   (RACE)
!
! Simulates a series of ten races among four horses.

randomize

for race = 1 to 10                    ! ten races

    let x = rnd                       ! get a random number

    if x < .3 then                    ! see if Acorn wins ...
        print  "Acorn wins"
    else if x < .7 then               ! or if Balky wins ...
        print  "Balky wins"
    else if x < .9 then               ! or Chestnut ...
        print  "Chestnut wins"
    else                              ! if no one else has won ...
        print  "Dolby wins"          ! ... then Dolby must have.
    end if

next race

end
```

Running this program resulted in the outcome:

```
Balky wins
Acorn wins
Acorn wins
Balky wins
Chestnut wins
Dolby wins
Dolby wins
Acorn wins
Acorn wins
Dolby wins
```

We see that Acorn won 40 percent of the time, Balky 20 percent of the time, Chestnut 10 percent of the time, and Dolby 30 percent of the time. A larger number of races would be necessary to have better agreement with the past experience.

Finally, we give a program **General Simulation** that will allow the user to put in any set of probabilities and simulate n times an experiment whose outcomes occur with these probabilities.

```
! General Simulation  (GSIM)
!
! Simulates an experiment with outcomes 1,2,...,n  occurring with
! probabilities probability(1),probability(2),...,probability(n).  To do
! this, pick x = rnd, and let "outcome" be the smallest k such that
! x < sum of the probabilities up to the k-th.

randomize

dim probability(100), frequency(100)

read n
mat read probability(n)
data 4
data .3,.4,.2,.1

input prompt "Number of experiments? " : experiments

for experiment = 1 to experiments

    let upper = 0                    ! reset upper bound to zero
    let x = rnd
    for outcome = 1 to n
       let upper = upper + probability(outcome)
       if x < upper then
          let frequency(outcome) = frequency(outcome) + 1
          exit for
       end if
    next outcome

next experiment

print
print "Outcome", "Probability", "Proportion of times"
print
for outcome = 1 to n
   print outcome, probability(outcome), frequency(outcome)/experiments
next outcome
print

end
```

We have run the program to simulate 1000 races with our four horses. Although very tired after all these races, they performed in a manner quite consistent with our estimates of their abilities.

```
Number of experiments? 1000

Outcome         Probability     Proportion of times

   1               .3               .298
   2               .4               .394
   3               .2               .195
   4               .1               .113
```

☐

Historical Remarks

Anyone who plays the same chance game over and over is really carrying out a simulation, and in this sense the process of simulation has been going on for centuries. As we have remarked, many of the early problems of probability might well have been suggested by gamblers' experiences. For example, we remarked that the Chevalier de Méré found that in his experience getting a six in the first four rolls of a single die was too favorable a game and wanted to change the game to getting two sixes in the first 24 rolls of two dice.

It is natural for anyone trying to understand probability theory to try simple experiments by tossing coins, rolling dice, and so forth. The naturalist Buffon tossed a coin 4040 times, resulting in 2048 heads and 1992 tails. He also estimated the number π by throwing needles on a ruled surface and recording how many times the needles crossed a line (see Chapter 2 Section 2.1). The English biologist W. F. R. Weldon[1] recorded 26,306 throws of 12 dice, and the Swiss scientist, Rudolf Wolf[2] recorded 100,000 throws of a single die without a computer. Such experiments are very time-consuming and may not accurately represent the chance phenomena being studied. For example, for the dice experiments of Weldon and Wolf, further analysis of the recorded data showed a suspected bias in the dice. The statistician Karl Pearson analyzed a large number of outcomes at certain roulette tables and suggested that the wheels were biased. He wrote in 1894:

> Clearly, since the Casino does not serve the valuable end of huge laboratory for the preparation of probability statistics, it has no scientific *raison d'être*. Men of science cannot have their most refined theories disregarded in this shameless manner! The French Government must be urged by the hierarchy of science to close the gaming-saloons; it would be, of course, a graceful act to hand over the remaining resources of the Casino to the Académie des Sciences for the endowment of a laboratory of orthodox probability; in particular, of the new branch of that study, the application of the theory of chance to the biological problems of evolution, which is likely to occupy so much of men's thoughts in the near future.[3]

However, these early experiments were suggestive and led to important discoveries in probability and statistics. They led Pearson to the *chi-squared test*, which is of great importance in testing whether observed data fit a given probability distribution.

By the early 1900s it was clear that a better way to generate random numbers was needed. In 1927, L. H. C. Tippett published a list of 41,600 digits obtained by selecting

---

[1] T. C. Fry, *Probability and Its Engineering Uses*, 2d ed. (Princeton: Van Nostrand, 1965).

[2] E. Czuber, *Wahrscheinlichkeitsrechnung*, 3rd ed. (Berlin: Teubner, 1914).

[3] Karl Pearson, "Science and Monte Carlo," *Fortnightly Review* vol. 55 (1894), p. 193; cited in S. M. Stigler, *The History of Statistics* (Cambridge: Harvard University Press, 1986).

numbers haphazardly from census reports. In 1955, RAND Corporation printed a table of 1,000,000 random numbers generated from electronic noise. The advent of the high-speed computer raised the possibility of generating random numbers directly on the computer, and in the late 1940s John von Neumann suggested that this be done as follows: Suppose that you want a random sequence of four-digit numbers. Choose any four-digit number, say 6235, to start. Square this number to obtain 38,875,225. For the second number choose the middle four digits of this square (i.e., 8752). Do the same process starting with 8752 to get the third number, and so forth. More modern methods, including the method used by True BASIC,™ involve the concept of "a mod m." If a and m are integers, then by a mod m we mean the remainder when a is divided by m. For example, 10 mod 4 = 2, 8 mod 2 = 0, and so forth. To generate a random sequence X_0, X_1, X_2 of numbers choose a starting number X_0 and then obtain the numbers X_{n+1} from X_n by the formula

$$X_{n+1} = (aX_n + c) \bmod m,$$

where a, c, and m are carefully chosen constants.

For both von Neumann's squaring method and for the mod technique the sequence of numbers is actually completely determined by the first number. Thus, there is nothing really random about these sequences. However, they produce numbers that behave very much as theory would predict for random experiments. To obtain different sequences for different experiments the initial number X_0 is chosen by some other procedure that might involve, for example, the time of day.[4]

During the Second World War, physicists at the Los Almos Scientific Laboratory needed to know, for purposes of shielding, how far neutrons travel through various materials. This question was beyond the reach of theoretical calculations. Daniel Mc-Cracken, writing in the Scientific American, states:

> The physicists had most of the necessary basic data: they knew the average distance of a neutron of a given speed would travel in a given substance before it collided with an atomic nucleus, what the probabilities were that the neutron would bounce off instead of being absorbed by the nucleus, how much energy the neutron was likely to lose after a given collision and so on.[5]

John von Neumann and Stanislas Ulum suggested that the problem be solved by modeling the experiment by chance devices on a computer. Their work being secret, it was necessary to give it a code name. Von Neumann chose the name "Monte Carlo." Since that time, this method of simulation has been called the *Monte Carlo method*.

Professor William Feller indicated the possibilities of using computer simulations to illustrate basic concepts in probability in his book *Introduction to Probability Theory and its Applications*. In discussing the problem about the number of times in the lead in the game of "heads or tails" Feller writes:

> The results concerning fluctuations in coin tossing show that widely held beliefs about the law of large numbers are fallacious. These results are so amazing and so at variance with

---

[4]For a detailed discussion of random numbers, see Donald E. Knuth, *The Art of Computer Programming*, vol. II (Reading: Addison-Wesley, 1969).

[5]Daniel D. McCracken, "The Monte Carlo Method," *Scientific American*, vol. 192 (May 1955), p. 90.

common intuition that even sophisticated colleagues doubted that coins actually misbehave as theory predicts. The record of a simulated experiment is therefore included.[6]

Feller provides a plot showing the result of 10,000 plays of *heads or tails* similar to that in Figure 5.

The martingale betting system described in Exercise 10 has a long and interesting history. Russell Barnhart pointed out to the author that its use can be traced back at least to 1754, when Casanova, writing in his memoirs, *History of My Life,* writes

> She [Casanova's mistress] made me promise to go to the casino [the Ridotto in Venice] for money to play in partnership with her. I went there and took all the gold I found, and, determinedly doubling my stakes according to the system known as the martingale, I won three or four times a day during the rest of the Carnival. I never lost the sixth card. If I had lost it, I should have been out of funds, which amounted to two thousand zecchini.[7]

Even if there were no zeros on the roulette wheel so the game was perfectly fair, the martingale system, or any other system for that matter, cannot make the game into a favorable game. The idea that a fair game remains fair and unfair games remain unfair has been exploited by mathematicians to obtain important results in the study of probability.

The word *martingale* itself also has an interesting history. The origin of the word is obscure. The *Oxford English Dictionary* gives examples of its use in the early 1600s and says that its probable origin is the reference in Rabelais's Book One, Chapter 19:

> Everything was done as planned, the only thing being that Gargantua doubted if they would be able to find, right away, breeches suitable to the old fellow's legs; he was doubtful, also, as to what cut would be most becoming to the orator—the martingale, which has a draw-bridge effect in the seat, to permit doing one's business more easily; the sailor-style which affords more comfort for the kidneys; the Swiss, which is warmer on the belly; or the codfish-tail, which is cooler on the loins.[8]

In modern uses martingale has several different meanings, all related to *holding down,* in addition to the gambling use. For example, it is a strap on a horse's harness used to hold down the horse's head, and also a part of a sailing rig used to hold down the bowsprit.

The Labouchere system described in Exercise 9 is named after Henry du Pre Labouchere (1831–1912), an English journalist and member of parliament. Labouchere attributed the system to Condorcet. Condorcet (1743–1794) was a political leader during the time of the French revolution who was interested in applying probability theory to economics and politics. For example, he calculated the probability that a jury using majority vote will give a correct decision if each juror has the same probability of deciding correctly. His writings provided a wealth of ideas on how probability might be applied to human affairs[9]

[6]William Feller, *Introduction to Probability Theory and its Application,* vol. I, 3rd ed. (New York: John Wiley & Sons, 1968), p. xi.

[7]Giacomo Casanova, *History of My Life,* vol. IV, Chap. 7, trans. W.R. Trask (New York: Harcourt-Brace, 1968), p. 124.

[8]Quoted in *The Portable Rabelais,* ed. S. Putnam (New York: Viking, 1946), p. 113.

[9]Le Marquise de Condorcet, *Essai sur l'Application de l'Analyse à la Probabilité dès Décisions Rendues a la Pluralité des Voix* (Paris: Imprimerie Royale, 1785).

Exercises

1. Modify the program **Coin 2** to toss a coin n times and print out after every 100 tosses the proportion of heads minus $^1/_2$. Do these numbers appear to approach 0 as n increases? Modify the program again to print out, every 100 times, the number of heads minus half the number of tosses. Do these numbers appear to approach 0 as n increases?

2. Modify the program **Coin 2** so that it tosses a coin n times and records whether or not the proportion of heads is within .1 of .5 (i.e., between .4 and .6). Have your program repeat this experiment 100 times. About how large must n be so that approximately 95 out of 100 times the proportion of heads is between .4 and .6?

3. In the early 1600s, Galileo was asked to explain the fact that, although the number of triples of integers from 1 to 6 with sum 9 is the same as the number of such triples with sum 10, when three dice are rolled, a 9 seemed to come up less often than a 10—supposedly in the experience of gamblers.
   (a) Write a computer program to simulate the roll of three dice a large number of times and keep track of the proportion of times that the sum is 9 and the proportion of times it is 10.
   (b) Can you conclude from your simulations that the gamblers were correct?

4. In racketball, a player continues to serve as long as she is winning; a point is scored only when a player is serving and wins the volley. The first player to win 21 points wins the game. Assume that you serve first and have a probability .6 of winning a volley when you serve and probability .5 when your opponent serves. Estimate, by simulation, the probability that you will win a game.

5. Consider the bet that all three dice will turn up sixes at least once in n rolls of three dice. Determine the smallest value of n necessary for a favorable bet that three sixes will occur when three dice are rolled n times. (DeMoivre would say it should be about $216 \cdot \log(2) = 149.7$ and so would answer 150—see Exercise 12. Do you agree with him?)

6. In Las Vegas, a roulette wheel has 38 slots numbered 0,00,1,2, . . . ,36. The 0 and 00 slots are green and half of the remaining 36 slots are red and half are black. A croupier spins the wheel and throws in an ivory ball. If you bet 1 dollar on red, you win 1 dollar if the ball stops in a red slot and otherwise you lose 1 dollar. Write a program to find the total winnings for a player who makes 1000 bets on red.

7. Another form of bet for roulette is to bet that a specific number (say 17) will turn up. If the ball stops on your number, you get your dollar back plus 35 dollars. If not, you lose your dollar. Write a program that will plot your winnings when you make 500 plays of roulette at Las Vegas, first when you bet each time on red (see Exercise 6), and then for a second visit to Las Vegas when you make 500 plays betting each time on the number 17. What differences do you see in the graphs of your winnings on these two occasions?

8. An astute student noticed that, in our simulation of the games of heads and tails

(see Example 3), the proportion of times the player is always in the lead is very close to the proportion of times that the player's total winnings end up 0. Work out these probabilities by enumeration of all cases for two tosses and for four tosses, and see if you think that these probabilities are, in fact, the same.

9. The *Labouchere system* for roulette is played as follows. Write down a list of numbers, usually 1,2,3,4. Bet the sum of the first and last, $1 + 4 = 5$, on red. If you win, delete the first and last numbers from your list. If you lose, add the amount that you last bet to the end of your list. Then use the new list and bet the sum of the first and last numbers (if there is only one number, bet that amount). Continue until your list becomes empty. Show that, if this happens, you win the sum, $1 + 2 + 3 + 4 = 10$, of your original list. Simulate this system and see if you do always stop and, hence, always win. If so, why is this not a foolproof gambling system?

10. Another well-known gambling system is the *martingale doubling system*. Suppose that you are betting on red to turn up in roulette. Every time you win, bet 1 dollar next time. Every time you lose, double your previous bet. Continue to play until you have won at least 5 dollars or you have lost more than 100 dollars. Write a program to simulate this system and play it a number of times and see how you do. In his book *The Newcomes,* W. M. Thackeray remarks "You have not played as yet? Do not do so; above all avoid a martingale if you do."[10] Was this good advice?

11. Modify the program **HT Simulation** so that it keeps track of the maximum of Peter's winnings in each game of 12 tosses. Have your program print out the proportion of times in 1000 games that his maximum is 0,1,2, . . . ,12. Compare these with the proportion of times that your total winnings take on values 0,2,4, . . . ,12. Calculate the corresponding exact probabilities for games of two tosses and four tosses.

*12. Assume that the probability of "success" on a single experiment with n outcomes is $1/n$. Let m be the number of experiments necessary to make it a favorable bet that at least one success will occur (see Exercise 5).
   (a) Show that the probability that, in m trials, there are no successes is $(1 - 1/n)^m$.
   (b) (DeMoivre) Show that if $m = n \cdot \log(2)$ then

$$\lim_{n \to \infty} \left(1 - \frac{1}{n} \right)^m = \frac{1}{2}.$$

   Hint:

$$\lim_{n \to \infty} \left(1 - \frac{1}{n} \right)^n = e^{-1}.$$

   Hence for large n we should choose m to be about $n \cdot \log(2)$.
   (c) Would DeMoivre have been led to the correct answer for de Méré's two bets if he had used his approximation?

---

[10]W.M. Thackerey, *The Newcomes* (London: Bradbury and Evans, 1854–55).

13. In an upcoming national election for the president of the United States 48 percent of the voters plan to vote for the Republican candidate and 52 percent plan to vote for the Democratic candidate. A pollster plans to predict the winner by taking a random sample of 1000 voters and declaring that the winner will be the one obtaining the most votes in his sample. To get some idea of how reasonable this is, write a program to make this prediction by simulation. Repeat the simulation 100 times and see how many times the pollster's prediction would come true. Repeat your experiment, assuming now that 49 percent of the population plan to vote for the Republican candidate; first with a sample of 1000 and then with a sample of 3000. (The Gallup poll uses about 3000.)

14. The psychologist Tversky and his colleagues[11] say that about four out of five people will answer **(a)** to the following question:

A certain town is served by two hospitals. In the larger hospital about 45 babies are born each day, and in the smaller hospital 15 babies are born each day. Although the overall proportion of boys is about 50 percent, the actual proportion at either hospital may be more or less than 50 percent on any day. At the end of a year, which hospital will have the greater number of days on which more than 60 percent of the babies born were boys?

(a) the large hospital

(b) the small hospital

(c) neither—the number of days will be about the same (within 5 percent of each other)

Assume that the probability that a baby is a boy is .5 (actual estimates make this more like .513). Decide, by simulation, what the right answer is to this question. Can you suggest why so many people go wrong?

15. You are offered the following game. A coin will be tossed until the first time it comes up heads. If this occurs on the jth toss you are paid 2^j dollars. You are sure to win at least 2 dollars so you should be willing to pay to play this game—but how much? Few people would pay as much as 10 dollars to play this game. See if you can decide, by simulation, a reasonable amount to be willing to pay if you will be allowed to make a large number of plays of the game.

16. Tversky and his colleagues[12] studied the records of 48 of the Philadelphia 76ers basketball games in the 1980–81 season to see if a player had times when he was hot and every shot went in, and other times when he was cold and barely able to hit the backboard. The players estimated that they were about 25 percent more likely to make a shot after a hit than after a miss. In fact, the opposite was true—the 76ers were 6 percent more likely to score after a miss than after a hit. Tversky reports that the number of hot and cold streaks was about what one would expect by purely

[11]See Kevin McKean, "Decisions, Decisions," *Discover*, June 1985, pp. 22–31. Kevin McKean, Discover Magazine, © 1987 Family Media, Inc. Reprinted with permission. This popular article reports on the work of Tversky et al. in *Judgement Under Uncertainty: Heuristics and Biases* (Cambridge: Cambridge University Press, 1982).

[12]Ibid.

random effects. Assuming that a player has a fifty-fifty chance of making a shot and makes 20 shots a game, estimate by simulation the proportion of the games in which the player will have a streak of 5 or more hits.

17. Estimate, by simulation, the average number of children there would be in a family if all people had children until they had a boy. Do the same if all people had children until they had at least one boy and at least one girl. How many more children would you expect to find under the second scheme than under the first in 100,000 families? (Assume that boys and girls are equally likely).

18. Mathematicians have been known to get some of their best ideas while sitting in a cafe, riding on a bus, or strolling in the park. In the early 1900s the famous mathematician George Polya liked to walk in the park in Zurich and think about mathematics. One day, while on such a walk, he encountered a couple (probably romantically inclined). He continued his walk and encountered them several times in his random meanderings through the park. This set him to thinking about whether random walkers were destined to meet.

    Polya considered random walkers in one, two, and three dimensions. In one dimension, he envisioned the walker on a very long street. At each intersection the walker flips a fair coin to decide which direction to walk next (see Figure 6a). In two dimensions, the walker is walking on a grid of streets, and at each intersection he chooses one of the four possible directions with equal probability (see Figure 6b). In three dimensions (we might better speak of a random climber), the walker moves on a three-dimensional grid, and at each intersection there are now six different directions that the walker may choose, each with equal probability (see Figure 6c).

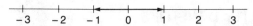

Figure 6a Random walk in one dimension.

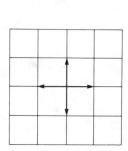

Figure 6b Random walk in two

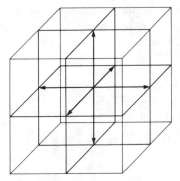

Figure 6c Random walk in three dimensions.

(a) Write a program to simulate random walk in one dimension starting at 0. Have your program print out the lengths of the times between returns to the starting point (returns to 0). See if you can guess from this simulation the answer to the following question: Will the walker always return to his starting point eventually, or might he drift away forever?

(b) The paths of two walkers in two dimensions who meet after n steps can be considered to be a single path that starts at $(0,0)$ and returns to $(0,0)$ after $2n$ steps. This means that the probability that two random walkers in two dimensions meet is the same as the probability that a single walker in two dimensions ever returns to the starting point. Thus the question of whether two walkers are sure to meet is the same as the question of whether a single walker is sure to return to the starting point.

Write a program to simulate a random walk in two dimensions and see if you think that the walker is sure to return to $(0,0)$. If so, Polya would be sure to keep meeting his friends in the park. Perhaps by now you have conjectured the answer to the question: Is a random walker in one or in two dimensions sure to return to the starting point? Polya answered the question: Is a random walker sure to return to the starting point? for random walks in each of the three dimensions. He established the remarkable result that the answer is *yes* in one and two dimensions and *no* in three dimensions.

(c) Write a program to simulate random walk in three dimensions and see whether, from this simulation and the results of (a) and (b), you could have guessed Polya's result.

1.2 DISCRETE PROBABILITY DENSITIES

In this book we shall study many different experiments from a probabilistic point of view. What is involved in this study will become evident as the theory is developed and examples are analyzed. However, the overall idea can be described and illustrated as follows: to each experiment that we consider there will be associated a set of possible outcomes, called the *sample space*. The subsets of the sample space will be regarded as *events,* and to each event there will be assigned a number between 0 and 1 which is the *probability* that the event occurs.

EXAMPLE 1

Consider an experiment in which a coin is tossed twice. We take as the set of possible outcomes (i.e., as the sample space) the 4-element set

{HH,HT,TH,TT},

where

HH is the outcome: heads on the first toss and heads on the second,

HT is the outcome: heads on the first toss and tails on the second,

TH is the outcome: tails on the first toss and heads on the second,

TT is the outcome: tails on the first toss and tails on the second.

Let E be the event that at least one head comes up on the two tosses. This event corresponds to the set of all outcomes with at least one H, which is the 3-element subset {HH,HT,TH} of the sample size. We write

E = {HH,HT,TH} = event that at least one head comes up.

In the same way, we have

F = {HH,HT} = event that heads occurs on the first toss,

E_1 = {HH} = elementary event corresponding to the outcome HH,

E_2 = {HT} = elementary event corresponding to the outcome HT,

E_3 = {TH} = elementary event corresponding to the outcome TH,

E_4 = {TT} = elementary event corresponding to the outcome TT.

Thus, we see that the possible events in the experiment of tossing a coin twice can be identified with the subsets of the sample space. $\square$

In this experiment, the most natural assumption is that all four outcomes are equally likely. Under that assumption, we should assign a probability of $^1/_4$ to each of the outcomes. Correspondingly, to the event E = {HH,HT,TH} that at least one head comes up on the two tosses, we should assign the probability $^3/_4$.

In this section, we are concerned with developing the basic mathematical theory that will enable us to analyze the probabilistic aspects of a wide range of experiments. Accordingly, we formalize the ideas suggested by our first example in the following definitions.

Samples Spaces

DEFINITION 1

A *sample space* is any nonempty set.

We generally denote a sample space by the capital Greek letter Ω. As stated above, in the correspondence between an experiment and the mathematical theory by which it is studied, the sample space Ω corresponds to the set of possible outcomes of the experiment. Thus, for the coin tossing experiment in our first example, we have Ω = {HH,HT,TH,TT}.

We now make two additional definitions. These are subsidiary to the definition of sample space and serve to make precise some of the common terminology used in conjunction with sample spaces. First of all, we define an *outcome,* ω (relative to a sample space Ω) to be an element of Ω (i.e., $\omega \in \Omega$). Second, an *event E* (relative to a sample space Ω) is subset of Ω (i.e., $E \subset \Omega$). Normally, we shall denote outcomes by lower case letters and events by capital letters.

EXAMPLE 2

A die is rolled once. We take as sample space for the experiment the 6-element set

$$\Omega = \{1,2,3,4,5,6\},$$

where each outcome i, for $i = 1, \ldots ,6$, corresponds to the number of dots on the face which turns up. The event

$$E = \{2,4,6\}$$

corresponds to the statement that the result of the roll is an even number. Unless there is reason to believe the die is loaded, the natural assumption is that every outcome is equally likely. Adopting this convention means that we assign a probability of $\frac{1}{6}$ to each of the six outcomes. □

Probability Densities

We next describe the assignment of probabilities. The definitions are motivated by the examples, in which we have assigned to each outcome of the sample space a nonnegative number such that the sum of the numbers assigned is equal to 1.

DEFINITION 2

A *probability density* on a finite sample space Ω is a real-valued function p whose domain is Ω and which satisfies:

(1) $p(\omega) \geqslant 0$ for all $\omega \in \Omega$.

(2) $\displaystyle\sum_{\omega \in \Omega} p(\omega) = 1$.

An event E is a subset of Ω, and we define the *probability* of E to be the number $P(E)$ given by

$$P(E) = \sum_{\omega \in E} p(\omega).$$

EXAMPLE 3

In the coin tossing experiment, we have $\Omega = \{HH,HT,TH,TT\}$, and the probability density corresponding to the assumption that all outcomes are equally likely is defined by

$$p(HH) = p(HT) = p(TH) = p(TT) = \frac{1}{4}.$$

The event $E = \{HH,HT,TH\}$ that at least one head comes up is assigned the probability

$$P(E) = p(HH) + p(HT) + p(TH)$$
$$= \frac{1}{4} + \frac{1}{4} + \frac{1}{4} = \frac{3}{4}.$$

The event $F = \{HH,HT\}$ that heads comes up on the first toss is assigned probability

$$P(F) = p(HH) + p(HT)$$
$$= \frac{1}{4} + \frac{1}{4} = \frac{1}{2}.$$ □

EXAMPLE 4

The sample space for the experiment in which the die is rolled is the 6-element set $\Omega = \{1,2,3,4,5,6\}$. Assuming a fair die, we choose the probability density defined by

$$p(i) = \frac{1}{6}, \quad \text{for } i = 1, \ldots, 6.$$

If E is the event that the result of the roll is an even number, then $E = \{2,4,6\}$ and

$$P(E) = p(2) + p(4) + p(6)$$
$$= \frac{1}{6} + \frac{1}{6} + \frac{1}{6} = \frac{1}{2}. \qquad \square$$

Notice that it is an immediate consequence of the above definitions that, for every $\omega \in \Omega$,

$$P(\{\omega\}) = p(\omega).$$

That is, the probability of the elementary event $\{\omega\}$, consisting of a single outcome ω, is equal to the value $p(\omega)$ assigned to the outcome ω by the probability density.

EXAMPLE 5

Three people, A, B, and C, are running for the same office, and we assume that one and only one of them wins. The sample space may be taken as the 3-element set $\Omega = \{A,B,C\}$ where each element corresponds to the outcome of that candidate's winning. Suppose that A and B have the same chance of winning, but that C has only $\frac{1}{2}$ the chance of A or B. Then we assign

$$p(A) = p(B) = 2p(C).$$

Since

$$p(A) + p(B) + p(C) = 1,$$

we see that

$$2p(C) + 2p(C) + p(C) = 1,$$

which implies that $5p(C) = 1$. Hence,

$$p(A) = \frac{2}{5}, \qquad p(B) = \frac{2}{5}, \qquad p(C) = \frac{1}{5}.$$

Let E be the event that either A or C wins. Then $E = \{A,C\}$, and

$$p(E) = p(A) + p(C) = \frac{2}{5} + \frac{1}{5} = \frac{3}{5}. \qquad \square$$

We next derive the basic set-theoretic properties of the probabilities of events, described in terms of the standard constructions of set theory, such as union $\cup$, intersection $\cap$, difference $-$, and inclusion $\subset$. (We denote by $\tilde{A}$ *the* complement of a subset A of Ω, i.e., $\tilde{A} = \Omega - A$).

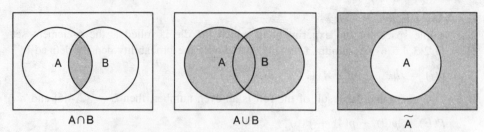

Figure 7 Basic set operations.

It will help to remember the Venn diagrams, which illustrate the basic set operations as shown in Figure 7.

Properties

THEOREM 1

The probabilities assigned to events by a density function on a sample space Ω satisfy the following properties:

    (1) $P(E) \geq 0$ for every $E \subset \Omega$.
    (2) $P(\Omega) = 1$.
    (3) If $E \subset F \subset \Omega$, then $P(E) \leq P(F)$.
    (4) If A and B are *disjoint* subsets of Ω, then $P(A \cup B) = P(A) + P(B)$.
    (5) $P(\tilde{A}) = 1 - P(A)$ for every $A \subset \Omega$.

Proof. For any event E the probability $P(E)$ is determined from the density p by

$$P(E) = \sum_{\omega \in E} p(\omega), \qquad \text{for every } E \subset \Omega.$$

Since the function p is nonnegative, it follows that $P(E)$ is also nonnegative, that is, (1) is true. Statement (2) is proved by the equations

$$P(\Omega) = \sum_{\omega \in \Omega} p(\omega) = 1.$$

Suppose that $E \subset F \subset \Omega$. Then every element ω that belongs to E also belongs to F, whence it follows that $\sum_{\omega \in E} p(\omega)$ is a summand of $\sum_{\omega \in F} p(\omega)$. Since all terms of $p(\omega)$ are nonnegative, we may conclude that

$$P(E) = \sum_{\omega \in E} p(\omega) \leq \sum_{\omega \in F} p(\omega) = P(F),$$

and (3) is proved. Suppose next that A and B are disjoint subsets of Ω. Then every element ω of $A \cup B$ lies either in A and not in B or in B and not in A. It follows that

$$P(A \cup B) = \sum_{\omega \in A \cup B} p(\omega) = \sum_{\omega \in A} p(\omega) + \sum_{\omega \in B} p(\omega)$$

$$= P(A) + P(B),$$

and (4) is proved. Finally, to prove (5), consider the disjoint union

$$\Omega = A \cup \tilde{A}.$$

Since $P(\Omega) = 1$, the property of disjoint additivity (4) implies that

$$1 = P(A) + P(\tilde{A}),$$

whence $P(\tilde{A}) = 1 - P(A)$. ∎

It is important to realize that statement (4) in Theorem 1 can be extended to more than two sets. The general finite additivity property, proved by mathematical induction, is the following:

(6) If $A_1, \ldots, A_n$ are pairwise disjoint subsets of Ω (i.e., $A_i \cap A_j = \emptyset$ for $i,j = 1, \ldots, n$ and $i \neq j$), then

$$P(A_1 \cup \ldots \cup A_n) = \sum_{i=1}^{n} P(A_i).$$

We shall often use the following consequence of (6).

THEOREM 2

Let $A_1, \ldots, A_n$ be pairwise disjoint events with $\Omega = A_1 \cup \ldots \cup A_n$, and let E be any event. Then

$$P(E) = \sum_{i=1}^{n} P(E \cap A_i).$$

Proof. $E \cap A_1, \ldots, E \cap A_n$ are disjoint sets whose union is the set E. Thus the theorem follows from property (6). ∎

COROLLARY 2

For any two events A and B,

$$P(A) = P(A \cap B) + P(A \cap \tilde{B}).$$

Statement (4) can be generalized in another way. Suppose that A and B are subsets of Ω which are not necessarily disjoint. Then:

(7) If A and B are subsets of Ω, then

$$P(A \cup B) = P(A) + P(B) - P(A \cap B). \tag{1}$$

Proof. The left side of Equation (1) is the sum of $p(\omega)$ for ω in either A or B. We must show that the right side of Equation (1) also adds $p(\omega)$ for ω in A or B. If ω is in exactly one of the two sets, then it is counted in only one of three terms on the right side of Equation (1). If it is in both A and B, it is added twice from the calculation of $P(A)$ and $P(B)$ and subtracted once for $P(A \cap B)$. Thus it is counted exactly once by the right side. Of course, if $A \cap B = \emptyset$, then (7) reduces to (4). ■

Tree Diagrams

EXAMPLE 6
Let us illustrate the properties of probabilities of events in terms of three tosses of a coin. When we have an experiment which takes place in stages such as this, we often find it convenient to represent the outcomes by a *tree diagram* as shown in Figure 8.

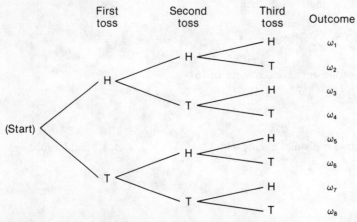

Figure 8 Tree diagram for three tosses of a coin.

A *path* through the tree corresponds to a possible outcome of the experiment. For the case of three tosses of a coin, we have eight paths $\omega_1, \omega_2, \ldots, \omega_8$ and, assuming each outcome to be equally likely, we assign equal weight, $1/8$, to each path. Let E be the event "at least one head turns up." Then $\tilde{E}$ is the event "no heads turn up." This event occurs for only one outcome, namely, $\omega_8 =$ TTT. Thus, $\tilde{E} = \{$TTT$\}$ and we have

$$P(\tilde{E}) = P(\{\text{TTT}\}) = p(\text{TTT}) = 1/8.$$

By property (5),

$$P(E) = 1 - P(\tilde{E}) = 1 - 1/8 = 7/8.$$

Note that we shall often find it is easier to compute the probability that an event does not happen rather than the probability that it does. We then use property (5) to obtain the desired probability.

Let A be the event "the first outcome is a head," and B the event "the second outcome is a tail." By looking at the paths in Figure 8, we see that

$$P(A) = P(B) = 1/2.$$

Moreover, $A \cap B = \{\omega_3, \omega_4\}$, and so $P(A \cap B) = {}^1/_4$. Using property (7), we obtain

$$P(A \cup B) = P(A) + P(B) - P(A \cap B)$$
$$= {}^1/_2 + {}^1/_2 - {}^1/_4 = {}^3/_4 .$$

Since $A \cup B$ is the 6-element set,

$$A \cup B = \{HHH, HHT, HTH, HTT, TTH, TTT\},$$

we see that we obtain the same result by direct enumeration. ☐

In our coin tossing examples and in the die rolling example, we have assigned an equal probability to each possible outcome of the experiment. Corresponding to this method of assigning probabilities, we have the following definitions.

Uniform Density

DEFINITION 3

The *uniform probability density* on a sample space Ω containing n elements is the function p defined by

$$p(\omega) = \frac{1}{n}, \qquad \text{for every } \omega \in \Omega .$$

It is important to realize that when an experiment is analyzed to describe its possible outcomes, there is no single correct choice of sample space. For the experiment of tossing a coin twice in Example 1, we selected the 4-element set $\Omega = \{HH, HT, TH, TT\}$ as a sample space and assigned the uniform probability density. These choices are certainly intuitively natural. On the other hand, for some purposes it may be more useful to consider the 3-element sample space $\overline{\Omega} = \{0, 1, 2\}$ in which 0 is the outcome "no heads turn up," 1 is the outcome "exactly one head turns up," and 2 is the outcome "two heads turn up." The probability density $\overline{p}$ on $\overline{\Omega}$ defined by the equations

$$\overline{p}(0) = {}^1/_4, \qquad \overline{p}(1) = {}^1/_2, \qquad \overline{p}(2) = {}^1/_4$$

is the one corresponding to the uniform probability density on the original sample space Ω. Notice that it is perfectly possible to choose a different probability density. For example, we may consider the uniform probability density on $\overline{\Omega}$, which is the function $\overline{q}$ defined by

$$\overline{q}(0) = \overline{q}(1) = \overline{q}(2) = {}^1/_3 .$$

Although $\overline{q}$ is a perfectly good probability density, it is not consistent with observed data on coin tossing.

EXAMPLE 7

Consider the experiment that consists of rolling a pair of dice. We take the sample space Ω the 36-element set of all ordered pairs (i,j) of integers with $1 \leqslant i \leqslant 6$ and $1 \leqslant j \leqslant 6$. Thus,

$$\Omega = \{(i,j) : 1 \leqslant i, j \leqslant 6\}.$$

Let us assume that the dice are not loaded. In mathematical terms, this means that we assume that each of the 36 outcomes is equally likely, or equivalently, that we adopt the equiprobable density on Ω by setting

$$p((i,j)) = \frac{1}{36}, \qquad 1 \leqslant i, j \leqslant 6.$$

What is the probability of getting a sum of 7 on the roll of two dice—or getting a sum of 11? The first event, denoted by E, is the subset

$$E = \{(1,6),(6,1),(2,5),(5,2),(3,4),(4,3)\}.$$

A sum of 11 is the subset F given by

$$F = \{(5,6),(6,5)\}.$$

Consequently,

$$P(E) = \sum_{\omega \in E} p(\omega) = 6 \cdot \frac{1}{36} = \frac{1}{6},$$

$$P(F) = \sum_{\omega \in F} p(\omega) = 2 \cdot \frac{1}{36} = \frac{1}{18}.$$

What is the probability of getting neither *double ones* (snakeeyes) nor *double sixes* (boxcars)? The event of getting either one of these two outcomes is the set

$$E = \{(1,1),(6,6)\}.$$

Hence, the probability of obtaining neither is given by

$$P(\tilde{E}) = 1 - P(E)$$

$$= 1 - \frac{2}{36} = \frac{17}{18}. \qquad \square$$

In the above coin tossing and the dice rolling experiments, we have assigned an equal probability to each outcome. That is, in each example, we have chosen the uniform probability density. These are the natural choices provided the coin is a fair one and the dice are not loaded. However, the decision as to which density to select to describe an experiment is *not* a part of the basic mathematical theory of probability. The latter begins only when the sample space and the probability density have already been defined.

Determination of Probabilities

It is still important to consider ways in which probability densities are determined in practice. One way is by *symmetry*. For the case of the toss of a coin, we do not see any physical difference between the two sides of a coin that should affect the chance of one side or the other turning up. Similarly, with an ordinary die there is no essential difference between any two sides of the die, and so by symmetry we assign the same probability for any possible outcome. In general, considerations of symmetry often suggest the uniform density. Care has to be used here. We should not always assume that, just because we do not know any reason to suggest that one outcome is more likely than another, it is appropriate to assign equal probabilities. For example, consider the experiment of guessing the sex of a newborn child. It has been observed that the proportion of newborn children who are boys is about .513. Thus, it is more appropriate to assign a probability density which assigns probability .513 to the outcome *boy* and probability .487 to the outcome *girl* than to assign probability $^1/_2$ to each outcome. This is an example where we use statistical observations to determine probabilities. Note that these probabilities may change with new studies and may vary from country to country. Genetic engineering might even allow an individual to influence this probability for a particular case.

Odds

Statistical estimates for probabilities are fine if the experiment under consideration can be repeated a number of times under similar circumstances. However, assume that, at the beginning of a football season, you want to assign a probability to the event that Dartmouth will beat Harvard. You really do not have data that relates to this year's football team. However, you can determine your own personal probability by seeing what kind of a bet you would be willing to make. For example, suppose that you are willing to make a 1 dollar bet giving 2 to 1 odds that Dartmouth will win. Then you are willing to pay 2 dollars if Dartmouth loses in return for receiving 1 dollar if Dartmouth wins. This means that you think the appropriate probability for Dartmouth winning is $^2/_3$.

Let us look more carefully at the relation between odds and probabilities. Assume that an event E has probability p of occurring. We want to offer a bet that E will occur. We ask for s dollars if E occurs and agree to pay r dollars if it does not occur. In a large number of bets we would expect to win s a fraction p of the times and lose r a fraction $1 - p$ of the times. Thus our average winnings per bet would be $sp - r(1 - p)$. To make the bet fair, we should make this average 0. That is, we should make $sp = r(1 - p)$, or $r/s = p/(1 - p)$. This determines the ratio of r to s. We write this ratio as $r : s$ and say that it gives us the *odds* in favor of E occurring.

DEFINITION 4

If $P(E) = p$, the *odds* in favor of the event E occurring are $r : s$ (r to s) where $r/s = p/(1 - p)$.

EXAMPLE 5 (continued)

In Example 5 we assigned probability $^1/_5$ to the event that candidate C wins the race. Thus the odds in favor of C winning are $^1/_5 : ^4/_5$. These odds could equally well have been written as $1 : 4$, $2 : 8$, and so forth. A bet that C wins is fair if we receive 4 dollars if C wins and pay 1 dollar if C loses.   □

Infinite Sample Spaces

If a sample space has an infinite number of points, then the way that a density is defined depends upon whether or not the sample space is countable. A sample space is *countably infinite* if the elements can be counted, i.e., can be put in one-to-one correspondence with the integers, and *noncountably infinite* otherwise. Infinite sample spaces require new concepts in general (see Chapter 2), but countably infinite spaces do not. If

$$\Omega = \{\omega_1, \omega_2, \omega_3, \ldots\}$$

is a countably infinite sample space, then a probability density is defined exactly as in Definition 2, except that the sum must now be a *convergent* infinite sum. Theorem 1 is still true, as are its extensions (6) and (7). One thing we cannot do on a countably infinite sample space that we could do on a finite sample space is to define a *uniform* probability density as in Definition 4. You are asked in Exercise 18 to explain why this is not possible.

EXAMPLE 8

A coin is tossed until the first time that a head turns up. Let the outcome of the experiment, ω, be the first time that a head turns up. Then the possible outcomes of our experiment are

$$\Omega = \{1, 2, 3, \ldots\}.$$

Note that even though the coin could come up tails every time we have not allowed for this possibility. We will explain why in a moment. The probability that heads comes up on the first toss is $1/2$. The probability that tails comes up on the first toss and heads on the second is $1/4$. The probability that we have two tails followed by a head is $1/8$, and so forth. This suggests assigning the density $p(n) = 1/2^n$ for $n = 1, 2, 3, \ldots$. To see that this is a density we must show that

$$\sum_{\omega} p(\omega) = \frac{1}{2} + \frac{1}{4} + \frac{1}{8} + \ldots = 1.$$

That this is true follows from the formula for the sum of a geometric series,

$$1 + r + r^2 + r^3 + \ldots = \frac{1}{1 - r},$$

or

$$r + r^2 + r^3 + \ldots = \frac{r}{1 - r} \qquad (0 < r < 1). \tag{2}$$

Putting $r = 1/2$, we see that we have a probability of 1 that the coin eventually turns up heads. The possible outcome of tails every time has to be assigned probability 0, so we omit it from our sample space of possible outcomes.

Let E be the event that the first time a head turns up is after an even number of tosses. Then

$$E = \{2, 4, 6, 8, \ldots\},$$

and

$$P(E) = \frac{1}{4} + \frac{1}{16} + \frac{1}{64} + \cdots.$$

Putting $r = \frac{1}{4}$ in (2) we see that

$$P(E) = \frac{1/4}{1 - 1/4} = \frac{1}{3}.$$

Thus the probability that a head turns up for the first time after an even number of tosses is $\frac{1}{3}$ and after an odd number of tosses is $\frac{2}{3}$. □

Historical Remarks

An interesting question in the history of science is: Why was probability not developed until the sixteenth century? We know that in the sixteenth century problems in gambling and games of chance made people start to think about probability. But gambling and games of chance are almost as old as civilization itself. In ancient Egypt (at the time of the First Dynasty, ca. 3500 B.C.) a game now called "Hounds and Jackals" was played. In this game the movement of the hounds and jackals was based on the outcome of the roll of four-sided dice made out of animal bones called astragali. Six-sided dice made of a variety of materials date back to the sixteenth century B.C. Gambling was widespread in ancient Greece and Rome. Indeed, in the Roman Empire it was sometimes found necessary to invoke laws against gambling. Why, then, were probabilities not calculated until the sixteenth century?

Several explanations have been advanced for this late development. One is that the relevant mathematics was not developed and was not easy to develop. The ancient mathematical notation made numerical calculation complicated, and our familiar algebraic notation was not developed until the sixteenth century. However, as we shall see, many of the combinatorial ideas needed to calculate probabilities were discussed long before the sixteenth century. Since many of the chance events of those times had to do with lotteries relating to religious affairs, it has been suggested that there may have been religious barriers to the study of chance and gambling. Another suggestion is that a stronger incentive, such as the development of commerce, was necessary. However, none of these explanations seems completely satisfactory, and people still wonder why it took so long for probability to be studied seriously. An interesting discussion of this problem can be found in Hacking.[13]

The first person to calculate probabilities systematically was Gerolamo Cardano (1501–1576) in his book *Liber de Ludo Aleae*. This was translated from the Latin by Gould and appears in the book *Cardano: The Gambling Scholar* by Ore.[14] Ore provides a fascinating discussion of the life of this colorful scholar with accounts of his interests in many different fields, including medicine, astrology, and mathematics. You will also find there a detailed account of Cardano's famous battle with Tartaglia over the solution to the cubic equation.

[13]Ian Hacking, *The Emergence of Probability* (Cambridge: Cambridge University Press, 1975).

[14]Oystein Ore, *Cardano, The Gambling Scholar* (Princeton: Princeton University Press, 1953).

In his book on probability Cardano dealt only with the special case that we have called the uniform density. This restriction to equiprobable outcomes was to continue for a long time. In this case Cardano realized that the probability that an event occurs is the ratio of the number of favorable outcomes to the total number of outcomes.

Many of Cardano's examples dealt with rolling dice. Here he realized that the outcomes for two rolls should be taken to be the 36 ordered pairs (i,j) rather than the 21 unordered pairs. This is a subtle point that was still causing problems much later for other writers on probability. For example, in the eighteenth century the famous French mathematician d'Alembert, author of several works on probability, claimed that when a coin is tossed three times the number of heads that turn up would be 0, 1, or 2, and hence we should assign equal probabilities for these three possible outcomes.[15] Cardano chose the correct sample space for his dice problems and calculated the correct probabilities for a variety of events.

Cardano's mathematical work is interspersed with a lot of advice to the potential gambler in short paragraphs, entitled, for example: "Who Should Play and When," "Why Gambling Was Condemned by Aristotle," "Do Those Who Teach Also Play Well?" and so forth. In a paragraph entitled "The Fundamental Principle of Gambling," Cardano writes:

> The most fundamental principle of all in gambling is simply equal conditions, e.g. of opponents, of bystanders, of money, of situation, of the dice box, and of the die itself. To the extent to which you depart from that equality, if it is in your opponent's favor, you are a fool, and if in your own, you are unjust.[16]

Cardano did make mistakes, and if he realized it later he did not go back and change his error. For example, for an event that is favorable in three out of four cases, Cardano assigned the correct odds 3 : 1 that the event will occur. But then he assigned odds by squaring these numbers (i.e., 9 : 1) for the event to happen twice in a row. Later, by considering the case where the odds are 1 : 1, he realized that this cannot be correct and was led to the correct result that when f out of n outcomes are favorable, the odds for a favorable outcome twice in a row are $f^2 : n^2 - f^2$. Ore points out that this is equivalent to the realization that if the probability that an event happens in one experiment is p, the probability that it happens twice is p^2. Cardano proceeded to established that for three successes the formula should be p^3 and for four successes p^4, making it clear that he understood that the probability is p^n for n successes in n independent repetitions of such an experiment. This will follow from the concept of independence that we introduce in Section 4.1.

Cardano did not always resolve his errors. For example he considered the problem we now call *de Méré's problem*. In the simplest version of this problem one asks how many times a single die should be rolled to make it a fair bet that at least one six will turn up. Cardano calls the six possible outcomes of a single toss a *circuit* and argues that it would be a fair bet if we take the number of tosses equal to one half the circuit, or three rolls. Actually, this would be a slightly unfavorable bet. He is led by this reasoning to a more serious error in determining the number of rolls necessary for a fair bet that a

---

[15]J. d'Alembert, "Croix ou Pile," in *L'Encyclopédie*, ed. Diderot, vol. 4 (Paris, 1754).

[16]Oystein Ore, *Cardano*, p. 189.

pair of sixes will turn up at least once when two dice are rolled a series of times. Since the circuit is now 36, Cardano says that 18 rolls would make a fair bet. There is some evidence that he was not happy with this line of reasoning, but he never corrected it. Pascal and Fermat had no trouble showing that, in fact, 24 rolls is still a unfavorable bet and 25 is a favorable bet.

It is fascinating to read Cardano's book as the first attempt at calculating probabilities systematically. Ore shows us that Cardano had many good ideas, but his book was not influential in the further development of probability. The incentive for further development came rather from the famous letters between Pascal and Fermat with their solution to the problem of points.[17] The problem of points was difficult enough to challenge these two great mathematicians and to lead Pascal to develop combinatorial concepts having to do with binomial coefficients that were to play such an essential role in probability.

The famous Dutch physicist Christian Huygens wrote in 1657 the first text book of probability, *Calculating in Games of Chance*. On visiting Paris, Huygens heard about the Pascal-Fermat correspondence. Although he was able to meet de Méré, he did not get to meet either Fermat or Pascal—Fermat lived in the country, and Pascal, although he lived in Port Royal, was apparently more interested in religious matters. Huygens did solve the problem of points for himself and corresponded with Pascal and Fermat. They verified his calculations and sent him additional problems. These problems, with two additional problems of his own, were put at the end of his text without solutions. They would appear later, with solutions, in the classic probability books of Bernoulli and de Moivre. The important concept of expected value of an experiment was formally defined first in Huygens's book.[18] We shall say more about this in our historical remarks in Section 7.1. Huygens's book was included as an appendix to a book by Francis van Shooten. In a letter to van Shooten, Huygens wrote, "I would like to believe that in considering these matters closely, the reader will observe that we are dealing not only with games but rather with foundations of a new theory, both deep and interesting."[19]

Exercises

1. Let $\Omega = \{a,b,c\}$ be a sample space. Let $p(a) = \frac{1}{2}$, $p(b) = \frac{1}{3}$, and $p(c) = \frac{1}{6}$. Find the probabilities for all eight subsets of Ω.

2. Give a possible sample space Ω for each of the following experiments:
   (a) An election decides between two candidates A and B.
   (b) A two-sided coin is tossed.
   (c) A student is asked for the month of the year and the day of the week on which her birthday falls.
   (d) A student is chosen at random from a class of ten students.
   (e) You receive a grade in this course.

[17]See F. N. David, *Games, Gods and Gambling* (London: Griffin, 1962), p. 229ff.

[18]Christian Huygens, *Calculating in Games of Chance*, trans. attributed to John Arbuthnot, *The Miscellaneous Works of the Late Dr. Arbuthnot*, 2d ed. (Glasgow: Carlisle, 1751).

[19]Cited in David, *Games, Gods and Gambling*, p. 115.

3. For which of the cases in Exercise 2 would it be reasonable to assign the equiprobable density?

4. Describe in words the events specified by the following subsets of $\Omega = \{$HHH, HHT, HTH, HTT, THH, THT, TTH, TTT$\}$ (see Example 6).
  (a) $E = \{$HHH, HHT, HTH, HTT$\}$.
  (b) $E = \{$HHH, TTT$\}$.
  (c) $E = \{$HHT, HTH, THH$\}$.
  (d) $E = \{$HHT, HTH, HTT, THH, THT, TTH, TTT$\}$.

5. What are the probabilities of the events described in Exercise 4?

6. A die is loaded in such a way that the probability of each face turning up is proportional to the number of dots on that face. (For example, a six is three times as probable as a two.) What is the probability of getting an even number in one throw?

7. Let A and B be events such that $P(A \cap B) = \frac{1}{4}$, $P(\tilde{A}) = \frac{1}{3}$, and $P(B) = \frac{1}{2}$. What is $P(A \cup B)$?

8. A student must choose one of the subjects, art, geology, or psychology, as an elective. She is equally likely to choose art or psychology and twice as likely to choose geology. What are the respective probabilities that she chooses art, geology, and psychology?

9. A student must choose exactly two out of three electives: art, French, and mathematics. He chooses art with probability $\frac{5}{8}$, French with probability $\frac{5}{8}$, and art and French together with probability $\frac{1}{4}$. What is the probability that he chooses mathematics? What is the probability that he chooses either art or French?

10. For a bill to come before the president of the United States, it must be passed by both the House of Representatives and the Senate. Assume that, of the bills presented to these two bodies, 60 percent pass the House, 80 percent pass the Senate, and 90 percent pass at least one of the two. Calculate the probability that the next bill presented to the two groups will come before the president.

11. What odds should a person give in favor of the following events?
  (a) A card chosen at random from a 52-card deck is an ace.
  (b) Two heads will turn up when a coin is tossed twice.
  (c) Boxcars (two sixes) will turn up when two dice are rolled.

12. You offer 3 : 1 odds that your friend Smith will be elected mayor of your city. What probability are you assigning to the event that Smith wins?

13. In a horse race, the odds that Romance will win are listed as 2 : 3 and that Downhill will win are 1 : 2. What odds should be given for the event that either Romance or Downhill wins?

*14. John and Mary are taking a mathematics course. The course has only three grades: A, B, and C. The probability that John gets a B is .3. The probability that Mary gets a B is .4. The probability that neither gets an A but at least one gets a B is .1. What is the probability that at least one gets a B but neither gets a C?

15. In a fierce battle, not less than 70 percent of the soldiers lost one eye, not less than 75 percent lost one ear, not less than 80 percent lost one hand and not less than 85 percent lost one leg. What is the minimal possible percentage of those who simultaneously lost one ear, one eye, one hand, and one leg?[20]

16. (a) For events $A_1, \ldots, A_n$, prove that $P(A_1 \cup \ldots \cup A_n) \leq P(A_1) + \cdots + P(A_n)$.
   (b) For events A and B, prove that

$$P(A \cap B) \geq P(A) + P(B) - 1.$$

17. (a) If A and B are any two events, show that $P(A \cup B) = P(A) + P(B) - P(A \cap B)$.
   (b) If A, B, and C are any three events, show that

$$\begin{aligned} P(A \cup B \cup C) = {} & P(A) + P(B) + P(C) \\ & - P(A \cap B) - P(B \cap C) - P(C \cap A) \\ & + P(A \cap B \cap C). \end{aligned}$$

18. Explain why it is not possible to define a uniform probability density (see Definition 3) on a countably infinite sample space. *Hint:* assume $p(\omega) = a$ for all ω, where $0 \leq a \leq 1$. Does $p(\omega)$ have all the properties of a density function?

19. In Example 8 find the probability that the coin turns up heads for the first time on the tenth, eleventh, or twelfth toss.

20. A die is rolled until the first time that a six turns up. We shall see that the probability that this occurs on the nth roll is $(5/6)^{n-1} \cdot (1/6)$. Using this fact, describe the appropriate infinite sample space and density for the experiment of rolling a die until a six turns up for the first time. Verify that for your density $\sum_\omega p(\omega) = 1$.

21. Let Ω be the sample space

$$\Omega = \{0, 1, 2, \ldots\},$$

and define a density by

$$p(\omega) = (1 - r)^j r \qquad \text{for some } r, \, 0 < r < 1.$$

Show that this is a density function for Ω.

22. Our calendar has a 400-year cycle. B. H. Brown noticed that the number of times the thirteenth of the month falls on each of the days of the week in the 4800 months of a cycle is as follows:

Sunday 687
Monday 685
Tuesday 685

---

[20]See Knot X, in Lewis Carroll, *Mathematical Recreations*, vol. 2 (Dover, 1958).

Wednesday 687

Thursday 684

Friday 688

Saturday 684

From this he deduced that the thirteenth was more likely to fall on Friday than on any other day. Explain what he meant by this.

*23. Prove that a calendar year has at least one and at most three Friday-the-thirteenths. For the origins of this problem and other interesting references to calendar problems see "Mathematics of the Gregorian Calendar" by V. Frederick Rickey.[21]

24. Tversky and Kahneman[22] asked a group of subjects to carry out the following task. They are told that:

Linda is 31, single, outspoken, and very bright. She majored in philosophy in college. As a student, she was deeply concerned with racial discrimination and other social issues, and participated in anti-nuclear demonstrations.

The subjects are then asked to rank the likelihood of various alternatives, such as:

(1) Linda is active in the feminist movement.

(2) Linda is a bank teller.

(3) Linda is a bank teller and active in the feminist movement.

Tversky and Kahneman found that between 85 and 90 percent of the subjects rated alternative (1) most likely, but alternative (3) more likely than alternative (2). Is it? They call this phenomenon the *conjunction fallacy,* and note that it appears to be unaffected by prior training in probability or statistics. Explain why this is a fallacy. Can you give a possible explanation for the subject's choices?

25. Two cards are drawn successively from a deck of 52 cards. Find the probability that the second card is higher in rank than the first card. *Hint:* show that $1 = P(\text{higher}) + P(\text{lower}) + P(\text{same})$ and use the fact that $P(\text{higher}) = P(\text{lower})$.

26. A *life table* is a table that lists for a given number of births the estimated number of people who will live to a given age. In Appendix C we give a life table based upon 100,000 births for ages from 0 to 85, both for women and for men. The data from this program are also incorporated in the computer program **Life Table.** Show how from this table you can estimate the probability $p(x)$ that a person born in 1981 would live to age x. Write a program to plot $p(x)$ both for men and for women, and comment on the differences that you see in the two cases.

*27. Suppose you are given a life table as in Exercise 26. Show that if you assume that the same number of births occur each year, then you can determine the age distribution of the total population in any one year.

[21]V. F. Rickey, "Mathematics of the Gregorian Calender," *Math Intelligencer*, vol. 7 (1985), pp. 53–56.

[22]McKean, "Decisions, Decisions," pp. 22–31.

*28. (a) What, intuitively, is the probability that a "randomly chosen" positive integer is a multiple of 3?

(b) Let $P_3(N)$ be the probability that an integer, chosen at random between 1 and N, is a multiple of 3 (since the sample space is finite, this is a legitimate probability). Show that the limit

$$P_3 = \lim_{N \to \infty} P_3(N)$$

exists and equals $^1/_3$. This formalizes the intuition in (a), and gives us a way to assign "probabilities" to certain events that are infinite subsets of the positive integers.

(c) In Chapter 4 we will define events A and B to be independent if $P(A \cap B) = P(A)P(B)$. Let A be the event "n is divisible by 3," B be the event "n is divisible by 4," and C the event "n is divisible by 6." Show that if we defined "probabilities" as in **(b)**, A and B are independent but B and C are not.

(d) If A is any set of positive integers, let $A(N)$ mean the number of elements of A which are less than or equal to N. Then define the "probability" of A as the limit

$$\lim_{N \to \infty} A(N)/N,$$

provided this limit exists. Show that this definition would assign probability 0 to any finite set and probability 1 to the set of all positive integers. Thus, the probability of the set of all integers is not the sum of the probabilities of the individual integers in this set. This means that the definition of probability given here is not a completely satisfactory definition.

Chapter 2

Continuous Probability Densities

2.1 COMPUTER SIMULATION OF CONTINUOUS PROBABILITIES

In this section we shall show how we can use computer simulations for experiments that have a whole continuum of possible outcomes.

Probabilities

EXAMPLE 1

To simulate an experiment for which an event has probability p we first introduced in Chapter 1, Section 1.1 the notion of a spinner with unit circumference. There we marked off an arc of length p and said that the event occurred if the spinner stopped in this arc. In this case it is convenient to think of the outcome of the spinner as a point on the circumference of the circle and hence any one of an infinite number of points. An event is then a subset of the points on the circumference. A typical event of interest is a subset consisting of an arc of the circle. To say that the spinner is equally likely to land anywhere

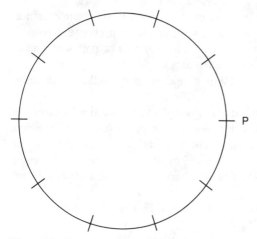

Figure 1 Ten arcs of equal length.

on the circumference is to say that it is equally likely to fall in arcs of the same length. Since the total circumference is 1, this suggests that the probability of falling in an arc should be equal to the length of the arc.

Lengths

We can check this assertion by simulation. Specifically, we take a circle of *unit circumference,* and divide the circumference into ten arcs of equal length (see Figure 1).

First we note that the points around the circumference can be described by their

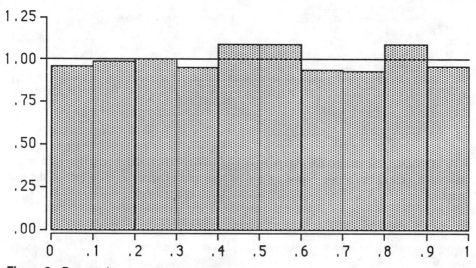

Figure 2 Bar graph.

distances counterclockwise around the circle from some fixed point P on the circle. Hence, if we choose a random number between 0 and 1, we can use it to choose a point *at random* on the circumference. We can then choose a large number of points at random and see what fraction of them fall in each of the ten arcs.

We have carried out this experiment 1000 times and summarized the results in the bar graph shown in Figure 2.

Here we have chosen each bar so that its *area* is equal to the fraction of outcomes falling within its arc, for reasons that we will make clear in the next section. We note here that the heights of the bars, and hence their areas, are approximately the same; in fact the heights are all nearly 1, and the areas are all nearly $1/10$ (i.e., nearly the length of each arc). Moreover, the total area of the first four bars is nearly the length of the arc $(0,4)$, and so forth.

The program **Demo Bargraph** produced the graph of Figure 2.

```
! Demo Bargraph      (DBARGRPH)
!
! Demonstrates sub bargraph(result(), trials, xmin, xmax, cells) in
! "Lib.prob"

library "Lib.prob*"

dim result(1000)

let xmin = 0
let xmax = 1
let ymin = 0
let ymax = 3/2

input prompt " Number of trials = ": trials
input prompt " Number of cells = ": cells

for trial = 1 to trials
    let result(trial) = rnd          ! Choose a random number
next trial

set window xmin, xmax, ymin, ymax

call bargraph(result, trials, xmin, xmax, cells)

plot 0,1; 1,1                        ! Theoretical curve

end
```

This program collects the outcomes in a list called **result** and then calls a subroutine **bargraph** in **Lib.Prob** that computes the number of outcomes in each cell of the bar graph.

```
! Bargraph
!
! Subroutine to make a histogram of a collection of data.
!
```

```
sub bargraph(result(),trials,xmin,xmax,cells)

    dim count(100)
    mat count = zer(0 to cells)

    let dx = (xmax - xmin)/cells

    for trial = 1 to trials

        let datum = result(trial)

        if datum >= xmin and datum <= xmax then
            let cell = int((datum-xmin)/dx)    ! Determine  the cell
        end if

        let count(cell) = count(cell) + 1     ! Count it

    next trial

    for cell = 0 to cells-1
        let height =  count(cell)/trials/dx
        box lines xmin+cell*dx, xmin+(cell+1)*dx,  0, height
    next cell

end sub
```

If we do this experiment again with more trials or with different arcs, we will gain support for our assertion that the fraction of outcomes falling in each arc should be approximately equal to the *length* of the arc. ☐

Areas

EXAMPLE 2

In our next example we show how simulation can be used to estimate areas of plane figures. Suppose we program our computer to provide a pair (x,y) of numbers, each chosen independently at random from the interval [0,1]. Then we can interpret this pair (x,y) as the coordinates of a point chosen *at random* from the unit square. Events then are subsets of the unit square. Our experience with Example 1 suggests that the point is equally likely to fall in subsets of equal area. Since the total area of the square is 1, the probability of the point falling in a specific subset E of the unit square should be equal to its area. Thus, we can estimate the area of any subset of the unit square by estimating the probability that a point chosen at random from this square falls in the subset.

We can use this method to estimate the area of the region E under the curve $y = x^2$ in the unit square (see Figure 3). We choose a large number of points (x,y) at random and record what fraction of them fall in the region $E = \{(x,y): y \leqslant x^2\}$.

The program **Monte Carlo** will carry out this experiment for us.

```
! Monte Carlo    (MONTE)
!
! Estimates an area by the Monte Carlo method.

read trials
data 10000

for trial = 1 to trials

    let x = rnd
    let y = rnd

    if y <= x^2 then let sum = sum + 1

next trial

print "Estimate for the area = "; round(sum/trials,3)

end
```

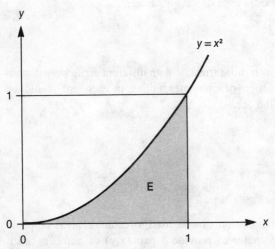

Figure 3 Area under $y = x^2$.

Running this program for 10,000 experiments gives:

```
Estimate for the area = .332
```

A graphical version of this program produced the picture shown in Figure 4.

From these experiments we would estimate the area to be about $1/3$. Of course, for this simple region we can find the exact area by calculus. In fact,

$$\text{Area of E} = \int_0^1 x^2 dx = \frac{1}{3}.$$

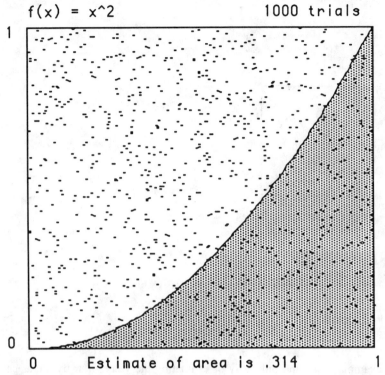

f(x) = x^2   1000 trials

0   Estimate of area is .314   1

Figure 4 Computing the area by simulation.

We will see later (in Chapter 9) that, when we simulate an experiment of this type n times to estimate a probability, we can expect the answer to be in error by at most $1/\sqrt{n}$ about 95 percent of the time. For 10,000 experiments we can expect an accuracy of 0.01, and our simulation did achieve this accuracy.

This same argument works for any region E of the unit square. For example, suppose E is the circle with center $(^1/_2, \, ^1/_2)$ and radius $^1/_2$ (see Figure 5). Then the probability that our random point (x,y) lies inside the circle is equal to the area of the circle, that is,

$$P(E) \;=\; \pi\left(\frac{1}{2}\right)^2 = \frac{\pi}{4} \, .$$

If we did not know the value of π, we could use this experiment, run a large number of times, to estimate it! □

Monte Carlo Procedure

The use of experiments involving chance to estimate the value of particular numbers in this way is often called a *Monte Carlo procedure* and is used in engineering applications, especially where other methods prove too difficult to carry out.

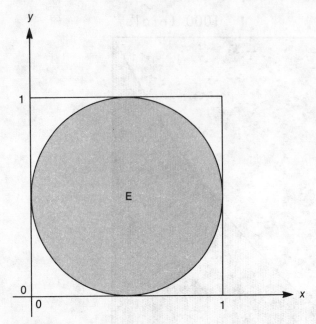

Figure 5 Circle in a square.

The above example is not the only way of estimating the value of π by a chance experiment. Here is another way, discovered by Buffon.[1]

Buffon's Needle

EXAMPLE 3

Suppose we take a card table and draw across the top surface a set of parallel lines a unit distance apart. We then drop a common needle of unit length at random on this surface and observe whether or not the needle lies across one of the lines. We can describe the possible outcomes of this experiment by coordinates as follows: Let d be the distance from the center of the needle to the nearest line, and let θ be the acute angle between the needle and the nearest line. Then certainly we have $0 \le d \le 1/2$, and $0 \le \theta \le \pi/2$. Moreover, we see that the needle lies across the nearest line if and only if the hypotenuse of the little triangle (see Figure 6) is less than half the length of the needle, that is,

$$\frac{d}{\sin\theta} < \frac{1}{2}$$

[1]G.L.L. Buffon, in "Essai d'Arithmétique Morale," *Oeuvres Complètes de Buffon avec Supplements*, tome iv, ed. Duménil (Paris, 1836).

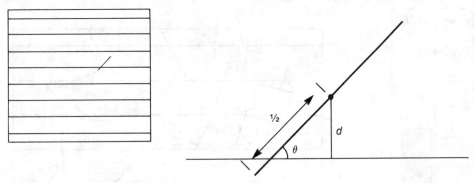

Figure 6   Buffon's experiment.

Now we assume that when the needle drops, the pair (θ, d) is chosen at random from the rectangle $0 \le \theta \le \pi/2, 0 \le d \le 1/2$. We observe whether the needle lies across the nearest line (i.e., whether $d \le 1/2 \sin\theta$). The probability of this event E is the fraction of the area of the rectangle which lies inside E (see Figure 7). Now the area of the rectangle is $\pi/4$, while the area of E is

$$\text{Area} = \int_0^{\pi/2} \frac{1}{2} \sin\theta \; d\theta$$

$$= \frac{1}{2} \; .$$

Hence, we get

$$P(E) = \frac{1/2}{\pi/4} = \frac{2}{\pi} \; .$$

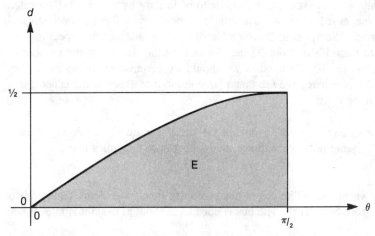

Figure 7   Set E of pairs (θ, d) with $d < \frac{1}{2} \sin\theta$.

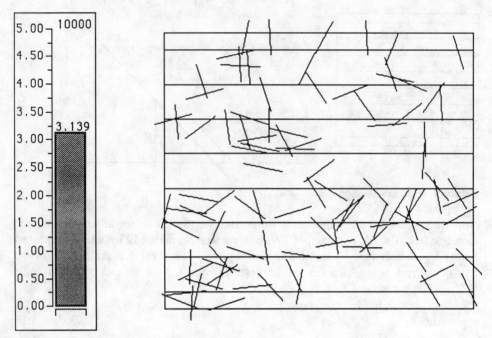

Figure 8 Simulation of Buffon's needle experiment.

The program **Buffon** simulates this experiment. We do not list the program here but we show the result of a run of the program dropping 10,000 needles. Figure 8 shows the position of every 100th needle.

Our final estimate for π is 3.139. While this was within 0.02 of the true value for π we had no right to expect such accuracy. The reason for this is that our simulation estimates $P(E)$. While we can expect this estimate to be in error by at most 0.01, a small error in $P(E)$ gets magnified when we use this to compute $\pi = 2/P(E)$. Perlman and Wichura, in their article "Sharpening Buffon's Needle"[2] show that we can expect to have an error of not more than $5/\sqrt{n}$ about 95 percent of the time. Here n is the number of needles dropped. Thus for 10,000 needles we should expect an error of no more than 0.05, and that was the case here. We see that a large number of experiments is necessary to get a decent estimate for π. $\qquad\square$

In each of our examples so far, events of the same size are equally likely. Here's an example where they are not. We will see many other such examples later.

EXAMPLE 4
Suppose you go down to the White River bus station to meet your Aunt Tilda who is coming in on a bus from New York. The bus is due at 12:00 but as usual it is late. When

[2]M.D. Perlman and M.J. Wichura, "Sharpening Buffon's Needle," *The American Statistician*, vol. 29, no. 4 (1975), pp. 157–163.

you ask at the window you learn that "it's coming any minute now," and you wonder how long you have to wait.

Suppose that in each minute after noon the bus, if it has not already arrived, will arrive with probability $p = {}^1/_{30}$. To see how this works, imagine that a biased coin is flipped every minute, biased so that it turns up heads with probability $^1/_{30}$. Most of the time, of course, it comes up tails, but eventually it will come up heads, and at that moment the bus arrives.

It is easy to write a computer program to simulate this situation. It will choose a random number in [0,1], test whether it is less than $^1/_{30}$ (a success) and if not, choose and test another random number, continuing until it finds a success. The program then records the total number of random numbers required to find a success. We have run such a program for 1000 experiments and made up a bar graph showing the fraction of the total number of experiments that required i random numbers to find a success, for $i = 1,2,3, \ldots$. The results are shown in Figure 9. We can interpret this graph in terms of our bus problem as giving the probability that we have to wait i minutes for the bus! This probability is just the area of the ith bar. Note that the probabilities are different for different i's: the bus is more likely to come in the first minute than in the tenth. The *heights* of the bars appear to fall along the graph of the function $y = (^1/_{30})e^{-(1/30)t}$. We shall see in the next section why this is so. □

Although the possible outcomes in this example (i.e., the possible waiting times for the bus) form the continuum of all positive real numbers, we have chosen to simulate it by a discrete approximation in which the possible outcomes (i.e., the waiting times *rounded off* to the nearest minute) form the discrete set of all positive integers. It is often possible to analyze a continuous problem in terms of a carefully chosen discrete approximation in this way, particularly when making numerical calculations or simulations, as we have done. It is also possible to simulate this problem directly without a discrete approximation, and we have indicated how this is done in Exercise 9.

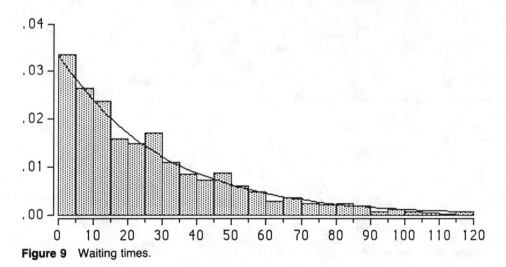

Figure 9 Waiting times.

Our last example explores the fundamental question of how probabilities are assigned.

Bertrand's Paradox

EXAMPLE 5

A chord is drawn *at random* in a unit circle. What is the probability that its length exceeds $\sqrt{3}$?

In this case, our answer will depend on what we mean by *at random*, which will depend, in turn, on what we choose for coordinates. The sample space Ω is the set of all possible chords in the circle. To find coordinates for these chords, we first introduce a rectangular coordinate system with origin at the center of the circle (see Figure 10). Then we can describe each chord by giving:

(1) The rectangular coordinates (x,y) of the midpoint M, or

(2) The polar coordinates (r,θ) of the midpoint M, or

(3) The polar coordinates $(1,\alpha)$ and $(1,\beta)$ of the endpoints A and B.

In each case we shall interpret *at random* to mean: choose these coordinates at random.

We can easily do this by computer simulation. In programming this simulation, it is convenient to include certain simplifications, which we describe in turn:

(1) To simulate this case, we choose values for x and y from $[-1,1]$ at random. Then we check whether $x^2 + y^2 \leq 1$. If not, the point M $= (x,y)$ lies outside

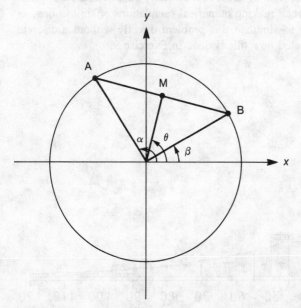

Figure 10 Random chord.

the circle and cannot be the midpoint of any chord, and we ignore it. Otherwise, M lies inside the circle and is the midpoint of a unique chord, whose length L is given by the formula:

$$L = 2\sqrt{1 - (x^2 + y^2)}.$$

(2) To simulate this case, we take account of the fact that any rotation of the circle does not change the length of the chord, so we might as well assume in advance that the chord is horizontal (i.e., that $\theta = \pi/2$). Then we choose r from $[-1,1]$ at random, and compute the length of the resulting chord with midpoint $(r, \pi/2)$ by the formula:

$$L = 2\sqrt{1 - r^2}.$$

(3) To simulate this case, we assume that one end point, say B, lies at $(1,0)$ (i.e., that $\beta = 0$). Then we choose a value for α from $[0,2\pi]$ at random and compute the length of the resulting chord, using the law of cosines, by the formula:

$$L = \sqrt{2 - 2\cos(\alpha)}.$$

The program **Bertrand's Paradox** carries out this simulation. Running this program produces the results shown in Figure 11. □

In each case we run the experiment a large number of times and record the fraction of these lengths that exceed $\sqrt{3}$. We have printed the results for every 100 trials up to 10,000 trials.

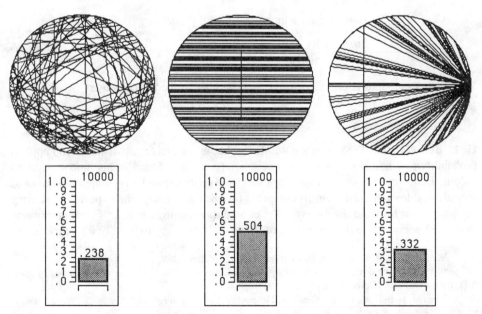

Figure 11 Bertrand's paradox.

It is interesting to observe that these fractions are *not* the same in the three cases: they depend on our choice of coordinates. This phenomenon was first observed by Bertrand, and is now known as *Bertrand's paradox*.[3] It is actually not a paradox at all; it is merely a reflection of the fact that different choices of coordinates will lead to different assignments of probabilities. Which assignment is "correct" depends on what application or interpretation of the model one has in mind.

One can argue that the "correct" assignment, that is, the assignment you should use to describe a real experiment involving throwing straws at a circle drawn on a card table, should not depend on where the circle lies on the card table, or where the card table sits in the room. Jaynes[4] has shown that the only assignment which meets this requirement is (1). In this sense, the assignment (1) is the natural, or "correct" one (see Exercise 11).

We can easily see in each case what the true probabilities are if we note that $\sqrt{3}$ is the length of the side of an inscribed equilateral triangle. Hence, a chord has length $L > \sqrt{3}$ if its midpoint has distance $d < \frac{1}{2}$ from the origin (see Figure 10). Hence, $L > \sqrt{3}$ if:

Case (1). (x,y) lies inside a circle of radius $\frac{1}{2}$, which occurs with probability

$$p = \frac{\pi(1/2)^2}{\pi 1^2} = \frac{1}{4}.$$

Case (2). $|r| < \frac{1}{2}$, which occurs with probability

$$\frac{1/2 - (-1/2)}{1 - (-1)} = \frac{1}{2}.$$

Case (3). $\frac{2\pi}{3} < \alpha < \frac{4\pi}{3}$, which occurs with probability

$$\frac{4\pi/3 - 2\pi/3}{2\pi - 0} = \frac{1}{3}.$$

We see that our simulations agree quite well with these theoretical values.

Historical Remarks

G. L. Buffon (1707–1788) was a natural scientist in the eighteenth century who applied probability to a number of his investigations. His work is found in his monumental 44 volume *Histoire Naturelle* and its supplements.[5] For example, he presented a number of mortality tables and used them to compute, for each age group, the expected remaining lifetime. From his table he observed: the expected remaining lifetime of an infant of one year is 33 years, while that of a man of 21 years is also approximately 33 years. Thus,

[3]J. Bertrand, *Calcul des Probabilités* (Paris: Gauthier-Villars, 1889).

[4]E.T. Jaynes, "The Well-Posed Problem," in *Papers on Probability, Statistics and Statistical Physics*, R.D. Rosencrantz, ed. (Dordrecht: D. Reidel, 1983), pp. 133–148.

[5]See G.L.L. Buffon, *Histoire Naturelle, Generali et Particular avec le Descriptión du Cabinet du Roy*, 44 vols. (Paris: L'Imprimerie Royale, 1749–1803).

a father who is not yet 21 can hope to live longer than his one year old son, but if the father is 40, the odds are already 3 to 2 that his son will outlive him.[6]

Buffon wanted to show that not all probability calculations relied only on algebra, but that some relied on geometrical calculations. One such problem was his famous "needle problem" as discussed in this chapter.[7] In his original formulation, Buffon describes a game in which two gamblers drop a loaf of french bread on a wide-board floor, and bet on whether or not the loaf falls across a crack in the floor. Buffon asked: what length L should the bread loaf be, relative to the width W of the floorboards, so that the game is fair. He found the correct answer $(L = {}^\pi/_4 W)$ using essentially the methods described in this chapter. He also considered the case of a checkerboard floor, but gave the wrong answer in this case. The correct answer was given later by Laplace.

The literature contains descriptions of a number of experiments that were actually carried out to estimate π by this method of dropping needles. N. T. Gridgeman[8] discusses the following experiments.

Experimenter	Length of needle	Number of casts	Number of crossings	Estimate for π
Wolf, 1850	.8	5000	2532	3.1596
Smith, 1855	.6	3204	1218.5	3.1553
De Morgan, c. 1860	1.0	600	382.5	3.137
Fox, 1864	.75	1030	489	3.1595
Lazzerini, 1901	.83	3408	1808	3.1415929
Reina, 1925	.5419	2520	859	3.1795

(The halves for the number of crossings comes from a compromise when it could not be decided if a crossing had actually occurred). He observes, as we have, that 10,000 casts could do no more than establish the first decimal place of π with reasonable confidence. Gridgeman points out that although none of the experiments used even 10,000 casts they are surprisingly good, and in some cases too good. The fact that the number of casts is not always a round number would suggest that the authors might have resorted to clever stopping to get a good answer. Gridgeman comments that Lazzerini's estimate turned out to agree with a well-known approximation to π, $355/113 = 3.1415929$, discovered by the fifth-century Chinese mathematician, Tsu Ch'ungchih. Gridgeman says that he did not have Lazzerini's original report, and while waiting for it (knowing only the needle crossed a line 1808 times in 3408 casts) deduced that the length of the needle must have been $^5/_6$. He calculated this from Buffon's formula, assuming $\pi = 355/113$:

$$L = \frac{\pi P(E)}{2} = \frac{1}{2}\left(\frac{355}{113}\right)\left(\frac{1808}{3408}\right) = \frac{5}{6} = .8333.$$

[6]Buffon, "Essai d'Arithmétique Morale," p. 301.

[7]*Ibid.*, pp. 277–278.

[8]N.T. Gridgeman, "Geometric Probability and the Number π" *Scripta Mathematika*, vol. 25, no. 3, (1960), pp. 183–195.

Even with careful planning one would have to be extremely lucky to be able to stop so cleverly.

The author likes to trace his interest in probability theory to the Chicago World's Fair of 1936 where he observed a mechanical device dropping needles and displaying the ever-changing estimates for the value of π.

Exercises

1. In the spinner problem (see Example 1) divide the unit circumference into three arcs of length $\frac{1}{2}$, $\frac{1}{3}$, and $\frac{1}{6}$. Write a program to simulate the spinner experiment 1000 times and print out what fraction of the outcomes fall in each of the three arcs. Now plot a bar graph whose bars have width $\frac{1}{2}$, $\frac{1}{3}$, and $\frac{1}{6}$, and areas equal to the corresponding fractions as determined by your simulation. Show that the heights of the bars are all nearly the same.

2. Do the same as in Exercise 1, but divide the unit circumference into five arcs of length $\frac{1}{3}$, $\frac{1}{4}$, $\frac{1}{5}$, $\frac{1}{6}$, and $\frac{1}{20}$.

3. Alter the program **Monte Carlo** to estimate the area of the circle, of radius $\frac{1}{2}$ with center at $(\frac{1}{2}, \frac{1}{2})$, inside the unit square by choosing 1000 points at random. Compare your results with the true value of $\pi/4$. Use your results to estimate the value of π. How accurate is your estimate?

4. Alter the program **Monte Carlo** to estimate the area under the graph of $y = \sin\pi x$ inside the unit square by choosing 10,000 points at random. Now calculate the true value of this area and use your results to estimate the value of π. How accurate is your estimate?

5. Alter the program **Monte Carlo** to estimate the area under the graph of $y = 1/(x + 1)$ in the unit square in the same way as in Exercise 4. Calculate the true value of this area, and use your simulation results to estimate the value of $\log(2)$. How accurate is your estimate?

6. To simulate the Buffon's needle problem we choose independently the distance d and the angle θ at random, with $0 \leq d \leq \frac{1}{2}$ and $0 \leq \theta \leq \pi/2$ and check whether $d \leq \frac{1}{2} \sin\theta$. Doing this a large number of times, we estimate π as $2/a$, where a is the fraction of the times that $d \leq \frac{1}{2} \sin\theta$. Write a program to estimate π by this method. Run your program for 100, 1000, and 10,000 experiments. Does the accuracy of π improve as the number of experiments increases?

7. For the Buffon's needle problem, Laplace[9] considered a grid with *horizontal* and *vertical* lines one unit apart. He showed that the probability that a needle of length $L \leq 1$ crosses at least one line is

$$p = \frac{4L - L^2}{\pi}.$$

---

[9]P.S. Laplace, *Theorie Analytique des Probabilités* (Paris: Courcier, 1812).

To simulate this experiment we choose at random an angle θ between 0 and $^\pi/_2$ and independently two numbers d_1 and d_2 between 0 and $^L/_2$. (The two numbers represent the distance from the center of the needle to the nearest horizontal and vertical line.) The needle crosses a line if either $d_1 \leq {}^L/_2 \sin\theta$ or $d_2 \leq {}^L/_2 \cos\theta$. We do this a large number of times and estimate π as

$$\bar{\pi} = \frac{4L - L^2}{a},$$

where a is the proportion of times that the needle crosses at least one line. Write a program to estimate π by this method, run your program for 100, 1000, and 10,000 experiments, and compare your results with Buffon's method described in Exercise 6. (Take $L = 1$.)

8. A long needle of length L much bigger than 1 is dropped on a grid with horizontal and vertical lines one unit apart. We will see (in Chapter 6 Section 6.3 Exercise 19) that the average number a of lines crossed will be approximately

$$a = \frac{4L}{\pi}.$$

To estimate π by simulation, pick an angle θ at random between 0 and $^\pi/_2$ and compute $L\sin\theta + L\cos\theta$. This may be used for the number of lines crossed. Repeat this many times and estimate π by

$$\bar{\pi} = \frac{4L}{a},$$

where a is the average number of lines crossed per experiment. Write a program to simulate this experiment and run your program for the number of experiments equal to 100, 1000, and 10,000. Compare your results with the methods of Laplace or Buffon for the same number of experiments. (Use $L = 100$.)

The following exercises involve experiments in which not all outcomes are equally likely. We shall consider such experiments in detail in the next section, but we invite you to explore a few simple cases here.

9. A large number of waiting time problems have an *exponential distribution* of outcomes. We shall see (in Chapter 5, Section 5.2) that such outcomes are simulated by computing $-\lambda\log(\text{rnd})$, where $\lambda > 0$. For waiting times produced in this way, the average waiting time is $1/\lambda$. For example, the times spent waiting for a bus, or the times between emissions of particles from a radioactive source, are simulated by a sequence of random numbers, each of which is chosen by computing $-\lambda\log(\text{rnd})$, where $1/\lambda$ is the average time between buses or emissions. Write a program to simulate the times between buses when the average time between buses is 30. Have your program compute a bar graph for these times by breaking the time interval from 0 to 120 into 24 subintervals. Compare your result with that of Example 4.

10. Heights of people, scores on SAT exams, errors in measurements, as well as many other natural phenomena, have a distribution that can be described by a *normal* *distribution* with mean μ and standard deviation σ. The mean μ is an average value for the outcomes, and the standard deviation σ is a measure of the spread of the outcomes away from the mean value μ. We shall see (in Chapter 9, Section 9.1) that the following function obtains a sample from a normal distribution.

```
! Computes a sample from a normal distribution with mean mu and
! standard deviation sigma.
!
function sample(mu, sigma)

let sum = 0

for k = 1 to 12
let sum = sum + rnd
next k

let sample = sigma * (sum - 6) + mu

end function
```

Use this function to write a program to simulate heights of 1000 males with average height 70 inches and standard deviation 1 inch. Plot a bar graph for the heights. Then do the same for a standard deviation of 2 inches and compare the two bar graphs.

11. Here is another way to pick a chord *at random* on the circle of unit radius. Imagine that the circle is inscribed in a square with center at the origin and sides of length 2 parallel to the coordinate axes. Now pick a point x_0, y_0 at random in the square, and an angle θ at random in the interval $(-\pi/2, \pi/2)$. Let $m = \tan(\theta)$. Then the equation of the line passing through (x_0, y_0) with slope m is

$$y = y_0 + m(x - x_0),$$

and the distance of this line from the center of the circle (i.e., the origin) is

$$d = \left| \frac{y_0 - mx_0}{\sqrt{m^2 + 1}} \right|.$$

We can use this distance formula to check whether the line intersects the circle (i.e., whether $d < 1$). If so, we consider the resulting chord a *random* chord. This describes an experiment of dropping a long straw at random on a table on which a circle is drawn.

Write a program to simulate this experiment 1000 times and estimate the probability that the length of the chord is greater than $\sqrt{3}$. How does your estimate compare with the results of Example 5?

2.2 CONTINUOUS PROBABILITY DENSITIES

In the previous section we have seen how to simulate experiments with a whole continuum of possible outcomes and have gained some experience in thinking about such experiments.

Now we turn to the general problem of assigning probabilities to the outcomes and events in such experiments. We shall restrict our attention here to those experiments whose sample space can be taken as a suitably chosen subset of the line, the plane, or some other Euclidean space. We begin with some simple examples.

Spinners

EXAMPLE 1

The spinner described in Section 2.1 consists of an arrow whose tail is pinned at the center of a circle of *unit circumference* and whose head is free to move around the circle (see Figure 12).

Suppose the spinner is spun once, and we observe where the head comes to rest. To describe the possible outcomes of this experiment, it is natural to take as our sample space the set of all points on the circle. To describe this sample space, we introduce as a *coordinate* the distance of each point (measured counterclockwise along the circle) from some fixed starting point (see Figure 12). Each outcome is then described by a value of ω, $0 \leq \omega < 1$. The event $E = \{\omega: 0 \leq \omega \leq \frac{1}{2}\}$, for example, then corresponds to the statement that the head of the spinner comes to rest in the upper half of the circle.

What probability should we assign to each elementary event, consisting of a single outcome? To begin with, it is natural to assume, unless there is reason to believe otherwise, that every outcome is equally likely. Suppose the probability $P\{\omega_1\}$ of the outcome ω_1 is a, where $0 \leq a \leq 1$. Then the probability $P\{\omega_1,\omega_2, \ldots ,\omega_n\}$ of any event consisting of n different outcomes is na. But if $a > 1/n$, then $na > 1$, which is contrary to our basic assumption that the probability of any event must lie between 0 and 1. From this we see that we must have $a \leq 1/n$ for every integer n, and so $a = P\{\omega\} = 0$. This argument applies to any experiment involving an infinite number of equally likely possible outcomes.

This does not at all mean that the probability of *every* event must be zero. On the contrary, the probability $P\{\omega: 0 \leq \omega < 1\}$, that the head of the spinner comes to rest

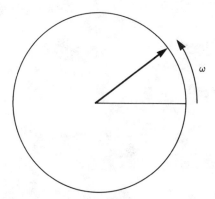

Figure 12   A spinner.

somewhere in the circle, should be equal to 1, and the probability that it comes to rest in the upper half of the circle should be the same as for the lower half, so that

$$P\left\{\omega: 0 \leq \omega < \frac{1}{2}\right\} = P\left\{\omega: \frac{1}{2} \leq \omega < 1\right\} = \frac{1}{2}.$$

More generally, the probability $P\{\omega: c \leq \omega < d\}$ that the head comes to rest in the interval $c \leq \omega < d$ should be determined by what fraction of the circle lies in the interval, that is,

$$P\{\omega: c \leq \omega < d\} = d - c.$$

We can verify this by simulation, as in Section 2.1. (Note that this holds whether or not we include the end points c and d of the interval.) □

We see in this example that, for experiments with a continuum of outcomes, the basic events are not the events consisting of a single outcome, as is the case for discrete sample spaces.

Darts

EXAMPLE 2

A game of darts involves throwing a dart at a circular target of unit *radius*. Suppose we throw a dart once so that it hits the target, and we observe where it lands (see Figure 13).

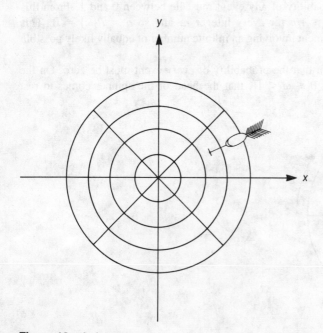

Figure 13 A dart game.

To describe the possible outcomes of this experiment, it is natural to take as our sample space the set Ω of all the points ω in the target. It is convenient to describe these points by their rectangular coordinates, relative to a coordinate system with origin at the center of the target, so that each pair (x,y) of coordinates with $x^2 + y^2 \leqslant 1$ describes a possible outcome of the experiment. Then $\Omega = \{(x,y): x^2 + y^2 \leqslant 1\}$ is a subset of the Euclidean plane, and the event $E = \{(x,y): y > 0\}$, for example, corresponds to the statement that the dart lands in the upper half of the target, and so forth. Unless there is reason to believe otherwise (and with experts at the game there may well be!), it is natural to assume that the coordinates are chosen *at random*. Then the arguments used in the preceding example show that the probability of any elementary event, consisting of a single outcome, must be zero, and suggest that the probability of the event that the dart lands in any subset E of the target should be determined by what fraction of the target area lies in E. Thus,

$$P(\text{E}) = \frac{\text{area of } E}{\text{area of target}} = \frac{\text{area of } E}{\pi}.$$

We can verify this by simulation as in Section 2.1. In particular, if $E = \{(x,y): x^2 + y^2 < a^2\}$ is the event that the dart lands within distance $a < 1$ of the center of the target, then

$$P(E) = \frac{\pi a^2}{\pi} = a^2.$$

For example, the probability that the dart lies within a distance $1/2$ of the center is $1/4$. $\square$

EXAMPLE 3
In the dart game experiment considered above, suppose that, instead of observing where the dart lands, we observe how far it lands from the center of the target.

In this case, we take as our sample space the set Ω of all circles with centers at the center of the target. It is convenient to describe these circles by their radii, so that each circle is identified by its radius r, $0 \leqslant r \leqslant 1$. In this way, we may regard Ω as the subset $[0,1]$ of the real line.

What probabilities should we assign to the events E of Ω? If $E = \{r: 0 \leqslant r < a\}$ then E corresponds to the statement that the dart lands within distance a of the center, that is, within the circle of radius a, and we saw in the previous example that under our assumptions the probability of this event is given by

$$P[0,a] = a^2.$$

More generally, if $E = \{r: a \leqslant r \leqslant b\}$, then, by our basic assumptions,

$$P(E) = P[a,b] = P[0,b] - P[0,a]$$

$$= b^2 - a^2$$

$$= (b - a)(b + a)$$

$$= 2(b - a)\frac{(b + a)}{2}.$$

Thus, $P(E) = 2(\text{length of } E)(\text{midpoint of } E)$. Here we see that the probability assigned

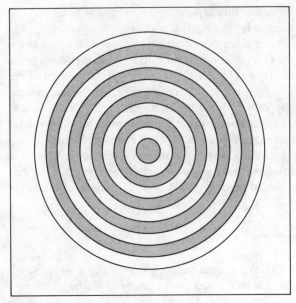

Figure 14 Dart board.

to the interval E depends not only on its length but also on its midpoint (i.e., not only on how long it is, but also on where it is). Roughly speaking, in this experiment events of the form $E = [a,b]$ are more likely if they are near the rim of the target and less likely if they are near the center. (A common experience for beginners! The conclusion might well be different if the beginner is replaced by an expert.)

Again we can verify this with a computer simulation as in Section 2.1. We divide the target area into ten concentric regions of equal thickness (see Figure 14).

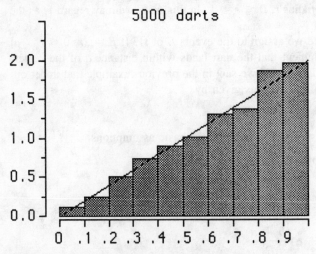

Figure 15 Distance of darts from center.

```
! Darts    (DARTS)
!
! Makes a histogram of darts falling in concentric regions of a board,
! and compares the graph of the theoretical density y = 2x.

library "Lib.prob*"
dim result(1000)

open #1:screen .1,.9,.1,.9
set window 0,1,0,2

input prompt " Number of darts = ":darts
mat result = zer(darts)

let count = 1

do
    let x = 2*rnd - 1
    let y = 2*rnd - 1

    let distance = sqr(x^2 + y^2)          ! Distance to center

    if distance <= 1 then                  ! See if dart hits target
        let result(count) = distance
        let count = count + 1
    end if

loop until count = darts + 1

call bargraph(result,darts,0,1,10)          ! Plot bargraph of results

plot 0,0;1,2                                ! Graph y = 2x

end
```

The computer program **Darts** throws n darts and records what fraction of the total falls in each of these concentric regions. The subroutine **bargraph** then plots a bar graph with the *area* of the ith bar equal to the fraction of the total falling in the ith region. Running the program for 5000 darts resulted in the bar graph of Figure 15.

Note that here the heights of the bars are not all equal, but grow approximately linearly with r. In fact, the linear function $y = 2r$ appears to fit our bar graph quite well. This suggests that the probability that the dart falls within a distance a of the center should be given by the *area* under the graph of the function $y = 2r$ between 0 and a. This area is a^2, which agrees with the probability we have assigned above to this event.   □

Bus Paradox

EXAMPLE 4

Suppose that at noon on Tuesday we arrive at the Hanover Inn to catch the shuttle bus. How long should we expect to wait? Past experience suggests that the bus makes a round

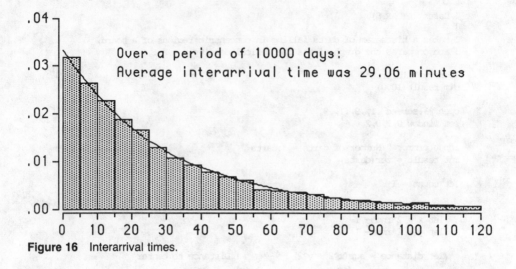

Figure 16 Interarrival times.

trip every 30 minutes on average, but that the times to make these round trips vary widely. We might expect that on the average we will arrive in the middle of one of these times, and so we should have to wait 15 minutes. On the other hand, we might expect that the bus is moving so randomly that it doesn't matter when we arrive, and on the average we will have to wait the full 30 minutes. These two apparently reasonable but obviously contradictory conjectures have caused this problem to be called the *bus paradox*.

Here we can resolve matters easily by simulation. We first simulate the time that the bus arrives back at the Hanover Inn in the same way that we did in Example 4 of Section 2.1, where we simulated the random time of arrival for your Aunt Tilda's bus. We assume that in any one minute either the bus arrives or it does not arrive, with the probability of arrival being 1/30. We simulate 10,000 round trips and construct a bar graph to give the fraction of the arrival times that fall in each 5 minute interval. We present the resulting bar graph in Figure 16. Of course, it is essentially the same as the bar graph in Figure 9 giving possible arrival times for Aunt Tilda's bus. The average interarrival time was about 30 minutes, as expected. The heights of the bars tend to fall along the exponential curve $y = \lambda e^{-\lambda}$ with $\lambda = {}^{1}/_{30}$, whose graph is superimposed on the bar graph. Note that the interarrival times are more likely to be short than long.

In this problem we have analyzed a continuous problem by replacing it with a discrete approximation. In the discrete approximation we have seen that the probability that the interarrival time falls in the interval $[a,b]$ is given by the sum of the areas of the bars lying between a and b. This fact, together with the fact that the heights of the bars fall along the exponential curve $y = \lambda e^{-\lambda t}$ with $\lambda = {}^{1}/_{30}$, suggests that for the original continuous problem the probability that the interarrival time falls in the interval $[a,b]$ should be given by the *area under the exponential curve* between a and b, that is,

$$P[a < t < b] = \int_a^b \lambda e^{-\lambda t} dt$$

$$= l e^{-\lambda b} - e^{-\lambda a}.$$

where $\lambda = 1/30$. Examples of this kind suggest that for continuous experiments we should assign probabilities for the outcomes to fall in given intervals as the areas under a suitably chosen curve over these intervals.

Now let us return to our original question. Suppose the bus first arrives at the inn at 8:00 AM and thereafter at random as described above. We are interested in the first time the bus arrives at the inn after noon. To determine this time we program the computer to produce a sequence $t_1, t_2, \ldots, t_n$ of interarrival times, each chosen as above, and compute the sum

$$s_n = t_1 + t_2 + \cdots + t_n.$$

Since we are interested in the first arrival time after noon, 240 minutes after 8:00 AM, we want to know the first time s_n exceeds 240. Thus,

$$y = s_n - 240$$

will be our waiting time (i.e., the time we must wait for the bus if we arrive at noon). The program **Bus Paradox** carries out this simulation and computes our average waiting time (see next page).

Running this program, we find that our average waiting time is indeed 30 minutes and not 15, thus resolving the bus paradox and confirming every commuter's worst suspicions. If we also plot the exponential curve $y = \lambda e^{-\lambda t}$ with $\lambda = {}^1/_{30}$ on the bar graph of the waiting times, we find again that the fit is quite good, leading us to conjecture that the distribution of probabilities for our waiting time is the same as that for the interarrival times (see Figure 17). It can be shown that this is in fact the case. □

Of course, you might ask what kind of bus runs in such a random fashion. Well, probably none. However, there are other less colorful phenomena that do behave in this way. For example, it is found that the times between emissions of a particle by a radioactive material do have this random character.

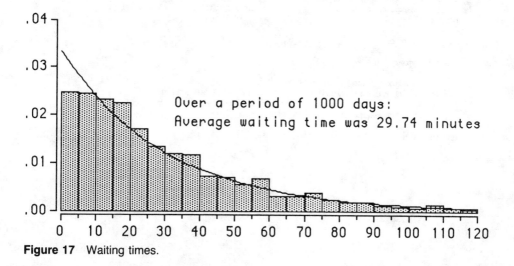

Figure 17 Waiting times.

```
! Bus Paradox   (BUS)
!
! Simulates your waiting times for a bus that arrives in any one
! minute time interval with probability 1/30.  Gives a bar graph
! of the waiting times and compares it with the exponential curve
! y = lambda * exp(-lambda*x), where lambda = 1/30.

library "Lib.cont*"
library "Lib.prob*"
declare function next_bus            ! Gets interarrival time until next bus.
declare function exponential         ! To compare exponential curve.
dim result(1000)
randomize

let noon = 240                       ! Noon is 240 minutes after 8 0'clock.
let xmax = 120                       ! Only look at waiting times ≤ 2 hours.
let cells = 30                       ! Number of partitions of the data.
let time_interval = 1                ! All times in minutes.
let probability = 1/30               ! Probability a bus arrives.
let lambda = probability             ! Parameter for exponential.
let ymax = lambda * 5/4              ! For setting window.

input prompt "   Number of days = ": number_days
mat result = zer(number_days)

for day = 1 to number_days
    let clock = 0                                    ! Start at ten oclock.
    do
       let interarrival_time = next_bus   ! Time until next bus.
       let clock = clock + interarrival_time  ! Time next bus arrives.
    loop until clock >= noon                 ! First bus after noon.
    let waiting_time = clock - noon
    let result(day) = waiting_time
next day

call sample_statistics(result,number_days,mean,std)   ! Find mean waiting time.

set window 0,xmax,0,ymax
call bargraph(result,number_days,0,xmax,cells)        ! Plot bar graph for waiting times.
let text$ = "Average waiting time was "&str$(round(mean,2))&" minutes"
plot text, at xmax/6, ymax * 7/8: text$

for x = 0 to xmax step xmax/100
    plot x,exponential(x,lambda);        ! Compare with exponential density.
next x

function next_bus

    let number_flips = 0
    do
       let number_flips = number_flips + 1
    loop until rnd < probability              ! Bus arrives.
    let minutes = (number_flips - 1/2)*time_interval ! Choose midpoint of last time.
    let next_bus = minutes

end function

end
```

We could also ask if the random character of the arrivals is really at the heart of the paradox. Well, if the bus always takes exactly 30 minutes and we arrived at a random time to get the bus, then we would have on the average only a 15 minute wait (see Exercise 9). But what about some other kind of interarrival times? In Exercises 10–11 you are asked to consider other possibilities. There you will find the even more paradoxical situation that it is possible to have the buses arriving on the average every 30 minutes and have your average waiting time *greater* than 30 minutes. Additional paradoxes related to this problem are illustrated in Exercise 12.

Sample Space Coordinates

These examples suggest that for continuous experiments of this sort we should assign probabilities for the outcomes to fall in given intervals by means of the area under a suitable function.

More generally, we suppose that suitable coordinates can be introduced into the sample space Ω, so that we can regard Ω as a connected subset of $\mathbf{R}^n$. We call such a sample space a *continuous sample space*. We then define a probability density for Ω as follows (cf. Definition 2 of Chapter 1, Section 1.2.).

Densities

DEFINITION 1

A *probability density* on the continuous sample space $\Omega \subset \mathbf{R}^n$ is a real-valued function p whose domain is Ω and which satisfies

(1) $p(\omega) \geq 0$ for all $\omega \in \Omega$.

(2) $\displaystyle\int_{\omega \in \Omega} p(\omega)d\omega = 1$.

It is often convenient, although not always necessary, to extend the domain of definition of p to all of $\mathbf{R}^n$ by stipulating that $p(\omega) = 0$ for $\omega \notin \Omega$ (i.e., that $p = 0$ on $\tilde{\Omega}$). *In general, we shall define our density functions for all of $\mathbf{R}^n$ in this way.*

Probabilities

In terms of the density $p(\omega)$, the *probability of an event $E \subset \Omega$* is the number $P(E)$ given by

$$P(E) = \int_{\omega \in E} p(\omega)d\omega.$$

The notation here assumes that E is a subset of Ω for which $\int_E p(\omega)d\omega$ makes sense. This formula then defines P as a real-valued function of such subsets which obeys all of the laws of probability described in Section 1.2.

EXAMPLE 1 (continued)

In the spinner experiment described above, we choose for our sample space the interval $0 \leq \omega < 1$, and for our probability density

$$p(\omega) = 1 \quad \text{if } 0 \leq \omega < 1,$$

$$= 0 \quad \text{otherwise.}$$

If E is the event that the head of the spinner falls in the upper half of the circle, then $E = \{\omega: 0 \leq \omega \leq 1\}$, and so

$$P(E) = \int_0^{1/2} 1 \, d\omega = \frac{1}{2}.$$

More generally, if E is the event that the head falls in the interval $[a,b]$, then

$$P[a,b] = \int_a^b 1 \, d\omega = b - a$$

(cf. Example 1). □

In terms of the bar graphs described in Example 1 of Chapter 2, Section 2.1, we see now that the density function in each subinterval is given approximately by the *height* of the bar, while the probability of that subinterval is given by the *area* of the bar (see Figure 2 of Chapter 2, Section 2.1).

EXAMPLE 2 (continued)

In the first dart game experiment, we choose for our sample space a disc of unit radius in the plane and for our probability density the function

$$p(x,y) = 1/\pi \quad \text{if } x^2 + y^2 \leq 1,$$

$$= 0 \quad \text{otherwise.}$$

The probability that the dart lands inside the subset E is then given by

$$P(E) = \iint_E \frac{1}{\pi} \, dxdy$$

$$= \frac{1}{\pi} (\text{area of } E)$$

(cf. Example 2). □

In these two examples, the probability density function is constant and does not depend on ω. It is often the case that experiments in which the coordinates are chosen *at random* can be described by *constant* probability densities, and, as in Section 1.2 of Chapter 1, we call such probability density functions *uniform* or *equiprobable*.

Not all experiments are of this type, however.

EXAMPLE 3 (continued)

In the second dart game experiment, we choose for our sample space the unit interval on the real line and for our probability density the function

$$p(r) = 2r \quad \text{if } 0 < r < 1,$$

$$= 0 \quad \text{otherwise.}$$

Then the probability that the dart lands at distance r, $a \leqslant r \leqslant b$, from the center of the target is given by

$$P[a,b] = \int_a^b 2r dr$$

$$= b^2 - a^2.$$

(cf. Example 3). Here again, since the density is small when r is near 0 and large when r is near 1, we see that in this experiment the dart is more likely to land near the rim of the target than near the center. In terms of the bar graph of Example 3, the heights of the bars approximate the density function, while the areas of the bars approximate the probabilities of the subintervals (see Figure 15). □

EXAMPLE 4 (continued)

In the case of the arrival times for a bus we take for our sample space the nonnegative t-axis, and introduce the probability density function

$$p(t) = \lambda e^{-\lambda t} \quad \text{if } 0 \leqslant t < \infty,$$

$$= 0 \quad \text{otherwise.}$$

where λ is a constant that will be determined by the average time between buses. (In Example 4, we choose $\lambda = \frac{1}{30}$.) Then with this density function (see Figure 18) we have

$$P[a,b] = \int_a^b (\frac{1}{30}) e^{-t/30} dt = e^{-a/30} - e^{-b/30}.$$

For example, if we assign this density for the arrival time for the bus, the probability that the bus arrives in the first five minutes, that is, in the time interval [0,5], is $1 - e^{-5/30} = .153$, and the probability that it arrives in the time interval [5,10] is $e^{-5/30} - e^{-10/30} = .129$. □

We see in this example that, unlike the case of discrete sample spaces, the value $p(\omega)$ of the probability density function for the outcome ω is *not* the probability of ω occurring (we have seen that this probability is always 0) and in general $p(\omega)$ is *not a probability at all*. In this example, if we take $\lambda = 2$ then $p(\frac{1}{4}) = 2e^{-.5}$ which is approximately 1.2, and so, being bigger than 1, cannot be a probability.

Nevertheless, the probability density function p does contain all the probability information about the experiment, since the probabilities of all events can be derived

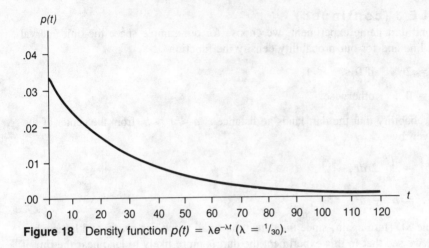

Figure 18 Density function $p(t) = \lambda e^{-\lambda t}$ $(\lambda = \frac{1}{30})$.

from it. In particular, the probability that the outcome of the experiment falls in an interval $[a,b]$ is given by

$$P[a,b] = \int_a^b p(\omega)d\omega,$$

that is, by the *area* under the graph of the density function in the interval $[a,b]$. Thus, there is a close connection here between probabilities and areas. We have been guided by this close connection in making up our bar graphs; each bar is chosen so that its *area*, and not its height, represents the relative frequency of occurrence, and hence estimates the probability of the outcome falling in the associated interval.

In the language of the calculus, we can say that the probability of occurrence of an event of the form $[\omega, \omega + d\omega]$, where $d\omega$ is small, is approximately given by

$$P[\omega, \omega + d\omega] \sim p(\omega)d\omega,$$

that is, by the area of the rectangle under the graph of p. Note that as $d\omega \to 0$, this probability $\to 0$, so that the probability $P\{\omega\}$ of a single point is again 0, as in Example 1.

A glance at the graph of a probability density function tells us immediately which events of an experiment are more likely. Roughly speaking, we can say that where the density is large the events are more likely, and where it is small the events are less likely. In Example 4 the density is monotone decreasing, and so in comparing intervals of the same length, we see that the outcome is more likely to fall in the interval nearer to 0. In Example 4 we saw that the bus is more likely to come in the time interval $[0,5]$ than in the time interval $[5,10]$, and so forth.

There are a large number of experiments of practical interest that may be described, after suitable coordinates have been introduced, by continuous sample spaces with one of the following standard probability density functions, which we introduce briefly in turn. (Note that in every case we have $p(\omega) \geq 0$ and $\int_\Omega p(\omega)d\omega = 1$.)

Uniform Density

EXAMPLE 5

Here the sample space is $\Omega = [a,b]$, and the probability density is

$$p(\omega) = \begin{cases} \dfrac{1}{b-a} & \text{if } a \leqslant \omega \leqslant b, \\ 0 & \text{otherwise.} \end{cases}$$

Here $[a,b]$ can be any finite interval on the real line (see Figure 19). This case is already familiar from the examples at the beginning of this section. Generally speaking, the uniform density is used to describe experiments with coordinates chosen *at random*. (Note that the interval cannot be infinite.) □

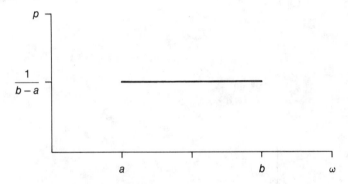

Figure 19 Uniform density.

Exponential Density

EXAMPLE 6

Here the sample space is $\Omega = [0,\infty)$ and the probability density is

$$p(\omega) = \begin{cases} \lambda e^{-\lambda\omega} & \text{if } 0 \leqslant \omega < \infty, \\ 0 & \text{otherwise.} \end{cases}$$

Here λ is any positive constant, depending on the experiment. This density is already familiar from the example of the bus paradox. In Figure 20 we show graphs of several exponential densities for different choices of λ. The exponential density is often used to describe experiments involving a question of the form: How long till something happens? For example, the exponential density is often used to study the time of emission of a particle from a radioactive source. □

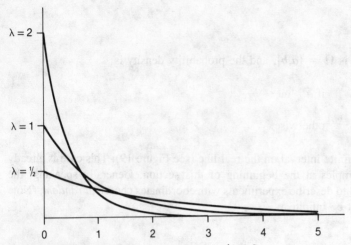

Figure 20 Exponential densities for $\lambda = {}^{1}/_{2}, 1, 2$.

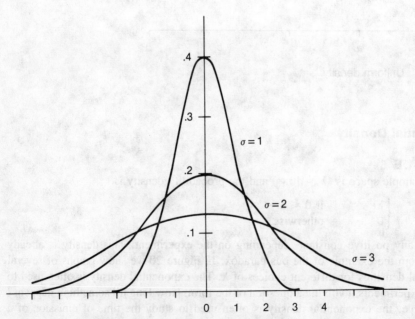

Figure 21 Normal density with $\mu = 0$ and $\sigma = 1, 2, 3$.

Normal Density

EXAMPLE 7

Here the sample space is $\Omega = (-\infty, \infty)$ and the probability density is

$$p(\omega) = \frac{1}{\sqrt{2\pi\sigma^2}}\, e^{-(\omega-\mu)^2/2\sigma^2}.$$

This density has for graph the celebrated *bell-shaped curve* (see Figure 21). The parameter μ determines the central value of the density function, called the *mean*, and the parameter σ is a measure of the spread of the density, called the *standard deviation*. We shall make these concepts more precise later (see Chapter 6). □

The normal density is perhaps the most fundamental of our examples. It is used to describe the outcomes of chance experiments which themselves are the sum of a lot of other small chance experiments. For example, your height might be considered to result from many small chance experiments, such as whether you ate your Wheaties on your seventh birthday, and so forth.

We must defer a full discussion of these applications of the normal density until Chapter 9, but we can give one suggestive example here.

Galton Board

EXAMPLE 8

A *Galton board* is a board in which a large number of BB-shots are dropped from a chute at the top of the board and deflected off a number of pins on their way down to the bottom of the board. The final position of each shot is the result of a number of random deflections either to the left or the right. We have written a program **Galton Board** to simulate this experiment.

We have run the program for the case of 20 rows of pins and 10,000 shots being dropped. We show the result of this simulation in Figure 22.

Note that the largest number of shots end up in the center box, which means that they underwent the same number of deflections to the left and to the right. The distribution of shots is quite symmetric about this center box and in some respects resembles the normal density. We shall see in Chapter 9 why this is so.

Note that if we write 0 every time the shot is deflected to the left, and 1 every time it is deflected to the right, then the path of the shot can be described by a sequence of 0s and 1s of length n, just as for the n-fold coin toss. □

In summary, we can say that in the case of continuous sample spaces, probabilities are assigned by giving a probability density function appropriate for the experiment under study, and that the probability of each event, and hence all probabilistic properties of the experiment, can be derived from this density function.

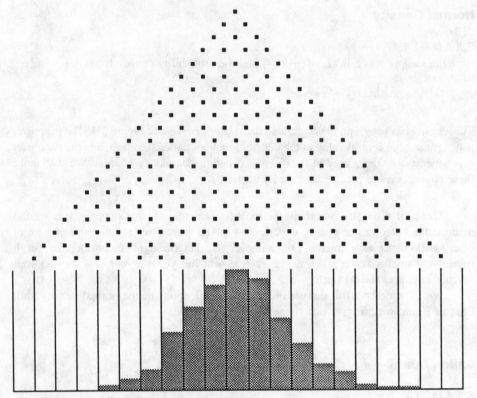

Figure 22 Simulation of the Galton board.

We have provided our standard density functions in our library **Lib.Cont** under the names

uniform(x,a,b)

exponential(x, lambda)

normal(x, mu, sigma).

Numerical Calculations

As we have mentioned, for continuous experiments we shall often be interested in the probability $P[a,b]$ that the outcome lies in an interval $[a,b]$. That is, we shall be interested in the integral of the density between a and b or the area under the density graph between a and b. For some densities this integral can be calculated using elementary functions, but for some it cannot. For example, we calculated this integral for the exponential density, but there is no simple antiderivative for the normal density, so areas under this curve cannot be calculated this way. However, any area can always be calculated approximately by numerical integration, and so we include in our library **Lib.Cont** a numerical integration program to calculate these areas. To use this program we write a simple call program which we have named **Demo Integral**. In this program we must denote the function to be integrated by integrand(x), and this function must appear at the end of the program. For example, to find the areas under the normal curve with $\mu = 0$, $\sigma = 1$, the program **Demo Integral** is:

```
! Demo integral    (DINTEGRL)
!
! Demonstrates the function integral(a,b,n) in Lib.cont, which uses
! Simpson's rule to integrate the function integrand(x), defined below,
! external to this main program.
!   The parameters a and b are the endpoints of the interval of
! integration; n is the number of subdivisions, hence must be even.

library "Lib.cont*"
declare function integral

do

    input prompt "Enpoints & number of subdivisions: a, b, n = ": a,b,n
    if n = 0 then stop

    print "The integral from"; a; "to"; b; "is"; integral(a,b,n)
    print

loop until a = b

end


function integrand(x)

    declare function normal
    let mu = 0
    let sigma = 1
    let integrand = normal(x,mu,sigma)

end function
```

Running this program for several intervals gives

```
Enpoints & number of subdivisions: a, b, n = -1,1,100
The integral from -1 to 1 is .682689

Enpoints & number of subdivisions: a, b, n = -2,2,100
The integral from -2 to 2 is .9545

Enpoints & number of subdivisions: a, b, n = -3,3,100
The integral from -3 to 3 is .9973

Enpoints & number of subdivisions: a, b, n = -4,4,100
The integral from -4 to 4 is .999937
```

Thus, we see that most of the area under the normal curve with $\mu = 0$, $\sigma = 1$ lies between -3 and 3 and that for all practical purposes we can assume that the outcome will lie between -4 and 4.

Of course, we can use the densities in **Lib.Cont**, but when we do this we must define the function $f(x)$ by a multiline definition. For example, for the exponential density with $\lambda = 1$ we put the following definition for integrand at the end of **Demo Integral**.

```
function integrand(x)

    declare function exponential
    let lambda = 1
    let integrand = exponential(x,lambda)

end function
```

Assignment of Probabilities

A fundamental question in practice is: How shall we choose the probability density function in describing any given experiment? The answer depends to a great extent on the amount and kind of information available to us about the experiment. In some cases, we can see that the outcomes are equally likely. In some cases, we can see that the experiment resembles another already described by a known density. In some cases, we can run the experiment a large number of times and make a reasonable guess at the density on the basis of the observed distribution of outcomes, as we did in Chapter 1. In general, the problem of choosing the right density function for a given experiment is a central problem for the experimenter and is not always easy to solve (see Chapter 1, Section 1.2, Example 5). We shall not examine this question in detail here but instead shall assume that the right density is already known for each of the experiments under study.

The introduction of suitable coordinates to describe a continuous sample space, and a suitable probability density to describe its probabilities, is not always so obvious, as our final example shows.

Infinite Tree

EXAMPLE 9

Consider an experiment in which a balanced coin is tossed repeatedly, without stopping. We have seen (Chapter 1, Section 1.2, Example 6) that, for a coin tossed n times, the natural sample space is a binary tree with n stages. On this evidence we expect that for a coin tossed repeatedly, the natural sample space is a binary tree with an unlimited number of stages, as indicated in Figure 23.

It is surprising to learn that, although the n-stage tree is obviously a finite sample space, the unlimited tree can be described as a continuous sample space. To see how this comes about, let us agree that a typical outcome of the unlimited coin tossing experiment can be described by a sequence of the form $\omega = \{ H H T H T T H \ldots \}$. If we write

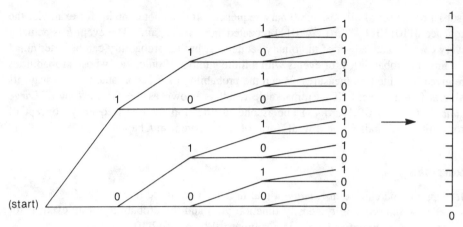

Figure 23 Tree for infinite number of tosses of a coin.

1 for H and 0 for T, then $\omega = \{1\ 1\ 0\ 1\ 0\ 0\ 1\ \ldots\}$. In this way, each outcome is described by a sequence of 0s and 1s.

Now suppose we think of this sequence of 0s and 1s as the binary expansion of some real number $x = .1101001\cdots$ lying between 0 and 1. (A *binary expansion* is like a decimal expansion but based on 2 instead of 10.) Then each outcome is described by a value of x, and in this way x becomes a coordinate for the sample space, taking on all real values between 0 and 1.

What probabilities should be assigned to the events of this sample space? Consider, for example, the event E consisting of all outcomes for which the first toss comes up heads and the second tails. Every such outcome has the form $.1\ 0\ *\ *\ *\ *\ \ldots$, where $*$ can be either 0 or 1. Now if x is our real-valued coordinate, then the value of x for every such outcome must lie between $\frac{1}{2} = .10000\cdots$ and $\frac{3}{4} = .11000\cdots$, and moreover, every value of x between $\frac{1}{2}$ and $\frac{3}{4}$ has a binary expansion of the form $.1\ 0\ *\ *\ *\ *.\ \ldots$. This means that $\omega \in E$ if and only if $\frac{1}{2} \leqslant x < \frac{3}{4}$, and in this way we see that we can describe E by the interval $[\frac{1}{2}, \frac{3}{4})$. More generally, every event consisting of outcomes for which the results of the first n tosses are prescribed is described by a binary interval of the form $[k/2^n, (k+1)/2^n)$.

Now we have already seen in Section 1.2 that in the experiment involving n tosses, the probability of any one outcome must be exactly $1/2^n$. It follows that in the unlimited toss experiment, the probability of any event consisting of outcomes for which the results of the first n tosses are prescribed must also be $1/2^n$. But $1/2^n$ is exactly the length of the interval of x-values describing E! Thus we see that, just as with the spinner experiment, the probability of an event E is determined by what fraction of the unit interval lies in E.

Consider again the statement: The probability is $\frac{1}{2}$ that a fair coin will turn up heads when tossed. We have suggested that one interpretation of this statement is that if we toss the coin indefinitely the proportion of heads will approach $\frac{1}{2}$. That is, in our correspondence with binary sequences we expect to get a binary sequence with the proportion of 1s tending to $\frac{1}{2}$. The event E of binary sequences for which this is true is a subset of the set of all possible binary sequences. It does not contain, for example, the sequence 011011011 . . . (i.e., (011) repeated again and again). The event E is actually a very complicated subset of the binary sequences, but its probability can be determined as a limit of probabilities for events with a finite number of outcomes whose probabilities are given by finite tree measures. When the probability of E is computed in this way, its value is found to be 1. This remarkable result is known as the *Strong Law of Large Numbers* (or *Law of Averages*) and is one justification for our frequency concept of probability. We shall prove a weak form of this theorem in Chapter 8. ☐

Exercises

1. Suppose you choose *at random* a real number x from the interval [2,10].
   (a) Find the probability density function $p(\omega)$ and the probability of an event E for this experiment, where E is a subinterval [a,b] of [2,10].
   (b) From (a), find the probability that $x > 5$, that $5 < x < 7$, and that $x^2 - 12x + 35 > 0$.

2. Suppose you choose a real number x from the interval [2,10] with a density function of the form

   $$p(\omega) = C\omega.$$

   (a) Find C.
   (b) Find $P(E)$, where $E = [a,b]$ is a subinterval of [2,10].
   (c) Find $P(x > 5)$, $P(x < 7)$, and $P(x^2 - 12x + 35 > 0)$.

3. Same as (2), but suppose

   $$p(\omega) = \frac{C}{\omega}.$$

4. Suppose you throw a dart at a circular target of radius 10 inches. Assuming that you hit the target and that the coordinates of the outcomes are chosen *at random*, find the probability that the dart falls
   (a) within 2 inches of the center.
   (b) within 2 inches of the rim.
   (c) within the first quadrant of the target.
   (d) within the first quadrant and within 2 inches of the rim.

5. Suppose you are watching a radioactive source that emits particles at a rate described by the exponential density

   $$p(t) = \lambda e^{-\lambda t}, \text{ where } \lambda = 0.1.$$

   so that the probability $P(0,T)$ that a particle will appear in the next T seconds is $P([0,T]) = \int_0^T \lambda e^{-\lambda t} \, dt$. Find the probability that a particle will appear
   (a) within the next second.
   (b) within the next 3 seconds.

(c) between the next 3 seconds and the next 4 seconds.

(d) after the next 4 seconds.

6. Assume that a new light bulb will burn out after t hours, where t is chosen from $[0,\infty)$ with an exponential density

$$p(\omega) = \lambda e^{-\lambda t}.$$

In this context, λ is often called the *failure rate* of the bulb.

(a) Assume that $\lambda = 0.01$, and find the probability that the bulb will *not* burn out before T hours. This probability is often called the *reliability* of the bulb.

(b) For what T is the reliability of the bulb = $^1/_2$?

7. Choose a number b *at random* from the interval $[0,1]$ with uniform density. Find the probability that

(a) $^1/_3 < b < ^2/_3$.

(b) $|b - ^1/_2| \le ^1/_4$.

(c) $b < ^1/_4$ or $1 - b < ^1/_4$.

(d) $3b^2 < b$.

8. Choose independently two numbers b and c *at random* from the interval $[0,1]$ with uniform density. Note that the point (b,c) is then chosen *at random* in the unit square. Find the probability that

(a) $b + c < ^1/_2$.

(b) $bc < ^1/_2$.

(c) $|b - c| < ^1/_2$.

(d) $\max\{b,c\} < ^1/_2$.

(e) $\min\{b,c\} < ^1/_2$.

(f) $b < ^1/_2$ and $1 - c < ^1/_2$.

(g) conditions (c) and (f) both hold.

(h) $b^2 + c^2 \le ^1/_2$.

(i) $(b - ^1/_2) + (c - ^1/_2)^2 < ^1/_4$.

9. In the bus problem (Example 4) assume that the bus starts in the morning at a *random* time between 7:45 and 8:15. Once it starts, each round trip takes exactly 30 minutes. Make a conjecture for the average time that you have to wait if you come to catch a bus at 12:00. Modify the program **Bus Paradox** to check your conjecture.

10. In the bus problem (Example 4) the bus company would probably assert (and would certainly hope) that the arrival times have a bell-shaped density around the mean of 30 minutes. Have the subroutine **next_bus** in the program **Bus Paradox** simulate this by tossing a fair coin 60 times, and setting the arrival time equal to the number of heads that come up. How does this effect the waiting times? Make a bar graph of the waiting times obtained in this way.

11. In the bus problem (Example 4) it might seem that at least you should not have to wait on the average *more* than 30 minutes if the average time between buses is 30 minutes. Alas, even this is not true. To see why, consider the following assumption about the times between buses. Assume that the interarrival time of the bus is either

9 minutes with probability .89 or 200 minutes with probability .11. Show by simulation that the average time between buses is 30 minutes, but your average waiting time is more than 30 minutes.

12. When the mathematics department bought a new Xerox machine from John Finn, Finn said that the average time between service calls should be about one month. Assume that there are 30 days in each month and the probability that a service call is necessary on any given day is $1/30$. Finn asks that you report to him once a year and tell him the length of time between service calls for the interval that includes January 1. Let R be the length of time since the last service call before January 1 and S the time until the first service call after January 1. Then $T = R + S$ is the time that you report to Finn. Modify the program **Bus Paradox** to estimate the average times for R and S, and determine what would be the average time for T, as reported to Finn, if the machine is functioning as he predicted.

13. Take a stick of unit length and break it into three pieces, choosing the breaks *at random*. What is the probability that the three pieces can be used to form a triangle? *Hint:* The sum of the lengths of any two pieces must exceed the length of the third, so each piece must have length $< 1/2$. Now use 8(g).

14. Choose independently two numbers b and c *at random* from the interval $[-1,1]$ with uniform distribution, and consider the quadratic equation

$$x^2 + bx + c = 0.$$

Find the probability that the roots of this equation
(a) are both real.
(b) are both positive.
   Hints: (a) requires $0 \leqslant b^2 - 4c$, (b) requires $0 \leqslant b^2 - 4c$, $b \leqslant 0$, $0 \leqslant c$.

15. At the Tunbridge World's Fair, a coin toss game works as follows. Quarters are tossed onto a checkerboard. The management keeps all the quarters, but for each quarter landing entirely within one square of the checkerboard the management pays a dollar. Assume that the edge of each square is twice the diameter of a quarter, and that the outcomes are described by coordinates chosen *at random*. Is this a fair game?

16. Three points are chosen *at random* on a circle of *unit circumference*. What is the probability that the triangle defined by these points as vertices has three acute angles? *Hint:* One of the angles is obtuse if and only if all three points lie in the same semicircle. Take the first point to be 0 and the other points to be at distance b and c around the circumference. Now use 8(d).

17. Write a program to choose a random number x in the interval $[2,10]$ 1000 times and record what fraction of the outcomes satisfy $x > 5$, what fraction satisfy $5 < x < 7$, and what fraction satisfy $x^2 - 12x + 35 > 0$. How do these results compare with those of Exercise 1?

18. Write a program to choose a point (x,y) *at random* in a square of side 20 inches, doing this 10,000 times, and recording what fraction of the outcomes fall within 10 inches of the center; of these, what fraction fall between 8 and 10 inches of the center; and, of these, what fraction fall within the first quadrant of the square. How do these results compare with those of Exercise 4?

19. Write a program to simulate the problem described in Exercise 7 (see Exercise 17). How do the simulation results compare with the results of Exercise 7?

20. Write a program to simulate the problem described in Exercise 13.

21. Write a program to simulate the problem described in Exercise 16.

22. Write a program to carry out the following experiment. A coin is tossed 100 times and the number of heads that turn up is recorded. This experiment is then repeated 1000 times. Have your program plot a bar graph for the proportion of the 1000 experiments in which the number of heads is n, for each n in the interval [35,65]. Now plot the normal density curve for $\mu = 50$ and $\sigma = \sqrt{5}$. Compare this curve with your bar graph.

23. Write a program that picks a random number between 0 and 1 and computes the negative of its logarithm. Repeat this process a large number of times and plot a bar graph to give the number of times that the outcome falls in each interval of length 0.1 in [0,10]. On this bar graph plot a graph of the density $p(x) = e^{-x}$. How well does this density fit your bar graph?

24. We will see many applications of the normal density. Books on probability or statistics contain tables of the areas under the normal density curve. Let **normal_area**(a,b) be the area under the normal curve from a to b with $a < b$. Some books give tables of **normal_area**$(0,x)$, others for **normal_area**$(-\infty,x)$, and still others give **normal_area**$(-x,x)$. Of course any one table can be obtained from any other. We have included in **Lib.Cont** a subroutine **normal_area**(a,b) that calculates the area under the normal curve between a and b.
    (a) Show how to obtain a table of **normal_area**$(-\infty,x)$ and **normal_area**$(-x,x)$ from a table of **normal_area**$(0,x)$.
    (b) Using the subroutine **normal_area**(a,b), write a program to produce a table of **normal_area**$(0,x)$ for $x = 0$ to 3.9 in increments of 0.01 (see the table in Appendix A).
    (c) Modify your program in (b) to produce tables of **normal_area**$(-\infty,x)$ and **normal_area**$(-x,x)$. *Save the tables from this exercise for later use.*

Chapter 3

Combinatorics

3.1 PERMUTATIONS

Many problems in probability theory require that we count the number of ways that a particular event can occur. For this, we study the topics of *permutations* and *combinations*. We consider permutations in this section and combinations in the next section.

Before discussing permutations, it is useful to introduce a general counting technique that will enable us to solve a variety of counting problems, including the problem of counting the number of possible permutations of n objects.

Counting Problems

Consider an experiment that takes place in several stages and is such that the number of outcomes m at the nth stage is independent of the outcomes of previous stages. The number m may be different for different stages. We want to count the number of ways that the entire experiment can be carried out.

EXAMPLE 1
You are eating at Émile's restaurant and the waiter informs you that you have (a) two choices for appetizers: soup or juice; (b) three for the main course: a meat, fish, or

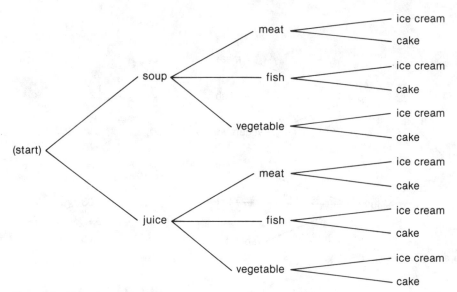

Figure 1 Tree for your menu.

vegetable dish; and (c) two for dessert: ice cream or cake. How many possible choices do you have for your complete meal?

We illustrate the possible meals by a tree diagram shown in Figure 1.

Your menu is decided in three stages—at each stage the number of possible choices does not depend on what is chosen in the previous stages: two choices at the first stage, three at the second, and two at the third. From the tree diagram we see that the total number of choices is the product of the number of choices at each stage. In this example we have $2 \cdot 3 \cdot 2 = 12$ possible menus. Our menu example is an example of the following general counting technique. ☐

A Counting Technique

A task is to be carried out in a sequence of r stages. There are n_1 ways to carry out the first stage; for each of these n_1 ways, there are n_2 ways to carry out the second stage; for each of these n_2 ways, there are n_3 ways to carry out the third stage, and so forth. Then the total number of ways in which the entire task can be accomplished is given by the product $N = n_1 \cdot n_2 \cdot \cdots \cdot n_r$.

Tree Diagrams

It will often be useful to use a tree diagram when studying probabilities of events relating to experiments that take place in stages and for which we are given the probabilities for the outcomes at each stage. For example, assume that the owner of Emile's restaurant has observed that 80 percent of his customers choose the soup for an appetizer and 20 percent choose juice. Of those who choose soup, 50 percent choose meat, 30 percent

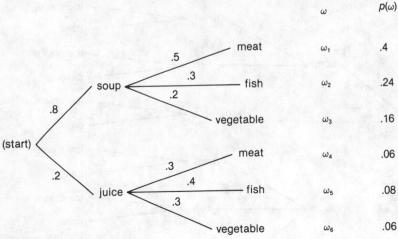

Figure 2 Two stage density.

choose fish, and 20 percent choose the vegetable dish. Of those who choose juice for an appetizer, 30 percent choose meat, 40 percent choose fish, and 30 percent choose the vegetable dish. We can use this to estimate the probabilities at the first two stages as indicated on the tree diagram of Figure 2.

We choose for our sample space the set Ω of all possible paths $\omega = \omega_1, \omega_2, \ldots, \omega_6$ through the tree. How should we assign our probability density? For example, what probability should we assign to the customer choosing soup and then the meat? If $^8/_{10}$ of the customers choose soup and then $^1/_2$ of these choose meat, a proportion $^8/_{10} \cdot ^1/_2 = ^4/_{10}$ of the customers choose soup and then meat. This suggests choosing our probability density for each path through the tree to be the *product* of the probabilities at each of the stages along the path. This results in the probability measure for the sample points ω indicated in Figure 2. (Note that $p(\omega_1) + \cdots + p(\omega_6) = 1$.) From this we see, for example, that the probability that a customer chooses meat is $p(\omega_1) + p(\omega_4) = .46$.

We shall say more about these tree measures later when we discuss the concept of conditional probability in Chapter 4. We return now to more counting problems.

EXAMPLE 2

We can show that there are at least two people in Columbus, Ohio, who have the same three initials. Assuming that each person has three initials, there are 26 possibilities for a person's first initial, 26 for the second, and 26 for the third. Therefore, there are $26^3 = 17,576$ possible sets of initials. This number is smaller than the number of people living in Columbus, Ohio; hence, there must be at least two people with the same three initials. □

We consider next the celebrated birthday problem—often used to show that naive intuition cannot always be trusted in probability.

Birthday Problem

EXAMPLE 3
How many people do we need to have in a room to make it a favorable bet (probability of success greater than $1/2$) that two people in the room will have the same birthday?

Since there are 365 possible birthdays, it is tempting to guess that we would need about $1/2$ this number, or 183. You would surely win this bet. In fact, the number required for a favorable bet is only 23. To show this, we find the probability p_r that, in a room with r people, there is no duplication of birthdays; we will have a favorable bet if this probability is less than one half.

Assume that there are 365 possible birthdays for each person (we ignore leap years). Order the people from 1 to r. For a sample point ω, we choose a possible sequence of length r of birthdays each chosen as one of the 365 possible dates. There are 365 possibilities for the first element of the sequence, and for each of these choices there are 365 for the second, and so forth, making 365^r possible sequences of birthdays. We must find the number of these sequences that have no duplication of birthdays. For such a sequence, we can choose any of the 365 days for the first element, then any of the remaining 364 for the second, 363 for the third, and so forth, until we make r choices. For the rth choice, there will be $365 - r + 1$ possibilities. Hence, the total number of sequences with no duplications is

$$365 \cdot 364 \cdot 363 \cdot \cdots \cdot (365 - r + 1)$$

Thus, assuming that each sequence is equally likely,

$$p_r = \frac{365 \cdot 364 \cdot \cdots \cdot (365 - r + 1)}{365^r}$$

The program **Birthday** carries out this computation and prints the probabilities for $r = 20$ to 25.

```
! Birthday.  (BIRTHDAY)
!
! Computes the probability that no two people in a group have the same
! birthday, where the size of the group ranges from a given minimum to
! a given maximium by a given increment.

Print "Minimum, maximum size of group, increment = ";
input prompt "": minimum, maximum, increment
print "Number of people    ";
print"Probability that all birthdays are different"
print
```

```
for size = minimum to maximum step increment

    let probability = 1

    for k = 365 to 365-size+1 step -1
        let probability = k/365*probability
    next k

    print size ,, using$(".#######",probability)

next size

end
```

Running this program, we get:

Number of people	Probability that all birthdays are different
20	.5885616
21	.5563117
22	.5243047
23	.4927028
24	.4616557
25	.4313003

As we asserted above, the probability for no duplication changes from greater than one half to less than one half as we move from 22 to 23 people. To see how unlikely it is that we would lose our bet for larger numbers of people, we have run the program again, printing out values from $r = 10$ to $r = 100$ in steps of 10.

Number of people	Probability that all birthdays are different
10	.8830518
20	.5885616
30	.2936838
40	.1087682
50	.0296264
60	.0058773
70	.0008404
80	.0000857
90	.0000062
100	.0000003

We see that in a room of 40 people the odds already heavily favor a duplication, and in a room of 100 the odds are overwhelmingly in favor of a duplication.

We have assumed that birthdays are equally likely to fall on any particular day. Statistical evidence suggests that this is not true. However, it is intuitively clear (but not easy to prove) that this makes it even more likely to have a duplication with a group of 23 people. □

We turn now to the problem of permutations.

Permutations

DEFINITION 1
Let A be any finite set. A *permutation of A* is a one-to-one mapping of A onto itself.

To specify a particular permutation we list the elements of A and, under them, show where each element is sent by the one-to-one mapping. For example, if $A = \{a,b,c\}$ a possible permutation σ would be

$$\sigma = \begin{pmatrix} a & b & c \\ b & c & a \end{pmatrix}.$$

By the permutation σ, a is sent to b, b is sent to c, and c is sent to a. The condition that the mapping be one-to-one means that no two elements of A are sent, by the mapping, into the same element of A.

We can put the elements of our set in some order and rename them $1, 2, \ldots, n$. Then, a typical permutation of the set $A = \{a_1, a_2, a_3, a_4\}$ can be written in the form

$$\sigma = \begin{pmatrix} 1 & 2 & 3 & 4 \\ 2 & 1 & 4 & 3 \end{pmatrix},$$

indicating that a_1 went to a_2, a_2 to a_1, a_3 to a_4, and a_4 to a_3.

If we always choose the top row to be 1 2 3 4 then, to prescribe the permutation, we need only give the bottom row, with the understanding that this tells us where 1 goes, 2 goes, and so forth, under the mapping. When this is done, the permutation is often called a *rearrangement* of the n objects $1, 2, 3, \ldots, n$. For example, all possible permutations, or rearrangements, of the numbers $A = \{1,2,3\}$ are:

123
132
213
231
312
321.

It is an easy matter to count the number of possible permutations of n objects. By our general counting principle, there are n ways to assign the first element, for each of these we have $n - 1$ ways to assign the second object, $n - 2$ for the third, and so forth. This proves the following theorem.

THEOREM 1

The total number of permutations of a set A of n elements is given by $n \cdot (n - 1) \cdot (n - 2) \cdot \cdots \cdot 1$.

Factorials

This number is called n *factorial,* and is denoted by $n!$. For example, $3! = 3 \cdot 2 \cdot 1 = 6$, $4! = 4 \cdot 3 \cdot 2 \cdot 1 = 24$, and so forth. We define $0! = 1$. (Note that $0! \neq 0$, as one might expect! This choice is made to make certain formulas come out simpler.)

The numbers $n!$ become large very fast. The program **Demo Factorial** prints out these numbers for $n = 1$ to 10.

```
! Demo Factorial    (DFACTRL)
!
! Demonstrates the function factorial(n) = n!

declare function factorial

input prompt "Factorials up to N! for N = " : largest

print
print " n"," n!"
print

for n = 1 to largest
    print n, factorial(n)
next n
print

end


function factorial(n)

    let product = 1
    for k = 1 to n
        let product = k * product
    next k

    let factorial = product

end function
```

Running this program for $N = 10$, we get:

```
Factorials up to N! for N = 10

 n              n!

 1              1
 2              2
 3              6
 4              24
 5              120
 6              720
 7              5040
 8              40320
 9              362880
 10             3628800
```

The number $10! = 3628800$ is sometimes taken to be the number of operations which it is reasonable to ask a computer to do. If an operation takes a millisecond, then 10! operations would take almost exactly 1 hour. This is a realistic estimate for a microcomputer. Leibnitz in 1666 computed the value of

$$24! = 6,204,484,017,332,394,339,360,000.$$

Stirling's Formula

The numbers $n!$ will enter into many of our calculations, and we shall need to have some estimate of its magnitude when n is large. It is clearly not practical to make exact calculations in this case. We shall instead use a result called *Stirling's formula*. Before stating this formula we need a definition.

DEFINITION 2

Let a_n and b_n be two sequences of numbers. We say that a_n is *asymptotically equal to* b_n if

$$\lim_{n \to \infty} \frac{a_n}{b_n} = 1.$$

In this case we write $a_n \sim b_n$.

EXAMPLE 4

If $a_n = n + \sqrt{n}$ and $b_n = n$ then, since $a_n/b_n = 1 + 1/\sqrt{n}$ and this ratio tends to 1 as n tends to infinity, we have $a_n \sim b_n$. $\square$

THEOREM 2 Stirling's Formula

The sequence $n!$ is asymptotically equal to

$$\sqrt{2\pi n}\, n^n e^{-n}.$$

The proof of Stirling's formula may be found at the end of this section. Let us verify this approximation by using the computer. We have modified the program **Demo Factorial** to **Stirling**, which prints $n!$, the Stirling approximations, and, finally, the ratio of these two numbers. Note that, while the ratio of the numbers is getting closer to 1, the difference between the exact value and the approximation is increasing, and indeed, this difference will tend to infinity as n tends to infinity, even though the ratio tends to 1. (This was also true in our Example 4 where $n + \sqrt{n} \sim n$ but the difference is $\sqrt{n}$)

```
Compare Stirling & factorial up to n = 10
```

n	n!	Stirling	n!/Stirling
1	1	.922137	1.08444
2	2	1.919	1.04221
3	6	5.83621	1.02806
4	24	23.5062	1.02101
5	120	118.019	1.01678
6	720	710.078	1.01397
7	5040	4980.4	1.01197
8	40320	39902.4	1.01047
9	362880	359537.	1.0093
10	3628800	3.5987e+6	1.00837

Fixed Points

There are many interesting problems that relate to properties of a permutation chosen at random from the set of all permutations of a given finite set. For example, since a permutation is a one-to-one mapping of the set onto itself, it is interesting to ask how many points are mapped onto themselves. We call such points *fixed points* of the mapping.

Let p_k be the probability that a random permutation has exactly k fixed points. We shall be particularly interested in p_0, the probability that there are no fixed points.

More picturesque versions of this problem are: You have arranged the books on your book shelf in alphabetical order by author and they get returned to your shelf at random; what is the probability that exactly k of the books end up in their correct position? (the library problem). In a restaurant n, hats are checked and they are hopelessly scrambled; what is the probability that no one gets his own hat back? (the hat check problem).

Although we shall be able, eventually, to solve this problem exactly, this is not possible for very similar problems, and so we shall see what we can learn about this problem by simulation.

Shuffles

When we shuffle a deck of cards, we are choosing a random permutation of the set of 52 cards. Consider the cards to be numbered from 1 to 52. After shuffling, our first card should be a random choice from the numbers from 1 to 52. Our second card should be a random choice from the remaining 51 cards, our third a random choice from the remaining 50 cards, and so forth. If we determine a tree measure for this experiment, each path at the first stage should be assigned a probability $1/52$, each path at the second stage a probability $1/51$, the third stage $1/50$, and so forth. Thus, each possible sequence of 52 cards would be assigned the product of these numbers and all would occur with the same probability.

This makes it easy to write a program to simulate a random shuffle or permutation. The subroutine **Shuffle** chooses a next random permutation from a previous permutation.

```
! Shuffle (list())
!
! Subroutine to shuffle a list.  Imagine the list of numbers to be a
! deck of cards. Randomly pick a card and exchange it with the bottom
! card.  Put the resuting bottom card aside.  Now repeat this for the
! remaining partial deck, etc.  When you're done, the pile of cards put
! aside, plus the single remaining card, constitute the shuffled deck.
!
sub shuffle (list())

    let length = ubound(list)

    for card = length to 2 step - 1
        let swap = int(card*rnd) + 1
        let copy = list(card)
        let list(card) = list(swap)
        let list(swap) = copy
    next card

end sub
!
```

We can describe the way this subroutine works in terms of our shuffling a deck of n cards. We choose a card at random and exchange this card with the bottom (nth) card. We then choose a card at random from the first $n - 1$ cards and exchange this with the $n - 1$st card. We continue this way until we get to the top of the deck. At each stage, the new card put in the jth position is equally likely to be any one of the top j cards.

```
! Random Permutations   (RANDPERM)
!
! Generates random permutations and counts the number of fixed points
! in each.  For each possible number of fixed points the proportion of
! simulations with that number of fixed points, if significant, is
! printed.  The average number of fixed points is also printed.
!

library "Lib.prob*"
randomize
dim permutation(100), count(0 to 100)
let significant = .0001

input prompt "Length of permutation = " : length
input prompt "Number of simulations = " : simulations
print

mat permutation = zer(length)
mat count = zer(0 to length)

for k = 1 to length                    !Start with identity permutation
    let permutation(k) = k
next k

for trial = 1 to simulations

    call shuffle(permutation)

    let fixed_points = 0
    for k = 1 to length
        if permutation(k) = k then let fixed_points = fixed_points + 1
    next k

    let count(fixed_points) = count(fixed_points) + 1

next trial

let sum = 0

for fixed_points = 0 to length
    let sum = sum + fixed_points*count(fixed_points)
    let proportion = count(fixed_points) / simulations
    if proportion > significant then print fixed_points, proportion
next fixed_points

let average = sum/simulations

print
print "Average number of fixed points =";average

end
```

The program **Random Permutations** (see p. 93) uses the subroutine **Shuffle** to generate random permutations. The program prints the proportion of times that there are k fixed points as well as the average number of fixed points. These can be used to estimate p_k when the number of simulations is large.

Running this program for 500 simulations for the cases $n = 10$, 20 and 30 gives:

```
Length of permutation = 10
Number of simulations = 500

0              .362
1              .368
2              .202
3              .052
4              .012
5              .004

Average number of fixed points = .996

Length of permutation = 20
Number of simulations = 500

0              .37
1              .396
2              .164
3              .06
4              .008
6              .002

Average number of fixed points = .948

Length of permutation = 30
Number of simulations = 500

0              .358
1              .358
2              .192
3              .07
4              .02
5              .002

Average number of fixed points = 1.042
```

Notice the rather surprising fact that our estimates for the probabilities do not seem to depend very heavily on the number of elements in the permutation. For example, the probability that no one gets his own hat back with 10, 20, or 30 people is estimated to be between .35 and .37. We shall see later that for $n \geq 10$ the exact probabilities are, to six decimal place accuracy, equal to $1/e = .367879$. Thus, for all practical purposes, after $n = 10$ the probability that no one gets his own hat back does not depend on the number of people. Also, it might be conjectured that the average number of fixed points will be close to 1, and we shall see that this is correct.

Records

Here is another interesting probability problem that involves permutations. Estimates for the amount of snow measured in inches in Hanover, New Hampshire, in the ten years 1974 to 1983 are:

1974	75
1975	88
1976	72
1977	110
1978	85
1979	30
1980	55
1981	86
1982	51
1983	64

Suppose we had started keeping records in 1974. Then our first year's snowfall could be considered a record snowfall starting from this year. 1975 established a new record; the next record was established in 1977, and there were no new records established after this year. Thus, in this ten-year period, there were three records established: 1974, 1975, and 1977. The question that we ask is: How many records should we expect to be established in such a ten-year period? We can count the number of records in terms of a permutation as follows: We number the years from 1 to 10. The actual amounts of snowfall are not important but their relative sizes are. We can, therefore, change the numbers measuring snowfalls to numbers 1 to 10 by replacing the smallest number by 1, the next smallest by 2, and so forth. (We assume that there are no ties.) For our example, we obtain

Year	1	2	3	4	5	6	7	8	9	10
Ranking	6	9	5	10	7	1	3	8	2	4

This gives us a permutation of the numbers from 1 to 10 and, from this permutation, we can read off the records: they are in years 1, 2 and 4. Thus we can define records for a permutation as follows:

DEFINITION 3

Let σ be a permutation of $1, \ldots, n$. Then i is a *record* of σ if either $i = 1$ or $\sigma(j) < \sigma(i)$ for every $j = 1, \ldots, i - 1$.

Now if we regard all rankings of snowfalls over an n-year period to be equally likely (and allow no ties), we can estimate the probability that there will be k records in n years as well as the average number of records by simulation.

We can modify **Random Permutations** to give a new program **Records** that counts the number of records in randomly chosen permutations by changing the middle block of **Random Permutations** to

```
for trial = 1 to simulations

    call shuffle(permutation)
    let current = permutation(1)   ! First year is always a record
    let records = 1

    for k = 1 to length
        if permutation(k) > current then   ! If it's a record ...
            let records = records + 1        ! ... count it ...
            let current = permutation(k)     ! ... and record it.
        end if
    next k

    let count(records) = count(records) + 1

next trial
```

Now s counts the number of records instead of the number of fixed points. We have run the new program **Records** for the cases $n = 10, 20, 30$.

```
Length of permutations = 10
Number of simulations = 500

        1               .092
        2               .282
        3               .31
        4               .216
        5               .082
        6               .018

Average number of records = 2.968

Length of permutations = 20
Number of simulations = 500

        1               .062
        2               .152
        3               .272
        4               .26
        5               .14
        6               .074
        7               .032
        8               .006
        9               .002

Average number of records = 3.656
```

```
Length of permutations = 30
Number of simulations = 500

1                   .036
2                   .14
3                   .24
4                   .234
5                   .182
6                   .118
7                   .036
8                   .008
9                   .006
```

Average number of records = 3.96

We see now that the averages increase, but very slowly. For $n = 10$ the average number of records is 2.968, for 20 it is 3.656, and for 30 it is 3.960.

The problem of finding the record in a series of measurements is the same as the problem of finding the maximum in a set of numbers. A typical program fragment to find the maximum in a list of n numbers would be:

```
let maximum = a(1)
for k = 2 to n
    if a(k) > maximum then let maximum = a(k)
next k
```

We see from this that, as the program is run, the number of times that the maximum is changed is the same as the number of records in the list. The speed of the program will depend on, among other things, the number of such changes that have to be made. For the computer scientist, our simulation results for records suggests that, for large n, the computer will make relatively few changes when looking for a maximum. We shall see later that the average number will be approximately $\log(n)$. Since $\log(10) = 2.3$, $\log(20) = 3$, and $\log(30) = 3.4$, this is consistent with the results of our simulations.

As remarked, we shall be able to obtain formulas for exact results of certain problems of the above type. However, only minor changes in the problem make this impossible. The power of simulation is that minor changes in a problem do not make the simulation much more difficult. (See Exercise 22 for an interesting variation of the hat check problem.)

List of Permutations

Another method to solve problems that is not sensitive to small changes in the problem is to have the computer simply list all possible permutations and count the fraction that have the desired property. When we try this, we run into a limitation on the use of the computer. The number of permutations of n increases so rapidly that, even to list all permutations of 20 objects is impractical.

We have included in **Lib.Prob** a subroutine **next_permutation** which generates the next permutation in a list in the order that you would naturally write them. The program **All Permutations** uses this subroutine to generate the set of all permutations of length n.

```
! All Permutations   (ALLPERMS)

! Generates (all) successive permutations on n objects, using the
! subroutine next_permutation(list(),flag) in Lib.prob.

library "Lib.prob*"

dim list(20)

input prompt "Length of permutations = " : length
print

mat list = zer(length)

let flag = 1

do
    call next_permutation(list,flag)
    mat print list;
loop until flag = 1

print

end
```

Running this program for $n = 3$ gives:

```
Length of permutations = 3

1  2  3

2  1  3

1  3  2

3  1  2

2  3  1

3  2  1
```

Historical Remarks

Our basic counting principle stated that if you can do one thing in r ways and for each of these another thing in s ways, then you can do the pair in rs ways. This is such a self-evident result that you might expect that it occurred very early in mathematics. N. L. Biggs suggests that we might trace an example of this principle as follows: First, he relates a popular nursery rhyme dating back to at least 1730:

> As I was going to St. Ives,
> I met a man with seven wives,
> Each wife had seven sacks,
> Each sack had seven cats,
> Each cat had seven kits,
> Kits, cats, sacks and wives,
> How many were going to St. Ives?

(You need our principle only if you are not clever enough to realize that you are supposed to answer *one*, since only the narrator is going to St. Ives; the others are going the other direction!)

Next he relates a very similar problem posed by Fibonacci in 1202:

> Seven old women are going to Rome; each of them has seven mules; each mule carries seven sacks; each sack contains seven loaves; each loaf has seven knives; and each knife has seven sheaths. What is the total number of things?

Finally, he gives a problem appearing on one of the oldest surviving mathematical manuscripts of about 1650 B.C., roughly translated as:

Houses	7
Cats	49
Mice	343
Wheat	2401
Hekat	<u>16807</u>
	19607

Biggs remarks that Rodet suggests this interpretation: there are seven houses, each with seven cats; each cat kills seven mice; each mouse would have eaten seven heads of wheat, each of which would have produced seven hekat measures of grain.[1]

One of the earliest uses of factorials was in Euclid's proof that there are infinitely many prime numbers. Euclid argued that there must be a prime number between n and $n! + 1$ as follows: $n!$ and $n! + 1$ cannot have common factors. Either $n! + 1$ is prime or it has a proper factor. In the latter case, this factor cannot divide $n!$ and hence must be between n and $n! + 1$. If this factor is not prime, then it has a factor that, by the same argument, must be bigger than n. In this way, we eventually reach a prime bigger than n, and this holds for all n.

The "$n!$" rule for the number of permutations seems to have occurred first in India. Examples have been found as early as 300 B.C., and by the eleventh century the general formula seems to have been well known in India and then in the Arab countries.

The *hat check problem* is found in an early probability book written by de Montmort first printed in 1708.[2] It appears in the form of a game called *Treize*. In a simplified version of this game considered by Montmort one turns over cards numbered from 1 to 13, calling out 1,2, . . . ,13 as the cards are examined. Montmort asked for the probability that no card that is turned up agrees with the number called out.

This probability is the same as the probability that a random permutation of 13 elements has no fixed point. Montmort solved this problem by the use of a recursion relation as follows: Let w_r be the number of permutations of r elements with no fixed point (complete permutations). Then

$$w_1 = 0 \quad \text{and} \quad w_2 = 1,$$

[1]N.L. Biggs, "The Roots of Combinatorics," *Historia Mathematica,* vol. 6 (1979), pp. 109–136.
[2]P.R. de Montmort, *Essay d'Analyse sur des Jeux de Hazard,* 2d ed. (Paris: Quillau, 1713).

and

$$w_n = (n-1)w_{n-1} + (n-1)w_{n-2} \qquad n = 3,4, \ldots .$$

This recurrence relation can be seen from the fact that any complete permutation of n numbers can be obtained either from a complete permutation of $n - 1$ numbers or from a permutation of $n - 1$ numbers that leave one number fixed. By induction this is equivalent to

$$w_n = nw_{n-1} + (-1)^n.$$

Then $p_i = \dfrac{w_i}{i!}$ satisfies

$$p_i - p_{i-1} = \frac{(-1)^i}{i!}.$$

Summing from $i = 2$ to n and using the fact that $p_1 = 0$ gives

$$p_n = \frac{1}{2!} - \frac{1}{3!} + \cdots + \frac{(-1)^n}{n!}.$$

This agrees with the first $n + 1$ terms of the expansion for e^x for $x = -1$ and hence for large n is approximately $e^{-1} = .368$. David remarks that this was possibly the first uses of the exponential function in probability.[3] We shall see another way to derive Montmort's result in the next section.

The *birthday problem* does not seem to have a very old history. It was made popular in the 1950s by Feller's book.[4]

Stirling presented his formula

$$n! \simeq \sqrt{2\pi n} \left(\frac{n}{e}\right)^n$$

in his work *Methodus Differentialis* published in 1730.[5] This approximation was used by de Moivre in establishing his celebrated central limit theorem that we will study in Chapter 9. De Moivre himself had independently established this approximation, but without identifying the constant π. Having established the approximation

$$\frac{2B}{\sqrt{n}}$$

for the central term of the binomial density, where the constant B was determined by an infinite series, de Moivre writes:

> . . . my worthy and learned Friend, Mr. James Stirling, who had applied himself after me to that inquiry, found that the Quantity B did denote the Square-root of the Circumference

---

[3] F.N. David, *Games, Gods and Gambling* (London: Griffin, 1962), p. 146.

[4] W. Feller, *Introduction to Probability Theory and Its Applications* vol. 1, 3rd ed. (New York: John Wiley and Sons, 1968).

[5] J. Stirling, *Methodus Differentialis*, (London: Bowyer, 1730).

of a Circle whose Radius is Unity, so that if that Circumference be called c the Ratio of the middle Term to the Sum of all Terms will be expressed by $2/\sqrt{nc}$ . . . .[6]

Exercises

1. Four people are to be arranged in a row to have their picture taken. In how many ways can this be done?

2. An automobile manufacturer has four colors available for automobile exteriors and three for interiors. How many different color combinations can he produce?

3. Assume that a typical computation on the computer takes a microsecond (one millionth of a second). Estimate the time required to carry out a program which makes 10! computations.

4. In a digital computer, a *bit* is one of the integers {0,1}, and a *word* is any string of 32 bits. How many different words are possible?

5. What is the probability that at least 2 of the presidents of the United States have died on the same day of the year? If you bet this has happened, would you win your bet?

6. There are three different routes connecting city A to city B. How many ways can a round trip be made from A to B and back? How many ways if it is desired to take a different route on the way back?

7. In arranging people around a circular table, we take into account their seats relative to each other, not the actual position of any one person. Show that n people can be arranged around a circular table in $(n - 1)!$ ways.

8. Five people get on an elevator that stops at five floors. Assuming that each has an equal probability of going to any one floor, find the probability that they all get off at different floors.

9. A finite set Ω has n elements. Show that if we count the empty set and Ω as subsets, there are 2^n subsets of Ω.

10. A more refined inequality for approximating $n!$ is given by (cf. Theorem 2)

$$\sqrt{2\pi n}.\left(\frac{n}{e}\right)^n e^{\left(\frac{1}{12n+1}\right)} < n! < \sqrt{2\pi n}\left(\frac{n}{e}\right)^n e^{\left(\frac{1}{12n}\right)}.$$

Write a computer program to illustrate this inequality for $n = 1$ to 9.

11. A deck of ordinary cards is shuffled and 13 cards are dealt. What is the probability that the last card dealt is an ace?

12. There are n applicants for the director of computing. The applicants are interviewed independently by each member of the three-person search committee and ranked from

---

[6]A. de Moivre, *The Doctrine of Chances*, 3rd ed. (London: Millar, 1756).

1 to n. A candidate will be hired if he or she is ranked first by at least two of the three interviewers. Find the probability that a candidate will be accepted if the members of the committee really have no ability at all to judge the candidates and just rank the candidates randomly. In particular, compare this probability for the case of three candidates and the case of ten candidates.

13. A symphony orchestra has in its repertoire 30 Haydn symphonies, 15 modern works, and 9 Beethoven symphonies. Its program always consists of a Haydn symphony followed by a modern work, and then a Beethoven symphony.
    (a) How many different programs can it play?
    (b) How many different programs are there if the three symphonies can be played in any order?
    (c) How many different three-piece programs are there if more than one piece from the same category can be played and they can be played in any order?

14. A certain state has license plates showing three numbers and three letters. How many different license plates are possible
    (a) if the numbers must come before the letters?
    (b) if there is no restriction on where the letters and numbers appear?

15. The door on the computer center has a lock which has five buttons numbered from 1 to 5. The combination of numbers that opens the lock is a sequence of five numbers and is reset every week.
    (a) How many combinations are possible if every button must be used once?
    (b) Assume that the lock can also have combinations that require you to push two buttons simultaneously and then the other three one at a time. How many more combinations does this permit?

16. A computing center has 3 processors that receive n jobs, with the jobs assigned to the processors purely at random so that all of the 3^n possible assignments are equally likely. Find the probability that exactly one processor has no jobs.

17. Prove that at least two people in Atlanta, Georgia, have the same four-digit phone number.

18. Modify the program **All Permutations** to compute the probability that in the hat check problem exactly k out of n people get their own hats back. Find these probabilities for $n = 2$ to 6.

19. Find a formula for the probability that among a set of n people, at least two have their birthdays in the same month of the year (assuming the months are equally likely for birthdays).

20. It is asserted in Kemeny, Snell, and Kurtz[7] that in the Land of Oz, there are 525 days in a year. You are asked to find the number of Munchkins who must be present

---

[7]J.G. Kemeny, J.L. Snell and T.E. Kurtz, *Computing for a Course in Finite Mathematics*, (Reading: Addison-Wesley, 1985).

to have a probability greater than $^1/_2$ that two have the same birthday. What should your answer be?

21. Consider the problem of finding the probability of more than one coincidence of birthdays in a group of n people. These include, for example, three people with the same birthday, or two pairs of people with the same birthday, or larger coincidences. Show how you could compute this probability, and write a computer program to carry out this computation. Use your program to find the smallest number of people for which it would be a favorable bet that there would be more than one coincidence of birthdays.

22. At a mathematical conference, ten participants are randomly seated around a circular table for meals. Using simulation, estimate the probability that no two people sit next to each other at both lunch and dinner. Can you make an intelligent conjecture for the case of n participants when n is large?

23. Modify the program **All Permutations** to count the number of permutations of n objects that have exactly j fixed points for $j = 0,1,2, \ldots ,n$. Run your program for $n = 2$ to 6. Make a conjecture for the relation between the number that have 0 fixed points and the number that have exactly 1 fixed point. For a proof of the correct conjecture, see "A Bijection in the Theory of Derangements" by Wilf.[8]

24. Mr. Wimply Dimple, one of London's most prestigious watch makers, has come to Holmes in a panic, having discovered that someone has been producing and selling crude counterfeits of his best selling watch. The 16 counterfeits so far discovered bear stamped numbers, all of which fall between 1 and 56, and Dimple is anxious to know the extent of the forger's work. All present agree that it seems reasonable to assume that the counterfeits thus far produced bear consecutive numbers from 1 to whatever the total number is.

"Chin up, Dimple," opines Watson. "I shouldn't worry overly much if I were you; the Maximum Likelihood Principle, which estimates the total number as precisely that which gives the highest probability for the series of numbers found, suggests that we guess 56 itself as the total. Thus, your forgers are not a big operation, and we shall have them safely behind bars before your business suffers significantly."

"Stuff, nonsense, and bother your fancy principles, Watson!" counters Holmes. "Anyone can see that, of course, there must be quite a few more than 56 watches— why the odds of our having discovered precisely the highest numbered watch made are laughably negligible. A much better guess would be *twice* 56."

(a) Show that Watson is correct that the Maximum Likelihood Principle gives 56.

(b) Write a computer program to compare Holmes's and Watson's guessing strategies as follows: fix a total N and choose 16 integers randomly between 1 and N. Let m denote the largest of these. Then Watson's guess for N is m, while Holmes's is $2m$. See which of these is closer to N. Repeat this experiment (with N still

[8]H.S. Wilf, "A Bijection in the Theory of Derangements," *Mathematics Magazine*, vol. 57, no. 1 (1984), pp. 37–40.

fixed) a hundred or more times, and determine the proportion of times that each comes closer. Whose seems to be the better strategy?

25. Barbara Smith is interviewing candidates to be her secretary. As she interviews the candidates, she can determine the relative rank of the candidates but not the true rank. Thus, if there are six candidates and their true rank is 6,1,4,2,3,5, (where 1 is best) then after she had interviewed the first three candidates she would rank them 3,1,2. As she interviews each candidate, she must either accept or reject the candidate. If she does not accept the candidate after the interview, the candidate is lost to her. She wants to decide on a strategy for deciding when to stop and accept a candidate that will maximize the probability of getting the best candidate. Assume that there are n candidates and they arrive in a random rank order.

   (a) What is the probability that Barbara gets the best candidate if she interviews all of the candidates? What is it if she chooses the first candidate?

   (b) Assume that Barbara decides to interview the first half of the candidates and then continue interviewing until getting a candidate better than any candidate seen so far. Show that she has a better than 25 percent chance of ending up with the best candidate.

26. For the task described in Exercise 25, it can be shown[9] that the best strategy is to pass over the first $k - 1$ candidates where k is the smallest integer for which

$$\frac{1}{k} + \frac{1}{k+1} + \cdots + \frac{1}{n-1} \leq 1.$$

Using this strategy the probability of getting the best candidate is approximately $1/e = .368$. Write a program to simulate Barbara Smith's interviewing if she uses this optimal strategy, using $n = 10$, and see if you can verify that the probability of success is approximately $1/e$.

Appendix: Proof of Stirling's Formula

To prove Stirling's formula we shall follow an approach suggested by J. G. Kemeny[10] and prove a more general theorem which implies Stirling's formula as well as other asymptotic expressions needed later.

Let $f(x)$ be a function defined on an interval $[a,n]$ with a and n integers and with $f(x) \geq 0$, $f'(x) \geq 0$, and $f''(x) \leq 0$. The graph of such a function is increasing and concave downward as illustrated in Figure 3.

We denote by $A_{a,n}$ the area under the curve from a to n. Then

$$A_{a,n} = \int_a^n f(x)dx = F(n) - F(a),$$

[9]E.B. Dynkin and A.A. Yushkevich, *Markov Processes: Theorems and Problems*, trans. J.S. Wood (New York: Plenum, 1969).

[10]Unpublished communication.

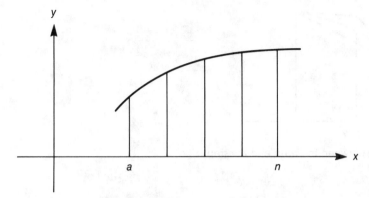

Figure 3 Approximating the area under $f(x)$.

where $F(x)$ is an antiderivative of $f(x)$, that is, $F'(x) = f(x)$. We denote by $T_{a,n}$ the sum of the areas of approximating trapezoids with unit base as indicated in Figure 3. Then

$$T_{a,n} = \frac{f(a)+f(a+1)}{2} + \frac{f(a+1)+f(a+2)}{2} + \cdots + \frac{f(n-1)+f(n)}{2}$$

$$= \frac{f(a)}{2} + f(a+1) + \cdots + f(n-1) + \frac{f(n)}{2}.$$

The difference $D_{a,n} = A_{a,n} - T_{a,n}$ is the area between the approximating trapezoids and the curve. It is increasing as $n \to \infty$ with a limiting value $D_a = \lim_{n \to \infty} D_{a,n}$, as the following theorem proves.

THEOREM 3

Let $f(x)$ be a function with $f(x) \geq 0$, $f'(x) \geq 0$, and $f''(x) \leq 0$ on the interval $[a,n]$ with a and n integers. Let $D_{a,n} = A_{a,n} - T_{a,n}$ be the difference between the area under the curve and the trapezoid approximation. Then $D_{a,n}$ increases to D_a as $n \to \infty$ with

$$0 \leq D_a \leq \frac{1}{8} f'(a).$$

Proof. Let d_k be the difference between the area under the curve between k and $k + 1$ and the trapezoid with base $[k,k + 1]$ and top connecting the points $(k,f(k))$ and $(k + 1,f(k + .1))$, as shown in Figure 4. We consider two trapezoids that lie above the curve, the first with base $[k,k + \frac{1}{2}]$ and the top formed by the tangent line at $f(k)$

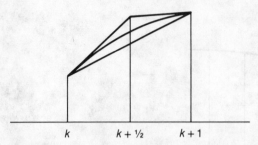

k   k + ½   k + 1

Figure 4 Difference between the area and the trapezoid approximation.

intersecting the vertical line through $k + \frac{1}{2}$ at the point $A = (k + \frac{1}{2}, f(k) + \frac{1}{2}f'(k))$. The second trapezoid has base $[k + \frac{1}{2}, k + 1]$ and the top determined by the tangent at $f(k + 1)$ intersecting the vertical line from $k + \frac{1}{2}$ at the point $B = (k + \frac{1}{2}, f(k + 1) - \frac{1}{2}f'(k + 1))$. These trapezoids have areas

$$\frac{1}{2}(f(k) + f(k) + \frac{1}{2}f'(k)) \cdot \frac{1}{2}$$

and

$$\frac{1}{2}(f(k+1) - \frac{1}{2}f'(k+1) + f(k+1)) \cdot \frac{1}{2}.$$

The trapezoid with unit base under the curve has area

$$\frac{1}{2}(f(k) + f(k+1))$$

Taking the difference between the sum of the areas of the two upper trapezoids and the area of the lower trapezoid we have

$$0 \le d_k \le \frac{1}{8}(f'(k) - f'(k+1)).$$

Now, $D_{a,n}$ is less than the sum of these d_k, so

$$0 \le D_{a,n} \le \frac{1}{8}(f'(a) - f'(a+1) + f'(a+1) - f'(a+2) + \cdots + f'(n-1) - f'(n))$$

$$= \frac{1}{8}(f'(a) - f'(n)) \le \frac{1}{8}f'(a),$$

as was to be proved. ∎

EXAMPLE 5   Stirling's Formula

Let $f(x) = \log(x)$ and $a = 1$. Then $f'(x) = \frac{1}{x} \ge 0$, $f''(x) = -\frac{1}{x^2} \le 0$, $F(x) =$

$x \log(x) - x$ for the interval $[1,n]$.

$$D_{1,n} = F(n) - F(1) - \left[\frac{1}{2}\log(1) + \log(2) + \log(3) + \ldots + \log(n-1) + \frac{1}{2}\log(n) \right]$$

$$= n\log(n) - n + 1 - \log(n!) + \frac{1}{2}\log(n).$$

Thus, by Theorem 3, $D_{1,n}$ approaches D_1 as $n \to \infty$ with $0 \le D_1 \le \frac{1}{8} f'(1) = \frac{1}{8}$, and so

$$\log(n!) - [\log(n^n) + \log(n^{1/2}) - n] \to 1 - D_1,$$

or

$$n! \sim cn^n \sqrt{n}\, e^{-n}, \tag{1}$$

with $e^{7/8} \le c \le e$. This gives $2.39 \ldots \le c \le 2.71 \ldots$. The exact value for $c = \sqrt{2\pi} \simeq 2.5$ can be obtained as follows. Integration by parts gives the integrals

$$I_{2n} = \int_0^{\pi/2} \sin^{2n}\theta\, d\theta = \frac{1 \cdot 3 \cdot 5 \ldots (2n-1)}{2 \cdot 4 \cdot 6 \ldots 2n} \frac{\pi}{2}$$

and

$$I_{2n+1} = \int_0^{\pi/2} \sin^{2n+1}\theta\, d\theta = \frac{2 \cdot 4 \cdot 6 \ldots 2n}{3 \cdot 5 \ldots (2n+1)}.$$

Since

$$I_{2n+1} < I_{2n} < I_{2n-1},$$

we have

$$\frac{(2 \cdot 4 \cdot 6 \ldots 2n-2)^2 (2n)^2}{(3 \cdot 5 \ldots 2n-1)^2 (2n+1)} < \frac{1}{2}\pi < \frac{(2 \cdot 4 \cdot 6 \ldots 2n-2)^2 (2n)}{(3 \cdot 5 \ldots 2n-1)^2}.$$

Both sides of this inequality have the same limit, giving Wallis's formula

$$\pi = \lim_{n \to \infty} \frac{2^{4n} (n!)^4}{n((2n)!)^2}. \tag{2}$$

Putting Equation (1) into Equation (2) gives $c = \sqrt{2\pi}$ and thus Stirling's formula

$$n! \sim \sqrt{2\pi}\, n^n \sqrt{n}\, e^{-n}. \qquad \square$$

THEOREM 4

Let $f(x)$ be a function defined on the interval $[a,n]$ with a,n integers and $f(x) \ge 0$, $f'(x) \le 0$, $f''(x) \ge 0$. Then if $D_{a,n} = T_{a,n} - A_{a,n}$, $D_{a,n}$ increases to D_a as $n \to \infty$ with $0 \le D_a \le -\frac{1}{8} f'(a)$.

Proof. The proof is the same as that of Theorem 1, but with the picture now given by Figure 5. ∎

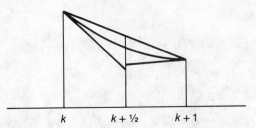

k $k + \frac{1}{2}$ $k + 1$

Figure 5 Approximating the area by trapezoids.

EXAMPLE 6   The Harmonic Series

Let $f(x) = \dfrac{1}{x}$ on the interval $[1,n]$. Then $f(x) \geq 0$, $f'(x) = -\dfrac{1}{x^2} \leq 0$, and

$f''(x) = \dfrac{2}{x^3} \geq 0$. Thus, by Theorem 4

$$D_{1,n} = \left(\frac{1}{2} + \frac{1}{2} + \frac{1}{3} + \cdots + \frac{1}{n-1} + \frac{1}{2n}\right) - (\log(n) - \log(1)) \to D_1,$$

with $0 \leq D_1 \leq -\frac{1}{8} f'(1) = \frac{1}{8}$. Therefore,

$$1 + \frac{1}{2} + \frac{1}{3} + \cdots + \frac{1}{n} \sim \log(n) + \gamma + \frac{1}{2n},$$

with $\frac{1}{2} \leq \gamma \leq \frac{5}{8}$ or $.5 \leq \gamma \leq .625$. The exact value of γ is *Euler's constant*: $\gamma = .5772156649 \ldots$. We shall not prove this here. $\qquad\qquad\square$

Exercises

1. Use Theorem 3 to find an asymptotic expression for $1 + 2 + \ldots + n$. Determine the exact value of the constant D_0.

2. Use Theorem 4 to find an asymptotic expression for

$$1 + \frac{1}{\sqrt{2}} + \frac{1}{\sqrt{3}} + \cdots + \frac{1}{\sqrt{n}}.$$

3. Write a program to compare the exact values of the harmonic series $1 + \frac{1}{2} + \cdots + \frac{1}{n}$ with the asymptotic results obtained in Example 6 (use $\gamma = .57722$).

3.2 BERNOULLI TRIALS

Having mastered permutations, we now consider combinations. Let U be a set with n elements; we want to count the number of distinct subsets of the set U that have exactly j elements. The empty set and the set U are considered to be subsets of U.

EXAMPLE 1

Let $U = \{a,b,c\}$. The subsets of U are:

$\emptyset$
$\{a\}$
$\{b\}$
$\{c\}$
$\{a,b\}$
$\{a,c\}$
$\{b,c\}$
$\{a,b,c\}$ □

Binomial Coefficients

We denote by $c(n,j)$ the number of distinct subsets with j elements that can be chosen from a set with n elements. A more common notation for $c(n,j)$ is $\binom{n}{j}$, pronounced "n choose j." We shall use both notations. The matrix notation $c(n,j)$ will be used in computer programs. The number $\binom{n}{j}$ is called a *binomial coefficient*. This terminology comes from an application to algebra which will be discussed later in this section.

In the above example, there is one subset with no elements, three subsets with exactly 1 element, three subsets with exactly 2 elements, and one subset with exactly 3 elements. Thus, $\binom{3}{0} = 1$, $\binom{3}{1} = 3$, $\binom{3}{2} = 3$, and $\binom{3}{3} = 1$. Note that there are $2^3 = 8$ subsets in all. (We have already seen that a set with n elements has 2^n subsets; see Exercise 9 in Section 3.1.) It follows that

$$\binom{3}{0} + \binom{3}{1} + \binom{3}{2} + \binom{3}{3} = 2^3 = 8,$$

$$\binom{n}{0} = \binom{n}{n} = 1.$$

Assume that $n > 0$. Then, since there is only one way to choose a set with no elements and only one way to choose a set with n elements, the remaining values of $\binom{n}{j}$ are determined by the following *recurrence relation:*

THEOREM 5

For $0 < j < n$, the binomial coefficients satisfy:

$$\binom{n}{j} = \binom{n-1}{j} + \binom{n-1}{j-1}. \tag{1}$$

Proof. We wish to choose a subset of j elements. Choose an element u of U. Assume first that we do not want u in the subset. Then we must choose the j elements from a set of $n - 1$ elements; this can be done in $\binom{n-1}{j}$ ways. On the other hand, assume that we do want u in the subset. Then we must choose the other $j - 1$ elements from the remaining $n - 1$ elements of U; this can be done in $\binom{n-1}{j-1}$ ways. Since u is either in our subset or not, the number of ways that we can choose a subset of j elements is the sum of the number of subsets of j elements which have u as a member and the number which do not—this is what Equation (1) states. ∎

Pascal's Triangle

The relation Equation (1), together with the knowledge that

$$\binom{n}{0} = \binom{n}{n} = 1$$

determines completely the numbers $\binom{n}{j}$. We can use these relations to determine the famous *triangle of Pascal*, which exhibits all these numbers in matrix form (see Figure 6).

The nth row of this triangle has the entries $\binom{n}{0}, \binom{n}{1}, \ldots, \binom{n}{n}$. We know that the first and last of these numbers are 1. The remaining numbers are determined by the recurrence relation Equation (1); that is, the entry $c(n,j) = \binom{n}{j}$ for $0 < j < n$ in the nth

	$j = 0$	1	2	3	4	5	6	7	8	9	10
$n = 0$	1										
1	1	1									
2	1	2	1								
3	1	3	3	1							
4	1	4	6	4	1						
5	1	5	10	10	5	1					
6	1	6	15	20	15	6	1				
7	1	7	21	35	35	21	7	1			
8	1	8	28	56	70	56	28	8	1		
9	1	9	36	84	126	126	84	36	9	1	
10	1	10	45	120	210	252	210	120	45	10	1

Figure 6. Pascal's triangle.

row of Pascal's triangle is the *sum* of the entry immediately above and the one immediately to its left in the $(n - 1)$st row. For example, $\binom{5}{2} = 6 + 4 = 10$.

This algorithm for constructing Pascal's triangle can be used to write a computer program to compute the binomial coefficients. You are asked to do this in Exercise 5.

While Pascal's triangle provides a way to construct recursively the binomial coefficients, it is also possible to give a formula for $\binom{n}{j}$.

THEOREM 6

The binomial coefficients are given by the formula

$$\binom{n}{j} = \frac{n!}{j!(n - j)!} .$$ (2)

Proof. We note first that the formula gives the value 1 for $j = 0$ and $j = n$ as it should. (Recall that $0! = 1$.) We shall prove, by induction, that it is true for all values of n. Assume that it is true for values of $m \leqslant n - 1$. Then from Equation (1) and our induction hypothesis,

$$\binom{n}{j} = \binom{n - 1}{j} + \binom{n - 1}{j - 1}$$

$$= \frac{(n - 1)!}{j!(n - j - 1)!} + \frac{(n - 1)!}{(j - 1)!(n - j)!}$$

$$= \frac{(n - j)(n - 1)!}{j!(n - j)!} + \frac{j(n - 1)!}{j!(n - j)!}$$

$$= \frac{n!}{j!(n - j)!} ,$$

and our formula is true for n. ∎

For computation purposes it is better to write the expression Equation (2) in the form

$$\binom{n}{j} = \frac{n \cdot (n - 1) \cdot (n - 2) \cdot \cdots \cdot (n - j + 1)}{1 \cdot 2 \cdot 3 \cdot \cdots \cdot j} .$$

The subroutine **choose** (n, k) in **Lib.Prob**, which uses this form to calculate binomial coefficients, is demonstrated by **Demo Choose**.

```
! Demo Choose    (DCHOOSE)
!
! Demonstrates the function choose(n,k), which returns the number of
! ways of choosing k objects out of n.  As a check, this compares the
!
!              n                           n
!             Σ choose(n,k)      with     2
!             k=0

declare function choose

do

   input prompt "n = ": n

   let sum = 0

   for k = 0 to n
       let value = round(choose(n,k))
       print "choose(" & str$(n) & "," & str$(k) & ") = " & str$(value)
       let sum = sum + value
   next k

   print "sum = " &  str$(sum) & "; 2^" & str$(n) & " ="; 2^n
   print "------------------------"

loop until n = 0

end


! choose(n,k)
!
! Subroutine to compute binomial coefficients: choose(n,k) is the number of ways of
! choosing k objects out of n.  Returns 0 if k is negative or greater
! than n. To save time, this computes choose(n,n-k) (which is equal to
! choose(n,k)) if n-k is smaller than k; e.g., it does choose(100,3)
! instead of choose(100,97).
!
function choose(n,k)

    if k < 0 or k > n then
       let choose = 0
    else
       let product = 1
       for j = 1 to min(k,n-k)
           let product = product * (n-j+1)/j
       next j
       let choose = product
    end if

end function
```

We have run this program for $n = 20$:

```
n = 20
choose(20,0) = 1
choose(20,1) = 20
choose(20,2) = 190
choose(20,3) = 1140
choose(20,4) = 4845
choose(20,5) = 15504
```

```
choose (20, 6)  = 38760
choose (20, 7)  = 77520
choose (20, 8)  = 125970
choose (20, 9)  = 167960
choose (20, 10) = 184756
choose (20, 11) = 167960
choose (20, 12) = 125970
choose (20, 13) = 77520
choose (20, 14) = 38760
choose (20, 15) = 15504
choose (20, 16) = 4845
choose (20, 17) = 1140
choose (20, 18) = 190
choose (20, 19) = 20
choose (20, 20) = 1
sum = 1048576;  2^20 = 1048576
```

Note that the number of distinct subsets of 10 elements in a set of 20 elements is quite large, namely 184756. Although there are far fewer subsets of 5 elements, namely 15504, this is still a large number of subsets.

Poker Hands

EXAMPLE 2

Poker players sometimes wonder why a *four of a kind* beats a *full house*. A poker hand is a random subset of 5 elements from a deck of 52 cards. A hand has four of a kind if it has four cards with the same value—for example, four sixes or four kings. It is a full house if it has three of one value and two of a second—for example, three twos and two queens. Let us see which hand is more likely. How many hands have four of a kind? There are 13 ways that we can specify the value for the four cards. For each of these, there are 48 possibilities for the fifth card. Thus, the number of four-of-a-kind hands is $13 \cdot 48 = 624$. Since the total number of possible hands is $\binom{52}{5} = 2598960$, the probability of a hand with four of a kind is $624/2598960 = .00024$.

Now consider the case of a full house; how many such hands are there? There are 13 choices for the value which occurs three times; for each of these there are $\binom{4}{3} = 4$ choices for the particular three cards of this value that are in the hand. Having picked these three cards, there are 12 possibilities for the value which occurs twice; for each of these there are $\binom{4}{2} = 6$ possibilities for the particular pair of this value. Thus, the number of full houses is $13 \cdot 4 \cdot 12 \cdot 6 = 3744$, and the probability of obtaining a hand with a full house is $3744/2598960 = .0014$. Thus, while both types of hands are unlikely, you are six times more likely to obtain a full house than four of a kind. □

Bernoulli Trials

Our principal use of the binomial coefficients will occur in the study of one of the important chance processes called *Bernoulli trials*.

DEFINITION 4

A *Bernoulli trials process* is a sequence of n chance experiments such that

(1) Each experiment has two possible outcomes, which we may call *success* and *failure*.

(2) The probability p of success on each experiment is the same for each experiment, and this probability is not affected by any knowledge of previous outcomes. The probability q of failure is given by $q = 1 - p$.

EXAMPLE 3

The following are Bernoulli trials processes:

(1) A coin is tossed ten times. The two possible outcomes are heads and tails. The probability of heads on any one toss is 1/2.

(2) An opinion poll is carried out by asking 1000 people, randomly chosen from the population, if they favor the ERA amendment—the two outcomes being yes and no. The probability p of a yes answer (i.e., a success) indicates the proportion of people in the entire population that favor the ERA amendment.

(3) A gambler makes a sequence of 1-dollar bets, betting each time on black at roulette at Las Vegas. Here a success is winning 1 dollar and a failure is losing

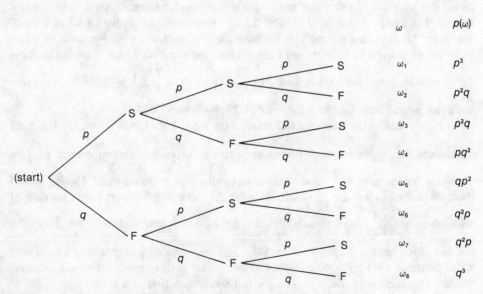

Figure 7 Tree diagram of three Bernoulli trials.

1 dollar. Since in American roulette the gambler wins if the ball stops on one of 18 out of 38 positions and loses otherwise, the probability of winning is $p = 18/38 = .474$. □

To analyze a Bernoulli trials process, we choose as our sample space a binary tree and assign a probability measure to the paths in this tree. Suppose, for example, that we have three Bernoulli trials. The possible outcomes are indicated in the tree diagram shown in Figure 7.

The probabilities assigned to the branches of the tree represent the probability for each individual trial. Since we have assumed that outcomes on any one trial do not affect those on another, we assign the same probabilities at each level of the tree. An outcome ω for the entire experiment will be a path through the tree. For example, ω_3 represents the outcomes SFS. Our frequency interpretation of probability would lead us to expect a fraction p of success on the first experiment; of these, a fraction q of failures on the second; and, of these, a fraction p of successes on the third experiment. This suggests assigning probability pqp to the outcome ω_3. More generally, we assign a probability density $p(\omega)$ for paths ω by defining $p(\omega)$ to be the product of the branch probabilities along the path ω.

If $\omega = $ (S,S,F,F,S) is a path in the tree for five Bernoulli trials, then

$$p(\omega) = p(S,S,F,F,S) = p(S)p(S)p(F)p(F)p(S)$$

where $p(S) = p$ is the probability of success on any one trial and $p(F) = q = 1 - p$ is the probability of failure on any one trial. Thus, the probability that the five events S,S,F,F,S happen in this order is the product of the probabilities for the individual events. We shall see in the next chapter that this means that the events involved are *independent* in the sense that the knowledge of outcome of one event does not affect our prediction for the occurrences of the other events.

Binomial Probabilities

We shall be particularly interested in the probability that in n Bernoulli trials there are exactly j successes. We denote this probability by $b(n,p,j)$. Let us calculate the particular value $b(3,p,2)$ from our tree measure. We see that there are three paths which have exactly two successes and one failure, namely $\omega_2, \omega_3, \omega_5$. Each of these paths has the same probability p^2q. Thus $b(3,p,2) = 3p^2q$. Considering all possible numbers of successes we have

$$b(3,p,0) = q^3$$
$$b(3,p,1) = 3pq^2$$
$$b(3,p,2) = 3p^2q$$
$$b(3,p,3) = p^3$$

We can, in the same manner, carry out a tree and tree measure for n experiments and determine $b(n,p,j)$ for the general case of n Bernoulli trials.

THEOREM 7

Given n Bernoulli trials with probability p of success on each experiment, the probability of exactly j successes is

$$b(n,p,j) = \binom{n}{j} p^j q^{(n-j)}$$

where $q = 1 - p$.

Proof. We construct a tree measure as described above. We want to find the sum of the probabilities for all paths which have exactly j successes and $n - j$ failures. Each such path is assigned a probability $p^j q^{(n-j)}$. How many such paths are there? To specify a path, we have to say which of the n outcomes were successes and which were failures. That is, we have to pick a subset of j elements out of the n possible trial numbers. We can do this in $\binom{n}{j}$ ways. Thus the sum of the probabilities is

$$b(n,p,j) = \binom{n}{j} p^j q^{(n-j)}. \qquad \blacksquare$$

EXAMPLE 4

A fair coin is tossed six times. What is the probability that exactly three heads turn up? The answer is

$$b(6,.5,3) = \binom{6}{3}\left(\frac{1}{2}\right)^3 \left(\frac{1}{2}\right)^3 = 20 \cdot \frac{1}{64} = .3125. \qquad \square$$

EXAMPLE 5

A die is rolled four times. What is the probability that we obtain exactly one 6? We treat this as Bernoulli trials with *success* = "rolling a 6" and *failure* = "rolling some number other than a 6." Then $p = 1/6$, and the probability of exactly one success in four trials is

$$b(4,1/6,1) = \binom{4}{1}\left(\frac{1}{6}\right)^1 \left(\frac{5}{6}\right)^3 = .386. \qquad \square$$

To compute binomial probabilities using the computer, multiply the function choose (n,j) by $p^j q^{n-j}$. The program **Demo Binomial** shows the result.

```
! Demo Binomial     (DBINOM)
!
! Demonstrates the function binomial(n,p,k)
!

declare function binomial
```

```
input prompt "Number of trials, probability of success = ": n,p
print "Probabilities for successes from kmin to kmax for kmin, kmax = ";
input prompt "": kmin, kmax

for k = kmin to kmax
    print "binomial(" & str$(n) & "," & str$(p) & ","&str$(k) & ") = ";
    print str$(binomial(n,p,k))
next k

end

! binomial(n,p,k)
!
! Function which returns the probability of getting k successes in n
! Bernoulli trials with probability p for success.  This uses the
! function choose(n,k), which returns binomial coefficients

function binomial(n,p,k)

    library "Lib.prob*"
    declare function choose

    let q = 1 - p
    let binomial = choose(n,k) * p^k * q^(n-k)

end function
```

We have run this program for $n = 100, p = 1/2$, and kmin $= 45$ and kmax $= 55$. Note that the individual probabilities are quite small.

```
Number of trials, probability of success = 100,.5
Probabilities for successes from kmin to kmax for kmin, kmax = 45,55

binomial(100,.5,45) = 4.84743e-2
binomial(100,.5,46) = 5.79584e-2
binomial(100,.5,47) = 6.65905e-2
binomial(100,.5,48) = .073527
binomial(100,.5,49) = 7.80287e-2
binomial(100,.5,50) = 7.95892e-2
binomial(100,.5,51) = 7.80287e-2
binomial(100,.5,52) = .073527
binomial(100,.5,53) = 6.65905e-2
binomial(100,.5,54) = 5.79584e-2
binomial(100,.5,55) = 4.84743e-2
```

The probability of exactly 50 heads in 100 tosses of a coin is actually quite small, about .08. Our intuition tells us that this is the most likely outcome, which is correct; but, all the same, it is not a very likely outcome.

Binomial Densities

DEFINITION 5

For given values of n and p, probability density $b(n,p,j)$ for $j = 0,1,2, \ldots ,n$ is called the *binomial density*.

We can get a better idea about the binomial density by graphing this density for different values of n and p (see Figure 8). The program **Binomial Plot** modifies **Demo Binomial** to plot the binomial density.

```
! Binomial Plot    (BINOMP)
!
! Plots densities for Bernoulli trials

library "Lib.prob*"
declare function binomial

input prompt "Probability for success? " : p

let q = 1-p
let min_trials = 20
let max_trials = 160
let min_peak_at = int(p*(min_trials + 1))
let xmin = 0
let xmax = int(min(max_trials,max_trials*p+4*sqr(max_trials*p*q)))+1/2
let ymin = 0
let ymax = 5/4 * binomial(min_trials,p,min_peak_at)

open #1:screen .1,.9,.1,.9          ! Open window for graph
set window xmin, xmax,ymin, ymax    ! Scale the window
plot xmin,ymax;xmin,ymin; xmax,ymin ! Plot axes in the window

for experiment = 1 to 4

    let trials = 10 * 2^experiment

    let sigma = sqr(trials*p*q)    ! standard deviation
    let kmin = int(max(0,trials*p-4*sigma))
    let kmax = int(min(trials,trials*p+4*sigma))

    for k = kmin to kmax
        let height = binomial(trials,p,k)
        box lines k-1/2, k+1/2, 0, height
    next k

next experiment

end
```

We have run this program for $p = .5$ and $p = .3$. Note that even for $p = .3$ the graphs are quite symmetric. We shall have an explanation for this in Chapter 9. We also note that the highest probability occurs around the value np, but that these highest probabilities get smaller as n increases. We shall see in Chapter 6 that np is the *mean* or *expected* value of the binomial density $b(n, p, j)$.

Hypothesis Testing

EXAMPLE 6
Suppose that ordinary aspirin has been found effective against headache 60 percent of the time, and that a drug company claims that its new aspirin with a special additive is more effective. We can test this claim as follows: we call their claim the *alternate hypothesis*, and its negation, that the additive has no appreciable effect, the *null hypothesis*. Thus the null hypothesis is that $p = .6$, and the alternate hypothesis that $p > .6$, where p is the probability that the new aspirin is effective.

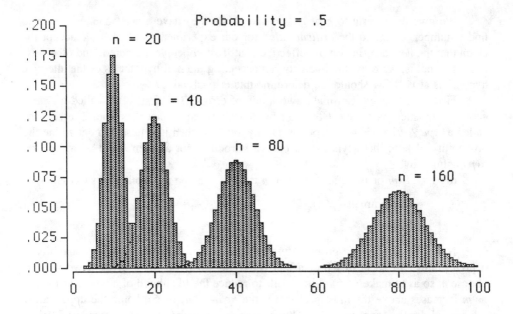

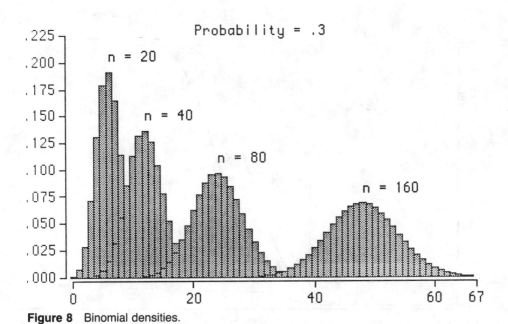

Figure 8 Binomial densities.

We give the aspirin to n people to take when they have a headache. We want to find a number m, called the *critical value* for our experiment, such that we accept the claim that the new aspirin is more effective if at least m people are cured, and otherwise reject it. That is, we draw the line between accepting the null hypothesis or the alternate hypothesis at m. How should we determine this critical value?

First note that we can make two kinds of errors. The first, often called a *type 1 error* in statistics, is to reject the null hypothesis when in fact it is true. The second, called a *type 2 error*, is to accept the null hypothesis when it is false. To determine the probability of both these types of errors we introduce, for a given n and m, a function $\alpha(p)$ defined by

$\alpha(p) = P(m$ or more successes in n trials if p is the probability of success).

$= \Sigma \text{ binomial}(n,p,k).$

$m \leqslant k \leqslant n$

Note that $\alpha(.6)$ is the probability of a type 1 error, since this is the probability of a high number of successes for an ineffective additive. So for a given n we want to choose m so as to make $\alpha(.6)$ quite small, to reduce the likelihood of a type 1 error. But as m increases above the most probable value $np = .6n$, $\alpha(.6)$, being the upper tail of a binomial density, approaches 0. Thus *increasing m* makes a type 1 error less likely.

Now suppose that the additive really is effective, so that p is appreciably greater than .6; say $p = .8$. Then choosing m well below $np = .8n$ will increase $\alpha(.8)$, since

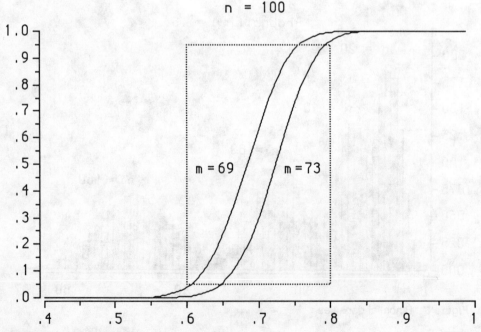

Figure 9 The power curve.

now $\alpha(.8)$ is all but the lower tail of a binomial density. Indeed, if we put $\beta(.8) = 1 - \alpha(.8)$, then $\beta(.8)$ gives us the probability of a type 2 error, and so *decreasing* m makes a type 2 error less likely.

What we hope to do then, for a given test population n, is to choose an m which simultaneously minimizes these two probabilities. If we make a type 1 error we end up buying a lot of essentially ordinary aspirin at an inflated price; a type 2 error means we miss a bargain on a superior medication. Let us say that we want our critical number m to make each of these undesirable events less than 5 percent probable.

We write a program **Power** to plot, for $n = 100$ and selected values of m, the function $\alpha(p)$, for p ranging from .4 to 1. The result is shown in Figure 9. We include in our graph a box (in dotted lines) from .6 to .8, with bottom and top at heights .05 and .95. Then a value for m satisfies our requirements if and only if the graph of α enters the box from the bottom, and leaves from the top (why?—which is the type 1 and which the type 2 criterion?). As m increases, the graph of α moves to the right. A few experiments have shown us that $m = 69$ is the smallest value for m that thwarts a type 1 error, while $m = 73$ is the largest which thwarts a type 2. So we may choose our critical value between 69 and 73. If we're more intent on avoiding a type 1 error we favor 73, and similarly we favor 69 if we regard a type 2 error as worse. Of course, the drug company may not be happy with having as much as a 5 percent chance of an error. They might insist on having a 1 percent chance of an error. For this we would have to increase the number n of trials (see Exercise 29). □

Binomial Expansion

We next remind the reader of an application of the binomial coefficients to algebra. This is the *binomial expansion,* from which we get the term binomial coefficient.

THEOREM 8

The quantity $(a + b)^n$ can be expressed in the form

$$(a + b)^n = \sum_{j = 0}^{n} \binom{n}{j} a^j b^{(n - j)}.$$

Proof. To see that this expansion is correct, write

$$(a + b)^n = (a + b)(a + b) \ldots (a + b).$$

When we multiply this out we will have a sum of terms each of which results from a choice of an a or b for each of n factors. When we choose j a's and $(n - j)$ b's, we obtain a term of the form $a^j b^{(n - j)}$. To determine such a term, we have to specify j of the n terms in the product from which we choose the a. This can be done in $\binom{n}{j}$ ways.

Thus, collecting these terms in the sum contributes a term $\binom{n}{j} a^j b^{(n-j)}$. ■

For example, we have

$(a + b)^0 = 1$

$(a + b)^1 = a + b$

$(a + b)^2 = a^2 + 2ab + b^2$

$(a + b)^3 = a^3 + 3a^2b + 3ab^2 + b^3$

We see here that the coefficients of successive powers do indeed yield Pascal's triangle.

COROLLARY 8

The sum of the elements in the nth row of Pascal's triangle is 2^n. If the elements in the nth row of Pascal's triangle are added with alternating signs, the sum is 0.

Proof. The first statement in the corollary follows from the fact that

$$2^n = (1 + 1)^n = \binom{n}{0} + \binom{n}{1} + \binom{n}{2} + \ldots + \binom{n}{n},$$

and the second from the fact that

$$0 = (1 - 1)^n = \binom{n}{0} - \binom{n}{1} + \binom{n}{2} - \ldots \pm \binom{n}{n}. \quad \blacksquare$$

The first statement of the corollary tells us that the number of subsets of a set of n elements is 2^n. We shall use the second statement in our next application of the binomial theorem.

We have seen that, when A and B are any two events (cf. Chapter 1, Section 1.2),

$$P(A \cup B) = P(A) + P(B) - P(A \cap B)$$

We now extend this theorem to a more general version, which will enable us to find the probability that at least one of a number of events occurs.

Inclusion-Exclusion Principle

THEOREM 9

Let P be a probability measure on a sample space Ω, and let $A_1, A_2, \ldots A_n$ be a sequence of events. Then

$$P(A_1 \cup A_2 \cup \ldots \cup A_n) = \sum_{i=1}^{n} P(A_i) - \sum_{1 \leq i < j \leq n} P(A_i \cap A_j)$$

$$+ \sum_{1 \leq i < j < k \leq n} P(A_i \cap A_j \cap A_k) - \cdots. \quad (3)$$

That is, to find the probability that at least one of n events occurs, first add the probability of each event, then substract the probabilities of all possible two-way intersections, add the probability of all three-way intersections, and so forth.

Proof. If ω occurs in at least one of the events, its probability is added exactly once by the left side of Equation (3). We must show that it is added exactly once by the right side of Equation (3).

Assume that ω is in exactly k of the sets. Then it is added k times in the first term, subtracted $\binom{k}{2}$ in the second, added $\binom{k}{3}$ in the third term, and so forth. Thus, the total number of times that it is added is

$$\binom{k}{1} - \binom{k}{2} + \binom{k}{3} - \cdots \pm \binom{k}{k}.$$

But

$$0 = (1 - 1)^k = \sum_{j=0}^{k} \binom{k}{j}(-1)^j = \binom{k}{0} - \sum_{j=1}^{k} \binom{k}{j}(-1)^{j-1}.$$

Hence,

$$1 = \binom{k}{0} = \sum_{j=1}^{k} \binom{k}{j}(-1)^{j-1}. \qquad \blacksquare$$

Hat Check Problem

EXAMPLE 8

We return to the hat check problem discussed in Section 3.1, that is, the problem of finding the probability that a random permutation contains at least one fixed point. Recall that a permutation is a one-to-one map of a set $A = \{a_1, a_2, \ldots, a_n\}$ onto itself. Let A_i be the event that the ith element a_i remains fixed under this map. If we require that a_i is fixed, then the map of the remaining $n - 1$ elements provides an arbitrary permutation of $(n - 1)$ objects. Since there are $(n - 1)!$ such permutations, $P(A_i) = \dfrac{(n-1)!}{n!} = 1/n$. Since there are n choices for a_i, the first term of Equation (3) is 1. In the same way, to have a particular pair (a_i, a_j) fixed, we can choose any permutation of the remaining $n - 2$ elements; there are $(n - 2)!$ such choices and thus

$$P(A_i \cap A_j) = \frac{(n-2)!}{n!} = \frac{1}{n \cdot (n-1)}.$$

The number of terms of this form in the right side of Equation (3) is

$$\binom{n}{2} = \frac{n \cdot (n-1)}{2!}.$$

Hence, the second term of Equation (3) is

$$-\frac{n \cdot (n-1)}{2!} \cdot \frac{1}{n \cdot (n-1)} = -\frac{1}{2!}.$$

Similarly, for any specific three events A_i, A_j, A_k

$$P(A_i \cap A_j \cap A_k) = \frac{(n-3)!}{(n)!} = \frac{1}{n \cdot (n-1) \cdot (n-2)},$$

and the number of such terms is

$$\binom{n}{3} = \frac{n \cdot (n-1) \cdot (n-2)}{3!},$$

making the third term of Equation (3) equal to $\frac{1}{3!}$. Continuing in this way, we obtain

$$P(\text{at least one fixed point}) = 1 - \frac{1}{2!} + \frac{1}{3!} - \cdots \pm \frac{1}{n!}.$$

and

$$P(\text{no fixed point}) = \frac{1}{2!} - \frac{1}{3!} + \cdots \mp \frac{1}{n!}.$$

From calculus we learn that

$$e^x = 1 + x + \frac{1}{2!} x^2 + \frac{1}{3!} x^3 + \cdots + \frac{1}{n!} x^n + \cdots .$$

Thus, if $x = -1$, we have

$$e^{-1} = \frac{1}{2!} - \frac{1}{3!} + \cdots + \frac{(-1)^n}{n!} + \cdots$$
$$= .3678794.$$

Therefore, the probability that there is no fixed point—that none of the n people gets his own hat back—is equal to the sum of the first n terms in the expression for e^{-1}. This series converges very fast. Calculating the partial sums for $n = 3$ to 10 gives:

n	Probability that no one gets his own hat back
3	.333333
4	.375
5	.366667
6	.368056
7	.367857
8	.367882
9	.367879
10	.367879

After $n = 9$ the probabilities are essentially the same to six significant figures. Interestingly, the probability of no fixed point alternately increases and decreases as n

increases. Finally, we note that our exact results are in good agreement with our simulations reported in the previous section. □

Historical Remarks

The binomial coefficients have a long and colorful history leading up to Pascal's *Treatise on the Arithmetical Triangle*,[11] where Pascal displayed the binomial coefficients in the triangle that bears his name. In this treatise Pascal developed many important properties of these numbers. This history is set forth in the book *Pascal's Arithmetical Triangle* by A. W. F. Edwards.[12] Pascal wrote his triangle in the form

1	1	1	1	1	1	1	1	1	1
1	2	3	4	5	6	7	8	9	
1	3	6	10	15	21	28	36		
1	4	10	20	35	56	84			
1	5	15	35	70	126				
1	6	21	56	126					
1	7	28	84						
1	8	36							
1	9								
1									

Edwards traces three different ways that the binomial coefficients arose. He refers to these as the *figurate numbers*, the *combinatorial numbers*, and the *binomial numbers*. They are all names for the same thing (which we have called binomial coefficients) but that they are all the same was not appreciated until the sixteenth century.

The *figurate numbers* date back to the Pythagorean interest in number patterns around 540 B.C. The Pythagoreans considered, for example, triangular patterns shown in Figure 10. The sequence of numbers

$$1, 3, 6, 10, \ldots$$

obtained as the number of points in each triangle are called *triangular numbers*. From the triangles it is clear that the nth triangular number is simply the sum of the first n integers. The tetrahedral numbers are the sums of the triangular numbers and were obtained by the Greek mathematicians Theon and Nicomachus at the beginning of the second century B.C. The tetrahedral number 10, for example, has the geometric representation

[11]B. Pascal, *Traité du Triangle Arithmétique* (Paris: Desprez, 1665).

[12]A.W.F. Edwards, *Pascal's Arithmetical Triangle* (London: Griffin, 1987).

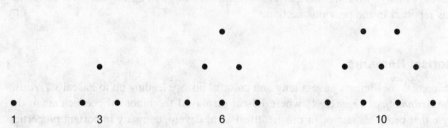

Figure 10 Pythagorean triangular patterns.

shown in Figure 11. The triangular and tetrahedral numbers can be represented in tabular form starting with the sequence of all 1s as follows.

	1	1	1	1	1	1	1	1	1
natural numbers	1	2	3	4	5	6	7	8	9
triangular numbers	1	3	6	10	15	21	28	36	45
tetrahedral numbers	1	4	10	20	35	56	84	120	165

These numbers provide the first four rows of Pascal's triangle, but the table was not to be completed in the West until the sixteenth century.

In the East, Hindu mathematicians began to encounter the binomial coefficients in combinatorial problems. Bhaskara in his *Lilavati* of 1150 gave a rule to find the number of medicinal preparations using 1, 2, 3, 4, 5, or 6 or six possible ingredients.[13] His rule is equivalent to our formula

$$\binom{n}{j} = \frac{n(n-1)(n-2)\ldots(n-r+1)}{1\cdot 2\cdot 3\cdots r}$$

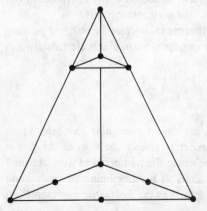

Figure 11 Geometric representation of the tetrahedral number 10.

[13]Ibid., p. 27.

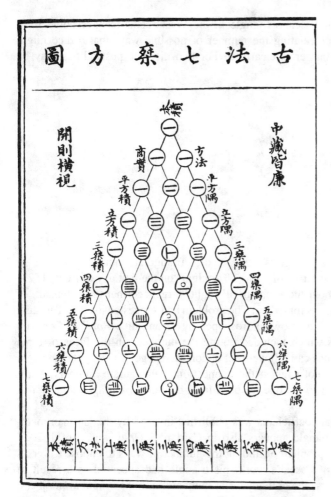

Figure 12 Chu Shih-chieh's triangle. [From J. Needham,
Science and Civilization in China, vol. 3 (New York: Cambridge
University Press, 1959), p. 135. Reprinted with permission.]

The binomial numbers as coefficients of $(a + b)^n$ appeared in the works of mathematicians in China around 1100. There are references about this time to "the tabulation system for unlocking binomial coefficients." The triangle to provide the coefficients up to the eighth power is given by Chu Shih-chieh in a book written around 1303 (see Figure 12).[14] The original manuscript of Chu's book has been lost, but copies have survived.

Edwards notes that there is an error in this copy of Chu's triangle. Can you find it? *Hint:* two numbers which should be equal are not. Other copies do not show this error.

[14]See J. Needham, *Science and Civilization in China*, vol. 3 (New York: Cambridge University Press, 1959), p. 135.

The first appearance of Pascal's triangle in the West seems to have come from calculations of Tartaglia in calculating the number of possible ways that n dice might turn up.[15] For one die the answer is clearly 6. For two dice the possibilities may be displayed as

11

12 22

13 23 33

14 24 34 44

15 25 35 45 55

16 26 36 46 56 66

Displaying them this way suggests the sixth triangular number $1 + 2 + 3 + 4 + 5 + 6 = 21$ for the throw of 2 dice. Tartalgia "on the first day of Lent, 1523, in Verona, having thought about the problem all night"[16] realized that the extension of the figurate table gave the answers for n dice. The problem had suggested itself to Tartalgia from watching people casting their own horoscopes by means of a *Book of Fortune*, selecting verses by a process which included noting the numbers on the faces of three dice. The 56 ways that three dice can fall were set out on each page. The way the numbers were written in the book did not suggest the connection with figurate numbers, but a method of enumeration similar to the one we used for 2 dice does. Tartaglia's table was not published until 1556.

A table for the Binomial coefficients was published in 1554 by the German mathematician Stifel.[17] Pascal's triangle appears also in Cardano's *Opus novum* of 1570.[18] Cardano was interested in the problem of finding the number of ways to choose r objects out of n. Thus by the time of Pascal's work, his triangle had appeared as a result of looking at the figurate numbers, the combinatorial numbers, and the binomial numbers, and the fact that all three were the same was presumably pretty well understood.

Pascal's interest in the binomial numbers came from his letters with Fermat that we described in the Introduction. Recall that the problem of points was as follows: Two teams A and B are playing a sequence of games and the first player to win n games wins the match. It is desired to find the probability that A wins the match at a time when A has won m games and B has won r games. Pascal solved the problem by backward induction, much the way we would do today in writing a computer program for its solution. He referred to the combinatorial method of Fermat which proceeds as follows: If A needs m games and B needs n games to win, we require that the players continue to play until they have played $m + n - 1$ games. The winner in this extended series

[15]N. Tartaglia, *General Trattato di Numeri et Misure* (Vinegia, 1556).

[16]Quoted in Edwards, *Pascal's Arithmetical Triangle*, p. 37.

[17]M. Stifel, *Arithmetica Integra* (Norimburgae, 1544).

[18]G. Cardano, *Opus Novum de Proportionibus Numerorum* (Basilea, 1570).

will be the same as the winner in the original series. The probability that A wins in the extended series and hence in the original series is

$$\sum_{r=m}^{m+n-1} \frac{1}{2^{m+n-1}} \binom{m+n-1}{r}.$$

Even at the time of the letters Pascal seemed to understand this formula. For example, he studied the value of winning a particular game. By this he meant how much more your expected winnings will be if you win this game. He showed that in a series of $2n$ games in a sequence in which each player puts up a stake of x, the value of the first game is

$$\frac{1 \cdot 3 \cdot 5 \cdots (2n - 1)}{2 \cdot 4 \cdot 6 \cdots (2n)}.$$

His proof of this seems to use Fermat's formula and the fact that the above ratio of products of odd to even numbers is equal to the probability of exactly n heads in $2n$ tosses of a coin. (See Exercise 39.)

Pascal presented Fermat with the following table:

If each one stakes 256 in

		6 games	5 games	4 games	3 games	2 games	1 game
From my opponent's 256 pistoles I get, for the	1st game	63	70	80	96	128	256
	2nd game	63	70	80	96	128	
	3rd game	56	60	64	64		
	4th game	42	40	32			
	5th game	24	16				
	6th game	8					

He states:

> You will see as always, that the value of the first game is equal to that of the second, which is easily shown by combinations.
> You will see, in the same way, that the numbers in the first line are always increasing; so also are those in the second; and those in the third.
> But those in the fourth line are decreasing, and those in the fifth, etc. This seems odd.[19]

The student can pursue this question further using the computer and Pascal's backward iteration method for computing the expected payoff at any point in the series.

In his treatise, Pascal gave a formal proof of Fermat's combinatorial formula as well as proofs of many other basic properties of binomial numbers. Many of his proofs involved induction and represent some of the first proofs by this method. His book brought together all the different aspects of the numbers in the Pascal triangle as known in 1654,

---

[19]Quoted in David, *Games, Gods and Gambling*, p. 235.

and, as Edwards states, "That the Arithmetical Triangle should bear Pascal's name cannot be disputed."[20]

The serious study of the Bernoulli density was undertaken by James Bernoulli in his *Ars Conjectandi* published in 1713.[21] We shall return to this work in the historical remarks in Chapter 8.

Exercises

1. Compute the following:
   - **(a)** $c(6,3)$
   - **(b)** $b(5,.2,4)$
   - **(c)** $c(7,2)$
   - **(d)** $c(26,26)$
   - **(e)** $b(4,.2,3)$
   - **(f)** $c(6,2)$
   - **(g)** $c(10,9)$

2. In how many ways can we choose five people from a group of ten to form a committee?

3. A fair coin is thrown ten times. What is the probability that seven or more heads turn up?

4. How many seven-element subsets are there in a set of nine elements?

5. Using the relation Equation (1), write a program to compute Pascal's triangle, putting the results in a matrix. Have your program print the triangle for $n = 10$.

6. A die is rolled 30 times. What is the probability that a 6 turns up exactly 5 times? What is the most probable number of times that a 6 will turn up?

7. Modify the program **Demo Binomial** so that it computes the probability that the number of successes in n independent trials lies between A and B. Use the program to find the probability that, in 100 tosses of a fair coin, the number of heads that turns up lies between 35 and 65, between 40 and 60, and between 45 and 55.

8. Charles claims that he can distinguish between beer and ale 75 percent of the time. Ruth bets that he cannot and, in fact, just guesses. To settle this, a bet is made: Charles is to be given ten small glasses, each having been filled with beer or ale, chosen by tossing a fair coin. He wins the bet if he gets seven or more correct. Find the probability that Charles wins if he has the ability that he claims. Find the probability that Ruth wins if Charles is guessing.

9. Show that for $j \geq 1$ that $b(n,p,j) = \left(\dfrac{p}{q}\right)\left(\dfrac{n - j + 1}{j}\right)b(n,p,j - 1)$. Use this fact to determine the value or values of j which give $b(n,p,j)$ its greatest value. *Hint:* Consider the successive ratios as j increases.

---

[20]Edwards, *Pascal's Arithmetical Triangle*, p. ix.

[21]J. Bernoulli, *Ars Conjectandi* (Basil: Thurnisiorum, 1713).

10. Find integers n and r such that the following equation is true:

$$\binom{13}{5} + 2\binom{13}{6} + \binom{13}{7} = \binom{n}{r}$$

11. In a ten-question true-false exam, find the probability that a student gets a grade of 70 percent or better by guessing (see Exercise 3).

12. A restaurant offers apple and blueberry pies and stocks an equal number of each kind of pie. Each day ten customers request pie. They choose, with equal probabilities, one of the two kinds of pie. How many pieces of each kind of pie should the owner provide so that the probability is about .95 that each customer gets the pie of his or her own choice?

13. A poker hand is a set of 5 cards randomly chosen from a deck of 52 cards. Find the probability of a
    (a) royal flush (ten, jack, queen, king, ace in a single suit).
    (b) straight flush (five in a sequence in a single suit, but not a royal flush).
    (c) four of a kind (four cards of the same face value).
    (d) full house (one pair and one triple, each of the same face value).
    (e) flush (five cards in a single suit but not a straight or royal flush).
    (f) straight (five cards in a sequence, not all the same suit).
    (Note that in straights, an ace counts high or low.)

14. If a set has $2n$ elements, show that it has more subsets with n elements than with any other number of elements. *Hint:* Consider the ratio $\dfrac{\binom{2n}{i}}{\binom{2n}{i-1}}$ for $i = 1, 2, \ldots, n$.

15. Let $b(2n,.5,n)$ be the probability that in $2n$ tosses of a fair coin exactly n heads turn up. Using Stirling's formula, show that $b(2n,.5,n) \sim \dfrac{1}{\sqrt{\pi n}}$. Modify the program **Demo Binomial** to compare this with the exact value for $n = 10$ to 25.

16. A baseball player, Smith, has a batting average of 300 and in a typical game comes to bat three times. Assume that Smith's hits in a game can be considered to be a Bernoulli trials process with probability .3 for *success*. Find the probability that Smith gets 0,1,2, and 3 hits.

17. The Siwash University football team plays eight games in a season, winning three, losing three, and ending two in a tie. Show that the number of ways that this can happen is $\binom{8}{3}\binom{5}{3} = \dfrac{8!}{3!3!2!}$.

18. Using the technique of Exercise 17, show that the number of ways that one can put n different objects into three boxes with a in the first, b in the second, and c in the third is $\dfrac{n!}{a!b!c!}$.

19. Baumgartner, Prosser, and Crowell are grading a calculus exam. There is a true-false question with ten parts. Baumgartner notices that one student has only two out of the ten correct and remarks, "The student was not even bright enough to have flipped a coin to determine his answers." "Not so clear," says Prosser. "With 340 students I bet that if they all flipped coins to determine their answers there would be at least one exam with two or less answers correct." Crowell says, "I'm with Prosser. In fact, I bet that we should expect at least one exam in which no answer is correct if everyone is just guessing." Who is right in all this?

20. A gin hand consists of 10 cards from a deck of 52 cards. Find the probability that a gin hand has
(a) all 10 cards of the same suit.
(b) exactly 4 cards in one suit and 3 in two other suits.
(c) a 4,3,2,1 distribution of suits.

21. A six-card hand is dealt from an ordinary deck of cards. Find the probability that:
(a) All six cards are hearts.
(b) There are three aces, two kings, and one queen.
(c) There are three cards of one suit and three of another suit.

22. A lady wishes to color her fingernails on one hand using at most two of the colors red, yellow, and blue. How many ways can she do this?

23. How many ways can six indistinguishable letters be put in three mail boxes? *Hint:* We can represent one way that this can be done by a sequence |LL|L|LLL| where the |'s represent the partitions for the boxes and the L's the letters. Any possible way can be so described. Note that we need two bars at the ends and the remaining two bars and the six L's can be put in any order.

24. Using the method for the hint in Exercise 23, show that r indistinguishable objects can be put in n boxes in $\binom{n + r - 1}{n - 1} = \binom{n + r - 1}{r}$ different ways.

25. A travel bureau estimates that when 20 tourists go to a resort with ten hotels they distribute themselves as if the bureau were putting 20 indistinguishable objects into ten boxes. Assuming this model is correct, find the probability that no hotel is left vacant when the first group of 20 tourists arrives.

26. An elevator takes on six passengers and stops at ten floors. We can assign two different equiprobable measures for the ways that the passengers are discharged: (a) we consider the passengers to be distinguishable or (b) we consider them to be indistinguishable (see Exercise 24 for this case). For each case, calculate the probability that all the passengers get off at different floors.

27. You are playing *heads* or *tails* with Prosser but you suspect that his coin is unfair. Von Neumann suggested that you proceed as follows: Toss Prosser's coin twice. If the outcome is HT call the result *win*, if it is TH call the result *lose*. If it is TT or HH ignore the outcome and toss Prosser's twice again. Keep going until you get either an HT or a TH and call the result win or lose in a single play. Repeat this procedure for each play. Assume that Prosser's coin turns up heads with probability p.

(a) Find the probability of HT, TH, HH, TT with two tosses of Prosser's coin.

(b) Using part **(a)**, show that the probability of a win on any one play is $1/2$, no matter what p is.

28. John claims that he has extrasensory powers and can tell which of two symbols is on a card turned face down (see Example 5). To test his ability he is asked to do this for a sequence of trials. Let the null hypothesis be that he is just guessing, so that the probability is $1/2$ of his getting it right each time, and let the alternative hypothesis be that he can name the symbol correctly more than half the time. Devise a test with the property that the probability of a type 1 error is less than .05 and the probability of a type 2 error is less than .05 if John can name the symbol correctly 75 percent of the time.

29. In Example 6 assume the alternative hypothesis is that $p = .8$ and that it is desired to have the probability of each type of error less than .01. Use the program **Power** to determine values of n and m that will achieve this. Choose n as small as possible.

30. A drug is assumed to be effective with an unknown probability p. To estimate p the drug is given to n patients. It is found to be effective for m patients. The *method of maximum likelihood* for estimating p states that we should choose the value for p that gives the highest probability of getting what we got on the experiment. Assuming that the experiment can be considered as a Bernoulli trial process with probability p for success, show that the maximum likelihood estimate for p is the proportion m/n of successes.

31. Recall that in the World Series the first team to win four games wins the series. The series can go at most seven games. Assume that the Red Sox and the Mets are playing the series. Assume that the Mets win each game with probability p. Fermat observed that even though the series might not go seven games, the probability that the Mets win the series is the same as the probability that they win four or more games in a series that was forced to go seven games no matter who wins the individual games.

(a) Using the program **Power** of Example 5 find the probability that the Mets win the series for the cases $p = .5$, $p = .6$, $p = .7$.

(b) Assume that the Mets have probability .6 of winning each game. Use the program **Power** to find a value of n so that, if the series goes to the first team to win more than half the games, the Mets will have a 95 percent chance of winning the series. Choose n as small as possible.

32. Each of the four engines on an airplane functions correctly on a given flight with probability .99, and the engines function independently of each other. Assume that the plane can make a safe landing if at least two of its engines are functioning correctly. What is the probability that the engines will allow for a safe landing?

33. A small boy is lost coming down Mount Washington. The leader of the search team estimates that there is a probability p that he came down on the east side and a probability $1 - p$ that he came down on the west side. He has n people in his search team who will search independently and, if the boy is on the side being searched, each member will find the boy with probability u. Determine how he should divide the n people into two groups to search the two sides of the mountain so that he will have the highest probability of finding the boy. How does this depend on u?

*34. $2n$ balls are chosen at random from a total of $2n$ red balls and $2n$ blue balls. Find a combinatorial expression for the probability that the chosen balls are equally divided in color. Use Stirling's formula to estimate this probability. Using **Demo Binomial**, compare the exact value with Stirling's approximation for $n = 20$.

35. Assume that every time you buy a box of Wheaties, you receive one of the pictures of the n players on the New York Yankees. Over a period of time, you buy $m \geq n$ boxes of Wheaties.

    (a) Use Theorem 9 to show that the probability that you get all n pictures is

    $$1 - \binom{n}{1}\left(\frac{n-1}{n}\right)^m + \binom{n}{2}\left(\frac{n-2}{n}\right)^m - \cdots + (-1)^{n-1}\binom{n}{n-1}\left(\frac{1}{n}\right)^m.$$

    Hint: Let E_k be the event that you do not get the kth player's picture.

    (b) Write a computer program to compute this probability. Use this program to find, for given n, the smallest value of m which will give probability $\geq .5$ of getting all n pictures. Consider $n = 50$, 100, and 150 and show that $m = \text{int}(n \log n - n \log (\log 2))$ is a good estimate for the number of boxes needed.

*36. Prove the following *binomial identity*

    $$\binom{2n}{n} = \sum_{j=0}^{n} \binom{n}{j}^2.$$

    Hint: Consider an urn with n red balls and n blue balls inside. Show that each side of the equation equals the number of ways to choose n balls from the urn.

37. Let $n \bmod m$ denote the remainder when the integer n is divided by the integer m. Write a computer program to compute the numbers $\binom{n}{j} \bmod m$ where $\binom{n}{j}$ is a binomial coefficient and m is an integer. You can do this by using the recursion relations for generating binomial coefficients, doing all arithmetic using the basic function $\text{mod}(n,m)$. Try to write your program to make as large a table as possible. Run your program for the cases $m = 2$ to 7. Do you see any patterns? In particular, for the case $m = 2$ and n a power of 2, verify that all the entries in the $(n - 1)$st row are 1. (The corresponding binomial numbers are odd.) Use your pictures to explain why this is true.

38. Kemeny has observed the following general result relating to Exercise 37. If m is any prime number, then $\binom{n}{j} \bmod m$ can be found as follows: Expand n and j in

base m as $n = s_0 + s_1 m + s_2 m^2 + \cdots + s_k m^k$ and $j = r_0 + r_1 m^1 + r_2 m^2 + \cdots + r_k m^k$, respectively. (Here k is chosen large enough to represent all numbers from 0 to n in base m using k digits.) Then set $s = (s_0, s_1, s_2, \ldots, s_k)$ and $r = (r_0, r_1, r_2, \ldots, r_k)$, and show that

$$\binom{n}{j} \bmod m = \prod_{i=0}^{k} \binom{s_i}{r_i} \bmod m.$$

For example, if $m = 7$, $n = 12$, and $j = 9$, then

$$12 = 5 \cdot 7^0 + 1 \cdot 7^1 \quad \text{so} \quad s = (5,1)$$
$$9 = 2 \cdot 7^0, + 1 \cdot 7^1 \quad \text{so} \quad r = (2,1)$$

and this result states that

$$\binom{12}{9} \bmod 7 = \binom{5}{2}\binom{1}{1} \bmod 7.$$

Since $\binom{12}{9} = 220 = 3 \bmod 7$, and $\binom{5}{2} = 10 = 3 \bmod 7$, we see that the result is correct for this example.

Show that this result implies that, for $m = 2$, the $(m^k - 1)$st row of your triangle in Exercise 37 has no zeros.

39. Prove that the probability of exactly n heads in $2n$ tosses of a fair coin is given by the product of the odd numbers up to $2n - 1$ divided by the product of the even numbers up to $2n$.

Chapter *4*

Conditional Probability

4.1 DISCRETE CONDITIONAL PROBABILITY

Conditional Probability

In this section we ask and answer the following question. Suppose we assign a probability measure to a sample space and then learn that an event E has occurred. How should we change the probabilities of the remaining events? We shall call the new probability for an event F the *conditional probability of F given E* and denote it by $P(F \mid E)$.

EXAMPLE 1
A die is rolled. Let F be the event "a six turns up." Let E be the event "a number bigger than 4 turns up." Before the experiment $P(F) = \frac{1}{6}$. Now we are told that the event E has occurred. This leaves only two possible outcomes: 5 and 6. In the absence of any other information, we would still regard these outcomes to be equally likely, so the probability of F becomes $\frac{1}{2}$, making $P(F \mid E) = \frac{1}{2}$. $\square$

EXAMPLE 2
Consider our voting example from Chapter 1, Section 1.2: three candidates A, B, and C are running for office. We decided that A and B have an equal chance of winning and C is only $\frac{1}{2}$ as likely to win as A. Let A be the event "A wins," B that "B wins," and

C that "C wins." Hence, we assigned probabilities $P(A) = \frac{2}{5}, P(B) = \frac{2}{5}$, and $P(C) = \frac{1}{5}$. We now learn that A has dropped out of the race. In the absence of any other information, we may reasonably assume that B is still twice as likely to win as C and so $P(B) = 2P(C)$. Since now either B or C will win, we want $P(B) + P(C) = 1$. Thus, we assign probability $\frac{2}{3}$ to B winning and $\frac{1}{3}$ to C winning. Thus $P(B \mid \bar{A}) = \frac{2}{3}$. Note that our reassessment of the probabilities would not be reasonable if we had additional information that the majority of those who would have voted for A will now vote for B. □

In these examples we had assigned a probability measure and then were given new information that determined a new sample space, consisting of the outcomes that are still possible, and caused us to assign a new probability measure to this space.

We want to make formal the procedure carried out in these examples. Let $\Omega = \{\omega_1, \omega_2, \ldots, \omega_r\}$ be the original sample space with a probability density $p(\omega_j)$ assigned. Suppose we learn that the event E has occurred. We want to assign a new probability density $p(\omega_j \mid E)$ to Ω to reflect this fact. Clearly, if a sample point ω_j is not in E, we want $p(\omega_j \mid E) = 0$. Moreover, in the absence of information to the contrary, it is reasonable to assume that the probabilities for ω_k in E should have the same relative magnitudes that they had before we learned that E occurred. For this we require that

$$p(\omega_k \mid E) = cp(\omega_k)$$

for all ω_k in E, and c some positive constant. But we must also have

$$\sum_E p(\omega_k \mid E) = c \sum_E p(\omega_k) = 1.$$

Thus,

$$c = \frac{1}{\sum_E p(\omega_k)} = \frac{1}{P(E)}.$$

This means we should define

$$p(\omega_k \mid E) = \frac{p(\omega_k)}{P(E)}$$

for ω_k in E. For a general event F, this gives

$$P(F \mid E) = \sum_{F \cap E} p(\omega_k \mid E) = \frac{P(F \cap E)}{P(E)}.$$

The above discussion is meant to motivate our definition of the conditional probability of the event F given that the event E occurs.

DEFINITION 1

If E and F are events with $P(E) > 0$, then the *conditional probability of F occurring given that E occurs*, denoted by $P(F \mid E)$, is

$$P(F \mid E) = \frac{P(F \cap E)}{P(E)}.$$

EXAMPLE 2 (continued)

Let us return to the example of three candidates A, B, and C running for office. We assigned $P(A) = P(B) = {}^2/_5$ and $P(C) = {}^1/_5$, and then we learned that A has dropped out of the race. Let E be the event "B or C wins" and B the event "B wins." Then without other information, we assume that

$$P(B \mid E) = \frac{P(B \cap E)}{P(E)} = \frac{2/5}{2/5 + 1/5} = \frac{2}{3}.$$

Since $P(A \mid E) = 0$, $P(C \mid E) = {}^1/_3$. We note that B is still twice as likely as C to win. ☐

Tree Measures

We have seen that, when we analyze an experiment that takes place in a sequence of steps, we often find it convenient to represent the sample space by the set of all paths through a tree. A probability measure is assigned by first considering the conditional probabilities appropriate for the outcome of the jth step, given all previous outcomes. These weights are assigned at the appropriate branches of the tree, and then the weight for a path through the tree is the product of the branch weights along the path. This process yields a probability measure with the desired conditional probabilities. We will call this a *tree measure*.

It should be emphasized that, in assigning a tree measure, we think of the branch probabilities as if they were conditional probabilities. They only become conditional probabilities after the tree measure is assigned. We will illustrate this in our next example, but we will not give a general proof of this consistency requirement.

EXAMPLE 3

We have two urns, I and II. Urn I contains 2 black balls and 3 white balls. Urn II contains 1 black and 1 white ball. An urn is drawn at random and a ball is chosen at random from it. We can represent the sample space as the paths through a tree as shown in Figure 1.

In this example, our experiment takes place in two stages. We have information

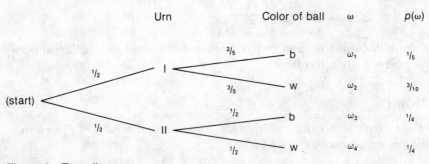

Figure 1 Tree diagram.

that suggests the appropriate probabilities for the outcomes of the first stage and the conditional probabilities for the outcomes of the second stage given the outcome of the first stage. These are indicated on the branches of the tree in Figure 1. Thus, a sample point ω of Ω is a path through the tree, and we assign as the probability for a specific path the product of all the probabilities along the path. The resulting tree measure is shown in Figure 1.

Let B be the event "a black ball is drawn," and I the event "urn I is chosen." Then

$$P(B \mid I) = \frac{P(B \cap I)}{P(I)}$$

$$= \frac{P(\omega_1)}{P(\omega_1) + P(\omega_2)}$$

$$= \frac{1/5}{1/5 + 3/10} = \frac{2}{5}.$$

Thus, the conditional probability, computed in terms of the assigned tree measure, agrees with that which we used informally to construct the tree measure.

From the tree measure we can compute any probability relating to the two experiments. For example, suppose that you are told that a black ball was drawn but not told which urn was chosen. What is the probability that urn I was chosen? That is, what is $P(I \mid B)$? From the definition of conditional probability and the fact that $P(B) = P(B \cap I) + P(B \cap II)$,

$$P(I \mid B) = \frac{P(I \cap B)}{P(B)}$$

$$= \frac{P(I \cap B)}{P(B \cap I) + P(B \cap II)}$$

$$= \frac{1/5}{1/5 + 1/4}$$

$$= \frac{4}{9}. \qquad \square$$

Bayes Probabilities

Our original tree measure gave us the probabilities for drawing a ball of a given color, given the urn chosen. We have just calculated the *inverse probability* that a particular urn was chosen, given the color of the ball. Such an inverse probability is called a *Bayes probability* and may be obtained by a formula that we shall develop later. Bayes probabilities can also be obtained by simply constructing the tree measure for the two-stage experiment carried out in reverse order. We show this tree in Figure 2.

The paths through the reverse tree are the same as for the forward tree and so are

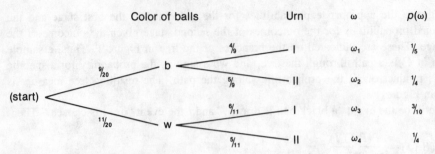

Figure 2 Reverse tree diagram.

assigned the same probabilities. From the forward tree, we find that the probability of a black ball is

$$\frac{1}{2} \cdot \frac{2}{5} + \frac{1}{2} \cdot \frac{1}{2} = \frac{9}{20}.$$

The probabilities for the branches at the second level are found by simple division. For example, if x is the probability to be assigned to the top branch at the second level, we must have

$$\frac{9}{20} \cdot x = \frac{1}{5}$$

or $x = \frac{4}{9}$. Thus, $P(I \mid B) = \frac{4}{9}$, in agreement with our previous calculations. The reverse tree then displays all of the inverse, or Bayes, probabilities. Drawing the reverse tree is a good project for the computer, and the program **Tree** carries out the computations and shows the results graphically. In Figure 3 we show the output of this program for Example 3.

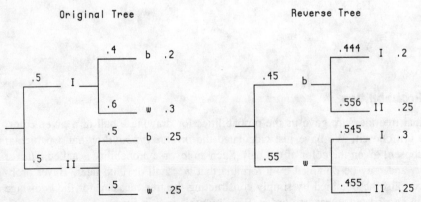

Figure 3 Forward and reverse tree diagrams.

EXAMPLE 4

Three men, Abel, Baker, and Charlie, are in jail, and one of them is to be executed. The guard knows which is the unlucky man, but Abel does not and assumes it is equally likely that each of them will be executed. Abel says to the guard, "I know that either Baker or Charlie will not be executed. Therefore you won't really be giving me any real information if you tell me the name of one of those who will go free. If both are to go free, just toss a coin to decide which name to tell me." The guard considers the request and then says, "No, that would not be fair to you. At the moment, you think that you have probability $1/3$ of being executed. If I tell you the name of the one who will go free, you will then have probability $1/2$ and will not sleep so well tonight." Was the guard right? To answer this, Abel examines the possible outcomes as a two-stage process, the first stage being the choice of the man to be executed, and the second the guard's answer. We assign the tree measures shown in Figure 4.

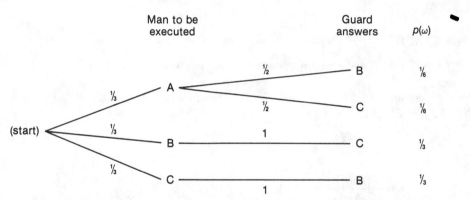

Figure 4 Tree diagram.

Let E be the event "the guard says Baker" and F the event "Abel is to be executed." Then Abel computes the probability that he is to be executed, given that the guard says Baker.

$$P(F \mid E) = \frac{P(E \cap F)}{P(E)} = \frac{1/6}{1/3 \, + \, 1/6} = \frac{1}{3}.$$

By symmetry, the probability that Abel is to be executed, given that the guard says Charlie, is also $1/3$. Hence the guard is wrong. His answer makes no difference to Abel; either way his probability is $1/3$. □

Independence

It often happens that the knowledge of the outcome of one event has no effect on the probability that you would assign to another event occurring, that is, that $P(F \mid E) = P(F)$.

In this case we might say that F is *independent* of E. For example, you would not expect the knowledge of the outcome of the first toss of a coin to change the probability that you would assign to the possible outcomes of the second toss, that is, you would not expect that the second toss depends on the first. This idea is formalized in the following more symmetrical definition of independent events.

DEFINITION 2

Two events E and F are *independent* if

$$P(E \cap F) = P(E)P(F).$$

The following theorem then provides the more intuitive form of independence. (Note the hypothesis that $P(E) > 0$.)

THEOREM 1

If $P(E) > 0$, then E and F are independent if and only if $P(F \mid E) = P(F)$.

Proof. Assume first that E and F are independent and $P(E) > 0$. Then $P(F \cap E) = P(F)P(E)$, and so

$$P(F \mid E) = \frac{P(F \cap E)}{P(E)}$$

$$= \frac{P(F)P(E)}{P(E)} = P(F).$$

Assume next that $P(F \mid E) = P(F)$ and $P(E) > 0$. Then

$$P(F \mid E) = \frac{P(F \cap E)}{P(E)} = P(F),$$

and so

$$P(E \cap F) = P(E)P(F),$$

making E and F independent. ∎

Thus, two events with positive probability are independent if knowing the outcome of one event does not affect the probability of the other event.

EXAMPLE 5

A coin is tossed twice. Let E be the event that heads turns up on the first toss and F the event that tails turns up on the second toss. Then $P(E) = P(F) = \frac{1}{2}$ and $P(E \cap F) = \frac{1}{4}$. Since $P(E)P(F) = \frac{1}{2} \cdot \frac{1}{2} = \frac{1}{4} = P(E \cap F)$, E and F are independent events. □

EXAMPLE 6

It is often, but not always, intuitively clear when two events are independent. In Example 5, let A be the event "the first toss is a head" and B the event "the two outcomes are the same." Then

$$P(B \mid A) = \frac{P(B \cap A)}{P(A)} = \frac{P\{HH\}}{P\{HH,HT\}} = \frac{1/4}{1/2} = \frac{1}{2} = P(B).$$

Therefore, A and B are independent, but the result was not so obvious. □

EXAMPLE 7

Finally, let us give an example of two events that are not independent. In Example 5, let I be the event "heads on the first toss" and J be the event "two heads turn up." Then $P(I) = \frac{1}{2}$ and $P(J) = \frac{1}{4}$. The event $I \cap J$ is the event "heads on both tosses" and has probability $\frac{1}{4}$. Thus, I and J are not independent since $P(I)P(J) = \frac{1}{8} \neq P(I \cap J)$. □

We can extend the concept of independence to any finite set of events $A_1, A_2, \ldots, A_n$.

DEFINITION 3

A set of events $A_1, A_2, \ldots, A_n$ is said to be *mutually independent* if for any subset A_i, $A_j, \ldots, A_m$ of these events we have

$$P(A_i \cap A_j \cap \ldots \cap A_m) = P(A_i)P(A_j) \ldots P(A_m),$$

or equivalently, if for any sequence $\overline{A}_1, \overline{A}_2, \ldots, \overline{A}_n$ with $\overline{A}_j = A_j$ or $\tilde{A}_j$,

$$P(\overline{A}_1 \cap \overline{A}_2 \cap \ldots \cap \overline{A}_n) = P(\overline{A}_1)P(\overline{A}_2) \ldots P(\overline{A}_n).$$

(For a proof of the equivalence, see Exercise 30.)

EXAMPLE 8

A coin is tossed three times. Let A be the event "heads on the first toss," B the event "tails on the second toss," and C the event "heads on the third toss." Then A, B, and C are mutually independent. This follows easily from the way that we construct the tree measure. □

The last example is a special case of the fact that any sequence of possible outcomes (S,S,F,F,S, . . . ,S) of a Bernoulli trials process forms a sequence of mutually independent events.

It is natural to ask: If all pairs of a set of events are independent, is the whole set mutually independent? The answer is *not necessarily*, and an example is given in Exercise 6.

In our examples, we have considered conditional probabilities of the following form: Given the outcome of the second stage of a two-stage experiment, find the probability for an outcome at the first stage. We have remarked that these probabilities are called *Bayes probabilities*.

We return now to the calculation of more general Bayes probabilities. Suppose we have a set of events $H_1, H_2, \ldots, H_m$ that are pairwise disjoint and such that

$$\Omega = H_1 \cup H_2 \cup \cdots \cup H_m.$$

We call these events *hypotheses*. We also have an event E that gives us some information about which hypothesis is correct. We call this event *evidence*.

Before we receive the evidence, then we have a set of *prior probabilities* $P(H_1), P(H_2), \ldots, P(H_m)$ for the hypotheses. If we know the correct hypothesis, we know the probability for the evidence. That is, we know $P(E \mid H_i)$ for all i. We want to find the probabilities for the hypotheses given the evidence. That is, we want to find the conditional probabilities $P(H_i \mid E)$. These probabilities are called the *posterior probabilities*.

To find these probabilities, we write them in the form

$$P(H_i \mid E) = \frac{P(H_i \cap E)}{P(E)}. \tag{1}$$

We can calculate the numerator from our given information by

$$P(H_i \cap E) = P(H_i)P(E \mid H_i). \tag{2}$$

Since one and only one of the events $H_1, H_2, \ldots, H_m$ can occur, we can write the probability of E as

$$\begin{aligned} P(E) &= P(H_1 \cap E) + P(H_2 \cap E) + \cdots + P(H_m \cap E) \\ &= P(H_1)P(E \mid H_1) + P(H_2)P(E \mid H_2) + \cdots + P(H_m)P(E \mid H_m). \end{aligned} \tag{3}$$

Bayes's Formula

Expressing the conditional probability Equation (1) as the ratio of the expressions Equation (2) and Equation (3) yields *Bayes's formula:*

$$P(H_i \mid E) = \frac{P(H_i)P(E \mid H_i)}{\displaystyle\sum_{k=1}^{m} P(H_k)P(E \mid H_k)}.$$

Although this is a very famous formula, we will rarely use it. If the number of hypotheses is small, a simple tree measure calculation is easily carried out, as we have done in our examples. If the number of hypotheses is large, we should then want to use the computer.

Bayes's probabilities are particularly appropriate for medical diagnosis. A doctor is anxious to know which of several diseases a patient might have. She collects evidence in the form of the outcomes of certain tests. From statistical studies the doctor can find the prior probabilities of the various diseases before the tests, and the probabilities for specific test outcomes, given a particular disease. What the doctor wants to know is the posterior probability for the particular disease, given the outcomes of the tests.

EXAMPLE 9

A doctor is trying to decide if a patient has one of three diseases d_1, d_2, or d_3. Two tests are to be carried out, each of which results in a positive ($+$) or a negative ($-$) outcome. There are four possible test patterns $++$, $+-$, $-+$, and $--$. National records have indicated that, for 10,000 people having one of these three diseases, the distribution of diseases and test results are as in the following table.

Disease	Number having this disease	Test results			
		$++$	$+-$	$-+$	$--$
d_1	3215	2110	301	704	100
d_2	2125	396	132	1187	410
d_3	4660	510	3568	73	509
Total	10000				

From this data, we can estimate the prior probabilities for each of the diseases and, given a particular disease, the probability of a particular test outcome. For example, the prior probability of disease d_1 may be estimated to be 3215/10,000 $=$ .3215. The probability of the test result $+-$, given disease d_1, may be estimated to be 301/3215 $=$ .094. $\qquad\square$

In the last example we would want to use a computer program to carry out our calculations for us. The program **Bayes** is such a program. Assume that the possible test results are described by the events E_1, E_2, . . . , E_k. In this program the ith entry in the vector *prior* is the prior probability $P(H_i)$, the ijth entry in the matrix *conditional* is the conditional probability $P(E_j \mid H_i)$, the ith entry of the vector *probability* gives the probability of event E_i calculated by Equation (3). The ijth entry in the matrix *posterior* is the posterior probability $P(H_j \mid E_i)$. (That is, the *givens* are the rows.) The program **Bayes** computes the posterior probabilities by means of the two formulas

$$P(E_j) = \sum_{k=1}^{m} P(H_k)P(E_j \mid H_k)$$

and

$$P(H_j \mid E_i) = \frac{P(H_j)P(E_i \mid H_j)}{P(E_i)}.$$

Hence,

$$\text{probability}(i) = \sum_{k=1}^{m} \text{prior}(k)\text{conditional}(k,i)$$

and

$$\text{posterior}(i,j) = \frac{\text{prior}(j)\text{conditional}(j,i)}{\text{probability}(i)}.$$

```
! Bayes
!
! Calculates posterior probabilities for m hypotheses and n possible
! evidences.

library "Lib.Markov*"              ! For labels
dim row$(10),column$(10)
dim prior(10), conditional(10,10), probability(10), posterior(10,10)

read m,n                           ! Dimensions
data 3,4
mat read row$(m)                   ! Row labels
data d1, d2, d3
mat read column$(n)                ! Column labels
data ++, +-, -+, --

mat posterior = zer(n,m)

mat read prior(m)                  ! Entries for prior probabilities
data .322, .214, .464

print
print "Prior probabilities"
call vector_labels(prior,row$," .###")

mat read conditional(m,n)          ! Probability of e given hypothesis h
data   .656, .094, .219, .031
data   .186, .062, .559, .424
data   .109, .766, .016, .109

print
print "Conditional probabilities"
call matrix_labels(conditional,row$,column$," .###")

for e = 1 to n                     ! Find probability of evidence e
   for h = 1 to m
      let probability(e) = probability(e) + prior(h) * conditional(h,e)
   next h
next e

for e = 1 to n                     ! Find probability of hypothesis given evidence
   for h = 1 to m
      let posterior(e,h) = prior(h)*conditional(h,e)/probability(e)
   next h
next e

print
print "Posterior probabilities"
call matrix_labels(posterior,column$,row$," .###")

end
```

We obtain from the data estimates for the prior probabilities and the conditional probabilities for the symptoms given the diseases. We put these into the program **Bayes** as data (we have rounded the data to three decimal places). Running the program **Bayes** then gives the results:

```
Prior probabilities
    ++   +-   -+
   .322 .214 .464

Conditional probabilities
      ++   +-   -+   --
d1  .656 .094 .219 .031
d2  .186 .062 .559 .424
d3  .109 .766 .016 .109

Posterior probabilities
      d1   d2   d3
++  .700 .132 .168
+-  .076 .033 .891
-+  .357 .605 .038
--  .066 .600 .334
```

We note from the outcomes that, when the test result is $+ +$, the disease d_1 has a significantly higher probability than the other two. When the outcome is $+ -$, this is true for disease d_3. If the outcome is $- +$ or $- -$, the most probable disease is d_2 but the information is less definitive in these cases.

Our final example shows that one has to be careful when the prior probabilities are small.

EXAMPLE 10

A doctor gives a patient a test for a particular cancer. Before the results of the test, the only evidence the doctor has to go on is that 1 woman in 1000 has this cancer. Experience has shown that, in 99 percent of the cases in which cancer is present, the test is positive; and in 95 percent of the cases in which it is not present, it is negative. If the test turns out to be positive, what probability should the doctor assign to the event that cancer is present? When a group of second-year medical students was asked this question, over half of the students incorrectly guessed the probability to be greater than .5.

We could use our program **Bayes** to investigate these probabilities. But since there are only two possibilities, we can also use our program **Tree**. We are given that

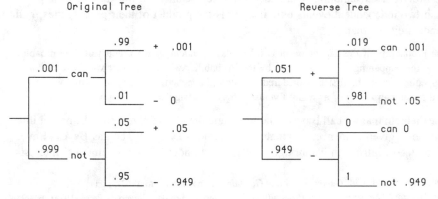

Figure 5 Forward and reverse tree diagrams.

prior(cancer) $= .001$ and prior(not cancer) $= .999$. We know also that $P(+ \mid \text{cancer}) = .99$, $P(- \mid \text{cancer}) = .01$, $P(+ \mid \text{not cancer}) = .05$, and $P(- \mid \text{not cancer}) = .95$. Using this data for the program **Tree** gives the result shown in Figure 5.

We see now that the probability of cancer given a positive test has only increased from .001 to .019. While this is nearly a twenty-fold increase, the probability that the patient has the cancer is still small. □

Historical Remarks

Conditional probability was used long before it was formally defined. When Pascal and Fermat were solving the problem of points they were solving a conditional probability problem: namely, given that team A has won m games and team B has won n games, what is the probability that A will win the series? In his book, Huygens gave a number of problems, one of which was:

> Three gamblers, A, B and C, take 12 balls of which 4 are white and 8 black. They play with the rules that the drawer is blindfolded, A is to draw first, then B and then C, the winner to be the one who first draws a white ball. What is the ratio of their chances?[1]

From his answer it is clear that Huygens meant that each ball is replaced after drawing. However, John Hudde, the mayor of Amsterdam, assumed that he meant to sample without replacement and corresponded with Huygens about the difference in their answers. Hacking remarks that "Neither party can understand what the other is doing."[2]

By the time of de Moivre's book, *The Doctrine of Chances*, these distinctions were well understood. De Moivre defined independence and dependence as follows:

> Two Events are independent, when they have no connexion one with the other, and that the happening of one neither forwards nor obstructs the happening of the other.
>
> Two Events are dependent, when they are so connected together as that the Probability of either's happening is altered by the happening of the other.[3]

De Moivre used sampling with and without replacement to illustrate that the probability that two independent events both happen is the product of their probabilities, and for dependent events that:

> The Probability of the happening of two Events dependent, is the product of the Probability of the happening of one of them, by the Probability which the other will have of happening, when the first is considered as having happened; and the same Rule will extend to the happening of as many Events as may be assigned.[4]

The theorem that we call Bayes's theorem, and the idea of computing the probability of a hypothesis given evidence, originated in a famous essay of Thomas Bayes. Bayes was an ordained minister in Tunbridge Wells near London. His mathematical interests

---

[1]Quoted in F.N. David, *Games, Gods and Gambling* (London: Griffin, 1962), p. 119.
[2]Ian Hacking, *The Emergence of Probability* (Cambridge: Cambridge University Press, 1975), p. 99.
[3]A. de Moivre, *The Doctrine of Chances*, 3rd ed. (New York: Chelsea, 1967), p. 6.
[4]Ibid, p. 7.

led him to be elected to the Royal Society in 1742, but none of his results were published within his lifetime. The work upon which his fame rests, "An Essay toward solving a Problem in the Doctrine of Chances," was published in 1763, three years after his death.[5] Bayes reviewed some of the basic concepts of probability and then considered a new kind of inverse probability problem requiring the use of conditional probability.

Bernoulli, in his study of processes that we now call Bernoulli trials, had proven his famous law of large numbers which we will study in Chapter 8. This theorem assured the experimenter that if he knew the probability p for success, he could predict that the proportion of successes would approach this value as he increased the number of experiments. Bernoulli himself realized that in most interesting cases you do not know the value of p and saw his theorem as an important step in showing that you could determine p by experimentation.

To study this problem further, Bayes started by assuming that the probability p for success is itself determined by a random experiment. He assumed in fact that this experiment was such that this value for p is equally likely to be any value between 0 and 1. Without knowing this value we carry out n experiments and observe m successes. Bayes proposed the problem of finding the conditional probability that the unknown probability p lies between a and b. He obtained the answer:

$$P(a \leq p < b \mid m \text{ successes in } n \text{ trials}) = \frac{\int_a^b x^m(1 - x)^{n-m}dx}{\int_0^1 x^m(1 - x)^{n-m}dx}.$$

We shall see in the next section how this result is obtained. Bayes clearly wanted to show that the conditional probability density, given the outcomes of more and more experiments, becomes concentrated around the true value of p. Thus, Bayes was trying to solve an *inverse problem*. The computation of the integrals were too difficult for exact solutions except for small values of j and n, and so Bayes tried approximate methods. His methods were not very satisfactory and it has been suggested that this discouraged him from publishing his results.

However, his paper was the first in a series of important studies carried out by Laplace, Gauss and other great mathematicians to solve inverse problems. They studied this problem in terms of errors in measurements in astronomy. If an astronomer were to know the true value of a distance and the nature of the random errors caused by his measuring device he could predict the probabilistic nature of his measurements. In fact, however, he is presented with the inverse problem of knowing the nature of the random errors, and the values of the measurements, and wanting to make inferences about the unknown true value.

As Maistrov remarks, the theorem that we have called Bayes's theorem does not appear in his essay. Laplace gave it this name when he studied these inverse problems.[6]

[5]T. Bayes, "An Essay Toward Solving a Problem in the Doctrine of Chances," *Phil. Trans. Royal Soc. London*, vol. 53 (1763), pp. 370–418.

[6]L.E. Maistrov, *Probability Theory: A Historical Sketch*, trans. and ed. Samuel Kotz (New York: Academic Press, 1974), p. 100.

The computation of inverse probabilities is fundamental to statistics and has led to an important branch of statistics called Bayesian analysis, assuring Bayes eternal fame for his brief essay.

Exercises

1. A coin is tossed three times. What is the probability that exactly two heads occur, given that
   (a) the first outcome was a head?
   (b) the first outcome was a tail?
   (c) the first two outcomes were heads?
   (d) the first two outcomes were tails?
   (e) the first outcome was a head and the third outcome was a head?

2. A die is rolled twice. What is the probability that the sum of the faces is greater than 7, given that
   (a) the first outcome was a 4?
   (b) the first outcome was greater than 3?
   (c) the first outcome was a 1?
   (d) the first outcome was less than 5?

3. A card is drawn at random from a deck of cards. What is the probability that
   (a) it is a heart, given that it is red?
   (b) it is higher than a 10, given that it is a heart? (Interpret J,Q,K,A as 11,12,13,14.)
   (c) it is a jack, given that it is red?

4. A coin is tossed three times. Consider the following events.
   A: Heads on the first toss.
   B: Tails on the second.
   C: Heads on the third toss.
   D: All three outcomes the same (HHH or TTT).
   E: Exactly one head turns up.
   (a) Which of the following pairs of these events are independent?
      (1) A,B
      (2) A,D
      (3) A,E
      (4) D,E
   (b) Which of the following triples of these events are mutually independent?
      (1) A,B,C
      (2) A,B,D
      (3) C,D,E

5. From a deck of five cards numbered 2, 4, 6, 8 and 10, respectively, a card is drawn at random and replaced. This is done three times. What is the probability that the card numbered 2 was drawn exactly two times, given that the sum of the numbers on the three draws is 12?

6. A coin is tossed twice. Consider the following events.
   A: Heads on the first toss.
   B: Heads on the second toss.
   C: The two tosses come out the same.
   (a) Show that A,B,C are pairwise independent but not mutually independent.
   (b) Show that C is independent of A and B but not of $A \cap B$.

7. Let $\Omega = \{a,b,c,d,e,f\}$. Assume that $p(a) = p(b) = \frac{1}{8}$ and $p(c) = p(d) = p(e)$ $= p(f) = \frac{3}{16}$. Let A, B and C be the events
   $A = \{d,e,a\}$
   $B = \{c,e,a\}$
   $C = \{c,d,a\}$.
   Show that $P(A \cap B \cap C) = P(A)P(B)P(C)$ but no two of these events are independent.

8. What is the probability that a family of two children has
   (a) two boys given that it has a least one boy?
   (b) two boys given that the first child is a boy?

9. In Example 10, how large must the prior probability of cancer be to give a posterior probability of .5 for cancer given a positive test?

10. Two cards are drawn from a bridge deck. What is the probability that the second card drawn is red?

11. If $P(\bar{B}) = \frac{1}{4}$ and $P(A \mid B) = \frac{1}{2}$, what is $P(A \cap B)$?

12. (a) What is the probability that your bridge partner has exactly two aces, given that she has at least one ace?
    (b) What is the probability that your bridge partner has exactly two aces, given that she has the ace of spades?

13. Prove that for any three events A,B,C, each having positive probability,

$$P(A \cap B \cap C) = P(A)P(B \mid A)P(C \mid A \cap B).$$

14. Prove that if A and B are independent so are
    (a) A and $\bar{B}$.
    (b) $\tilde{A}$ and $\bar{B}$.

15. A doctor assumes that a patient has one of three diseases $d1$, $d2$, or $d3$. Before any test, he assumes an equal probability for each disease. He carries out a test that will be positive with probability .8 if the patient has $d1$, .6 if he has disease $d2$, and .4 if he has disease $d3$. Given that the outcome of the test was positive, what probabilities should the doctor now assign to the three possible diseases?

16. In a poker hand, John has a very strong hand and bets 5 dollars. The probability that Mary has a better hand is .04. If Mary had a better hand she would raise with probability .9, but with a poorer hand she would only raise with probability .1. If Mary raises, what is the probability that she has the winning hand?

17. The Polya urn model for contagion is as follows: We start with an urn which contains one white ball and one black ball. At each second we choose a ball at random from the urn and replace this ball and add one more of the color chosen. Write a program to simulate this model, and see if you can make any predictions about the proportion of white balls in the urn after a large number of draws. Is there a tendency to have a large fraction of balls of the same color in the long run?

18. It is desired to find the probability that in a bridge deal each player receives an ace. A student argues as follows. It does not matter where the first ace goes. The second ace must go to one of the other three players and this occurs with probability $^3/_4$. Then the next must go to one of two, an event of probability $^1/_2$, and finally the last ace must go to the player who does not have an ace. This occurs with probability $^1/_4$. The probability that all these events occur is the product $(^3/_4)(^1/_2)(^1/_4) = {}^3/_{32}$. Is this argument correct?

19. One coin in a collection of 65 has two heads. The rest are fair. If a coin, chosen at random from the lot and then tossed, turns up heads 6 times in a row, what is the probability that it is the two-headed coin?

20. You are given two urns and fifty balls. Half of the balls are white and half are black. You are asked to distribute the balls in the urns with no restriction placed on the number of either type in an urn. How should you distribute the balls in the urns to maximize the probability of obtaining a white ball if an urn is chosen at random and a ball drawn out at random? Justify your answer.

21. A fair coin is thrown n times. Show that the conditional probability of a head on any specified trial, given a total of k heads over the n trials, is k/n $(k > 0)$.

22. (Johnsonbough)[7] A coin with probability p for heads is tossed n times. Let E be the event "a head is obtained on the first toss" and F_k the event "exactly k heads are obtained." For which pairs (n,k) are E and F_k independent?

23. Suppose that A and B are events such that $P(A \mid B) = P(B \mid A)$ and $P(A \cup B) = 1$ and $P(A \cap B) > 0$. Prove that $P(A) > {}^1/_2$.

24. In London it rains three out of every four days. The weather forecaster is correct $^3/_4$ of the time. When rain is forecast, Mr. Pickwick takes his umbrella. When rain is not forecast, he takes it with probability $^1/_2$. Find
    (a) the probability that Pickwick is caught in the rain without an umbrella.
    (b) the probability that Pickwick carries an umbrella when it does not rain.

25. Probability theory was used in a famous court case: *People v. Collins*.[8] In this case a purse was snatched from an elderly person in a Los Angeles suburb. A couple seen running from the scene were described as a black man with a beard and a mustache and a blond girl with hair in a ponytail. Witnesses said they drove off in a partly yellow car. Malcolm and Janet Collins were arrested. He was black and though clean shaven when arrested had evidence of recently having had a beard and a mustache.

[7]R. Johnsonbough, "Problem #103," *Two Year College Math Journal*, vol. 8 (1977), p. 292.

[8]M.W. Gray, "Statistics and the Law," *Mathematics Magazine*, vol. 56 (1983), pp. 67–81.

She was blond and usually wore her hair in a ponytail. They drove a partly yellow Lincoln. The prosecution called a professor of mathematics as a witness who suggested that a conservative set of probabilities for the characteristics noted by the witnesses would be:

man with mustache	1/4
girl with blond hair	1/3
girl with ponytail	1/10
black man with beard	1/10
interracial couple in a car	1/1000
partly yellow car	1/10

The prosecution then argued that the probability that all of these characteristics are met by a randomly chosen couple is the product of the probabilities or 1/12,000,000, which is very small. He claimed this was proof beyond a reasonable doubt that the defendants were guilty. The jury agreed and handed down a verdict of guilty of second-degree robbery.

If you were the lawyer for the Collins couple how would you have countered the above argument? (The appeal of this case is discussed in Chapter 9, Section 9.3, Exercise 23.)

26. A student is applying to Harvard and Dartmouth. He estimates that he has a probability of .5 of being accepted at Dartmouth and .3 of being accepted at Harvard. He further estimates the probability that he will be accepted by both is .2. What is the probability that he is accepted by Dartmouth if he is accepted by Harvard? Is the event "accepted at Harvard" independent of the event "accepted at Dartmouth"?

27. Luxco, a wholesale lightbulb manufacturer, has two factories. Factory A sells bulbs in lots that consist of 1000 regular and 2000 *softglow* bulbs each. Random sampling has shown that on the average there tend to be about 2 bad regular bulbs and 11 bad softglow bulbs per lot. At factory B the lot size is reversed—there are 2000 regular and 1000 softglow per lot—and there tend to be 5 bad regular and 6 bad softglow bulbs per lot.

The manager of factory A asserts, "We're obviously the better producer; our bad bulb rates are .2 percent and .55 percent compared to B's .25 and .6 percent. We're better at both regular and softglow bulbs by half of a tenth of a percent each."

"Au contraire," counters the manager of B, "each of our 3000 bulb lots contains only 11 bad bulbs, while A's 3000 bulb lots contain 13. So our .37 percent bad bulb rates beats their .43 percent.

Who is right?

28. Using the Life Table for 1981 given in Appendix A, find the probability that a male of age 60 in 1981 lives to age 80. Find the same probability for a female.

29. (a) There has been a blizzard and Helen is trying to drive from Woodstock to Tunbridge, which are connected like this:

Here p and q are the probabilities that the two roads are passable. What is the probability that Helen can get from Woodstock to Tunbridge?

(b) Now suppose that Woodstock and Tunbridge are connected like this:

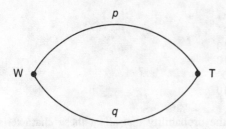

What now is the probability that she can get from W to T? Note that if we think of the roads as being components of a system, then in (a) and (b) we have computed the *reliability* of a system whose components are (a) *in series* and (b) *in parallel*.

(c) Now suppose W and T are connected like this:

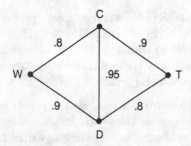

Find the probability of Helen's getting from W to T. *Hint:* If the road from C to D is impassable, it might as well not be there at all; if it is passable, it is as though C and D were one and the same town.

30. Prove that the events A_1, A_2, A_3 are mutually independent if and only if $P(B_1 \cap B_2 \cap B_3) = P(B_1)P(B_2)P(B_3)$, where each B_i is either A_i or its complement $\tilde{A}_i$.

31. Let E be an event with $P(E) > 0$ and define $p_E(\omega)$ by $p_E(\omega) = p(\omega \mid E)$.

Prove that $p_E(\omega)$ is a density function on E, that is, that $p_E(\omega) \geqslant 0$ and that $\sum_{\omega \in \Omega} p_E(\omega) = 1$. p_E is called the *conditional density given E*.

32. You are given two urns each containing two biased coins. The coins in urn I come up heads with probability p_1, and the coins in urn II come up heads with probability $p_2 \neq p_1$. You are given a choice of (a) choosing an urn at random and tossing the two coins in this urn or (b) choosing one coin from each urn and tossing these two coins. You win a prize if both coins turn up heads. Show that you are better off selecting choice (a).

33. Prove that, if $A_1, A_2, \ldots, A_n$ are mutually independent events defined on a sample space Ω and if $0 < P(A_j) < 1$ for all j, then Ω must have at least 2^n points.

34. Prove that if

$$P(A \mid C) \geq P(B \mid C) \text{ and } P(A \mid \tilde{C}) \geq P(B \mid \tilde{C}),$$

then $P(A) \geq P(B)$.

35. A coin is in one of n boxes. The probability that it is in the ith box is p_i. If you search in the ith box and it is there, you find it with probability a_i. Show that the probability that the coin is in the jth box, given that you have looked in the ith box and not found it, is

$$\frac{p_j}{1 - a_i p_i} \quad \text{if} \quad j \neq i,$$

$$\frac{(1 - a_i)p_i}{1 - a_i p_i} \quad \text{if} \quad j = i.$$

36. George Wolford has suggested the following variation on the Linda problem (see Exercise 24 of Chapter 1, Section 1.2). The registrar is carrying John and Mary's registration cards and drops them in a puddle. When he picks them up he cannot read the names but on the first card he picked up he can make out mathematics 23 and government 35, and on the second card he can make out only mathematics 23. He asks you if you can help him decide which card belongs to Mary. You know that Mary likes government but does not like mathematics. You know nothing about John and assume that he is just a typical Dartmouth student. From this you estimate:

P(Mary takes government 35) = .5
P(Mary takes mathematics 23) = .1
P(John takes government 35) = .3
P(John takes mathematics 23) = .2

   Assume that their choices for courses are independent events. Show that the card with mathematics 23 and government 35 showing is more likely to be Mary's than John's. The conjunction fallacy referred to in the Linda problem would be to assume that the event "Mary takes mathematics 23 and government 35" is more likely than the event "Mary takes mathematics 23." Why are we not making this fallacy here?

37. (Suggested by Eisenberg and Ghosh)[9] A deck of playing cards can be described as a Cartesian product

Deck = Suit × Rank,

where Suit = {♣,♦,♥,♠} and Rank = {2,3, . . . ,10,J,Q,K,A}. This just means that every card may be thought of as an ordered pair like (♦,2). By a *suit event* we mean any event A contained in Deck which is described in terms of Suit alone. For instance, if A is "the suit is red," then

A = {♦,♥} × Rank,

so that A consists of all cards of the form (♦,r) or (♥,r), where r is any rank.

(a) Show that if A is any suit event and B any rank event, then A and B are *independent*. (We can express this briefly by saying that suit and rank are independent.)
(b) Throw away the ace of spades. Show that now no nontrivial (i.e., neither empty nor the whole space) suit event A is independent of any nontrivial rank event B. *Hint:* here independence comes down to

$$c/51 = (a/51) \cdot (b/51),$$

where a,b,c are the respective sizes of A,B and $A \cap B$. It follows that 51 must divide ab, hence that 3 must divide one of a and b, and 17 the other. But the possible sizes for suit and rank events preclude this.
(c) Show that the deck in (b) nevertheless does have pairs A, B of nontrivial independent events. *Hint:* find 2 events A and B of sizes 3 and 17, respectively, which intersect in a single point.
(d) Add a joker to a full deck. Show that now there is no pair A,B of nontrivial independent events. *Hint:* see the hint in (b); 53 is prime.

The following problems are suggested by Stanley Gudder in his article "Do Good Hands Attract?"[10] Gudder says that event A *attracts* event B if $P(B \mid A) > P(B)$ and *repels B* if $P(B \mid A) < P(B)$.

38. Let R_i be the event that the ith player in a poker game has a royal flush. Show that a royal flush (A,K,Q,J,10 of one suit) is attractive, that is $P(R_2 \mid R_1) > P(R_1)$. Show that a royal flush repels full houses.

39. Prove that A attracts B if and only if B attracts A. Hence we can say that A and B are *mutually attractive* if A attracts B.

40. Prove that A neither attracts nor repels B if and only if A and B are independent.

41. Prove that A and B are mutually attractive if and only if $P(B \mid A) > P(B \mid \tilde{A})$.

42. Prove that if A attracts B, then A repels $\tilde{B}$.

43. Prove that if A attracts both B and C, and A repels $B \cap C$, then A attracts $B \cup C$. Is there any example in which A attracts both B and C and repels $B \cup C$?

44. Prove that if $B_1, . . . ,B_n$ are mutually disjoint and collectively exhaustive, and if A attracts some B_i, then A must repel some B_j.

[9]B. Eisenberg and B.K. Ghosh, "Independent Events in a Discrete Uniform Probability Space," *The American Statistician*, vol. 41, no. 1 (1987), pp. 52–56.

[10]S. Gudder, "Do Good Hands Attract?" *Mathematics Magazine*, vol. 54, no. 1 (1981), pp. 13–16.

4.2 CONTINUOUS CONDITIONAL PROBABILITY

In the previous section we introduced the concept of the conditional probability $P(F|E)$ as the probability of the event F, given that the event E has occurred. We argued there that this probability should be given by the definition

$$P(F \mid E) = \frac{P(F \cap E)}{P(E)}$$

(cf. Definition 1).

Conditional Probabilities

We shall adopt this same definition in situations where the sample space is continuous. In this case, the probability of an event E is determined by a probability density function $p(\omega)$:

$$p(E) = \int_E p(\omega)d\omega.$$

It follows that

$$P(F|E) = \frac{\int_{F \cap E} p(\omega)d\omega}{\int_E p(\omega)d\omega}$$

$$= \int_{F \cap E} \frac{p(\omega)}{P(E)}d\omega.$$

This suggests that we define the *conditional probability density function* $p(\omega|E)$ by

$$p(\omega|E) = \begin{cases} \dfrac{p(\omega)}{P(E)} & \text{if } \omega \in E \\ \\ 0 & \text{if } \omega \notin E \end{cases}$$

(cf. Definition 1). Then

$$P(F|E) = \int_F p(\omega|E)d\omega.$$

We can think of the conditional density function as being 0 except on E, and normalized to have integral 1 over E. Note that if the original density is a uniform density corresponding to an experiment in which all events of equal size are *equally likely*, then the same will be true for the conditional density.

EXAMPLE 1

In the spinner experiment (cf. Chapter 2, Section 2.2, Example 1), suppose we know that the spinner has stopped with head in the upper half of the circle, $0 \leq \omega \leq \frac{1}{2}$. What is the probability that $\frac{1}{6} \leq \omega \leq \frac{1}{3}$?

Here $E = [0, \frac{1}{2}]$, $F = [\frac{1}{6}, \frac{1}{3}]$, and $F \cap E = F$. Hence

$$P(F|E) = \frac{P(F \cap E)}{P(E)}$$

$$= \frac{\frac{1}{6}}{\frac{1}{2}}$$

$$= \frac{1}{3},$$

which is reasonable, since F is $\frac{1}{3}$ the size of E. The conditional density function here is given by

$$p(\omega|E) = 2 \quad \text{if } 0 \leq \omega < \frac{1}{2}$$
$$= 0 \quad \text{if } \frac{1}{2} \leq \omega < 1.$$

Thus the conditional density function is nonzero only on $[0, \frac{1}{2}]$, and is uniform there.

□

EXAMPLE 2

In the dart game (cf. Chapter 2, Section 2.2, Example 2), suppose we know that the dart lands in the upper half of the target. What is the probability that its distance from the center is less than $\frac{1}{2}$?

Here $E = \{(x,y): y \geq 0\}$, and $F = \{(x,y): x^2 + y^2 < (\frac{1}{2})^2\}$. Hence,

$$P(F|E) = \frac{P(F \cap E)}{P(E)} = \frac{\frac{1}{\pi}[\frac{1}{2} \cdot \frac{\pi}{4}]}{\frac{1}{\pi}[\frac{\pi}{2}]}$$

$$= \frac{1}{4}.$$

Here again, the size of $F \cap E$ is $\frac{1}{4}$ the size of E. The conditional density function is

$$p((x,y)|E) = \begin{cases} \dfrac{p(x,y)}{P(E)} = \dfrac{\frac{1}{\pi}}{\frac{1}{\pi} \cdot \frac{\pi}{2}} = \dfrac{2}{\pi} & \text{if } (x,y) \in E, \\\\ 0 & \text{if } (x,y) \notin E. \end{cases}$$

□

EXAMPLE 3

We return to the bus example (cf. Chapter 2, Section 2.2, Example 4) and ask for the probability that a bus arrives after time $t = r + s$, given that it has not arrived by time r.

Let $G(t)$ be the probability that the bus arrives after time t. Then

$$G(t) = \int_t^\infty \lambda e^{-\lambda x} dx$$

$$= -e^{-\lambda x} \Big|_t^\infty = e^{-\lambda t}.$$

Let E be the event "the bus arrives after time r" and F the event "the bus arrives after time $r + s$." Then

$$P(F|E) = \frac{P(F \cap E)}{P(E)}$$
$$= \frac{G(r+s)}{G(r)}$$
$$= \frac{e^{-\lambda(r+s)}}{e^{-\lambda r}}$$
$$= e^{-\lambda s}.$$

This tells us the rather surprising fact that the probability that we have to wait s seconds more for the bus, given that it has not arrived by time r, is *independent* of the time r. This property (the *forgetting* property) is unique to the exponential density function and suggests the use of the exponential density to describe experiments in which this property is observed. ☐

Independence

In the previous section we also introduced the concept of independence: Two events E and F are *independent* if $P(E \cap F) = P(E) \cdot P(F)$. We showed there that: If $P(E) > 0$, then E and F are independent if and only if $P(F|E) = P(F)$, so that knowing the outcome of E does not affect the probability of F.

In the case of continuous sample spaces, this idea still makes good sense, and we can carry over the same definition and the same theorem. In this case, however, the probability P is given in terms of a probability density function p, and so

$$P(E \cap F) = P(E) \cdot P(F)$$

becomes

$$\int_{E \cap F} p(\omega) d\omega = \left(\int_{E} p(\omega) d\omega \right) \left(\int_{F} p(\omega) d\omega \right),$$

and this can hold only under rather special circumstances.

EXAMPLE 2 (continued)
In the dart game (see Example 2), let E be the event that the dart lands in the *upper* half of the target ($y \geq 0$) and F the event that the dart lands in the *right* half of the target ($x \geq 0$). Then $P(E \cap F)$ is the probability that the dart lies in the first quadrant of the target, and

$$P(E \cap F) = \frac{1}{\pi} \int_{E \cap F} 1 \, dxdy$$
$$= \text{Area}(E \cap F)$$
$$= \text{Area}(E)\text{Area}(F)$$
$$= \left(\frac{1}{\pi} \int_{E} 1 \, dxdy \right) \left(\frac{1}{\pi} \int_{F} 1 \, dxdy \right)$$
$$= P(E)P(F)$$

so that E and F are independent. What makes this work is that the events E and F are described by restricting different coordinates. This example suggests the following general rule: If the sample space Ω can be described by two coordinates (x,y), and if the probability density function $p(x,y)$ can be written in the form

$$p(x,y) = p_1(x) \, p_2(y),$$

then events E and F described by restricting x and y, respectively, are always independent. $\qquad\qquad\square$

Beta Density

We consider next an example which involves a sample space with both discrete and continuous coordinates. For this example we shall need a new density function called the *beta density*. This density has two parameters α, β and is defined by

$$B(\alpha,\beta,x) = \frac{1}{B(\alpha,\beta)} \, x^{\alpha-1} \, (1-x)^{\beta-1} \qquad \text{if } 0 \leq x \leq 1,$$

$$= 0 \qquad \text{otherwise.}$$

Here α and β are any positive numbers, and the beta function $B(\alpha,\beta)$ is given by the area under the graph of $x^{\alpha-1} \, (1-x)^{\beta-1}$ between 0 and 1:

$$B(\alpha,\beta) = \int_0^1 x^{\alpha-1} \, (1-x)^{\beta-1} dx.$$

Note that when $\alpha = \beta = 1$ the beta density is the uniform density. When α and β are greater than 1 the density is bell-shaped, but when they are less than 1 it is U-shaped as suggested by the examples in Figure 6.

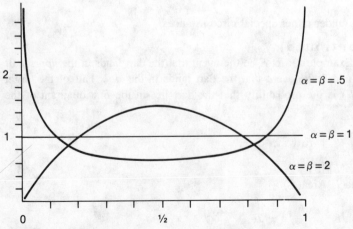

Figure 6 Beta density for $\alpha = \beta = .5, 1, 2$.

We shall need the values of the beta function only for integer values of α and β, and in this case

$$B(\alpha,\beta) = \frac{(\alpha-1)!(\beta-1)!}{(\alpha+\beta-1)!}.$$

Effectiveness of Drugs

EXAMPLE 4

In medical problems it is often assumed that a drug is effective with a probability x each time it is used and that the various trials are independent, so that one is in effect tossing a biased coin with probability x for heads. Before experimentation little is known about the value of x. The beta densities provide a convenient class of densities to describe the possible states of information before experimentation. The choice $\alpha = \beta = 1$ (the uniform density) would be appropriate if we have absolutely no information before we do any experimentation.

Assume that the experimenter has chosen a beta density to describe the state of his knowledge about x before the experiment. Then he gives the drug to n subjects and records the number i of successes. In this case the sample space may be conveniently described by two coordinates (x,i), where x is the probability of success in each trial, and i is the number of successes in n trials. In such a case we can say that the sample space is neither discrete nor continuous, but *mixed*.

Now let us calculate the probability density $p(i|x)$ that we observe i successes knowing the value of x. This is given by the binomial density with probability x for success:

$$p(i|x) = b(n,x,i) = \binom{n}{i} x^i(1-x)^j,$$

where $j = n - i$. If x is chosen at random from $[0,1]$ with a beta density $B(\alpha,\beta,x)$, then the density function for the outcome of the pair (x,i) is

$$\begin{aligned}
p(x,i) &= p(i|x)B(\alpha,\beta,x) \\
&= \binom{n}{i} x^i(1-x)^j \frac{1}{B(\alpha,\beta)} x^{\alpha-1}(1-x)^{\beta-1} \\
&= \binom{n}{i} \frac{1}{B(\alpha,\beta)} x^{\alpha+i-1}(1-x)^{\beta+j-1}.
\end{aligned}$$

Now let $p(i)$ be the probability that we observe i successes *not* knowing the value of x. Then

$$\begin{aligned}
p(i) &= \int_0^1 p(i|x) B(\alpha,\beta,x)\, dx \\
&= \binom{n}{i}\frac{1}{B(\alpha,\beta)} \int_0^1 x^{\alpha+i-1}(1-x)^{\beta+j-1}dx \\
&= \binom{n}{i}\frac{B(\alpha+i,\,\beta+j)}{B(\alpha,\beta)}.
\end{aligned}$$

Hence, the probability density $p(x|i)$ for x, given that i successes were observed, is

$$p(x|i) = \frac{p(x,i)}{p(i)}$$

$$= \frac{x^{\alpha+i-1}(1-x)^{\beta+j-1}}{B(\alpha+i, \beta+j)},$$

that is, $p(x|i)$ is another beta density. This says that if we observe i successes and j failures in n subjects, then the new density for the probability that the drug is effective is again a beta density but with parameters $\alpha + i, \beta + j$.

Assume, for example, that before the experiment we choose a beta density with $\alpha = \beta = 1$ (that is, the uniform density), and that in the experiment we obtain i successes in n trials. Then the new density for x after the experiment should be a beta density with parameters $i + 1$ and $j + 1$. This means that after the experiment the probability that the drug is effective on the next subject is

$$p = \frac{1}{B(i+1,j+1)}\int_0^1 x{\cdot}x^i(1-x)^j dx$$

$$= \frac{B(i+2,j+1)}{B(i+1,j+1)}$$

$$= \frac{(i+1)!j!}{(n+2)!}\cdot\frac{(n+1)!}{i!j!}$$

$$= \frac{i+1}{n+2}.$$

Thus, our estimate for the probability of success after the experiment is approximately the proportion of successes observed in the experiment, which is certainly a reasonable conclusion. ☐

Winning Strategies

EXAMPLE 5   Two-armed bandit problem

You are in a casino and confronted by two slot machines. Each machine pays off either 1 dollar or nothing. The probability that the first machine pays off a dollar is x and that the second machine pays off a dollar is y. We assume that x and y are random numbers chosen independently from the interval $[0,1]$ and unknown to you. You are permitted to make a series of ten plays, each time choosing one machine or the other. How should you choose to maximize the number of times that you win?

One strategy that sounds reasonable is to calculate, at every stage, the probability that each machine will pay off and choose the machine with the higher probability. Let win (i), for $i = 1$ or 2, be the number of times that you have won on the ith machine. Similarly, let lose(i) be the number of times you have lost on the ith machine. Then, from Example 4, the probability $p(i)$ that you win if you choose the ith machine is

$$p(i) = \frac{\text{win}(i) + 1}{\text{win}(i) + \text{lose}(i) + 2}.$$

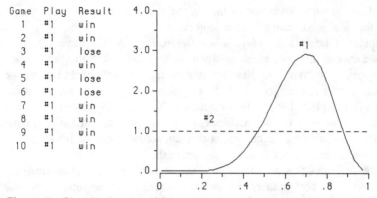

Game	Play	Result
1	#1	win
2	#1	win
3	#1	lose
4	#1	win
5	#1	lose
6	#1	lose
7	#1	win
8	#1	win
9	#1	win
10	#1	win

Figure 7 Play the best machine.

Thus, if $p(1) > p(2)$ you would play machine 1 and otherwise you would play machine 2. We have written a program **Two Arm** to simulate this experiment. In the program, the user specifies the initial values for x and y (but these are unknown to the experimenter). The program calculates at each stage the two conditional densities for x and y, given the outcomes of the previous trials, and then computes $p(i)$ for $i = 1,2$. It then chooses the machine with the highest value for the probability of winning for the next play. The program prints the machine chosen on each play and the outcome of this play. It also plots the new densities for x (solid line) and y (dotted line), showing only the current densities. We have run the program for ten plays for the case $x = .6$ and $y = .7$. The result is shown in Figure 7.

The run of the program shows the weakness of this strategy. Our initial probability for winning on the better of the two machines is .7. We start with the poorer machine and our outcomes are such that we always have a probability greater than .6 of winning and so we just keep playing this machine even though the other machine is better. If we had lost on the first play we would have switched machines. Our final density for x is the same as our initial density, namely, the uniform density. Our final density for y is different and reflects a much more accurate knowledge about y. The computer did pretty

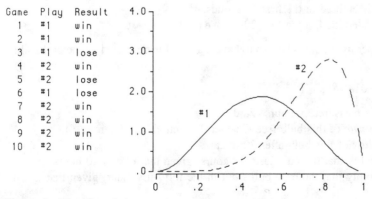

Game	Play	Result
1	#1	win
2	#1	win
3	#1	lose
4	#2	win
5	#2	lose
6	#1	lose
7	#2	win
8	#2	win
9	#2	win
10	#2	win

Figure 8 Play the winner.

well with this strategy, winning seven out of the ten trials, but ten trials are not enough to judge whether this is a good strategy in the long run.

Another popular strategy is the *play-the-winner strategy*. As the name suggests, for this strategy we choose the same machine when we win and switch machines when we lose. The program **Two Arm** will simulate this strategy as well. In Figure 8, we show the results of running this program with the play-the-winner strategy and the same true probabilities of .6 and .7 for the two machines. Now we do change machines frequently and learn about both of the machines. After ten plays our densities for the unknown probabilities of winning suggest to us that the second machine is indeed the better of the two. We again won seven out of the ten trials.

Neither of the strategies that we simulated is the best one in terms of maximizing our average winnings. This best strategy is very complicated but is reasonably approximated by the play-the-winner strategy. Variations on this example have played an important role in the problem of clinical tests of drugs where experimenters face a similar situation. □

Exercises

1. Pick a point x at random (with uniform density) in the interval $[0,1]$. Find the probability that $x > \frac{1}{2}$, given that
   (a) $x > \frac{1}{4}$.
   (b) $x < \frac{3}{4}$.
   (c) $|x - \frac{1}{2}| < \frac{1}{4}$.
   (d) $x^2 - x + \frac{2}{9} < 0$.

2. A radioactive material emits α-particles at a rate described by the probability density function

   $$p(t) = .1e^{-.1t}.$$

   (see Chapter 2, Section 2.2, Exercise 5). Find the probability that a particle is emitted in the first 10 seconds, given that
   (a) no particle is emitted in the first second.
   (b) no particle is emitted in the first 5 seconds.
   (c) a particle is emitted in the first 3 seconds.
   (d) a particle is emitted in the first 20 seconds.

3. The Acme Super light bulb is known to have a useful life described by the probability density function

   $$p(t) = .01e^{-.01t},$$

   where time t is measured in hours. Find
   (a) the *failure rate* of this bulb (see Chapter 2, Section 2.2, Exercise 6).
   (b) the *reliability* of this bulb after 20 hours.
   (c) the probability that the bulb lasts 40 hours, given that it lasts 20 hours.
   (d) the probability that the bulb burns out in the forty-first hour, given that it lasts 40 hours.

4. Suppose you toss a dart at a circular target of radius 10 inches. Given that the dart lands in the upper half of the target, find the probability that
   (a) it lands in the right half of the target.
   (b) its distance from the center is less than 5 inches.
   (c) its distance from the center is greater than 5 inches.
   (d) it lands within 5 inches of the point (0,5).

5. Suppose you choose two numbers x and y, independently at random from the interval [0,1]. Given that their sum lies in the interval [0,1], find the probability that
   (a) $|x - y| < 1$.
   (b) $xy < 1/2$.
   (c) $\max\{x,y\} < 1/2$.
   (d) $x^2 + y^2 < 1/4$.
   (e) $x > y$.

6. Find the conditional density functions for the following experiments.
   (a) A number x is chosen at random in the interval [0,1], given that $x > 1/4$.
   (b) A number t is chosen at random in the interval $[0,\infty]$ with exponential density e^{-t}, given that $1 < t < 10$.
   (c) A dart is thrown at a circular target of radius 10 inches, given that it falls in the upper half of the target.
   (d) Two numbers x and y are chosen at random in the interval [0,1], given that $x > y$.

7. Let x and y be chosen at random from the interval [0,1]. Show that the events $x > 1/3$ and $y > 2/3$ are independent events.

8. Let x and y be chosen at random from the interval [0,1]. Which pairs of the following events are independent?
   (a) $x > 1/3$.
   (b) $y > 2/3$.
   (c) $x > y$.
   (d) $x + y < 1$.

*9. In Chapter 2, Section 2.2, Exercise 13 you proved the following: If you take a stick of unit length and break it in into three pieces, choosing the breaks at random, then the probability that the three pieces form a triangle is $1/4$. Consider now a similar experiment: First break the stick at random, then break the longer piece at random. Show that the two experiments are actually quite different, as follows.
   (a) Write a program which simulates both cases for a run of 1000 trials, prints out the proportion of successes for each run, and repeats this process ten times. (Call a trial a success if the three pieces do form a triangle.) Have your program pick (x,y) at random in the unit square, and in each case use x and y to find the two breaks. For each experiment, have it plot (x,y) if (x,y) gives a success.
   (b) Show that in the second experiment the theoretical probability of success is actually $2(\log 2 - 1/2)$.

10. A coin has an unknown bias p that is assumed to be uniformly distributed between 0 and 1. The coin is tossed n times and heads turns up j times and tails turns up k times. We have seen that the probability that heads turns up next time is

$$\frac{j+1}{n+2}.$$

Show that this is the same as the probability that the next ball is black for the Polya urn model of Exercise 17 of Chapter 4, Section 4.1. Use this result to explain why, in the Polya urn model, the proportion of black balls does not tend to 0 or 1 as one might expect but rather to a uniform distribution on the interval [0,1].

11. Previous experience with a drug suggests that the probability p that the drug is effective is a random quantity having a beta density with parameters $\alpha = 2$ and $\beta = 3$. The drug is used on ten subjects and found to be successful in four out of the ten patients. What density should we now assign to the probability p? What is the probability that the drug will be successful the next time it is used?

12. Write a program to allow you to compare the strategies play-the-winner and play-the-best-machine for the two-armed-bandit problem of Example 5. Have your program determine the initial payoff probabilities for each machine by choosing a pair of random numbers between 0 and 1. Have your program carry out 20 plays and keep track of the number of wins for each of the two strategies. Finally, have your program make 1000 repetitions of the 20 plays and compute the average winning per 20 plays. Which strategy seems to be the best?

13. Consider the two-armed bandit problem of Example 5. Bruce Barnes proposed the following strategy, which is a variation on the play-the-best-machine strategy. The machine with the greatest probability of winning is played *unless* the following two conditions hold: (a) the difference in the probabilities for winning is less than .08, and (b) the ratio of the number of times played on the more often played machine to the number of times played on the less often played machine is greater than 1.4. If the above two conditions hold, then the machine with the smaller probability of winning is played. Write a program to simulate this strategy. Have your program choose the initial payoff probabilities at random from the unit interval [0,1], make 20 plays, and keep track of the number of wins. Repeat this experiment 1000 times and obtain the average number of wins per 20 plays. Implement a second strategy— for example, play-the-best-machine or one of your own choice, and see how this second strategy compares with Bruce's on average wins.

Chapter 5

Random Variables

5.1 DISCRETE RANDOM VARIABLES

We have already observed that, in a chance experiment, it is often not the actual outcome that concerns us but some quantity that depends upon the outcome. For example, when we toss a coin ten times, we may wish to discuss the number of heads that turn up rather than the exact outcome of each toss. When a gas is considered to be a collection of molecules moving randomly, it may be the pressure or the temperature that we can measure. For this purpose we introduce the notion of a function defined on a sample space.

Random Variables

DEFINITION 1

A *random variable* is a function whose domain is a sample space Ω.

The term random variable is customary, but unfortunate, since a random variable is neither random nor a variable. It is simply a function. In calculus we sometimes write

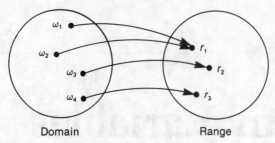

Figure 1 Random variable.

a function as $f(x)$ and, sometimes, as simply f. In probability, when we speak of random variables, we shall sometimes write $X(\omega)$ and sometimes simply X. While the values of random variables will often be numerical, this is not necessary. Recall that we can represent a function as a map from its domain to its range. Such a map is shown in Figure 1. The notation $\{\omega: X(\omega) = r\}$ denotes the set of all sample points $\omega \in \Omega$ such that $X(\omega) = r$. We usually abbreviate this set by $(X(\omega) = r)$, or simply by $(X = r)$. Since this set is an event, we can determine its probability. We obtain

$$P(X = r) = P(\{\omega: X(\omega) = r\}) = \sum_{\omega \in E} p(\omega),$$

where $E = \{\omega: X(\omega) = r\} = (X = r)$.

Density Functions

DEFINITION 2

Let X be a random variable defined on a finite sample space Ω, and let R be the range of X. The *density* of X is the function p_X with domain R defined by

$$p_X(r) = p(X = r), \qquad \text{for every } r \text{ in } R.$$

The density p_X of a random variable is a probability density defined on the *range* R of X. Suppose that $R = \{r_1, \ldots, r_s\}$. Then we may abbreviate $p_X(r_j)$ by p_j and write

$$p_j = P(X = r_j), \qquad \text{for } j = 1, \ldots, s.$$

The density function itself we normally denote by

$$p_X = \begin{pmatrix} r_1, r_2, \ldots, r_s \\ p_1, p_2, \ldots, p_s \end{pmatrix}.$$

EXAMPLE 1

If $\Omega = \{1, 2, \ldots, n\}$ is a sample space with probability density

$$p = \begin{Bmatrix} 1, 2, \ldots, n \\ p_1, p_2, \ldots, p_n \end{Bmatrix},$$

and if $X(i) = i$, then X is a random variable with density $p_X = p$. ☐

EXAMPLE 2

A fair coin is tossed three times. Let

$$\Omega = \{HHH, HHT, HTH, HTT, THH, THT, TTH, TTT\}.$$

Assign to Ω the equiprobable measure. The outcome X_1 of the first toss is a random variable. The range of X_1 is $R = \{H, T\}$. If $\omega = (HTH)$ then $X_1(\omega) = H$. The random variable X_1 has density

$$p_{X_1} = \begin{pmatrix} H & T \\ \dfrac{1}{2} & \dfrac{1}{2} \end{pmatrix}.$$

If we let X_2 be the outcome of the second toss, X_2 will have the density

$$p_{X_2} = \begin{pmatrix} H & T \\ \dfrac{1}{2} & \dfrac{1}{2} \end{pmatrix}.$$

This is the same density as X_1. Although these densities are the same, the random variables X_1 and X_2 are different functions. For example, if $\omega = (HTH)$, $X_1(\omega) = H$, and $X_2(\omega) = T$.

As another example of a random variable with domain Ω, let Y be the total number of heads that turn up. Then Y has density

$$p_Y = \begin{pmatrix} 0 & 1 & 2 & 3 \\ \dfrac{1}{8} & \dfrac{3}{8} & \dfrac{3}{8} & \dfrac{1}{8} \end{pmatrix}.$$

Note that Y has the binomial density $b(3, \frac{1}{2}, j)$ as its density. $\qquad \square$

DEFINITION 3

Let $X_1, \ldots, X_n$ be random variables defined on a sample space Ω, and let R_j be the range of X_j for $j = 1, \ldots, n$. The *joint density* of $X_1, \ldots, X_n$ is the probability density p defined on the set

$$R^* = \{(r_1, \ldots, r_n): r_1 \in R_1, \ldots, r_n \in R_n\}$$

by

$$p(r_1, \ldots, r_n) = P(X_1 = r_1, \ldots, X_n = r_n).$$

The set R^* is called the *Cartesian product* of $R_1, R_2, \ldots, R_n$, and is generally denoted by $R^* = R_1 \times \cdots \times R_n$.

EXAMPLE 3

In a group of 60 people, the numbers who do or do not smoke and do or do not have cancer are reported as:

	Not smoke	Smoke	Total
Not cancer	40	10	50
Cancer	7	3	10
Totals	47	13	60

Let Ω be the sample space consisting of these 60 people. A person is chosen at random from the group. Let $C(\omega) = 1$ if this person has cancer and 0 if not, and $S(\omega) = 1$ if this person smokes and 0 if not. Then the joint density of $\{C,S\}$ is given by the table

$$
\begin{array}{c|cc}
 & \multicolumn{2}{c}{S} \\
 & 0 & 1 \\
\hline
0 & \dfrac{40}{60} & \dfrac{10}{60} \\
C & & \\
1 & \dfrac{7}{60} & \dfrac{3}{60}
\end{array}
$$

For example $P(C = 0, S = 0) = \dfrac{40}{60}$, $P(C = 0, S = 1) = \dfrac{10}{60}$, and so forth. The densities of the individual random variables are called *marginal densities*. The marginal densities of C and S are:

$$
p_C = \begin{pmatrix} 0 & 1 \\ \dfrac{50}{60} & \dfrac{10}{60} \end{pmatrix},
$$

$$
p_S = \begin{pmatrix} 0 & 1 \\ \dfrac{47}{60} & \dfrac{13}{60} \end{pmatrix}.
$$

Independence

We now introduce a concept of independent random variables analogous to that of independent events.

DEFINITION 4

The random variables $X_1, X_2, \ldots, X_n$ are *mutually independent* if

$$P(X_1 = r_1, X_2 = r_2, \ldots, X_n = r_n) = P(X_1 = r_1)P(X_2 = r_2) \cdots P(X_n = r_n)$$

for any choice of $r_1, r_2, \ldots, r_n$.

We note that, in the case of mutually independent random variables, the joint density is the product of the individual densities. When two random variables are mutually independent, we shall say more briefly that they are *independent*.

EXAMPLE 2 (continued)

A coin is tossed three times. The random variables $X =$ number of heads, and $Y =$ the number of tails, that turn up are not independent, since $P(X = 3, Y = 3) = 0$ but $P(X = 3) = \frac{1}{8}$ and $P(Y = 3) = \frac{1}{8}$, and thus $P(X = 3, Y = 3) \neq P(X = 3)\,P(Y = 3)$.

On the other hand, if $X_j = 1$ when the jth outcome is heads and 0 when it is tails, then each X_j has the same density

$$p_{X_j} = \begin{pmatrix} 0 & 1 \\ \dfrac{1}{2} & \dfrac{1}{2} \end{pmatrix}.$$

The probability of any three values of these random variables occurring, for example, $P(X_1 = 1, X_2 = 0, X_3 = 1)$, is $\frac{1}{8}$, and this is equal to the product

$$P(X_1 = 1)P(X_2 = 0)P(X_3 = 1) = \frac{1}{2} \cdot \frac{1}{2} \cdot \frac{1}{2} = \frac{1}{8}.$$

Thus X_1, X_2, X_3 are mutually independent. $\qquad\square$

EXAMPLE 3 (continued)

The random variables S and C are not mutually independent, since

$$P(C = 1, S = 1) = \frac{3}{60} = .05,$$

$$P(C = 1)P(S = 1) = \frac{10}{60} \cdot \frac{13}{60} = .036.$$

Note that we would also see this from the fact that

$$P(C = 1 \mid S = 1) = \frac{3}{13} = .23,$$

$$P(C = 1) = \frac{1}{6} = .167.$$

$\qquad\square$

Independent Trials

The study of random variables proceeds by considering special classes of random variables. The first such class that we shall study is the class of *independent trials*.

DEFINITION 5

A sequence of random variables $X_1, X_2, \ldots, X_n$ that are mutually independent and that have the same density is called a sequence of independent trials or an *independent trials process*.

Independent trials processes arise naturally in the following way. We have a single experiment with range space $R = \{r_1, r_2, \ldots, r_s\}$ and a density

$$p_X = \begin{pmatrix} r_1, & \ldots & ,r_s \\ p_1, & \ldots & ,p_s \end{pmatrix}.$$

We repeat this experiment n times. To describe this total experiment, we choose as sample space the space

$$\Omega = R \times R \times \cdots \times R.$$

consisting of all possible sequences $\omega = (\omega_1, \omega_2, \ldots, \omega_n)$ where the value of each ω_j is chosen from R. We assign a probability density to be the *product density*

$$p(\omega) = p(\omega_1) \cdots p(\omega_n),$$

with $p(\omega_j) = p_k$ when $\omega_j = r_k$. Then we define random variables on this space by $X_j(\omega) = \omega_j$. The random variables $X_1, \ldots, X_n$ form an independent trials process.

EXAMPLE 4

A die is rolled three times. The common density is

$$p_X = \begin{pmatrix} 1 & 2 & 3 & 4 & 5 & 6 \\ \dfrac{1}{6} & \dfrac{1}{6} & \dfrac{1}{6} & \dfrac{1}{6} & \dfrac{1}{6} & \dfrac{1}{6} \end{pmatrix}.$$

The sample space is $R^3 = R \times R \times R$ with $R = \{1,2,3,4,5,6\}$. If $\omega = (1,3,6)$, then $X_1(\omega) = 1$, $X_2(\omega) = 3$, and $X_3(\omega) = 6$ indicating that the first roll was a 1, the second was a 3, and the third was a 6. The probability assigned to any sample point is

$$P(\omega) = \frac{1}{6} \cdot \frac{1}{6} \cdot \frac{1}{6} = \frac{1}{216}. \qquad \square$$

EXAMPLE 5

Consider next a Bernoulli trials process with probability p for success on each experiment.

Let $X_j(\omega) = 1$ if the jth outcome is success and $X_j(\omega) = 0$ if it is a failure. Then $X_1, X_2, \ldots, X_n$ is an independent trials process. Each X_j has the same density

$$p_{X_j} = \begin{pmatrix} 0 & 1 \\ q & p \end{pmatrix},$$

where $q = 1 - p$.

If $S_n = X_1 + X_2 + \cdots + X_n$, then

$$P(S_n = j) = \binom{n}{j} p^j q^{n-j},$$

and S_n has, as density, the binomial density $b(n,p,j)$. $\qquad\qquad\qquad\square$

Heads or Tails

EXAMPLE 6

Let us return to the game of Heads and Tails (see Chapter 1, Section 1.1, Example 3). A coin is tossed a sequence of times and Peter wins 1 penny if heads turns up and loses 1 penny if tails turns up. Then, for n plays, we can represent the sample space Ω as the set of all sequences $\omega = (\omega_1, \omega_2, \ldots, \omega_n)$ where each ω_j is 0 or 1, a 0 indicating a loss and a 1 indicating a win. For example, for three plays the sample points can be listed as

```
0 0 0
0 0 1
0 1 0
0 1 1
1 0 0
1 0 1
1 1 0
1 1 1.
```

In Chapter 1, Section 1.1, we studied, by simulation, two random variables: Peter's total winnings W_n and the number of times in the lead L_n. Recall that Peter is in the lead if his fortune is positive, or if it is 0 and it was positive last time. The values of these random variables for $n = 3$ are

ω			W_3	L_3
0	0	0	-3	0
0	0	1	-1	0
0	1	0	-1	0
0	1	1	1	1
1	0	0	-1	2
1	0	1	1	3
1	1	0	1	3
1	1	1	3	3

Thus the density for W_3 and L_3 are

$$p_{W_3} = \begin{pmatrix} -3 & -1 & 1 & 3 \\ \dfrac{1}{8} & \dfrac{3}{8} & \dfrac{3}{8} & \dfrac{1}{8} \end{pmatrix}$$

$$p_{L_3} = \begin{pmatrix} 0 & 1 & 2 & 3 \\ \dfrac{3}{8} & \dfrac{1}{8} & \dfrac{1}{8} & \dfrac{3}{8} \end{pmatrix}.$$

We can find the density of W_n by using the fact that W_n is simply related to the random variable Z_n defined as the number of times heads turns up. In fact

$$W_n = Z_n - (n - Z_n) = 2Z_n - n$$

or

$$Z_n = \frac{W_n + n}{2}.$$

Thus,

$$P(W_n = j) = P\left(Z_n = \frac{j + n}{2} \right).$$

But the density of Z_n is the binomial density $b(n, 1/2, j)$. Thus in ten plays,

$$P(W_{10} = 6) = P\left(Z_{10} = \frac{6 + 10}{2} \right) = P(Z_{10} = 8)$$
$$= b(10, 1/2, 8) = .044.$$

Therefore, it is an easy matter to modify the program **Binomial Plot** to compute the density of Peter's winnings and to plot this density. Figure 2 shows the output of the resulting program **Win Plot**.

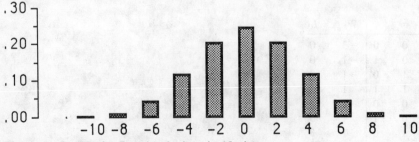

Figure 2 Density for Peter's winnings in 10 plays.

We have not yet learned how to compute the density for the random variable L_n equal to the number of times Peter is in the lead. We found the density of L_3 by simply listing all possible outcomes and counting the number for which L_3 takes on each specific value. For larger values we can ask the computer to do this for us.

There are many ways to list systematically all possible sequences of 0s and 1s. One of the easiest ways is to start with 0 and add 1 each time, using binary arithmetic. In binary arithmetic, $0 + 0 = 0$, $0 + 1 = 1 + 0 = 1$, and $1 + 1 = 0$. Thus, for sequences of length 3, we start with 0 0 0 and obtain the eight sequences

```
0 0 0
0 0 1
0 1 0
0 1 1
1 0 0
1 0 1
1 1 0
1 1 1.
```

The program **Lead** carries out this process and counts, for each sequence, the number of times Peter is in the lead. We have put in the **Lib.Prob** library a subroutine **next_diadic (list, flag)** which returns the next binary sequence and sets **flag** $= 1$ when this sequence is all 0s (see page 176).

We have run the program for $n = 10$. The density is

Times in lead	Probability
0	.2461
2	.1367
4	.1172
6	.1172
8	.1367
10	.2461

A bar graph of the density is obtained from the program **Lead Plot**, and is shown in Figure 3.

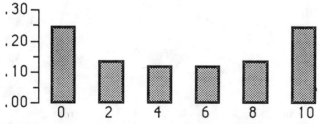

Figure 3 Density for the number of times in the lead.

```
! Lead    (LEAD)
!
! Computes the probability of being in the lead k times in the game of
! heads or tails.  The uses the subroutine next_diadic in Lib.prob to
! get every possible sequence of 0's and 1's.

library "Lib.prob*"
dim heads(20), count(20)

input prompt "Number of plays = " : plays

let sequences = 2^plays
mat heads = zer(plays)                  ! Zero and redimension arrays
mat count = zer(0 to plays)
let flag = 1                            ! Starting signal for next_diadic

do

    call next_diadic(heads,flag)        ! Get a new sequence

    let win, old_win, times_in_lead = 0   ! Reset counters to zero

    for toss = 1 to plays

        if heads(toss) = 1 then
            let win = win + 1           ! if it's heads
        else
            let win = win - 1           ! if it's tails
        end if

        if win >= 0 and old_win >= 0 then   ! See if in lead
        let times_in_lead = times_in_lead + 1
        end if

        let old_win = win                   ! Update counter

    next toss

    let count(times_in_lead) = count(times_in_lead) + 1

loop until flag = 1                          ! Stop when sequence exhausted

print
print "Times in lead", "Probability"
print

for times_in_lead = 0 to plays step 2
    print times_in_lead, round(count(times_in_lead)/sequences,4)
next times_in_lead

end
```

We have seen that the graph for the density of Peter's winnings is a bell-shaped curve with most probable value 0. In contrast, the graph for the density of the number of times Peter is in the lead is U-shaped, with the most probable values being always in the lead and never in the lead. Note that our exact computations are in good agreement with those obtained in Chapter 1, Section 1.1, by simulation, and that we have additional confirmation for the conjecture made there that the probability that Peter is always in the lead equals the probability that his final fortune is 0. □

Geometric Densities

EXAMPLE 7

Consider a Bernoulli trials process continued for an infinite number of trials; for example, a coin tossed an infinite sequence of times. We showed in Chapter 2, Section 2.2, how to assign a probability measure to the infinite tree. Now, we can determine the density for any random variable X relating to the experiment provided $P(X = a)$ can be computed in terms of a finite number of trials. For example, let T be the number of trials before the first success. Then

$$P(T = 1) = p$$

$$P(T = 2) = qp$$

$$P(T = 3) = q^2p$$

$$\cdots$$

To show that this is a density, we must show that

$$p + qp + q^2p + \cdots = 1. \tag{1}$$

Recall that for any x with $|x| < 1$,

$$1 + x + x^2 + \cdots = \frac{1}{1 - x}. \tag{2}$$

Thus, from Equation (1) and Equation (2),

$$p + qp + q^2p + \cdots = p(1 + q + q^2 + \cdots)$$

$$= \frac{p}{1 - q} = \frac{p}{p} = 1.$$

In Figure 4 we have plotted this density using the program **Geometric Plot** for the cases $p = .5, .4, .3, .2$. We see that as p decreases we are more likely to get large values for T, as would be expected. In each case, the most probable value for T is 1. This will always be true since

$$\frac{P(T = j + 1)}{P(T = j)} = q < 1.$$

□

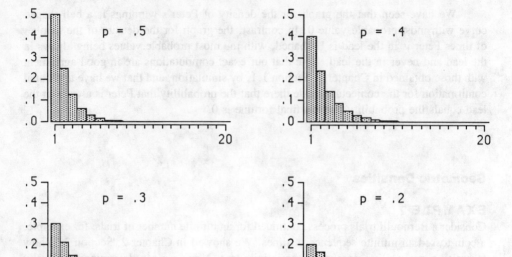

Figure 4 Geometric densities.

DEFINITION 6

A random variable T has a *geometric density* if $P(T = j) = q^{j-1}p, j = 1,2,3, \ldots,$
that is

$$p_T = \begin{pmatrix} 1 & 2 & 3 & \cdots \\ p & qp & q^2p & \cdots \end{pmatrix}.$$

Queues

The geometric density plays an important role in the theory of queues, or waiting lines.
For example, suppose a line of customers waits for service at a counter. It is often assumed
that, in each small time unit, either 0 or 1 new customers arrive at the counter. The
probability that a customer arrives is p and that no customer arrives is $q = 1 - p$. Then
the time T until the next arrival has a *geometric density*. It is natural to ask for the
probability that no customer arrives in the next k time units, that is, for $P(T > k)$. This
is given by

$$P(T > k) = \sum_{j=k}^{\infty} q^j p = q^k(p + qp + q^2p + \cdots)$$
$$= q^k.$$

It is often assumed that the length of time required to service a customer also has
a geometric distribution but with a different value for p. This requires a rather special

property of the service time. To see this, let us compute the conditional probability

$$P(T > r+s \mid T > r) = \frac{P(T > r+s)}{P(T > r)} = \frac{q^{r+s}}{q^r} = q^s.$$

Thus, the probability that the customer's service takes s more time units is independent of the length of time r that the customer has already been served. (Fortunately, not too many service stations have this property.)

Exercises

1. Peter and Paul are matching pennies as in Example 6. Let W_7 be Peter's fortune after seven tosses. Find $W_7(\omega)$ for
   (a) $\omega = (1,1,0,0,0,1,0)$.
   (b) $\omega = (1,1,1,0,1,1,0)$.
   (c) $\omega = (0,0,1,0,1,1,0)$.
   (d) $\omega = (1,0,1,0,0,1,0)$.

2. Ruth is playing the following game: A die is rolled a sequence of times. On each roll, Ruth wins a dollar if either a five or a six turns up and loses a dollar otherwise. Let W_n be Ruth's fortune after n plays. What is $W_6(\omega)$ for the following outcome sequences?
   (a) $\omega = 1,3,6,4,1,3$.
   (b) $\omega = 6,6,2,1,5,2$.
   (c) $\omega = 3,2,6,5,5,3$.
   (d) $\omega = 1,4,4,5,4,6$.

3. In the game of Exercise 2, Ruth wins 2 dollars for each time a five or six turns up and loses 1 dollar otherwise. What is her fortune after each of the following outcome sequences occurs?
   (a) $\omega = 1,1,6,5,2,3$.
   (b) $\omega = 5,5,6,4,1,6$.
   (c) $\omega = 4,5,4,1,6,3$.
   (d) $\omega = 2,5,1,3,4,4$.

4. Four women, A, B, C, and D, check their hats, and the hats are returned in a random manner. Let Ω be the set of all possible permutations of A,B,C,D. Let $X_j(\omega) = 1$ if the jth woman gets her own hat and 0 otherwise. What is the density of $X_j(\omega)$? Are $X_1(\omega), X_2(\omega), X_3(\omega), X_4(\omega)$ mutually independent?

5. A box has numbers from 1 to 10. A number is drawn at random. Let X_1 be the number drawn. This number is replaced, and the ten numbers mixed. A second number X_2 is drawn. Find the densities of X_1 and X_2. Are X_1 and X_2 independent? Answer the same questions if the first number is not replaced before the second is drawn.

6. A die is thrown twice. Let X_1 and X_2 be the outcomes. Define $X(\omega) = \min(X_1(\omega), X_2(\omega))$. For example, if the first outcome is 1 and the second outcome is 3, $\omega = (1,3)$ and $X(\omega) = \min(1,3) = 1$. Find the density of X.

*7. Given that $P(X = a) = r$, $P(\max(X,Y) = a) = s$, and $P(\min(X,Y) = a) = t$, show that you can determine $u = P(Y = a)$ in terms of r, s, and t.

8. A fair coin is tossed three times. Let X be the number of heads that turn up on the first two tosses and Y the number of heads that turn up on the third toss. Give the density of
(a) the random variables X and Y.
(b) the random variable $Z = X + Y$.
(c) the random variable $W = X - Y$.

9. Modify the program **Lead** to find the density of the *maximum value* of Peter's fortune in ten penny matches (see Example 6). Compare this density with that obtained by the program **Lead**.

10. Assume that the random variables X and Y have the joint density given by

		Y			
		-1	0	1	2
	-1	0	1/36	1/6	1/12
X	0	1/18	0	1/18	0
	1	0	1/36	1/6	1/12
	2	1/12	0	1/12	1/6

(a) What is $P(X \geq 1$ and $Y \leq 0)$?
(b) What is the conditional probability that $Y \leq 0$ given that $X = 2$?
(c) Are X and Y independent?
(d) What is the probability density of $Z = XY$?

11. In the *problem of points* (see Introduction), two players, A and B, play a series of points in a game with player A winning each point with probability p and player B winning each point with probability $q = 1 - p$. The first player to win N points wins the game. Assume that $N = 3$. Let X be a random variable that has the value 1 if player A wins the series and 0 otherwise. Let Y be a random variable with value the number of points played in a game. Find the distribution of X and Y when $p = \frac{1}{2}$. Are X and Y independent in this case? Answer the same questions for the case $p = \frac{2}{3}$.

12. The letters between Pascal and Fermat, which are often credited with having started probability theory, dealt mostly with the *problem of points* described in Exercise 11. Pascal and Fermat considered the problem of finding a fair division of stakes if the game must be called off when the first player has won r games and the second player has won s games, with $r < N$ and $s < N$. Let $P(r,s)$ be the probability that player A wins the game if he has already won r points and player B has won s points. Then
(a) $P(r,N) = 0$ if $r < N$,
(b) $P(N,s) = 1$ if $s < N$,
(c) $P(r,s) = pP(r + 1,s) + qP(r,s + 1)$ if $r < N$, $s < N$;
and **(a)**, **(b)**, and **(c)** determine $P(r,s)$ for $r \leq N$ and $s \leq N$. Pascal used these facts to find $P(r,s)$ by working backward: He first obtained $P(N - 1,j)$ for $j = N - 1$,

$N - 2, \ldots ,0$; then, from these values, he obtained $P(N - 2,j)$ for $j = N - 1$, $N - 2, \ldots ,0$ and, continuing backward, obtained all the values $P(r,s)$. Write a program to compute $P(r,s)$ for given N,a,b and p. *Warning:* Follow Pascal and you will be able to run $N = 100$; use recursion and you will not be able to run $N = 20$.

13. Fermat solved the *problem of points* (see Exercise 11) as follows: He realized that the problem was difficult because the possible ways the play might go are not equally likely. For example, when the first player needs two more games and the second needs three to win, two possible ways the series might go for first player are WLW and LWLW. These sequences are not equally likely. To avoid this difficulty, Fermat extended the play, adding fictitious plays so that the series went the maximum number of games needed (four in this case). He obtained equally likely outcomes and used, in effect, the Pascal triangle to calculate $P(r,s)$. Show that this leads to a *formula* for $P(r,s)$ even for the case $p \neq \frac{1}{2}$.

14. The Yankees are playing the Dodgers in a world series. The Yankees win each game with probability .6. What is the probability that the Yankees win the series? (The series is won by the first team to win four games.)

15. C. L. Anderson[1] has used Fermat's argument for the *problem of points* to prove the following result due to J. G. Kingston. You are playing the *game of points* (see Exercise 11) but, at each point, when you serve you win with probability p, and when your opponent serves you win with probability $\bar{p}$. You will serve first, but you can choose one of the following two conventions for serving: for the first convention you alternate service (tennis), and for the second the person serving continues to serve until he loses a point and then the other player serves (volleyball). The first player to win N points wins the match. The problem is to show that the probability of winning the match is the same under either convention.
    (a) Show that, under either convention, you will serve at most N games and your opponent at most $N - 1$ games.
    (b) Extend the number of games to $2N - 1$ so that you serve N games and your opponent serves $N - 1$. For example, you serve any additional games necessary to make N serves and then your opponent serves any additional games necessary to make him serve $N - 1$ games. The winner is now the person, in the extended match, who wins the most points. Show that playing these additional games has not changed the winner.
    (c) Show that (a) and (b) prove that you have the same probability of winning under either convention.

16. A die is rolled until the first time T that a six turns up.
    (a) What is the density for T?
    (b) Find $P(T > 3)$.
    (c) Find $P(T > 6 \mid T > 3)$.

[1]C.L. Anderson, "Note on the Advantage of First Serve," *Journal of Combinatorial Theory*, Series A, vol. 23 (1977), p. 363.

17. Let T be the number of trials until the second success in a Bernoulli trials process. Write a program to simulate this experiment a number of times and plot the proportion of times that $T = j$. See if you think T has a geometric density. *Hint:* Estimate the most probable outcome for $p = .7$.

18. If a coin is tossed a sequence of times, what is the probability that the first head will occur after the fifth toss, given that it has not occurred in the first two tosses?

19. A poker hand consists of 5 cards dealt from a deck of 52 cards. Let X and Y be, respectively, the number of aces and kings in a poker hand. Find the joint density of X and Y.

20. A manufactured lot of brass turnbuckles has S items of which D are defective. A sample of s items is drawn without replacement. Let X be a random variable that gives the number of defective items in the sample. Let $p(d) = P(X = d)$.
    (a) Show that

    $$p(d) = \frac{\binom{D}{d} \binom{S-D}{s-d}}{\binom{S}{s}}.$$

    This density p for the random variable X is called the *hypergeometric* density.
    (b) Prove the following identity, known as *Euler's formula:*

    $$\sum_{j=1}^{\min(D,s)} \binom{D}{j}\binom{S-D}{s-j} = \binom{S}{s}.$$

21. In a manufactured lot of S turnbuckles the number D of defectives is unknown. A sample of s items is tested and d items are found to be defective. The *maximum likelihood principle* of statistics says that you can estimate D as the number which gives the highest probability for getting the observed sample. Write a computer program to find this number. In a manufactured lot of 1000 items 48 were found to be defective. Use your program to estimate by the maximum likelihood principle the true proportion of defective items in the lot.

22. There are an unknown number of moose on Isle Royale (a National Park in Lake Superior). To estimate the number of moose, 50 moose are captured and tagged. Six months later 200 moose are captured and it is found that 8 of these were tagged. Use your computer program and the maximum likelihood principle (see Exercise 21) to estimate the number of moose on Isle Royale.

23. A manufactured lot of buggy whips has 20 items, of which 5 are defective. A random sample of 5 items is chosen to be inspected. Find the probability that the sample contains exactly one defective item
    (a) if the sampling is done with replacement.
    (b) if the sampling is done without replacement.

24. A bridge deck has 52 cards with 13 cards in each of four suits: spades, hearts, diamonds, and clubs. A hand of 13 cards is dealt from a shuffled deck. Find the probability that the hand has
   (a) a distribution of suits 4,4,3,2 (for example, four spades, four hearts, three diamonds, three clubs).
   (b) a distribution of suits 5,3,2,2.

25. Let X_1 and X_2 be independent random variables and let $Y_1 = \phi_1(X_1)$ and $Y_2 = \phi_2(X_2)$.
   (a) Show that

$$P(Y_1 = r, Y_2 = s) = \sum_{\substack{\phi_1(a) = r \\ \phi_2(b) = s}} P(X_1 = a, X_2 = b).$$

   (b) Using (a), show that $P(Y_1 = r, Y_2 = s) = P(Y_1 = r)P(Y_2 = s)$ so that Y_1 and Y_2 are independent.

5.2 CONTINUOUS RANDOM VARIABLES

In the previous section we introduced, for discrete sample spaces, the notion of a random variable as a function whose domain is a discrete sample space Ω and whose range is a set R, usually of real numbers. For continuous sample spaces we adopt here the same notion, but we shall usually restrict our attention to functions that are *real-valued continuous* functions of the coordinates. We make the definition as in Section 5.1.

Random Variables

DEFINITION 7

Let Ω be a continuous sample space. A (continuous) *random variable* $X: \Omega \to R \subset \mathbf{R}$ is a real-valued function defined on Ω which depends continuously (or piecewise continuously) on the coordinates of Ω.

Let Ω be a continuous sample space and $X: \Omega \to R \subset \mathbf{R}$ a (real-valued continuous) random variable. As in the previous section, we can use X to make the range R into a probability space as follows. Let E be a subset of R, and let A be the corresponding subset of Ω consisting of all points $\omega \in \Omega$ for which $X(\omega) \in E$:

$$A = \{\omega: X(\omega) \in E\}.$$

Then we can define the probability $P(E)$ of E by the rule

$$\begin{aligned} P(E) &= P\{X(\omega) \in E\} \\ &= P\{\omega \in A\} = P(A). \end{aligned}$$

It is not hard to check that this probability has all the properties discussed in Chapter 1, Section 1.2. The probabilities defined in this way can be conveniently described in terms of a probability distribution function F_X defined as follows.

Probability Distributions

DEFINITION 8

Let $X: \Omega \to R$ be a random variable. The probability distribution function F_X of X is the function $F_X: \mathbf{R} \to \mathbf{R}$ defined by

$$F_X(x) = P\{\omega: X(\omega) \leq x\}.$$

(Note that F_X is defined for all $x \in \mathbf{R}$ in this way.)

In terms of F_X, the probability $P(E)$ of an interval $E = (a,b] \subset \mathbf{R}$ is then given by

$$\begin{aligned} P((a,b]) &= P\{\omega: X(\omega) \leq b\} - P\{\omega: X(\omega) \leq a\} \\ &= F_X(b) - F_X(a). \end{aligned}$$

It is not hard to verify the following proposition.

PROPOSITION 1

The probability distribution function F_X has the properties

(1) $F_X(-\infty) = 0$, $F_X(+\infty) = 1$,

(2) if $x \leq y$ then $F_X(x) \leq F_X(y)$.

The probability distribution function F_X can in turn be conveniently described in terms of a probability density f_X, defined as follows.

Probability Densities

DEFINITION 9

The probability density function f_X of X is the function $f_X: \mathbf{R} \to \mathbf{R}$ defined by

$$f_X(x) = \frac{d}{dx} F_X(x).$$

This definition assumes that F_X is a differentiable function. In that case, we have

$$F_X(x) = \int_{-\infty}^{x} f_X(u)\,du.$$

Moreover, it is not hard to verify the following proposition.

PROPOSITION 2

The probability density function f_X has the properties

(1) $f_X(x) \geq 0$,

(2) $\displaystyle\int_{-\infty}^{+\infty} f_X(u)\,du = 1$.

It follows that if $X: \Omega \to R$ is a random variable, then the range R, together with the probability density function f_X, form a continuous probability space as defined in Chapter 2, Section 2.2. Thus, as in the discrete case, if we are interested only in events relating to the values of X, we can take for our sample space the range R of X, with probabilities determined by the density function f_X.

Let us look at some examples.

EXAMPLE 1

Let Ω be any continuous sample space described by a single coordinate ω and probability density function $p(\omega)$.

Now define the function X on Ω by setting

$$X(\omega) = \omega.$$

Then X is a random variable with density

$$f_X(x) = p(x)$$

and distribution

$$F_X(x) = \int_{-\infty}^{x} p(u)du.$$

In particular, all of the one-dimensional examples at the end of Chapter 2, Section 2.2 (Examples 5–7), can be described in this way. If the density $f_X(x)$ is the exponential or normal density, then we say the random variable X is exponentially or normally distributed, and so forth.

In these cases, all of the probabilistic information in Ω is contained in the random variable X, since X is essentially a coordinate for Ω. □

EXAMPLE 2

In Chapter 2, Section 2.2, we considered the exponential density function

$$f_T(t) = \lambda e^{-\lambda t}$$

in connection with the arrival time T of a bus. In this case, T is a random variable whose distribution function F_T is given by

$$F_T(t) = 0 \quad \text{if } t < 0,$$

$$F_T(t) = \int_{0}^{t} f_T(u)du$$

$$= \int_{0}^{t} \lambda e^{-\lambda u}du$$

$$= 1 - e^{-\lambda t} \quad \text{if } t \geq 0.$$ □

EXAMPLE 3

A number is chosen at random from $[0,1]$ with uniform probability, and then this number is squared. What is the distribution of the square? What is its density?

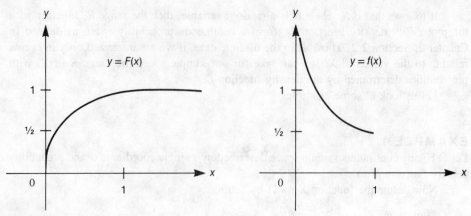

Figure 5 Distribution and density for $X(\omega) = \omega^2$.

Let $\Omega = [0,1]$, with uniform density $p(\omega) \equiv 1$. Let $\omega \in \Omega$ be the number chosen, and let $X = \omega^2$ be its square. Then X is a random variable with domain $\Omega = [0,1]$ and range $R = [0,1]$. The probability distribution F_X of X (see Figure 5) is given by

$$F_X(x) = P\{X \le x\}$$

$$= P\{\omega^2 \le x\}$$

$$= P\{\omega \le \sqrt{x}\}$$

$$= \begin{cases} 0 & \text{if } x \le 0, \\ \sqrt{x} & \text{if } 0 \le x \le 1, \\ 1 & \text{if } 1 \le x. \end{cases}$$

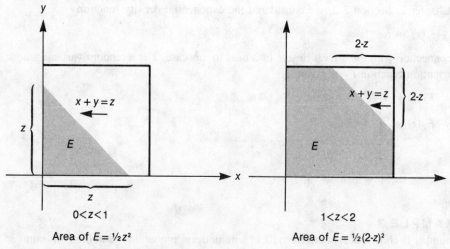

Figure 6 Calculation of $F_Z(z)$ for Example 4.

The corresponding density function f_X is given by:

$$f_X(x) = \frac{d}{dx} F_X(x)$$

$$= \begin{cases} 0 & \text{if } x \leq 0, \\ \dfrac{1}{2\sqrt{x}} & \text{if } 0 \leq x \leq 1, \\ 0 & \text{if } 1 \leq x. \end{cases}$$

(Note that F_X is continuous, but f_X is not.) $\square$

EXAMPLE 4

Two numbers are independently chosen at random from [0,1] and then added together. What is the distribution of the sum? What is the density?

Here we take for our sample space Ω the unit square in $\mathbf{R}^2$ with uniform density. A point $\omega \in \Omega$ then consists of a pair (x,y) of numbers chosen at random. Let $X(\omega) = x$, $Y(\omega) = y$, and $Z(\omega) = X(\omega) + Y(\omega) = x + y$. Then $0 \leq Z(\omega) \leq 2$, and the probability distribution F_Z of Z (see Figure 6) is given by

$$F_Z(z) = P\{Z \leq z\} = \text{Area of } E$$

$$= \begin{cases} 0 & \text{if } z < 0, \\ 1/2 \, z^2 & \text{if } 0 \leq z \leq 1, \\ 1 - 1/2(2-z)^2 & \text{if } 1 \leq z \leq 2, \\ 1 & \text{if } 2 < z. \end{cases}$$

The probability density f_Z for Z is just the derivative of F_Z (see Figure 7)

$$f_Z(z) = \begin{cases} 0 & \text{if } z < 0, \\ z & \text{if } 0 \leq z \leq 1, \\ 2 - z & \text{if } 1 \leq z \leq 2, \\ 0 & \text{if } 2 < z. \end{cases}$$

(Notice that the value of the sum Z is more likely to be near 1 than near anything else.) $\square$

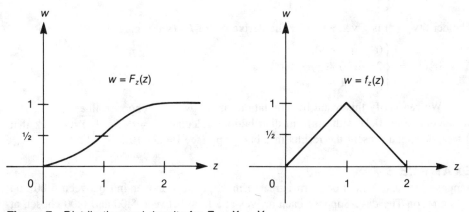

Figure 7 Distribution and density for $Z = X + Y$.

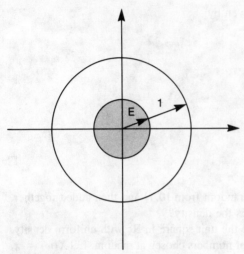

Figure 8 Calculation of F_Z for Example 5.

EXAMPLE 5

In the dart game described in Example 2 of Chapter 2, Section 2.2, what is the distribution of the distance of the dart from the center of the target? What is its density?

Here, as before, our sample space Ω is the unit circle in $\mathbf{R}^2$, with coordinates (x,y). As in Example 4, let $X(\omega) = x$, $Y(\omega) = y$, and now let $Z(\omega) = \sqrt{X^2(\omega) + Y^2(\omega)} =$ distance from the center of the target. Then the distribution function F_Z of Z (see Figure 8) is given by

$$F_Z(z) = P\{Z \leqslant z\}$$

$$= \frac{\text{Area of } E}{\text{Area of target}}$$

$$= \begin{cases} 0 & \text{if } z < 0, \\ \dfrac{\pi z^2}{\pi} = z^2 & \text{if } 0 \leqslant z \leqslant 1, \\ 1 & \text{if } 1 < z \end{cases}$$

The density $f_Z(z)$ is given again by the derivative of F_Z (see Figure 9)

$$f_Z(z) = \begin{cases} 0 & \text{if } z < 0, \\ 2z & \text{if } 0 \leqslant z \leqslant 1, \\ 0 & \text{if } 1 < z. \end{cases}$$

We can verify this result by simulation, as follows: We choose values for X and Y at random from $[0,1]$ with uniform distribution, calculate $Z = \sqrt{X^2 + Y^2}$, check that $0 \leqslant Z \leqslant 1$, and present the results in a bar graph (see Figure 10). $\qquad\square$

EXAMPLE 6

Suppose Mr. and Mrs. Lockhorn agree to meet at the Hanover Inn between 5:00 and 6:00 P.M. on Tuesday. Suppose each arrives at a time between 5:00 and 6:00 chosen at

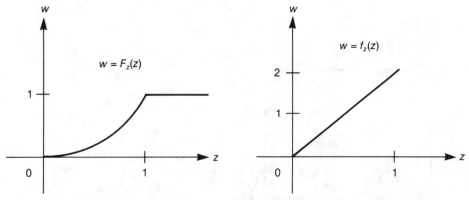

Figure 9 Distribution and density for $Z = \sqrt{X^2 + Y^2}$.

random with uniform probability. What is the distribution function for the length of time that the first to arrive has to wait for the other? What is the density function?

Here again we can take Ω as the unit square and $\omega = (\omega_1,\omega_2)$ as the arrival times (after 5:00 P.M.) of the Lockhorns. Let $X = \omega_1$, $Y = \omega_2$ and $Z = |X - Y|$. Then, since ω_1 and ω_2 are chosen from a uniform distribution, we have $F_X(x) = x$ and $F_Y(y) = y$. Moreover (see Figure 11),

$$F_Z(z) = P\{Z \leq z\}$$

$$= P\{|X - Y| \leq z\}$$

$$= \text{Area of } E$$

$$= \begin{cases} 0 & \text{if } z \leq 0, \\ 1 - (1 - z)^2 & \text{if } 0 \leq z \leq 1, \\ 1 & \text{if } 1 \leq z. \end{cases}$$

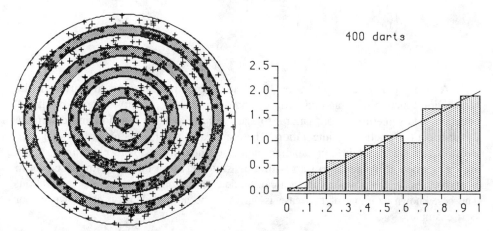

Figure 10 Simulation results for dart example.

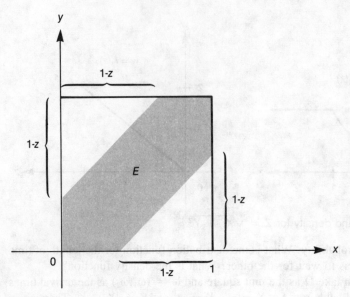

Total area of $\widetilde{E} = (1\text{-}z)^2$

Figure 11 Calculation of F_Z.

The density $f_Z(z)$ is given again by differentiation:

$$
\begin{aligned}
f_Z(z) &= \frac{d}{dz} F_Z(z) \\
&= \begin{cases}
0 & \text{if } z \le 0, \\
2\,(1 - z) & \text{if } 0 \le z \le 1, \\
0 & \text{if } 1 \le z.
\end{cases}
\end{aligned}
$$

    □

    As the previous examples show, it is sometimes more natural to start with the distribution function of a random variable and determine the density function by differentiation, and sometimes more natural to start with the density function and determine the distribution function by integration. There are cases where it is natural to start with a distribution that is not differentiable; in such cases the density is not well-defined. There are cases where it is natural to start with a density that is not integrable in closed form; in such cases the distribution function can be determined only by numerical integration. The best known example of this case is, in fact, the normal density, as shown in our next example.

Normal Distributions

EXAMPLE 7

It is often assumed that college board scores in a typical year are normally distributed with parameters μ and σ determined by the particular college board examination. Let X be the score of a randomly chosen student. Then, by assumption, X has a normal density function, namely

$$f_X(x) = \frac{1}{\sqrt{2\pi}\,\sigma}\, e^{-\frac{(x-\mu)^2}{2\sigma^2}}.$$

The distribution function $F_X(x)$ is then given by

$$F_X(x) = \int_{-\infty}^{x} \frac{1}{\sqrt{2\pi}\,\sigma}\, e^{-\frac{(u-\mu)^2}{2\sigma^2}}\, du. \qquad \square$$

This integral, however, cannot be carried out in terms of simple functions, and so we must determine F_X by numerical integration. We have in **Lib.Cont** a function **integral(a,b,n)** that approximates an integral on $[a,b]$ using Simpson's rule with n subdivisions. If X has the normal density f_X, then the distribution function is $F_X(x) =$ integral(a,x,n) where $a = -\infty$. Fortunately, the normal density is nearly zero if $\left|\dfrac{x-\mu}{\sigma}\right| > 4$, so we can choose $a = \mu - 4\sigma$ with negligible error. The program **Normal Distribution** uses the function **integral** to plot the normal distribution (see page 192). In Figure 12 we have included for comparison a plot of the normal density and normal distribution for the case of $\mu = 0$, $\sigma = 1$.

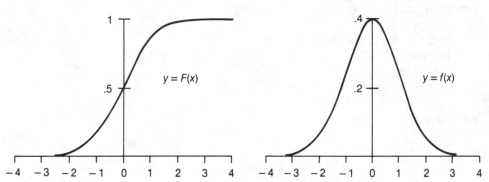

Figure 12 Normal distribution and density for parameters $\mu = 0$ and $\sigma = 1$.

```
! Normal Distribution   (NORMDIST)
!
! Plots the normal distribution function.  This uses the function
! integral(a,b,n) in Lib.cont, which approximates an integral on [a,b]
! using Simpson's rule with n subdivisions.

library "Lib.cont*"
declare function integral


let xmin = -4
let xmax = 4
let ymin = 0
let ymax = 1
let steps = 30
let minus_infinity = -10
let subdivisions = 20

set window xmin, xmax, ymin, ymax

plot xmin,0; xmax,0
plot 0,ymin; 0,ymax

for x = xmin to xmax step (xmax-xmin)/steps
    plot x,integral(minus_infinity,x, subdivisions);
next x

end


function integrand(x)

    declare function normal
    let mu = 0
    let sigma = 1
    let integrand = normal(x,mu, sigma)

end function
```

Functions of a Random Variable

Now let X and Y be random variables defined on the same sample space Ω, and suppose Y can be written as a function of X: $Y = \phi(X)$, that is,

$$Y(\omega) = \phi(X(\omega)) \qquad \text{for all } \omega \in \Omega.$$

where ϕ is a continuous function. Then how is F_Y related to F_X?

First, suppose ϕ is a *strictly increasing* function on the range of X, that is, $\phi(x_1) < \phi(x_2)$ if $x_1 < x_2$ in the range of X. Then ϕ is an invertible function there, and we may write $X = \phi^{-1}(Y)$. To see how F_Y is related to F_X we note that

$$F_Y(y) = P(Y \leq y) = P(\phi(X) \leq y)$$
$$= P(X \leq \phi^{-1}(y))$$
$$= F_X(\phi^{-1}(y)).$$

This gives us the following theorem.

THEOREM 1

Let X and Y be random variables defined on the same sample space Ω, with distribution functions F_X and F_Y. Suppose $Y = \phi(X)$ for some continuous function ϕ that is strictly increasing on the range of X. Then F_Y and F_X are related by

$$F_Y(y) = F_X(\phi^{-1}(y)).$$ ∎

Suppose, for example, that $Y = X^3$. Then $\phi(x) = x^3$, ϕ is strictly increasing for all x, and $\phi^{-1}(y) = y^{1/3}$. Then we have

$$F_Y(y) = F_X(y^{1/3}).$$

For example, assume that U has a uniform distribution on the interval $[0,1]$ and $Y = U^3$. Then, since $F_U(u) = u$ if $0 \leq u \leq 1$, the distribution of Y is given by

$$F_Y(y) = \begin{cases} 0 & \text{if } y < 0, \\ y^{1/3} & \text{if } 0 \leq y \leq 1, \\ 1 & \text{if } y > 1. \end{cases}$$

As a second example, assume that X has positive range and $Y = \log(X)$. Then $\phi(y) = \log(x)$ and $\phi^{-1}(y) = e^y$. In this case

$$F_Y(y) = F_X(e^y).$$

If U has a uniform distribution on the interval $[0,1]$, then $Y = \log(U)$ has the distribution

$$F_Y(y) = \begin{cases} e^y & \text{if } y \leq 0, \\ 1 & \text{if } y > 0. \end{cases}$$

The relation between the density functions f_X and f_Y now follows by differentiation: If ϕ is differentiable, and $y = \phi(x)$, then by the chain rule

$$F_Y(y) = \frac{d}{dy} F_Y(y)$$

$$= \frac{d}{dy} F_X(\phi^{-1}(y))$$

$$= F_X(\phi^{-1}(y)) \cdot \frac{d}{dy} (\phi^{-1}(y)).$$

(Note that if ϕ is differentiable, then ϕ^{-1} is differentiable.) Hence we have the following.

COROLLARY 1a

Under the assumptions of Theorem 1, with ϕ differentiable, we have

$$f_Y(y) = f_X(\phi^{-1}(y)) \cdot \frac{d}{dy} (\phi^{-1}(y)).$$ ∎

If, for example, $Y = X^3$, then $\phi(x) = x^3$, $\phi^{-1}(x) = y^{1/3}$, and

$$\frac{d}{dy}(\phi^{-1}(y)) = \frac{1}{3} y^{-2/3},$$

and we get

$$f_Y(y) = \begin{cases} f_X(y^{1/3}) \dfrac{1}{3} y^{-2/3} & \text{if } 0 \leqslant y \leqslant 1, \\ 0 & \text{otherwise.} \end{cases}$$

If U has a uniform distribution on $[0,1]$, then the density of U is 1 on this interval, and so the density of $Y = U^3$ would be

$$f_Y(y) = \begin{cases} \dfrac{1}{3} y^{-2/3} & \text{if } 0 \leqslant y \leqslant 1, \\ 0 & \text{otherwise.} \end{cases}$$

If $Y = \log(X)$, then $\phi(x) = \log(x)$, $\phi^{-1}(y) = e^y$, and

$$\frac{d}{dy}(\phi^{-1}(y)) = e^y.$$

so that

$$f_Y(y) = f_X(e^y) \cdot e^y.$$

Thus, if U is a uniform random variable on $[0,1]$ and $Y = \log(U)$, then Y has the density

$$f_Y(y) = \begin{cases} e^y & \text{if } y < 0, \\ 0 & \text{otherwise.} \end{cases}$$

A similar result holds if the function $\phi(x)$ is *strictly decreasing* on the range of X, so that $\phi(x_1) > \phi(x_2)$ if $x_1 < x_2$ there. Then ϕ reverses inequalities, and we have

$$F_Y(y) = P(Y \leq y) = P(\phi(X) \leq y)$$
$$= P(X \geq \phi^{-1}(y))$$
$$= 1 - P(X < \phi^{-1}(y))$$
$$= 1 - F_X(\phi^{-1}(y)).$$

It follows that

$$f_Y(y) = -f_X(\phi^{-1}(y))\frac{d}{dy}(\phi^{-1}(y)).$$

For example, if the range of X is positive, and $Y = 1/X$, then $\phi(x) = \dfrac{1}{x}$, $\phi^{-1}(y) = \dfrac{1}{y}$ and

$$F_Y(y) = 1 - F_X\left(\frac{1}{y}\right),$$

$$f_Y(y) = -f_X\left(\frac{1}{y}\right)\left(-\frac{1}{y^2}\right).$$

If the function ϕ is neither strictly increasing nor strictly decreasing, then the situation is somewhat more complicated but can be treated by the same methods. For example, suppose that $Y = X^2$. Then $\phi(x) = x^2$, and

$$F_Y(y) = P(Y \leq y)$$
$$= P(-\sqrt{y} \leq X \leq +\sqrt{y})$$
$$= P(X \leq +\sqrt{y}) - P(X \leq -\sqrt{y})$$
$$= F_X(\sqrt{y}) - F_X(-\sqrt{y}).$$

Moreover,

$$f_Y(y) = \frac{d}{dy}F_Y(y)$$

$$= \frac{d}{dy}(F_X(\sqrt{y}) - F_X(-\sqrt{y}))$$

$$= (f_X(\sqrt{y}) + f_X(-\sqrt{y}))\frac{1}{2\sqrt{y}}.$$

For example, if X has a normal density

$$f_X(x) = \frac{1}{\sqrt{2\pi}} e^{-x^2/2},$$

then $Y = X^2$ has the density

$$f_Y(y) = \frac{1}{\sqrt{2\pi y}} e^{-y/2}.$$

In general, we see that in order to express F_Y in terms of F_X when $Y = \phi(X)$, we have to express $P(Y \le y)$ in terms of $P(X \le x)$, and this process will depend in general upon the structure of ϕ.

Simulation

Theorem 1 tells us, among other things, how to simulate on the computer a random variable Y with a prescribed distribution function F. We assume that $F(y)$ is strictly increasing for those values of y where $0 < F(y) < 1$. For this purpose, let $\Omega = [0,1]$ with uniform density, and let U be the uniform random variable defined on Ω by

$$U(\omega) = \omega.$$

Then U has distribution function $F_U(u) = u$. Now, if F is the prescribed distribution function for Y, then to write Y in terms of U we first solve the equation

$$F(y) = u$$

for y in terms of u: $y = F^{-1}(u)$. Note that since F is an increasing function this equation always has a unique solution (see Figure 13). Then we set $Y = F^{-1}(U)$ and obtain, by Theorem 1,

$$F_Y(y) = F_U(F(y)) = F(y).$$

since $F_U(u) = u$. Summarizing, we have the following.

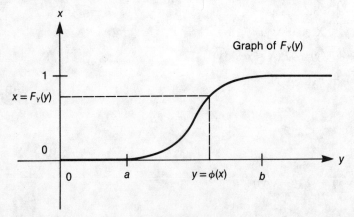

Figure 13 Converting a uniform distribution F_X into a prescribed distribution F_Y.

COROLLARY 1b

If $F(y)$ is a given distribution function that is strictly increasing when $0 < F(y) < 1$ and if U is a random variable with uniform distribution on $[0,1]$, then

$$Y = F^{-1}(U)$$

has the distribution $F(y)$. ∎

     Thus, to simulate a random variable with a given distribution F we need only set $Y = F^{-1}$ (rnd).

Exponential Distribution

EXAMPLE 8

Suppose we want to simulate a random variable Y with an exponential distribution function

$$F(y) = \begin{cases} 1 - e^{-\lambda y} & \text{for } y > 0, \\ 0 & \text{otherwise.} \end{cases}$$

with λ given. We solve for y

$$1 - e^{-\lambda y} = u,$$

getting

$$y = -\frac{1}{\lambda}\log(1 - u).$$

Then we set

$$Y = -\frac{1}{\lambda}\log(1 - \text{rnd}),$$

and Y then has the distribution

$$F_Y(y) \begin{cases} 1 - e^{-\lambda y} & \text{if } y > 0, \\ 0 & \text{otherwise.} \end{cases}$$

Note that since $1 - \text{rnd}$ is also uniform, we could just as well set $Y = -\frac{1}{\lambda}\log(\text{rnd})$, and this is what is normally done. □

     We could have used this procedure in simulating the exponential distribution in the bus program in Chapter 2, Section 2.2 (see Exercise 32 below). Instead we chose there to use a discrete approximation to the exponential distribution (the geometric distribution), which doesn't require Theorem 1, and gives very nearly the same result. In fact, all of our continuous distributions discussed here could also be simulated by discrete approximations in the same way, and we could obtain the continuous theory in this way as a limiting case of the discrete theory.

Normal Distribution

EXAMPLE 9

For the important case of the normal distribution, it is not possible to give a closed form expression for the distribution function F, and so we cannot solve the equation $F(y) = x$. For this reason, special methods have been developed for simulating a normal distribution. One such method relies on the fact that if U and V are independent random variables with uniform densities on $[0,1]$, then the random variables

$$X = \sqrt{-2\log(U)}\cos(2\pi V)$$

and

$$Y = \sqrt{-2\log(U)}\sin(2\pi V)$$

are independent, and have normal distribution functions with parameters $\mu = 0$ and $\sigma = 1$.

To get a random variable Z having a normal distribution function with other values of the parameters μ and σ, we need only set

$$Z = \sigma X + \mu.$$

Then by Theorem 1, we have $\phi(x) = \sigma x + \mu$, $\phi^{-1}(z) = \dfrac{z - \mu}{\sigma}$, and

$$F_Z(z) = F_X\left(\frac{z - \mu}{\sigma}\right)$$

$$f_Z(z) = f_X\left(\frac{z - \mu}{\sigma}\right) \cdot \frac{1}{\sigma}$$

$$= \frac{1}{\sqrt{2\pi}\sigma}\, e^{-\frac{(z-\mu)^2}{2\sigma^2}}.$$

Thus, if f_X is the normal density function with parameters $\mu = 0$ and $\sigma = 1$, then f_Z is the normal density function with parameters μ and σ prescribed.

In this way, we see that we can simulate any normal random variable. We also see that it is unnecessary to make tables of normal distribution functions with arbitrary μ and σ, since they can always be reduced to the case $\mu = 0$, $\sigma = 1$. Indeed, we always have

$$F_Z(z) = P(Z \leq z)$$

$$= P\left(X \leq \frac{z - \mu}{\sigma}\right)$$

$$= F_X\left(\frac{z - \mu}{\sigma}\right).$$

We often refer to F_X as the *standard* normal distribution function, and to $X = \dfrac{Z - \mu}{\sigma}$ as the *standardized version* of Z.

We shall see in the next sections that μ is the *mean value*, or average value, and σ the *standard deviation*, a measure of the *spread* of the distribution. When the normal distribution is used to describe test scores, it is customary to speak of a test score being a certain number of standard deviations from the mean and to compute probabilities of a given number of deviations from the mean. We have seen that these computations can all be done using a standardized normal density. For example, if Z has a normal distribution with mean μ and standard deviation σ and if

$$X = \frac{Z - \mu}{\sigma}$$

is the standardized version of Z, then

$$P(\mu - k\sigma < Z < \mu + k\sigma) = P(-k < X < k).$$

The area under the standard normal curve between -3 and 3 is .997. Thus, the probability that any normal random variable lies within three standard deviations of the mean is .997. In the college boards, for example, the mean value is 500 and the standard deviation is 100. All scores above 800 are reported as 800 and represent more than three standard deviations above the mean. □

Maxwell Distribution

EXAMPLE 10

Suppose that we drop a dart on a large table top, which we consider as the x-y plane, and suppose that the x and y coordinates of the dart point are independent and have a normal distribution with parameter $\mu = 0$ and $\sigma = 1$. What is the distribution of the distance of the point from the origin?

This problem arises in physics when it is assumed that a moving particle has x and y components of the velocity that are normally distributed and it is desired to find the distribution of the speed of the particle.

We can simulate this experiment by picking independently a pair of coordinates (x,y), each from a normal distribution with $\mu = 0$ and $\sigma = 1$ on $(-\infty,\infty)$, calculating the distance $r = \sqrt{(x^2 + y^2)}$ of the point (x,y) from the origin, repeating this process a large number of times, and then presenting the results in a bar graph. This requires only a slight change in our program **Darts** (Chapter 2, Section 2.2): we replace the lines

```
let x = 2*rnd - 1
let y = 2*rnd - 1
```

with the lines

```
let r = rnd
let s = rnd
let x = sqr(-2*log(r)) * cos(2*pi*s)
let y = sqr(-2*log(r)) * sin(2*pi*s)
```

The results are shown in Figure 14.

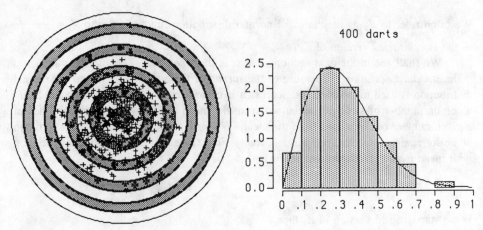

Figure 14 Density of distance from center.

We have also plotted the theoretical density

$$p(r) = re^{-r^2/2}.$$

We shall see in the next section why this is the density for this distance. □

Joint Distribution

Now suppose we have several random variables $X_1, X_2, \ldots, X_n$, all defined on the same sample space Ω, and let R_j be the range of X_j.

DEFINITION 10

The *joint distribution* of $X_1, \ldots, X_n$ is the function F, with domain

$$R^* = \{ (r_1, \ldots, r_n) : r_j \in R_j \} = R_1 \times R_2 \times \cdots \times R_n,$$

and range in **R**, defined by

$$F(r_1, \ldots, r_n) = \text{Prob } \{X_1 \leq r_1, X_2 \leq r_2, \ldots, X_n \leq r_n\}.$$

Independence

The joint distribution functions tells us to what extent the values of the X_j depend on each other. In particular, we have the following.

DEFINITION 11

The random variables $X_1, \ldots, X_n$ with individual distribution functions $F_1(r_1), \ldots, F_n(r_n)$ are *mutually independent* if

$$F(r_1, \ldots, r_n) = F_1(r_1) \cdot F_2(r_2) \cdots \cdot F_n(r_n).$$

Let's look at some examples.

EXAMPLE 11

Choose a point $\omega = (\omega_1, \omega_2)$ at random from the unit square. Set $X_1 = \omega_1^2$, $X_2 = \omega_2^2$, and $X_3 = \omega_1 + \omega_2$. Find the joint distributions $F_{12}(r_1,r_2)$ and $F_{23}(r_2,r_3)$.

We have already seen (see Example 3) that

$$F_1(r_1) = P(-\infty < X \leq r_1)$$

$$= \sqrt{r_1} \quad \text{if } 0 \leq r_1 \leq 1,$$

and similarly,

$$F_2(r_2) = \sqrt{r_2} \quad \text{if } 0 \leq r_2 \leq 1.$$

Now we calculate

$$F_{12}(r_1,r_2) = \text{Prob}(X_1 \leq r_1 \text{ and } X_2 \leq r_2)$$

$$= P(\omega_1 \leq \sqrt{r_1} \text{ and } \omega_2 \leq \sqrt{r_2})$$

$$= \text{Area of } E_1 \text{ (see Figure 15)}$$

$$= \sqrt{r_1} \sqrt{r_2}$$

$$= F_1(r_1)F_2(r_2).$$

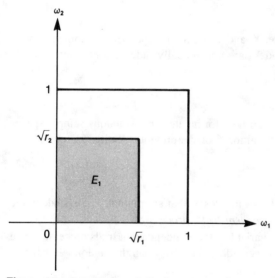

Figure 15 Calculation of $F_{12}(r_1, r_2)$.

In this case $F_{12}(r_1,r_2) = F_1(r_1)F_2(r_2)$ so that X_1 and X_2 are mutually independent. On the other hand, if $r_1 = {}^1/_4$ and $r_3 = 1$, then

$$F_{13}({}^1/_4,1) = P(X_1 \leq {}^1/_4, X_3 \leq 1)$$

$$= P(\omega_1 \leq {}^1/_2, \omega_1 + \omega_2 \leq 1)$$

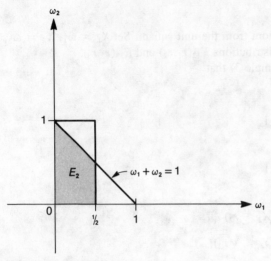

Figure 16 Calculation of $F_{13}(r_1, r_3)$.

$= $ Area of E_2 (see Figure 16)

$= {}^1/_2 - {}^1/_8 = {}^3/_8.$

But $F_1 ({}^1/_4) \cdot F_3 = {}^1/_2 \cdot {}^1/_2 = {}^1/_4$. Hence, X_1 and X_3 are not independent random variables. A similar calculation shows that X_2 and X_3 are not mutually independent either. ☐

Independent Trials

Using the notion of independence, we can now formulate for continuous sample spaces the notion of independent trials (see Definition 5 of the previous section).

DEFINITION 12

A sequence $X_1, X_2, X_3, \ldots, X_n$ of random variables X_i that are mutually independent and have the same density is called an *independent trials process*.

As in the case of discrete random variables, these independent trials processes arise naturally in situations where an experiment described by a single random variable is repeated n times.

Queues

EXAMPLE 12

Suppose that customers arrive at random times at a service station with one server, and suppose that each customer is served immediately if no one is ahead of him, but must wait his turn in line otherwise. How long should each customer expect to wait?

Let us assume that the interarrival times between successive customers are given by random variables $X_1, X_2, \ldots, X_n$ that are mutually independent and identically distributed with an exponential distribution function given by

$$F_X(t) = 1 - e^{-\lambda t}.$$

The X_j then form an independent trials process. Let us assume, too, that the service times for successive customers are given by random variables $Y_1, Y_2, \ldots, Y_n$ that again are mutually independent and identically distributed with another exponential distribution function given by

$$F_Y(t) = 1 - e^{-\mu t}.$$

The Y_j then form another independent trials process. We can guess that the length of time a customer will spend in the queue depends on how often the customers arrive and how fast they are served (i.e., on the relative size of the parameters λ and μ in the distribution functions above).

It is easy to verify this conjecture by simulation. The program **Queue** simulates this queueing process. Let $N(t)$ be the number of customers in the queue at time t. Then we plot $N(t)$ as a function of t for different choices of the parameters λ and μ (see Figure 17).

We note that when $\lambda < \mu$, $N(t)$ remains of reasonable size, but if $\lambda > \mu$ then $N(t)$ appears to grow without limit. If we think of λ as determining the *rate* at which customers *arrive* (a small λ means a slow arrival rate) and μ as determining the *service rate* (a small μ means a slow service rate) then the results of our simulation seem reasonable.

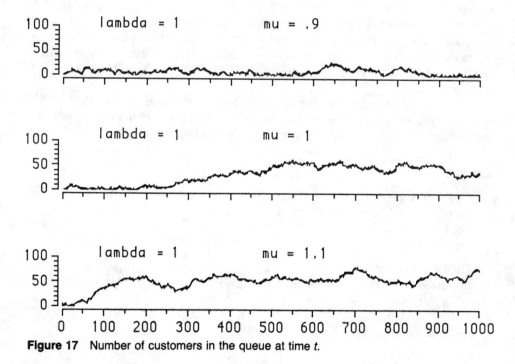

Figure 17 Number of customers in the queue at time t.

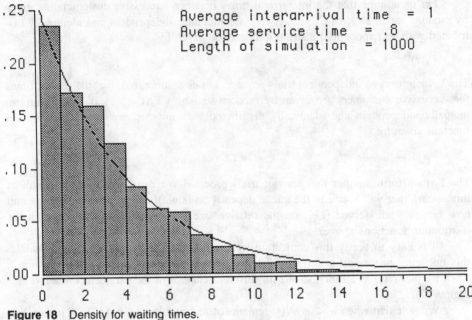

Figure 18 Density for waiting times.

We will see in the next chapter that under our assumptions here customers arrive at a rate of λ per unit time, on the average, so that the time between arrivals is $^1/_\lambda$, on the average.

We can now ask: How long will a customer have to wait in the queue for service? To examine this question, we let W_i be the length of time that the ith customer to arrive has to wait for service, assuming he has to wait at all. Then we can present these data in a bar graph, using the program **Queue**, to give some idea of how the W_i are distributed (see Figure 18).

We see here that these waiting times appear to be distributed exponentially. This is always the case when λ < μ. The proof of this fact is too complicated to give here, but we can verify it by simulation for different choices of λ and μ, as above. ☐

Exercises

1. Choose a number U from the interval [0,1] with uniform distribution. Find the distribution and density for the random variables
    (a) $Y = U + 2$.
    (b) $Y = U^3$.

2. Choose a number U from the interval [0,1] with uniform distribution. Find the distribution and density for the random variables
    (a) $Y = \dfrac{1}{U + 1}$.
    (b) $Y = \log(U + 1)$.

3. Suppose we know a random variable Y as a function of the uniform random variable $U : Y = \phi(U)$, and suppose we have calculated the distribution function $F_Y(y)$ and thence the density $f_Y(y)$. How can we check whether our answer is correct? An easy simulation provides the answer: Make a bar graph of $Y = \phi(\text{rnd})$ and compare the result with the graph of $f_Y(y)$. These graphs should look similar. Check your answers to Exercises 1 and 2 by this method.

4. Choose a number U from the interval $[0,1]$ with uniform distribution. Find the distribution and density for the random variables
   (a) $Y = |U - \frac{1}{2}|$.
   (b) $Y = (U - \frac{1}{2})^2$.

5. Check your results for Exercise 4 by simulation as described in Exercise 3.

6. Explain how you can generate a random variable whose distribution function is

$$F(x) = \begin{cases} 0 & x < 0, \\ x^2 & 0 \le x \le 1, \\ 1 & x > 1. \end{cases}$$

7. Write a program to generate a sample of 1000 random outcomes each of which is chosen from the distribution given in Exercise 6. Plot a bar graph of your results and compare this empirical density with the density for the distribution given in Exercise 6.

8. Let U, V be random numbers chosen independently from the interval $[0,1]$ with uniform distribution. Find the distribution and density of each of the variables
   (a) $Y = U + V$.
   (b) $Y = |U - V|$.

9. Let U, V be random numbers chosen independently from the interval $[0,1]$. Find the distribution and density for the random variables
   (a) $Y = \max(U,V)$.
   (b) $Y = \min(U,V)$.

10. Write a program to simulate the random variables of Exercises 8 and 9 and plot a bar graph of the results. Compare the resulting empirical density with the density found in Exercises 8 and 9.

11. A number U is chosen at random in the interval $[0,1]$. Find the probability that
   (a) $R = U^2 < \frac{1}{4}$.
   (b) $S = U(1 - U) < \frac{1}{4}$.
   (c) $T = \dfrac{U}{1 - U} < \frac{1}{4}$.

12. Find the distribution function F and the density function f for each of the random variables R, S, and T in Exercise 11.

13. A point P in the unit square has coordinates X and Y chosen at random in the interval $[0,1]$. Let D be the distance from P to the nearest edge of the square, and E the distance to the nearest corner. What is the probability that
   (a) $D < {}^1\!/_4$?
   (b) $E < {}^1\!/_4$?

14. In problem 13 find the distribution F and the density f for the random variable D.

15. Let X be a random variable with density function

$$f_X(x) = \begin{cases} cx(1 - x) & \text{if } 0 < x < 1, \\ 0 & \text{otherwise.} \end{cases}$$

   (a) What is the value of c?
   (b) What is the distribution function F_X for X?
   (c) What is the probability that $X < {}^1\!/_4$?

16. Let X be a random variable with distribution function

$$F(x) = \begin{cases} 0 & \text{if } x < 0, \\ \sin^2(\pi x/2) & \text{if } 0 < x < 1, \\ 1 & \text{if } 1 < x. \end{cases}$$

   (a) What is the density function f_X for X?
   (b) What is the probability that $X < {}^1\!/_4$?

17. Let X be a random variable with distribution function F_X, and let $Y = X + b$, $Z = aX$, and $W = aX + b$, where a and b are any constants. Find the distribution functions F_Y, F_Z, and F_W. *Hint:* the cases $a > 0$, $a = 0$, and $a < 0$ require different arguments.

18. Let X be a random variable with density function f_X, and let $Y = X + b$, $Z = aX$, and $W = aX + b$. Find the density functions f_Y, f_Z, and f_W. (See Exercise 17.)

19. Let X be a random variable uniformly distributed over $[c,d]$, and let $Y = aX + b$. For what choice of a and b is Y uniformly distributed over $[0,1]$?

20. Let X be a random variable with distribution function F strictly increasing on the range of F. Let $Y = F(X)$. Show that Y is uniformly distributed in the interval $[0,1]$. (The formula $X = F^{-1}(Y)$ then tells us how to construct X from a uniform random variable Y.)

21. Let X be a random variable with distribution function F. The *median* of X is the value m for which $F(m) = {}^1\!/_2$. Then $X < m$ with probability ${}^1\!/_2$ and $X > m$ with probability ${}^1\!/_2$. Find m if X is
   (a) uniformly distributed over the interval $[a,b]$.
   (b) normally distributed with parameters μ and σ.
   (c) exponentially distributed with parameter λ.

22. Let X be a random variable with density function f_X. The *mean* of X is the value $\mu = \int x f_X(x) dx$. Then μ gives an average value for X (see Chapter 6, Section 6.3). Find μ if X is distributed uniformly, normally, or exponentially, as in Exercise 21.

23. Let X be a random variable with density function f_X. The *mode* of X is the value M for which $f(M)$ is maximum. Then values of X near M are most likely to occur. Find M if X is distributed normally or exponentially, as in Exercise 21. What happens if X is distributed uniformly?

24. Let X be a random variable normally distributed with parameters $\mu = 70$, $\sigma = 10$. Estimate
    (a) $P(X > 50)$.
    (b) $P(X < 60)$.
    (c) $P(X > 90)$.
    (d) $P(60 < X < 80)$.

25. Bridies's Bearing Works manufactures bearing shafts whose diameters are normally distributed with parameters $\mu = 1$, $\sigma = .002$. The buyer's specifications require these diameters to be $1.000 \pm .003$ cm. What fraction of the manufacturer's shafts are likely to be rejected? If the manufacturer improves her quality control, she can reduce the value of σ. What value of σ will ensure that no more than 1 percent of her shafts are likely to be rejected?

26. A final examination at Podunk University is constructed so that the test scores are approximately normally distributed, with parameters μ and σ. The instructor assigns letter grades to the test scores as follows (this is the process of "grading on the curve").

Test Score x	Letter grade
$\mu + \sigma < x$	A
$\mu < x < \mu + \sigma$	B
$\mu - \sigma < x < \mu$	C
$\mu - 2\sigma < x < \mu - \sigma$	D
$x < \mu - 2\sigma$	F

What fraction of the class gets A, B, C, D, F?

27. (Ross)[2] An expert witness in a paternity suit testifies that the length (in days) of a pregnancy, from conception to delivery, is approximately normally distributed, with parameters $\mu = 270$, $\sigma = 10$. The defendant in the suit is able to prove that he was out of the country during the period from 290 to 240 days before the birth of the child. What is the probability that the defendant is actually the father of the child?

[2]S. Ross, *A First Course in Probability Theory*, 2d ed. (New York: Macmilllan, 1984).

28. Suppose that the time (in hours) required to repair a car is an exponentially distributed random variable with parameter $\lambda = \frac{1}{2}$. What is the probability that the repair time exceeds 4 hours? If it exceeds 4 hours what is the probability that it exceeds 8 hours?

29. Suppose that the number of years a car will run is exponentially distributed with parameter $\mu = \frac{1}{4}$. If Prosser buys a used car today, what is the probability that it will still run after 4 years?

30. Let U be a uniformly distributed random variable on $[0,1]$. What is the probability that the equation

$$x^2 + 4Ux + 1 = 0$$

has two distinct real roots x_1 and x_2?

31. Write a program to simulate the random variables whose densities are given by the following, making a suitable bar graph of each and comparing the exact density with the bar graph.
    (a) $f_X(x) = e^{-x}$ on $[0, \infty)$ (but just do it on $[0,10]$).
    (b) $f_X(x) = 2x$ on $[0,1]$.
    (c) $f_X(x) = 3x^2$ on $[0,1]$.
    (d) $f_X(x) = 4 | x - 1/2 |$ on $[0,1]$.

32. Write a program to simulate the Bus Paradox (see Example 4 of Chapter 2, Section 2.2). Assume that the time between arrivals has an *exponential density* with parameter $\lambda = \frac{1}{30}$ (average time between bus arrivals is 30 minutes). Suppose the bus starts from the Hanover Inn at 8:00 and you arrive at 12:00. Estimate your average waiting time.

33. Jones puts in two new lightbulbs: a 60 watt bulb and a 100 watt bulb. It is claimed that the lifetime of the 60 watt bulb has an exponential density with average lifetime 200 hours (parameter $\lambda = \frac{1}{200}$). The 100 watt bulb also has an exponential density but with average lifetime of only 100 hours (parameter $\frac{1}{100}$). Jones wonders what is the probability that the 100 watt bulb will outlast the 60 watt bulb.

   If X and Y are two independent random variables with exponential densities $f(x) = \lambda e^{-\lambda x}$ and $g(x) = \mu e^{-\mu x}$, respectively, then the probability that X is less than Y is given by

$$P(X < Y) = \int_0^\infty f(x)(1 - G(x))dx,$$

   where $G(x)$ is the distribution function for $g(x)$. Explain why this is the case. Use this to show that

$$P(X < Y) = \frac{\lambda}{\lambda + \mu}$$

   and to answer Jones's question.

34. Consider the simple queueing process of Example 12. Suppose that you watch the size of the queue. If there are j people in the queue the next time the queue size changes it will either decrease to $j - 1$ or increase to $j + 1$. Use the result of Exercise 33 to show that the probability that the queue size decreases to $j - 1$ is $\dfrac{\mu}{\mu + \lambda}$ and the probability that it increases to $j + 1$ is $\dfrac{\lambda}{\mu + \lambda}$. When the queue size is 0 it can only increase to 1. Write a program to simulate the queue size and use this to determine conditions on μ and λ that will ensure that the queue will have times when it is empty.

35. A radioactive source is emitting particles in such a way that the time between emissions has an exponential density with parameter λ. Let X_T be the number of particles that are emitted in time T. Then it can be shown that the density for X_T is the *Poisson density* given by

$$P(X_T = j) = \frac{e^{-m} \cdot m^j}{j!},$$

where $m = T\lambda$.

Write a program to simulate this process for $\lambda = .1$ and count the number of particles emitted in the first ten time units. Have your program repeat this simulation a large number of times and plot a bar graph for the proportion of the times that j particles were emitted in ten time units. Compare your bar graph with the Poisson density with $m = 1$. (This is a density that we shall study later in Chapter 9, Section 9.2).

36. Let X be a random variable having an exponential density with parameter λ. Find the density for the random variable $Y = rX$, where r is a positive real number.

37. Let X be a random variable having a normal density and consider the random variable $Y = e^X$. Then Y has a *log normal* density. Find this density of Y.

38. Let X_1 and X_2 be independent random variables and let $Y_i = \phi_i(X_i)$ where ϕ_i is strictly increasing on the range of X_i. Show that Y_1 and Y_2 are independent. Note that the same result is true without the assumption that ϕ_i is strictly increasing, but the proof is more difficult.

Chapter *6*

Expected Value and Variance

6.1 EXPECTED VALUE OF DISCRETE RANDOM VARIABLES

When a large collection of numbers is assembled, as in a census, we are usually interested not in the individual numbers, but rather in certain descriptive quantities such as the average or the median. In general, the same is true for the probability density of a numerically valued random variable. In this and in the next section, we shall discuss two such descriptive quantities: the *expected value* and the *variance*. Both of these quantities apply only to numerically valued random variables, and so we assume, in these sections, that all random variables have numerical values. To give some intuitive justification for our definition, we consider the following game:

Average Value

A die is rolled. If an odd number turns up, we win an amount equal to this number; if an even number turns up, we lose an amount equal to this number. For example, if a two turns up we lose 2, and, if a three comes up we win 3. We want to decide if this is a reasonable game to play. We first try simulation. The program **Die** carries out this simulation.

```
!  Die    (DIE)
!
! Simulates a dice game wherein an odd number yields a win, and an
! even number a loss, equal to the die's face.

!randomize
dim frequency(20)
declare function win
def roll = int(6*rnd)+1            ! Define a roll of the die

input prompt "Number of plays = " : plays
print "Winning", "Frequency", "Relative Frequency"
print

for play = 1 to plays
    let face = roll
    let frequency(face) = frequency(face)+1
    let winning = winning + win(face)
next play

for face = 1 to 6
    let proportion = round(frequency(face)/plays,5)
    print win(face), frequency(face), proportion
next face

print
print "Average winning = "; winning/plays

end


function win(face)

    if mod(face,2) = 1 then        ! Determine whether roll was odd.
        let win = face             ! If so, win the amount showing,..
    else                           ! ... otherwise...
        let win = -face            ! ...lose amount showing.
    end if

end function
```

The program prints the frequency and the relative frequency with which each outcome occurs. Finally it prints the average winnings.

We have run the program twice (see next page). In the first run we have played the game 100 times. In this run our average gain is −.57. It looks as if the game is unfavorable, and we wonder how unfavorable it really is. To get a better idea, we have played the game 10,000 times. In this case our average gain is −.4949.

We note that the relative frequency of each of the six possible outcomes is quite close to the probability $\frac{1}{6}$ for this outcome. This corresponds to our frequency interpre-

```
Number of plays = 100
Winning          Frequency          Relative Frequency

  1                 17                   .17
 -2                 17                   .17
  3                 16                   .16
 -4                 18                   .18
  5                 16                   .16
 -6                 16                   .16

Average winning = -.57
```

```
Number of plays = 10000
Winning          Frequency          Relative Frequency

  1               1681                 .1681
 -2               1678                 .1678
  3               1626                 .1626
 -4               1696                 .1696
  5               1686                 .1686
 -6               1633                 .1633

Average winning = -.4949
```

tation of probability. It also suggests that for very large numbers of plays, our average gain should be

$$\mu = 1\left(\frac{1}{6}\right) - 2\left(\frac{1}{6}\right) + 3\left(\frac{1}{6}\right) - 4\left(\frac{1}{6}\right) + 5\left(\frac{1}{6}\right) - 6\left(\frac{1}{6}\right)$$

$$= \frac{9}{6} - \frac{12}{6} = -\frac{3}{6} = -.5.$$

This agrees quite well with our average gain for 10,000 plays.

We note that the value we have chosen for the average gain is obtained by taking the possible outcomes, multiplying by the probability, and adding the results. This suggests the following definition for the expected outcome of an experiment:

Expected Value

DEFINITION 1

Let X be a numerically valued random variable defined on a finite sample space Ω with probability density p. The *expected value* $E(X)$ is defined by

$$E(X) = \sum_{\omega \in \Omega} X(\omega)p(\omega).$$

We often refer to the expected value as the *mean*, and denote $E(X)$ by μ for short.

EXAMPLE 1

Let X be the number of fixed points in a random permutation of the set $\{a,b,c\}$. Then each sample point has $p(\omega) = {}^1/_6$ and X has value:

ω	$X(\omega)$
$a\ b\ c$	3
$a\ c\ b$	1
$b\ a\ c$	1
$b\ c\ a$	0
$c\ a\ b$	0
$c\ b\ a$	1

Thus,

$$E(X) = 3\left(\frac{1}{6}\right) + 1\left(\frac{1}{6}\right) + 1\left(\frac{1}{6}\right) + 0\left(\frac{1}{6}\right) + 0\left(\frac{1}{6}\right) + 1\left(\frac{1}{6}\right) = 1.$$

We shall see later that the expected number of fixed points of a random permutation of n elements is always 1 no matter what n is. □

Of course, just as with the frequency interpretation of probability, to interpret expected value as an average outcome requires further justification. We know that for any finite experiment the average of the outcomes is not predictable. However, we shall eventually prove that the average will usually be close to $E(X)$ for a large number of experiments. We first need to develop some properties of the expected value. Using these properties, and those of the concept of the variance to be introduced in the next section, we shall be able to prove the *Law of Large Numbers*. This theorem will justify mathematically both our frequency concept of probability and the interpretation of expected value as the average value to be expected in a large number of experiments.

Now let us get down to work.

Properties of Expected Value

THEOREM 1

Let X and Y be random variables defined on the same sample space Ω. Then

$$E(X + Y) = E(X) + E(Y),$$

and if c is any constant,

$$E(cX) = cE(X).$$

Proof.

$$E(X + Y) = \sum_{\omega} (X(\omega) + Y(\omega)\, p(\omega)$$

$$= \sum_{\omega} X(\omega)p(\omega) + \sum_{\omega} Y(\omega)p(\omega)$$

$$= E(X) + E(Y).$$

If c is any constant,

$$E(cx) = \sum_{\omega} cX(\omega)p(\omega)$$

$$= c\sum_{\omega} X(\omega)p(\omega)$$

$$= cE(X). \qquad\blacksquare$$

It is easy to prove by mathematical induction that *the expected value of the sum of any finite number of random variables is the sum of the expected values of the individual random variables*.

Our next theorem shows that we can calculate the expected value of a random variable from its density alone.

Calculation of Expected Value

THEOREM 2

If X is a random variable with density

$$p_X = \begin{pmatrix} r_1, r_2, \ldots, r_n \\ p_1, p_2, \ldots, p_n \end{pmatrix},$$

then

$$E(X) = \sum r_j p_j.$$

In particular, if X and Y have the same density function, then $E(X) = E(Y)$.

Proof. Let $A_j = \{\omega: X(\omega) = r_j\}$. Then $p_j = P(A_j) = P(X = r_j)$ and

$$E(X) = \sum_{\omega} X(\omega)P(\omega)$$

$$= \sum_{j} \sum_{\omega \varepsilon A_j} X(\omega)p(\omega)$$

$$= \sum_{j} r_j P(X(\omega) = r_j)$$

$$= \sum_{j} r_j p_j. \qquad\blacksquare$$

EXAMPLE 2

A fair coin is tossed three times. Let $X_j = 1$ if the jth outcome is heads and 0 if it is tails. Then $S_3 = X_1 + X_2 + X_3$ gives the number of heads in three tosses. We know that S_3 has a binomial density $p_0 = {}^1\!/_8, p_1 = {}^3\!/_8, p_2 = {}^3\!/_8, p_3 = {}^1\!/_8$. Thus, by Theorem 2,

$$E(S_3) = 0\left(\frac{1}{8}\right) + 1\left(\frac{3}{8}\right) + 2\left(\frac{3}{8}\right) + 3\left(\frac{1}{8}\right)$$

$$= \frac{12}{8} = \frac{3}{2}.$$

A second way to compute this expected value is to use Theorem 1. We first find, for each X_j,

$$E(X_j) = 0\left(\frac{1}{2}\right) + 1\left(\frac{1}{2}\right) = \frac{1}{2}.$$

Then

$$E(S_3) = E(X_1) + E(X_2) + E(X_3)$$

$$= \frac{3}{2}. \qquad \Box$$

This example is a special case of Bernoulli trials, for which we can prove the following general theorem.

Bernoulli Trials

THEOREM 3

Let S_n be the number of successes in n Bernoulli trials with probability p for success on each trial. Then the expected number of successes is np. That is,

$$E(S_n) = np.$$

Proof. Let X_j be a random variable which has the value 1 if the jth outcome is a success and 0 if it is a failure. Then, for each X_j,

$$E(X_j) = 0 \cdot (1 - p) + 1 \cdot p = p.$$

Since

$$S_n = X_1 + X_2 + \cdots + X_n,$$

and the expected value of the sum is the sum of the expected values, we have

$$E(S_n) = E(X_1) + E(X_2) + \cdots + E(X_n)$$

$$= np. \qquad \blacksquare$$

If X and Y are two random variables, it is not true in general that $E(X \cdot Y) = E(X)E(Y)$. However, this is true if X and Y are *independent*.

Independence

THEOREM 4

If X and Y are independent random variables, then

$$E(X \cdot Y) = E(X)E(Y).$$

Proof.

$$E(X \cdot Y) = \sum_{\omega} X(\omega)Y(\omega)p(\omega)$$

$$= \sum_{j,k} r_j r_k P(X(\omega) = r_j, Y(\omega) = r_k).$$

But if X and Y are independent,

$$P(X(\omega) = r_j, Y(\omega) = r_k) = P(X(\omega) = r_j)P(Y(\omega) = r_k).$$

Thus,

$$E(X \cdot Y) = \sum_{j,k} r_j r_k P(X(\omega) = r_j)P(Y(\omega) = r_k)$$

$$= \left(\sum_{j} r_j P(X(\omega) = r_j) \right) \left(\sum_{k} r_k P(Y(\omega) = r_k) \right)$$

$$= E(X)E(Y). \qquad \blacksquare$$

EXAMPLE 3

A coin is tossed twice. $X_i = 1$ if the ith toss is heads and 0 otherwise. We know that X_1 and X_2 are independent. They each have expected value $1/2$. Thus $E(X_1 \cdot X_2) = E(X_1)E(X_2) = (1/2)(1/2) = 1/4$. $\qquad \square$

EXAMPLE 4

We next give a simple example to show that the expected values need not multiply if the random variables are not independent. To see this we consider a single toss of a coin. We define the random variable X to be 1 if heads turns up and 0 if tails turns up, and we set $Y = 1 - X$. Then $E(X) = E(Y) = 1/2$. But $X \cdot Y = 0$ for either outcome. Hence, $E(X \cdot Y) = 0 \neq E(X)E(Y)$. $\qquad \square$

We return to our records example of Chapter 3, Section 3.1, for another application of the result that the expected value of the sum of random variables is the sum of the expected values of the individual random variables.

Records

EXAMPLE 5   Record Snowfalls

We start keeping snowfall records this year and want to find the expected number of records that will occur in the next n years. The first year is necessarily a record. The second year will be a record if the snowfall in the second year is greater than that in the first year. By symmetry, this probability is $1/2$. More generally, let X_j be 1 if the jth year is a record and 0 otherwise. To find $E(X_j)$, we need only find the probability that the jth year is a record. But the record snowfall for the first j years is equally likely to fall in any one of these years, so $E(X_j) = 1/j$. Therefore, if S_n is the total number of records observed in the first n years,

$$E(S_n) = 1 + \frac{1}{2} + \frac{1}{3} + \cdots + \frac{1}{n}.$$

This is the famous *divergent harmonic series*. We have seen that

$$E(S_n) \sim \log(n) \qquad \text{as } n \to \infty.$$

(See Chapter 3, Section 3.1, Appendix.)

Therefore, in ten years the expected number of records is approximately $\log(10) = 2.3$; the exact value is the sum of the first ten terms of the harmonic series which is 2.9. We see that, even for such a small value as $n = 10$, $\log(n)$ is not a bad approximation. $\square$

Recall that this example could also be interpreted as the number of new assignments in a computer program to find the maximum (or minimum) of n different numbers (see Chapter 3, Section 3.1). Thus, when there are n elements in the list, the expected number of such assignments is approximately $\log(n)$—a pleasant fact for the computer scientist who wants to keep the number of computer operations small when n is large.

Craps

EXAMPLE 6

In the game of craps, the player makes a bet and rolls a pair of dice. If the sum of the numbers is 7 or 11 the player wins, if it is 2, 3 or 12 the player loses. If any other number results, say r, then r becomes the player's point and he continues to roll until either r or a 7 occurs. If r comes up first he wins, and if 7 comes up first he loses.

The program **Craps** simulates playing this game a number of times (see next page).

We have run the program for 1000 plays in which the player bets 1 dollar each time. The player's average winnings were $-.006$. The game of craps would seem to be only slightly unfavorable. Let us calculate the expected winnings on a single play and see if this is the case. We construct a two-stage tree measure as shown in Figure 1.

The first stage represents the possible sums for his first roll. The second stage represents the possible outcomes for the game if it is not ended on the first roll. In this stage we are representing the possible outcomes of a sequence of rolls required to determine

```
! Craps     (CRAPS)
!
! Simulates the game of craps.

randomize
def roll = int(6*rnd) + 1              ! Define roll of a die

input prompt "Number of plays = " : plays

for play = 1 to plays

    let result = roll + roll           ! Roll 2 dice

    select case result                 ! Examine the result:

    case 7, 11                         ! If a natural ...
        let winning = winning + 1      ! increase winnings

    case 2, 3, 12                      ! If crap out ...
        let winning = winning -1       ! reduce winnings

    case else                          ! Otherwise ...
        let point = result             ! determine point to make...

        do                             ! and roll until 7 or point
            let result = roll + roll
        loop until result = 7 or result = point

        if result = point then         ! If point made,...
            let winning = winning + 1  ! increase winnings
        else                           ! But if crap out,...
            let winning = winning -1   ! reduce winnings
        end if

    end select

next play

print
print "Average winning is   "; winning/plays

end
```

the final outcome. The branch probabilities for the first stage are computed in the usual way assuming all 36 possibilities for outcomes for the pair of dice are equally likely. For the second stage we assume that the game will eventually end, and we compute the conditional probabilities for obtaining either the point or a 7. For example, assume that the player's point is 6. Then the game will end when one of the eleven different pairs, (1,5), (2,4), (3,3), (4,2), (5,1), (1,6), (2,5), (3,4), (4,3), (5,2), (6,1), occurs. We assume that each of these possible pairs has the same probability. Then the player wins in the first five cases and loses in the last six. Thus the probability of winning is $^5/_{11}$ and losing $^6/_{11}$. From the path probabilities, we can find the probability that the player wins 1 dollar.

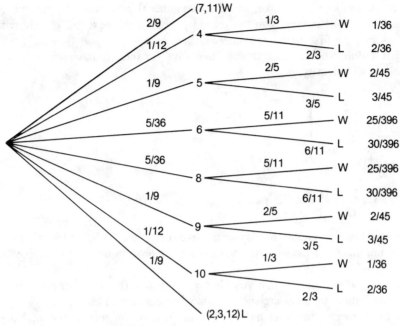

Figure 1 Tree measure for craps.

This is $^{244}/_{495}$. The probability of losing is then $^{251}/_{495}$. Thus if X is his winning for a dollar bet,

$$E(X) = 1\left(\frac{244}{495}\right) + (-1)\left(\frac{251}{495}\right)$$

$$= \frac{-7}{495} = -.0141.$$

The game is unfavorable, but only slightly. The player's expected loss in n plays is $-n(0.141)$. If n is not large, this is a small expected loss for the player. The casino makes a large number of plays and so can afford a small average winning per play and still expect a large profit. □

Roulette

EXAMPLE 7
In the roulette game in Las Vegas there are two 0s, but in Monte Carlo there is only one 0. If you bet on red and a 0 turns up, then in Las Vegas you lose, but in Monte Carlo you have two choices: (a) you can accept one half of your stake, or (b) you can allow your money to be put "in prison." If you elect (b) and the next roll is red, you win your

stake; if it is black you lose your stake; and if it is another 0 your money is put into a second prison. When your money is in the second prison, if the next roll is red your stake is put back into the first prison and otherwise it is lost.

If you bet 1 dollar on red and choose alternative (a) then your winnings are a random variable X with density:

$$p_X = \begin{pmatrix} -1 & -\dfrac{1}{2} & 1 \\ \dfrac{18}{37} & \dfrac{1}{37} & \dfrac{18}{37} \end{pmatrix},$$

and

$$E(X) = -1 \cdot \frac{18}{37} - \frac{1}{2} \cdot \frac{1}{37} + 1 \cdot \frac{18}{37} = -\frac{1}{74} = -.0135.$$

Assume now that you choose to play alternative (b). The calculation for this case is more difficult but illustrates the way that the early French probabilists worked problems like this.

Assume that you bet on red, that you choose alternative (b), and that a 0 comes up. Your possible future outcomes are shown in the tree diagram in Figure 2.

Here P_1 or P_2 means that your money is in the first or the second prison. Now assume that your money is in the first prison and let x be the probability that you lose your money. From the tree diagram we see that

$$x = \frac{18}{37} + \frac{1}{37} \left[\frac{19}{37} + \frac{18}{37} \cdot x \right].$$

Solving for x gives $x = .507$.

Assume now that you make a 1 dollar bet on red and choose alternative (b). You will win 1 dollar if the first roll is red (probability $^{18}/_{37}$), and lose 1 dollar if this roll is black (probability $^{18}/_{37}$). If the first roll is a 0 (probability $^1/_{37}$) you lose with probability $x = .507$. Thus in calculating your expected winning everything cancels out except for the case where a 0 turns up and you eventually lose your stake. The probability that this

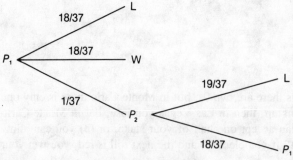

Figure 2 Your money is put in prison.

happens is $1/37 \cdot (.507) = .0137$, making your expected winnings $-.0137$. Therefore, you are slightly better off in roulette at Monte Carlo in choosing alternative (a).

If you bet 1 dollar on the number 17, then the density for your winnings X is

$$p_X = \begin{pmatrix} -1 & 35 \\ \dfrac{36}{37} & \dfrac{1}{37} \end{pmatrix}.$$

and the expected winnings are

$$-1 \cdot \frac{36}{37} + 35 \cdot \frac{1}{37} = -\frac{1}{37} = -.027.$$

Thus, at Monte Carlo different bets have different expected values. At Las Vegas almost all bets have the same expected value of $-2/38 = -.0526$. □

Infinite Sample Spaces

DEFINITION 2

If X is a random variable defined on a countably infinite sample space Ω, then the *expected value* of X is

$$E(X) = \sum_{\omega} X(\omega)p(\omega),$$

provided $\sum_{\omega} |X(\omega)|p(\omega)$ *is finite*. If this latter sum is infinite, we say that X does not have an expected value.

EXAMPLE 8

Let T be the time for the first success in a Bernoulli trials process. Then we take as sample space Ω the integers $1, 2, \ldots$ and assign the geometric density

$$p(j) = P(T = j) = q^{j-1}p.$$

Thus,

$$E(T) = 1 \cdot p + 2qp + 3q^2p + \cdots$$
$$= p(1 + 2q + 3q^2 + \cdots).$$

Now if $|x| < 1$, then

$$1 + x + x^2 + x^3 + \cdots = \frac{1}{1 - x}.$$

Differentiating this formula, we get

$$1 + 2x + 3x^2 + \cdots = \frac{1}{(1-x)^2},$$

so

$$E(T) = \frac{p}{(1-q)^2} = \frac{p}{p^2} = \frac{1}{p}.$$

In particular, we see that if we toss a fair coin a sequence of times, the expected time until the first heads is $\dfrac{1}{1/2} = 2$. If we roll a die a sequence of times, the expected number of rolls until the first six is $\dfrac{1}{1/6} = 6$. $\qquad\qquad\square$

EXAMPLE 6 (continued)

Assume that in a game of craps the roller establishes a point of four on the first roll. Let R be the number of additional rolls until the roller obtains either a four or a seven. The probability of this occurring on any one roll is $^9/_{36} = {}^1/_4$. Thus R has a geometric density with $P = {}^1/_4$ and $E(R) = 4$. $\qquad\qquad\square$

Conditional Expectation

DEFINITION 3

If F is any event and X is a random variable, then the *conditional expectation given F* is defined by

$$E(X|F) = \sum_{\omega} X(\omega)p(\omega|F).$$

In terms of the range values of X this is

$$E(X|F) = \sum_{j} r_j P(X = r_j|F).$$

Conditional expectation is used most often in the form provided by the following theorem.

THEOREM 5

If $F_1, F_2, \ldots, F_r$ are events such that $F_i \cap F_j = \emptyset$ for $i \neq j$ and $\Omega = \bigcup_j F_j$, then

$$E(X) = \sum_{j} E(X|F_j)P(F_j).$$

Proof.

$$\sum_j E(X|F_j)P(F_j) = \sum_j \sum_k kP(X = k|F_j)P(F_j)$$

$$= \sum_j \sum_k kP(X = k \text{ and } F_j \text{ occurs})$$

$$= \sum_k \sum_j kP(X = k \text{ and } F_j \text{ occurs})$$

$$= \sum_k kP(X = k)$$

$$= E(X). \qquad \blacksquare$$

EXAMPLE 6 (continued)

Let T be the number of rolls in a single play of craps. Let X be the roller's first number. Then by Theorem 1

$$E(T) = \sum_{j=2}^{12} E(T|X = j)P(X = j).$$

If $j = 7$, 11 or 2, 3, 12, then $E(T|X = j) = 1$. If $X = 4$ we have seen that the number of additional rolls has a geometric density with $p = \frac{1}{4}$, so the expected number of additional rolls is 4 and $E(T|X = 4) = 1 + 4 = 5$. Carrying out the corresponding calculations for the other possible values for X and using Theorem 5 gives

$$E(T) = \frac{2}{9}\cdot 1 + \frac{1}{12}\cdot 5 + \frac{1}{9}\cdot\frac{46}{10} + \frac{5}{36}\cdot\frac{47}{11} + \frac{5}{36}\cdot\frac{47}{11} + \frac{1}{9}\cdot\frac{46}{10} + \frac{1}{12}\cdot 5 + \frac{1}{9}\cdot 1$$

$$= 3.375 \ldots \qquad \square$$

Martingales

We can extend the notion of fairness to a player playing a sequence of games by using the concept of conditional expectation.

EXAMPLE 9

Let $S_1, S_2, \ldots, S_n$ be Peter's accumulated fortune in playing heads and tails (see Chapter 1, Section 1.1, Example 3). Then

$$E(S_n|S_{n-1} = a, \ldots, S_1 = r) = \frac{1}{2}(a + 1) + \frac{1}{2}(a - 1) = a.$$

We note that Peter's expected fortune after the next play is equal to his present fortune. When this occurs, we say the game is *fair*. A fair game is also called a *martingale*.

If the coin is biased and comes up heads with probability p and tails with probability $q = 1 - p$, then

$$E(S_n|S_{n-1} = a, \ldots, S_1 = r) = p(a + 1) + q(a - 1) = a + p - q.$$

Thus, if $p < q$, this game is unfavorable; and if $p > q$, it is favorable. □

If you are in a casino, you will see players adopting elaborate *systems* of plays to try to make unfavorable games favorable. Two such systems, the martingale doubling system and the more conservative Labouchere system, were described in Exercises 9 and 10 of Chapter 1, Section 1.1. Unfortunately, such systems cannot change even a fair game into a favorable game.

Even so, it is a favorite pastime of many people to develop systems of play for gambling games and for other games such as the stock market. We close this section with a simple illustration of such a system.

Stock Prices

EXAMPLE 10

Let us assume that a stock increases or decreases in value each day by 1 dollar, each with probability $1/2$. Then we can identify this simplified model with our familiar game of heads and tails. We assume that a buyer, Mr. Ace, adopts the following strategy. He buys the stock on the first day at its price V. He then waits until the price of the stock increases by one to $V + 1$ and sells. He then continues to watch the stock until its price falls back to V. He buys again and waits until it goes up to $V + 1$ and sells. Thus he holds the stock in intervals during which it increases by 1 dollar. In each such interval, he makes a profit of 1 dollar. However, we assume that he can do this only for a finite number of trading days. Thus he can lose if, in the last interval that he holds the stock, it does not get back up to $V + 1$; and this is the only way he can lose. In Figure 3 we illustrate a typical history if Mr. Ace must stop in ten days.

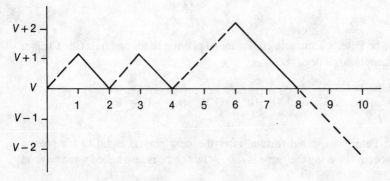

Figure 3 Mr. Ace's system.

Mr. Ace holds the stock under his system during the days indicated by broken lines. We note that his system nets him a gain of 3 dollars during the periods when his system is successful, but he loses 2 dollars during his last holding since it does not get back up to $V + 1$ before he must quit.

Since our model for the increases of the stock price is that of the heads and tails game, it is again an easy matter to modify the program **Lead** to keep track, for every possible sequence of stock gains over an N-day period, of the fortune of Mr. Ace using his system. The program **Stock System** is the appropriate modification; and a run of the program gives the density of the gain and the expected value of the gain, using his system over a ten-day period. We note from a run of the program that his expected profit is 0.

```
Number of days = 10
Profit        Probability
-10           .0010
-9            .0000
-8            .0088
-7            .0010
-6            .0342
-5            .0088
-4            .0742
-3            .0342
-2            .0967
-1            .0742
 0            .0752
 1            .3018
 2            .1914
 3            .0781
 4            .0186
 5            .0020
The expected profit is 0 ; the probability of being ahead is .5918
```

Although the expected profit remains 0, the probability that Mr. Ace is ahead after ten days is .5918. Thus, he would be able to tell his friends that his system gives him a better chance of being ahead than that of someone who simply buys the stock and holds it, if our simple random model is correct. There have been a number of studies to determine how random the stock market is. At least one congressman achieved public attention by claiming that he did better than the mutual funds by throwing darts at a dart board to determine which stocks to buy and sell. □

Historical Remarks

With 200 years of experience and the law of large numbers to bolster the frequency interpretation of probability, we find it natural to justify the definition of expected value in terms of the average outcome over a large number of repetitions of the experiment. The concept of expected value was used before it was formally defined; and when it was used, it was considered not as an average value but rather as the appropriate value for a gamble. For example, recall Pascal's way of finding the value of a three-game series that had to be called off before it is finished.

Pascal first observed that if each player has won only one game to win, then the stake of 64 pistoles should be divided evenly. Then he considered the case where one player has won two games and the other one.

> Then consider, Sir, if the first man wins, he gets 64 pistoles, if he loses he gets 32. Thus if they do not wish to risk this last game, but wish to separate without playing it, the first man must say: "I am certain to get 32 pistoles, even if I lose I still get them; but as for the other 32 pistoles, perhaps I will get them, perhaps you will get them, the chances are equal. Let us then divide these 32 pistoles in half and give one half to me as well as my 32 which are mine for sure." He will then have 48 pistoles and the other 16.[1]

Note that Pascal reduced the problem to a symmetric bet in which each player gets the same amount and takes it as obvious that in this case the stakes should be divided equally.

The first systematic study of expected value appears in Huygens's book. Like Pascal, Huygens finds the value of a gamble by assuming that the answer is obvious for certain symmetric situations and uses this to deduce the expected value for the general situation. He does this in steps. His first proposition is

> Prop. I. If I expect a or b, either of which, with equal probability, may fall to me, then my Expectation is worth $(a + b)/2$, that is, the half Sum of a and b.[2]

Huygens proved this as follows: Assume that two players A and B play a game in which each player puts up a stake of $(a + b)/2$ with an equal chance of winning the total stake. Then the value of this game to each player is $(a + b)/2$. For example, if the game had to be called off clearly each player should just get back his original stake. Now, by symmetry, this value is not changed if we add the condition that the winner of the game has to pay the loser an amount b as a consolation prize. Then for player A the value is still $(a + b)/2$. But what are his possible outcomes for this modified game? If he wins he gets the total stake $a + b$ and must pay B an amount b so ends up with a. If he loses he gets an amount b from player B. Thus player A wins a or b with equal chances and the value to him is $(a + b)/2$.

Huygens illustrated this proof in terms of an example. If you are offered a game in which you have an equal chance of winning 2 or 8, the expected value is 5, since this game is equivalent to the game in which each player stakes 5 and agrees to pay the loser 3—a game in which the value is obviously 5.

Huygens's second proposition is

> Prop. II. If I expect a, b, or c, either of which, with equal facility, may happen, then the Value of my Expectation is $(a + b + c)/3$, or the third of the Sum of a, b, and c.[3]

[1]Quoted in F. N. David, *Games, Gods and Gambling* (London: Griffin, 1962), p. 231.

[2]C. Huygens, *Calculating in Games of Chance*, translation attributed to John Arbuthnot (London, 1692), p. 34.

[3]Ibid., p. 35.

His argument here is similar. Three players, A, B, and C each stake $(a + b + c)/3$ in a game they have an equal chance of winning. The value of this game to player A is clearly $(a + b + c)/3$. Further, this value is not changed if A enters into an agreement with B that if one of them wins he pays the other a consolation prize of b and with C that if one of them wins he pays the other a consolation prize of c. By symmetry these agreements do not change the value of the game. In this modified game, if A wins he wins the total stake $a + b + c$ minus the consolation prizes $b + c$ giving him a final winning of a. If B wins, A wins b and if C wins, A wins c. Thus A finds himself in a game with value $(a + b + c)/3$ and with outcomes a, b, and c occurring with equal chance. This proves proposition II.

More generally, this reasoning shows that if you have n outcomes $a_1, a_2, \ldots, a_n$ all occurring with the same probability the expected value is

$$\frac{a_1 + a_2 + \cdots + a_n}{n}.$$

In his third proposition Huygens considered the case where you win a or b but with unequal probabilities. He assumed there are p chances of winning a, and q chances of winning b, all having the same probability. He then showed that the expected value is

$$E = \frac{p}{p + q} \cdot a + \frac{q}{p + q} \cdot b.$$

This follows by considering an equivalent gamble with $p + q$ outcomes all occurring with the same probability and with a payoff of a in p of the outcomes and b in q of the outcomes. This allowed Huygens to compute the expected value for experiments with unequal probabilities, at least when these probabilities are rational numbers.

Thus, instead of defining the expected value as a weighted average, Huygens assumed that the expected value of certain symmetric gambles are known and deduced the other values from these. Although this requires a good deal of clever manipulation, Huygens ended up with values that agree with those given by our modern definition of expected value. One advantage of this method is that it gives a justification for the expected value in cases where it is not reasonable to assume that you can repeat the experiment a large number of times, as for example, in betting that at least two presidents died on the same day of the year. (In fact, three did: All were signers of the Declaration of Independence, and all three died on July 4).

In his book, Huygens calculated the expected value of games using techniques similar to those which we used in computing the expected value for roulette at Monte Carlo. For example, his proposition XIV is:

Prop. XIV. If I were playing with another by turns, with two Dice, on this Condition, that if I throw 7 I gain, and if he throw 6 he gains allowing him the first Throw: To find the proportion of my Hazard to his.[4]

---

[4]Ibid., p. 47.

To solve this problem Huygens let x be his chance of winning when his opponent threw and y his chance of winning when he threw. Then on the first roll his opponent wins on 5 out of the 36 possible outcomes. Thus,

$$x = \frac{31}{36} \cdot y.$$

But when Huygens rolls he wins on 6 of the 36 possible outcomes, and in the other 30, he is led back to where his chances are x. Thus

$$x = \frac{31}{36} \cdot y + \frac{30}{36} \cdot x.$$

From these two equations Huygens found that $x = {}^{31}/_{61}$.

Another early use of expected value appeared in Pascal's argument to show that a rational person should believe in the existence of God.[5] Pascal said that we have to make a wager whether to believe or not to believe. His discussion suggests that we are playing a game with two strategies, believe and not believe, with payoffs as follows:

	God does not exist	God exists
Probability	p	$1-p$
believe	$-u$	v
not believe	0	$-x$

Here $-u$ represent the cost to you of passing up some worldly pleasures as a consequence of believing that God exists. If you do not believe, and God is a vengeful God, you will lose x. Now to determine which strategy is best you should compare the two expected values

$$-pu + (1 - p)v \quad \text{and} \quad p0 + (1 - p)(-x),$$

and choose the larger of the two. In general, the choice will depend upon the value of p. But Pascal assumed that the value of v is infinite and so the strategy of believing is best no matter what probability you assign for the existence of God. This example is considered by some to be the beginning of decision theory. Decision analyses of this kind appear today in many fields, and, in particular, are an important part of medical diagnostics and corporate business decisions.

Another early use of expected value was to decide the price of annuities. The study

[5]Quoted in I. Hacking, *The Emergence of Probability* (Cambridge: Cambridge Univ. Press, 1975).

of statistics has its origins in the use of the bills of mortality kept in the parishes in London from 1603. These records kept a weekly tally of christenings and burials. From these John Graunt made estimates for the population of London and also provided the first mortality table.[6] His mortality table was this:

Age	Survivors
0	100
6	64
16	40
26	25
36	16
46	10
56	6
66	3
76	1

As Hackings observes, Graunt apparently constructed this table by assuming that after the age of 6 there is a constant probability of about $5/8$ of surviving for another decade.[7] For example, of the 64 people who survive to age 6, $5/8$ of 64 or 40 survive to 16, $5/8$ of these 40 or 25 survive to 26, and so forth. Of course, he rounded off his figures to the nearest whole person.

Clearly, a constant mortality rate cannot be correct throughout the whole range, and later tables provided by Halley were more realistic in this respect.[8]

A *terminal annuity* provides a fixed amount of money during a period of *n* years. To determine the price of a terminal annuity one needs only to know the appropriate interest rate. A *life annuity* provides a fixed amount during each year of the buyer's life. The appropriate price for a life annuity is the price of a terminal annuity for the number of years equal to the expected lifetime of the buyer. Thus, the work of Huygens in introducing expected value and the work of Graunt and Halley in determining mortality tables led to a more rational method for pricing annuities. This was one of the first serious uses of probability theory outside the gambling houses.

Although expected value plays a role now in every branch of science, it retains its importance in the casino. In 1962, Edward Thorp's book *Beat the Dealer*[9] provided the reader with a strategy for playing the popular casino game of blackjack that would assure the player a positive expected winning. This book forevermore changed the belief of the casinos that they could not be beat.

[6]Ibid., p. 108.

[7]Ibid., p. 109.

[8]E. Halley, "An Estimate of The Degrees of Mortality of Mankind," *Phil. Trans. Royal Soc.*, vol. 17 (1693), pp. 596–610; 654–656.

[9]E. Thorp, *Beat the Dealer* (New York: Random House, 1962).

Exercises

1. A card is drawn at random from a deck consisting of cards numbered 2 through 10. A player wins 1 dollar if the number on the card is odd and loses 1 dollar if the number is even. What is the expected value of his winnings?

2. A card is drawn at random from a deck of playing cards. If it is red, the player wins 1 dollar; if it is black, the player loses 2 dollars. Find the expected value of the game.

3. In a class there are 20 students: 6 are age 18, 10 are age 19, and 4 are age 20. A student is chosen at random. What is the student's expected age?

4. In Las Vegas the roulette wheel has a 0 and a 00 and then the numbers 1 to 36 marked on equal slots; the wheel is spun and a ball stops randomly in one slot. When a player bets 1 dollar on a number, he receives 36 dollars if the ball stops on this number, for net gain of 35 dollars; otherwise, he loses his dollar bet. Find the expected value for his net winnings.

5. In a second version of roulette at Las Vegas, a player bets on red or black. Half of the numbers from 1 to 36 are red, and half are black. If a player bets a dollar on black, and if the ball stops on a black number, he gets his dollar back and another dollar. If the ball stops on a red number of on 0 or 00 he loses his dollar. Find the expected winnings for this bet.

6. A die is rolled twice. Let X denote the sum of the two numbers that turn up, and Y the difference of the numbers (specifically, the number on the first roll minus the number on the second). Show that $E(XY) = E(X)E(Y)$. Are X and Y independent?

*7. Show that, if X and Y are random variables taking on only two values each, and if $E(XY) = E(X)E(Y)$, then X and Y are independent.

8. A royal family has children until it has a boy or until it has three children. Assume that each child is a boy with probability $^1/_2$. Find the expected number of boys in this royal family and the expected number of girls.

9. If the first roll in a game of craps is neither a natural nor craps, the player can make an additional bet, equal to his original one, that he will make his point before a seven turns up. If his point is four or ten he is paid off at 2:1 odds; if it is a five or nine he is paid off at odds 3:2; and if it is a six or eight he is paid off at odds 6:5. Find the player's expected winnings if he makes this additional bet when he has the opportunity.

10. In Example 10, assume that Mr. Ace decides to buy the stock and hold it until it goes up 1 dollar and then sell and not buy again. Modify the program **Stock System** to find the density of his profit under this system after a ten-day period. Find the expected profit and the probability that he comes out ahead.

11. On September 26, 1980, the *New York Times* reported that a mysterious stranger strode into a Las Vegas casino, placed a single bet of 777,000 dollars on the "don't pass" line at the crap table, and walked away with more than 1.5 million dollars. In the "don't pass" bet, the bettor is essentially betting with the house. That is, the "don't pass" bettor wins if the roller loses and loses if the roller wins. An exception occurs if the roller rolls a 12 on the first roll. In this case, the roller loses and the "don't pass" bettor just gets back the money bet instead of winning. Show that the "don't pass" bettor has a more favorable bet than the roller.

12. Recall that, for the *martingale doubling system* (see Chapter 1, Section 1.1, Exercise 10), the player doubles his bet each time he loses and quits the first time he is ahead. Suppose that you are playing roulette in a *fair casino* where there are no 0s, and you bet on red each time. You then win with probability $1/2$ each time. Assume that you start with a 1-dollar bet and employ the martingale system. Since you entered the casino with 100 dollars, you also quit in the unlikely event that black turns up six times in a row so that you are down 63 dollars and cannot make the required 64-dollar bet. Find your expected winnings under this system of play.

13. You have 80 dollars and play the following game. An urn contains two white balls and two black balls. You draw the balls out one at a time without replacement until all the balls are gone. On each draw, you bet half of your present fortune that you will draw a white ball. What is your final fortune?

14. In the hat check problem (see Chapter 3, Section 3.1, Example 8), it was assumed that N people check their hats and the hats are handed back at random. Let $X_j = 1$ if the jth man gets his hat and 0 otherwise. Find $E(X_j)$ and $E(X_j \cdot X_k)$ for j not equal to k. Are X_j and X_k independent?

15. Let X be a random variable defined on a sample space Ω such that $X(\omega) \geq 0$ for all ω. Assume that $E(X) = 0$. Show that if $p(\omega) > 0$ then $X(\omega) = 0$.

16. A box contains two gold balls and three silver balls. You are allowed to choose successively balls from the box at random. You win 1 dollar each time you draw a gold ball and lose 1 dollar each time you draw a silver ball. After a draw, the ball is not replaced. Show that, if you draw until you are ahead by 1 dollar or until there are no more gold balls, this is a favorable game.

17. Gerolamo Cardano in his book, *The Gambling Scholar,* written in the early 1500s, considers the following carnival game. There are six dice. Each of the dice has five blank sides. The sixth side has a number between 1 and 6—a different number on each die. The six dice are rolled and the player wins a prize depending on the total of the numbers which turn up.
    (a) Find, as Cardano did, the expected total without finding its density.
    (b) Large prizes were given for large totals with a modest fee to play the game. Explain why this could be done.

18. Let X be the first time that a *failure* occurs in an infinite sequence of Bernoulli trials with probability p for success. Let $p_k = P(X = k)$ for $k = 1, 2, \ldots$ Show that $p_k = p^{k-1}q$ where $q = 1 - p$. Show that $\sum_k p_k = 1$. Show that $E(X) = 1/q$. What is the expected number of tosses of a coin required to obtain the first tail?

19. Exactly one of six similar keys opens a certain door. If you try the keys, one after another, what is the expected number of keys that you will have to try before success?

20. A multiple choice exam is given. A problem has four possible answers, and exactly one answer is correct. The student is allowed to choose a subset of the four possible answers as his answer. If his chosen subset contains the correct answer, the student receives three points, but he loses one point for each wrong answer in his chosen subset. Show that if he just guesses his expected score is zero.

21. You are offered the following game to play: a fair coin is tossed until heads turns up for the first time. If this occurs on the first toss you receive 2 dollars, if it occurs on the second toss you receive $2^2 = 4$ dollars and, in general, if heads turns up for the first time on the nth toss you receive 2^n dollars.

   (a) Show that the expected value of your winnings does not exist. (i.e., is given by a divergent sum) for this game. Does this mean that this game is favorable no matter how much you pay to play it?

   (b) Assume that you only receive 2^{10} dollars if any number greater than or equal to ten tosses are required to obtain the first head. Show that your expected value for this modified game is finite and find its value.

   (c) Assume that you pay 10 dollars for each play of the original game. Write a program to simulate 100 plays of the game and see how you do.

22. Recall that in exercise 14 of Chapter 1, Section 1.1, we considered a town with two hospitals. In the large hospital about 45 babies are born each day, and in the smaller hospital about 15 babies are born each day. We were interested in guessing which hospital would have on the average the largest number of days with the property that more than 60 percent of the children born on that day are boys. For each hospital find the expected number of days in a year that have the property that more than 60 percent of the children born on that day were boys.

23. An insurance company has 1,000 policies on men of age 50. The company estimates that the probability that a man of age 50 dies within a year is .01. Estimate the number of claims that the company can expect from beneficiaries of these men within a year.

24. Using the life table for 1981 in Appendix C, write a program to compute the expected lifetime for males and females of each possible age from 1 to 85. Compare the results for males and females. Comment on whether life insurance should be priced differently for males and females.

*25. A deck of ESP cards consists of 20 cards each of two types: say ten stars, ten circles (normally there are five types). The deck is shuffled and the cards turned up one at a time. You, the alleged percipient, are to name the symbol on each card *before* it is turned up.

    Suppose that you are really just guessing at the cards. If you do not get to see each card after you have made your guess, then it is easy to calculate the expected number of correct guesses, namely ten.

If, on the other hand, you are guessing with information, that is, if you see each card after your guess, then, of course, you might expect to get a higher score. This is indeed the case, but calculating the correct expectation is no longer easy.

But it is easy to do a computer simulation of this guessing with information, so we can get a good idea of the expectation by simulation. (This is similar to the way that skilled blackjack players make blackjack into a favorable game by observing the cards that have already been played. See Exercise 29.)

(a) First, do a simulation of guessing without information, repeating the experiment at least 1000 times. Estimate the expected number of correct answers and compare your result with the theoretical expectation.

(b) What is the best strategy for guessing with information?

(c) Do a simulation of guessing with information, using the strategy in (b). Repeat the experiment at least 1000 times, and estimate the expectation in this case.

(d) Let S be the number of stars and C the number of circles in the deck. Let $h(S,C)$ be the expected winnings using the optimal guessing strategy in (b). Show that $h(S,C)$ satisfies the recursion relation

$$h(S,C) = \frac{S}{S + C}h(S - 1, C) + \frac{C}{S + C}h(S, C - 1) + \frac{\max(S, C)}{S + C},$$

and $h(0,0) = h(-1,0) = h(0,-1) = 0$. Using this relation, write a program to compute $h(S,C)$ and find $h(10,10)$. Compare the computed value of $h(10,10)$ with the result of your simulation in (c). For more about this exercise and Exercise 26 see Diaconis and Graham.[10]

*26. Consider the ESP problem as described in Exercise 25. You are again guessing with information, and you are using the optimal guessing strategy of guessing *star* if the remaining deck has more stars, *circle* if more circles, and tossing a coin if the number of stars and circles are equal. Assume that $S \geq C$, where S is the number of stars and C the number of circles.

Now consider a random walk that starts at $(0,0)$ and moves up one step every time a star is turned up and down one every time a circle is turned up. For example, consider a deck with six stars and four circles. Then a typical graph would be like that shown in Figure 4.

(a) Show that, when the random walk is below the line L, the player guesses right when the graph goes up (star is turned up) and when the walk is above the line guesses right when the walk goes down (circle turned up). Show from this property that the subject is sure to have S correct guesses.

[10]P. Diaconis and R. Graham, "The Analysis of Sequential Experiments with Feedback to Subjects," *Annals of Statistics*, vol. 9 (1981), pp. 3–23.

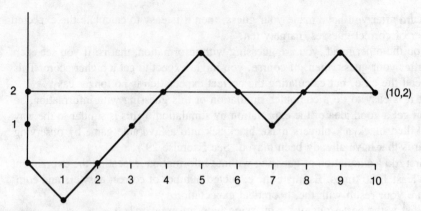

Figure 4 Random walk for ESP.

(b) When the walk is at a point (x,x) *on* the line L the number of stars and circles remaining is the same, and so the subject tosses a coin. Show that the probability that the walk reaches (x,x) is

$$\frac{\binom{S}{x}\binom{C}{x}}{\binom{S+C}{2x}}.$$

Hint: The outcome of $2x$ cards is a hypergeometric distribution (see Chapter 5, Section 5.1, Exercise 20).

(c) Using the results of (a) and (b) show that the expected number of correct guesses under intelligent guessing is

$$S + \sum_{x=1}^{C} \frac{\binom{S}{x}\binom{C}{x}}{\binom{S+C}{2x}} \cdot \frac{1}{2}.$$

27. It has been said[11] that a Dr. B. Muriel Bristol declined a cup of tea stating that she preferred a cup into which milk had been poured first. The famous statistician R. A. Fisher carried out a test to see if she could tell whether milk was put in before or after the tea. Assume that for the test Dr. Bristol was given eight cups of tea—four in which the milk was put in before the tea and four in which the milk was put in after the tea (cf., Chapter 3, Section 3.2, Exercise 8).

[11]J.F. Box, *R.A. Fisher, The Life of a Scientist* (New York: John Wiley and Sons, 1978).

(a) What is the expected number of correct guesses the lady would make if she had no information after each test and was just guessing?

(b) Using the result of Exercise 26 find the expected number of correct guesses if she was told the result of each guess and used an optimal guessing strategy.

28. In a popular computer game the computer picks an integer from 1 to n at random. The player is given k chances to guess the number. After each guess the computer responds "correct," "too small," or "too big."

(a) Show that if $n \leq 2^k - 1$, then there is a strategy that guarantees you will correctly guess the number in k tries.

(b) Show that if $n \geq 2^k - 1$, there is a strategy that assures you of identifying one of $2^k - 1$ numbers and hence gives a probability of $(2^k - 1)/n$ of winning. Why is this an optimal strategy? Illustrate your result in terms of the case $n = 9$ and $k = 3$.

29. In the casino game of blackjack the dealer is dealt two cards, one face up and one face down, and each player is dealt two cards, both face down. If the dealer is showing an ace the player can look at his down cards and then make a bet called an *insurance* bet. (Expert players will recognize why it is called insurance.) If you make this bet you will win the bet if the dealer's second card is a *ten card:* namely, a ten, jack, queen, or king. If you win, you are paid twice your insurance bet; otherwise you lose this bet. Show that, if the only cards you can see are the dealer's ace and your two cards and if your cards are not ten cards, then the insurance bet is an unfavorable bet. Show, however, that if you are playing two hands simultaneously, and you have no ten cards, then it is a favorable bet. (Thorpe[12] has shown that the game of blackjack is favorable to the player if he or she can keep good enough track of the cards that have been played.)

30. Assume that, every time you buy a box of Wheaties, you receive a picture of one of the n players for the New York Yankees (see Chapter 3, Section 3.2, Exercise 35). Let X_k be the number of additional boxes you have to buy, after you have obtained $k - 1$ different pictures, in order to obtain the next new picture. Thus $X_1 = 1$, X_2 is the number of boxes bought after this to obtain a picture different from the first picture obtained, and so forth.

(a) Show that X_k has a geometric density with $p = (n - k + 1)/n$.

(b) Simulate the experiment for a team with 26 players (25 would be more accurate but we want an even number). Carry out a number of simulations and estimate the expected time required to get the first 13 players and the expected time to get the second 13. How do these expectations compare?

(c) Show that, if there are $2n$ players, the expected time to get the first half of the players is

$$2n\left(\frac{1}{2n} + \frac{1}{2n - 1} + \cdots + \frac{1}{n + 1}\right),$$

[12]Thorpe, *Beat The Dealer*.

and the expected time to get the second half is

$$2n\left(\frac{1}{n} + \frac{1}{n-1} + \cdots + 1\right).$$

(d) In Chapter 3 Section 3.1 (Appendix) we showed that

$$1 + \frac{1}{2} + \frac{1}{3} + \cdots + \frac{1}{n} \sim \log(n) + .5772 + \frac{1}{2n}.$$

Use this to estimate the expressions in (c). Compare these estimates with the exact values and also with your estimates obtained by simulation for the case $n = 26$.

*31. (Feller)[13] A large number, N, of people are subjected to a blood test. This can be administered in two ways: (1) Each person can be tested separately, in this case N tests are required, (2) the blood samples of k persons can be pooled and analyzed together. If this test is *negative*, this one test suffices for the k people. If the test is *positive*, each of the k persons must be tested separately, and in all, $k + 1$ tests are required for the k people. Assume that the probability p that a test is positive is the same for all people and that these events are independent.
  (a) Find the probability that the test for a pooled sample of k people will be positive.
  (b) What is the expected value of the number X of tests necessary under plan (2)? (Assume that N is divisible by k.)
  (c) For small p, show that the value of k which will minimize the expected number of tests under the second plan is approximately $1/\sqrt{p}$.

32. Write a program to add random numbers chosen from $[0,1]$ until the first time the sum is greater than one. Have your program repeat this experiment a number of times to estimate the expected number of selections necessary in order that the sum of the chosen numbers first exceeds 1. On the basis of your experiments, what is your estimate for this number?

*33. The following related discrete problem also gives a good clue for the answer to the above problem. Randomly select with replacement $t_1, t_2, \ldots, t_r$ from the set $(^1/_n, ^2/_n, \ldots, ^n/_n)$. Let X be the smallest value of r satisfying

$$t_1 + t_2 + \cdots + t_r > 1.$$

Then $E(X) = (1 + ^1/_n)^n$. To prove this, we can just as well choose $t_1, t_2, \ldots$ randomly with replacement from the set $(1, 2, \ldots, n)$ and let X be the smallest value of r for which

$$t_1 + t_2 + \cdots + t_r > n.$$

[13]W. Feller, *Introduction to Probability Theory and Its Applications*, 3rd ed., vol. 1 (New York: John Wiley and Sons, 1968), p. 240.

It can be shown that

$$P(X \geq j + 1) = \binom{n}{j} \left(\frac{1}{n}\right)^j.$$

Show then that

$$E(X) = \sum_{j=0}^{n} P(X \geq j + 1).$$

From these two facts, the expression for $E(X)$ follows easily. This proof is given by Harris Schultz in the *Two-year College Mathematics Journal*.[14]

*34. (Banach's Matchbox)[15] A man carries in each of his two front pockets a box of matches originally containing N matches. Whenever he needs a match, he chooses a pocket at random and removes one from that box. One day he reaches into a pocket and finds the box empty.

    (a) Let p_r denote the probability that the other pocket contains r matches. Define a sequence of *counter* random variables as follows: Let $X_i = 1$ if the ith draw is from the left pocket, and 0 if it is from the right pocket. Interpret p_r in terms of $S_n = X_1 + X_2 + \cdots + X_n$. Find a binomial expression for p_r.

    (b) Write a computer program to compute the p_r, as well as the probability that the other pocket contains at least r matches, for $N = 100$ and r from 0 to 50.

    (c) Show that $(N - r)p_r = \frac{1}{2}(2N + 1)p_{r+1} - \frac{1}{2}(r + 1)p_{r+1}$.

    (d) Evaluate $\sum_r p_r$.

    (e) Use (c) and (d) to determine the expectation E of the density $\{p_r\}$.

    (f) Use Stirling's formula to obtain an approximation for E. How many matches must each box contain to ensure a value of about 13 for the expectation E? (Take $\pi = \frac{22}{7}$.)

35. A coin is tossed until the first time a head turns up. If this occurs on the nth toss and n is odd you win $2^n/n$, but if n is even then you lose $2^n/n$. Then if your expected winnings exist they are given by the convergent series

$$1 - \frac{1}{2} + \frac{1}{3} - \frac{1}{4} + \cdots$$

called the alternating *harmonic series*. It is tempting to say that this should be the expected value of the experiment. Show that if we were to do this, the expected value of an experiment would depend upon the order in which the outcomes are listed.

[14]H. Schultz, "An Expected Value Problem," *Two-Year Mathematics Journal*, vol. 10, no. 4 (1979), pp. 277–78.

[15]See Feller, *Introduction to Probability Theory*, p. 166.

6.2 VARIANCE OF DISCRETE RANDOM VARIABLES

The usefulness of the expected value as a prediction for the outcome of an experiment is increased when the outcome is not likely to deviate too much from the expected value. In this section we shall introduce a measure of this deviation, called the variance.

Variance

DEFINITION 4

Let X be a numerically valued random variable with expected value $\mu = E(X)$. Then the *variance* of X, denoted by $V(X)$, is

$$V(X) = E((X - \mu)^2).$$

Standard Deviation

The *standard deviation* of X, denoted by $D(X)$, is $D(X) = \sqrt{V(X)}$. We often write σ for $D(X)$ and σ^2 for $V(X)$.

Note that, from the definition of expected value, $V(X)$ is given by

$$V(X) = \sum_{\omega} (X(\omega) - \mu)^2 p(\omega). \tag{1}$$

EXAMPLE 1

Consider one roll of a die. Let X be the number that turns up. To find $V(X)$, we must first find the expected value of X. This is

$$\mu = E(X) = 1\left(\frac{1}{6}\right) + 2\left(\frac{1}{6}\right) + 3\left(\frac{1}{6}\right) + 4\left(\frac{1}{6}\right) + 5\left(\frac{1}{6}\right) + 6\left(\frac{1}{6}\right)$$

$$= \frac{7}{2}.$$

To find the variance of X, we now form the new random variable $(X - \mu)^2$ and compute its expectation. We can easily do this from the following table.

ω	$p(\omega)$	$X(\omega)$	$(X(\omega) - 7/2)^2$
1	1/6	1	25/4
2	1/6	2	9/4
3	1/6	3	1/4
4	1/6	4	1/4
5	1/6	5	9/4
6	1/6	6	25/4

From this table we find $E(X - \mu)^2$ is

$$V(X) = \frac{1}{6}\left(\frac{25}{4} + \frac{9}{4} + \frac{1}{4} + \frac{1}{4} + \frac{9}{4} + \frac{25}{4}\right)$$

$$= \frac{35}{12},$$

and the standard deviation $D(X) = \sqrt{35/12} = 1.707$. $\qquad\square$

Properties of Variance

The variance has properties very different from those of the expectation. If c is any constant, $E(cX) = cE(X)$ and $E(X+c) = E(X) + c$. In contrast, we have the following properties of the variance.

THEOREM 6

If X is any random variable and c is any constant, then

$$V(cX) = c^2 V(X),$$
$$V(X+c) = V(X).$$

Proof. Let $\mu = E(X)$. Then $E(cX) = c\mu$, and

$$V(cX) = E((cX - c\mu)^2) = E(c^2(X - \mu)^2)$$
$$= c^2 E((X - \mu)^2) = c^2 V(X).$$

To prove the second assertion, we note that, to compute $V(X+c)$, we would replace $X(\omega)$ by $X(\omega)+c$ and μ by $\mu+c$ in Equation (1). But the c's would cancel, leaving $V(X)$. $\qquad\blacksquare$

We next prove a theorem that gives us a useful alternative form for computing the variance.

Calculation of Variance

THEOREM 7

If X is any random variable with $E(X) = \mu$, then

$$V(X) = E(X^2) - \mu^2.$$

In particular, if X and Y have the same density function, then $V(X) = V(Y)$.

Proof.

$$V(X) = E((X - \mu)^2) = E(X^2 - 2\mu X + \mu^2)$$
$$= E(X^2) - 2\mu E(X) + \mu^2 = E(X^2) - \mu^2. \qquad \blacksquare$$

Using Theorem 7, we can compute the variance of the outcome of a roll of a die by first computing

$$E(X^2) = 1\left(\frac{1}{6}\right) + 4\left(\frac{1}{6}\right) + 9\left(\frac{1}{6}\right) + 16\left(\frac{1}{6}\right) + 25\left(\frac{1}{6}\right) + 36\left(\frac{1}{6}\right)$$

$$= \frac{91}{6},$$

and,

$$V(X) = E(X^2) - \mu^2 = \frac{91}{6} - \left(\frac{7}{2}\right)^2$$

$$= \frac{35}{12},$$

in agreement with the value obtained directly from the definition of $V(X)$.

We turn now to some general properties of the variance. Recall that if X and Y are any two random variables, $E(X + Y) = E(X) + E(Y)$. This is not always true for the case of the variance. For example, let X be any random variable and define $Y = -X$. Then $V(X) = V(Y)$, so that $V(X) + V(Y) = 2V(X)$. But $X + Y$ is always 0 and hence has variance 0. Thus $V(X + Y) \neq V(X) + V(Y)$ if $2V(X) \neq 0$.

Independence

In the important case of independent random variables, however, *the variance of the sum is the sum of the variances*.

THEOREM 8

Let X and Y be two *independent* random variables. Then $V(X + Y) = V(X) + V(Y)$.

Proof. Let $E(X) = a$ and $E(Y) = b$. Then

$$V(X + Y) = E((X + Y)^2) - (a + b)^2$$

$$= E(X^2) + 2E(XY) + E(Y^2) - a^2 - 2ab - b^2.$$

Since X and Y are independent, $E(XY) = E(X)E(Y) = ab$. Thus,

$$V(X + Y) = E(X^2) - a^2 + E(Y^2) - b^2 = V(X) + V(Y). \qquad \blacksquare$$

It is easy to extend this proof, by mathematical induction, to show that *the variance of the sum of any number of independent random variables is the sum of the individual variances*.

From this we have the following.

THEOREM 9

Let $X_1, X_2, \ldots, X_n$ be an independent trials process. Let

$$S_n = X_1 + X_2 + \cdots + X_n$$

be the sum, and

$$A_n = \frac{S_n}{n}$$

be the average. Then

$$E(S_n) = n\mu, \qquad V(S_n) = n\sigma^2,$$

$$E(A_n) = \mu, \qquad V(A_n) = \frac{\sigma^2}{n}.$$

Proof. Since all the random variables X_j have the same expected value, we have

$$E(S_n) = E(X_1) + \cdots + E(X_n) = n\mu,$$

and

$$V(S_n) = V(X_1) + \cdots + V(X_n) = n\sigma^2.$$

We have seen that, if we multiply a random variable X with mean μ and variance σ^2 by a constant c, the new random variable has expected value $c\mu$ and variance $c^2\sigma^2$. Thus, $E(A_n) = E\left(\dfrac{S_n}{n}\right) = \dfrac{n\mu}{n} = \mu$,

and

$$V(A_n) = V\left(\frac{S_n}{n}\right) = \frac{V(S_n)}{n^2} = \frac{n\sigma^2}{n^2} = \frac{\sigma^2}{n}. \qquad ■$$

EXAMPLE 2

Consider n rolls of a die. We have seen that, if X_j is the outcome of the jth roll, then $E(X_j) = 7/2$ and $V(X_j) = 35/12$. Thus, if S_n is the sum of the outcome, and $A_n = \dfrac{S_n}{n}$ is the average of the outcomes, we have $E(A_n) = 7/2$ and $V(A_n) = \dfrac{(35/12)}{n}$. Therefore, as n increases, the expected value of the average remains constant, but the variance tends to 0. If the variance is a measure of the expected deviation from the mean this would indicate that, for n large, we can expect the average to be very near the expected value. This is in fact the case, and we shall justify it in Chapter 8. $\qquad\qquad\square$

Bernoulli Trials

Consider next the general Bernoulli trials process. As usual, we let $X_j = 1$ if the jth outcome is a success and 0 if it is a failure. If p is the probability of a success, and $q = 1 - p$, then

$$E(X_j) = 0q + 1p = p,$$

$$E(X_j^2) = 0^2q + 1^2p = p,$$

and

$$V(X_j) = E(X_j^2) - (E(X_j))^2 = p - p^2 = pq.$$

Thus, for Bernoulli trials, if $S_n = X_1 + X_2 + \cdots + X_n$ is the number of successes, then $E(X_n) = np$, $V(S_n) = npq$, and $D(S_n) = \sqrt{npq}$. If $A_n = \dfrac{S_n}{n}$ is the average number of successes, then $E(A_n) = p$, $V(A_n) = \dfrac{pq}{n}$, and $D(A_n) = \sqrt{\dfrac{pq}{n}}$. We see that the expected proportion of successes remains p and the variance tends to 0. This suggests that the frequency interpretation of probability is a correct one. We shall make this more precise in Chapter 8.

EXAMPLE 3

Let us compute the variance for the number T of trials until the first success in a Bernoulli trials process. In Example 7 of Chapter 5, Section 5.1, we saw that

$$p_T = \begin{pmatrix} 1 & 2 & 3 & \cdots \\ p & qp & q^2p & \cdots \end{pmatrix}.$$

In Example 8 of Chapter 6, Section 6.1, we showed that $E(T) = \dfrac{1}{p}$. Thus, $V(T) = E(T^2) - \dfrac{1}{p^2}$ so we need only find

$$E(T^2) = 1p + 4qp + 9q^2p + \cdots$$
$$= p(1 + 4q + 9q^2 + \cdots).$$

To evaluate this sum, we start again with

$$1 + x + x^2 + \cdots = \frac{1}{1-x}.$$

Differentiating, we obtain

$$1 + 2x + 3x^2 + \cdots = \frac{1}{(1-x)^2}.$$

Multiplying by x,

$$x + 2x^2 + 3x^3 + \cdots = \frac{x}{(1-x)^2}.$$

Differentiating again gives

$$1 + 4x + 9x^2 + \cdots = \frac{1+x}{(1-x)^3}.$$

Thus,

$$E(T^2) = p\,\frac{1+q}{(1-q)^3} = \frac{1+q}{p^2}$$

and

$$V(T) = E(T^2) - (E(T))^2$$
$$= \frac{1+q}{p^2} - \frac{1}{p^2} = \frac{q}{p^2}.$$

For example, the variance for the number of tosses of a coin until the first head turns up is $\dfrac{1/2}{(1/2)^2} = 2$. The variance for the number of rolls of a die until the first six turns up is $\dfrac{5/6}{(1/6)^2} = 30$. Note that, as p decreases, the variance increases rapidly. This corresponds to the increased spread of the geometric density as p decreases (noted in Chapter 5, Section 5.1, Figure 4). $\qquad\square$

Exercises

1. A number is chosen at random from the set $S = \{-1,0,1\}$. Let X be the number chosen. Find the expected value, variance, and standard deviation of X.

2. A random variable X has the density

$$p_X = \begin{pmatrix} 0 & 1 & 2 & 4 \\ \dfrac{1}{3} & \dfrac{1}{3} & \dfrac{1}{6} & \dfrac{1}{6} \end{pmatrix}.$$

   Find the expected value, variance, and standard deviation of X.

3. You place a 1-dollar bet on the number 17 at Las Vegas, and your friend places a 1-dollar bet on black (see Exercises 6 and 7 of Chapter 1, Section 1.1). Let X be

your winnings and Y be her winnings. Compare $E(X)$, $E(Y)$ and $V(X)$, $V(Y)$. What do these computations tell you about the nature of your winnings if you and your friend make a sequence of bets, with you betting each time on a number and your friend betting on a color?

4. X is a random variable with $E(X) = 100$ and $V(X) = 15$. Find
   (a) $E(X^2)$.
   (b) $E(3X + 10)$.
   (c) $E(-X)$.
   (d) $V(-X)$.
   (e) $D(-X)$.

5. In a certain manufacturing process, the (Fahrenheit) temperature never varies by more than $2°$ from $62°$. The temperature is, in fact, a random variable F with density

$$p_F = \begin{pmatrix} 60 & 61 & 62 & 63 & 64 \\ \dfrac{1}{10} & \dfrac{2}{10} & \dfrac{4}{10} & \dfrac{2}{10} & \dfrac{1}{10} \end{pmatrix}.$$

   (a) Define $T = F - 62$. Find $E(T)$ and $V(T)$, and from these determine $E(F)$ and $V(F)$.
   (b) It is decided to report the temperature readings on a Celsius scale, that is, $C = 5/9(F - 32)$. What is the expected value and variance for the readings now?

6. Write a computer program to calculate the mean and variance of a density which you specify as data. Use the program to compare the variances for the following densities, both having expected value 0.

$$p_X = \begin{pmatrix} -2 & -1 & 0 & 1 & 2 \\ \dfrac{3}{11} & \dfrac{2}{11} & \dfrac{1}{11} & \dfrac{2}{11} & \dfrac{3}{11} \end{pmatrix},$$

$$p_Y = \begin{pmatrix} -2 & -1 & 0 & 1 & 2 \\ \dfrac{1}{11} & \dfrac{2}{11} & \dfrac{5}{11} & \dfrac{2}{11} & \dfrac{1}{11} \end{pmatrix}.$$

7. A coin is tossed three times. Let X be the number of heads that turn up. Find $V(X)$ and $D(X)$.

8. A random sample of 2400 people are asked if they favor a government proposal to develop new nuclear power plants. If 40 percent of the people in the country are in favor of this proposal, find the expected value and the standard deviation for the number S_{2400} of people in the sample who favor the proposal.

9. A die is loaded so that the probability of a face coming up is proportional to the number on that face. The die is rolled with outcome X. Find $V(X)$ and $D(X)$.

10. Prove the following facts about the standard deviation.
   (a) $D(X+c) = D(X)$.
   (b) $D(cX) = |c|D(X)$.

11. A number is chosen at random from the integers $1,2,3, \ldots ,n$. Let X be the number chosen. Show that $E(X) = \dfrac{(n+1)}{2}$ and $V(X) = \dfrac{(n-1)(n+1)}{12}$.

12. Prove that $V(X) = 0$ if and only if X is a constant function (except on a set of probability 0).

13. Let X be a random variable with $\mu = E(X)$ and $\sigma^2 = V(X)$. Define $X^* = \dfrac{(X-\mu)}{\sigma}$. The random variable X^* is called the *standardized random variable* associated with X. Show that this standardized random variable has expected value 0 and variance 1.

14. Peter and Paul play Heads and Tails (see Example 3 of Chapter 1, Section 1.1.) Let W_n be Peter's winnings after n matches. Show that $E(W_n) = 0$ and $V(W_n) = n$.

15. Find the expected value and the variance for the number of boys and the number of girls in a royal family that has children until there is a boy or until there are three children.

16. n people have their hats returned at random. Let $X_i = 1$ if the ith person gets his own hat back and 0 otherwise. Let $S_n = \sum\limits_{i=1}^{n} X_i$. Then S_n is the total number of people who get their own hats back. Show that
   (a) $E(X_i^2) = 1/n$.
   (b) $E(X_i \cdot X_j) = \dfrac{1}{n(n-1)}$ for $i \neq j$.
   (c) $E(S_n^2) = 2$ [using (a) and (b)].
   (d) $V(S_n) = 1$.

17. Let S_n be the number of successes in n independent trials. Modify the program **Demo Binomial** (Chapter 3, Section 3.2) to compute, for given n, p and k, the probability
$$P(-k\sqrt{npq} < S_n - np < k\sqrt{npq}).$$
   (a) Let $p = .5$, and compute this probability for $k = 1,2,3$ and $n = 10,30,50$. Do the same for $p = .2$.
   (b) Show that the *standardized random variable* $S_n^* = \dfrac{(S_n - np)}{\sqrt{npq}}$ has expected value 0 and variance 1. What do your results from (a) tell you about this standardized quantity S_n^*?

18. Let X be the outcome of a chance experiment with $E(X) = \mu$ and $V(X) = \sigma^2$. When μ and σ^2 are unknown, the statistician often estimates them by repeating the experiment n times with outcomes $x_1, x_2, \ldots, x_n$, estimating μ by the *sample mean*

$$\bar{x} = \frac{x_1 + x_2 + \cdots + x_n}{n},$$

and σ^2 by the *sample variance*

$$s^2 = \frac{(x_1 - \bar{x})^2 + (x_2 - \bar{x})^2 + \cdots + (x_n - \bar{x})^2}{n-1}.$$

Then s is the *sample standard deviation*.

Write a computer program that will roll a die n times and compute the sample mean and sample variance. Repeat this experiment several times for $n = 10$ and $n = 1000$. How well do the sample mean and sample variance estimate the true mean $^7/_2$ and variance $^{35}/_{12}$?

19. Show that, for the sample mean $\bar{x}$ and sample variance s^2 as defined in Exercise 18,
(a) $E(\bar{x}) = \mu$.
(b) $E(s^2) = \sigma^2$.
Hint: for (b) write

$$\sum_{i=1}^{n} (x_i - \mu)^2 = \sum_{i=1}^{n} (x_i - \bar{x} + \bar{x} - \mu)^2$$

$$= \sum_{i=1}^{n} (x_i - \bar{x})^2 + 2(\bar{x} - \mu) \sum_{i=1}^{n} (x_i - \bar{x}) + n(\bar{x} - \mu)^2$$

$$= \sum_{i=1}^{n} (x_i - \bar{x})^2 + n(\bar{x} - \mu)^2,$$

and take expectations of both sides.

*20. Let X be a random variable taking on values $a_1, a_2, \cdots, a_r$ with probabilities $p_1, p_2, \ldots, p_r$ and with $E(X) = \mu$. Assume that we had defined the standard deviation by:

$$\bar{\sigma} = \sum_{i=1}^{r} |a_i - \mu| p_i$$

and

$$\bar{V}(X) = \bar{\sigma}^2.$$

Show by an example that, with this definition of standard deviation and variance, it would not necessarily be true that the variance of the sum of two independent random variables is the sum of the individual variances nor, for that matter, that the standard deviation of the sum is the sum of the individual standard deviations.

21. We have two instruments that measure the distance between two points. The measurements given by the two instruments are random variables X_1 and X_2 that are independent with $E(X_1) = E(X_2) = \mu$, where μ is the true distance. From experience with these instruments, we know the values of the variances σ_1^2 and σ_2^2. These variances are not necessarily the same. From two measurements, we estimate μ by $\bar{\mu} = wX_1 + (1-w)X_2$. Here w is chosen in $[0,1]$ to minimize the variance of $\bar{\mu}$.
    (a) What is $E(\bar{\mu})$?
    (b) How should w be chosen in $[0,1]$ to minimize the variance of $\bar{\mu}$?

22. Let X be a random variable with $E(X) = \mu$ and $V(X) = \sigma^2$. Show that the function $f(x)$ defined by

$$f(x) = \sum_{\omega} (X(\omega) - x)^2 p(\omega)$$

has its minimum value when $x = \mu$.

23. Let X and Y be two random variables defined on the finite sample space Ω. Assume that $X, Y, X+Y$, and $X-Y$ all have the same density. Prove that $P(X = Y = 0) = 1$.

24. If X and Y are any two random variables, then the *covariance* of X and Y is defined as by $\text{Cov}(X,Y) = E((X - E(X))(Y - E(Y)))$. Note that $\text{Cov}(X,X) = V(X)$. Show that, if X and Y are independent, then $\text{Cov}(X,Y) = 0$; and show, by an example, that we can have $\text{Cov}(X,Y) = 0$ but X and Y not independent.

*25. A professor wishes to make up a true-false exam with n questions. She assumes that she can design the problems in such a way that a student will answer the jth problem correctly with probability p_j, and that the answers to the various problems may be considered independent experiments. Let S_n be the number of problems that a student will get correct. The professor wishes to choose p_j so that $E(S_n) = .7n$ and so that the variance of S_n is as large as possible. Show that, to achieve this, she should choose $p_j = .7$ for all j; that is, she should make all the problems have the same difficulty.

26. An urn contains exactly 5000 balls, of which an unknown number X are white and the rest red. X is a random variable with a probability distribution on the integers $0, 1, 2, \ldots, 5000$.
    (a) Suppose we know that $E(X) = \mu$. Show that this is enough to allow us to calculate the probability that a ball drawn at random from the urn will be white. What is this probability?
    (b) We draw a ball from the urn, examine its color, replace it, and then draw another. Under what conditions, if any, are the results of the two drawings independent; that is, does

$$Pr(\text{white,white}) = Pr(\text{white})^2?$$

(c) Suppose the variance of X is σ^2. What is the probability of drawing two white balls in part (b)?

27. For a sequence of Bernoulli trials, let X_1 be the number of trials until the first success. For $j \geqslant 2$, let X_j be the number of trials after the $j-1$ success until the jth success. Then $X_1, X_2, \ldots$ is an independent trials process.
    (a) What is the common density, expected value, and variance for X_j?
    (b) Let $T_n = X_1 + X_2 + \cdots + X_n$. Then T_n is the time until the nth success. Find $E(T_n)$ and $V(T_n)$.
    (c) Use the results of (b) to find the expected value and the variance for the number of tosses of a coin until nth occurrence of a head.

28. Referring to Exercise 30 of Section 6.1, find the variance for the number of boxes of Wheaties bought before getting half of the player's pictures and the variance for the number of additional boxes needed to get the second half of the player's pictures.

6.3 EXPECTED VALUE AND VARIANCE OF CONTINUOUS RANDOM VARIABLES

In this section we consider the properties of the expected value and the variance of a continuous random variable. These quantities are defined just as for discrete random variables and share the same properties.

For technical reasons, we consider first the case of random variables that are bounded, that is, whose range lies in a bounded interval. We consider the case of unbounded random variables after Corollary 15.

Expected Value and Variance

DEFINITION 5

Let X be a bounded random variable defined on a continuous sample space Ω with probability density p. The *expected value* $\mu = E(X)$ is defined by

$$\mu = E(X) = \int_\Omega X(\omega)p(\omega)d\omega.$$

The *variance* $\sigma^2 = V(X)$ is defined by

$$\sigma^2 = V(X) = E\left[(X-\mu)^2\right] = \int_\Omega (X(\omega)-\mu)^2 p(\omega)d\omega.$$

Compare these definitions with those made for discrete random variables in Sections 6.1 and 6.2. Note that since X is bounded, these integrals are surely finite.

Intuitively, we can interpret $E(X)$, as we did in the previous sections, as the value that we should expect to obtain if we perform a large number of independent experiments and average the resulting values of X. Similarly, we can interpret $V(X)$ as the value that we should expect to obtain if we average the resulting values of $(X - \mu)^2$, the square of the deviation of X from μ. We shall make these rather vague statements more precise in Chapter 8.

Meanwhile, we can summarize the properties of $E(X)$ as follows (cf. Theorem 1).

Properties of Expectation

THEOREM 10

If X and Y are bounded random variables on the same sample space Ω and c is any constant, then

$$E(X + Y) = E(X) + E(Y),$$
$$E(cX) = cE(X),$$
$$E(X + c) = E(X).$$

Proof.

$$
\begin{aligned}
E(X + Y) &= \int (X(\omega) + Y(\omega))p(\omega)d\omega \\
&= \int X(\omega)p(\omega)d\omega + \int Y(\omega)p(\omega)d\omega \\
&= E(X) + E(Y).
\end{aligned}
$$

$$
\begin{aligned}
E(cX) &= \int cX(\omega)p(\omega)d\omega \\
&= c \int X(\omega)p(\omega)d\omega = cE(X).
\end{aligned}
$$

$$
\begin{aligned}
E(X + c) &= \int (X(\omega) + c)p(\omega)d\omega \\
&= \int X(\omega)p(\omega)d\omega + c \int p(\omega)d\omega \\
&= E(X) + c.
\end{aligned}
$$

More generally, if $X_1, X_2, \ldots, X_n$ are n bounded random variables defined on Ω, and $c_1, c_2, \ldots, c_n$ are n constants, then

$$E(c_1X_1 + c_2X_2 + \cdots + c_nX_n) = c_1E(X_1) + c_2E(X_2) + \cdots + c_nE(X_n). \quad \blacksquare$$

Our next result shows that the expected value $E(X)$ and the variance $V(X)$ can be computed directly from the density function f_X without reference to the sample space Ω (cf. Theorem 2). More generally we have the following.

Calculation of Expectation

THEOREM 11

If X is a bounded random variable with range in the interval $[a,b]$, and if $\phi:[a,b] \to \mathbf{R}$ is a continuous real-valued function with domain $[a,b]$, then $\phi(X)$ is a bounded random variable, and

$$E(\phi(X)) = \int_a^b \phi(x)f_X(x)dx.$$

In particular,

$$\mu = E(X) = \int_a^b xf_X(x)dx$$

and

$$V(X) = E((X - \mu)^2) = \int_a^b (x - \mu)^2 f_X(x)dx.$$

Proof. First suppose that $X(\omega)$ is a step function, that is, a function that only a finite number of values x_i, $a \leqslant x_1 \leqslant x_2 \cdots \leqslant x_n \leqslant b$, in the interval $[a,b]$. Let $A_i = \{\omega: X(\omega) = x_i\}$. Then we can break the integral for $E(\phi(X))$ up into n pieces:

$$E(\phi(X)) = \int_\Omega \phi(X)(\omega)p(\omega)d\omega$$

$$= \sum_{i=1}^n \int_{A_i} \phi(X)(\omega)p(\omega)d\omega.$$

But on A_i, $X(\omega) = x_i$ and $\phi(X)(\omega) = \phi(x_i)$, so

$$E(\phi(X)) = \sum_{i=1}^n \phi(x_i)P(A_i)$$

$$= \sum_{i=1}^n \phi(x_i)P\{x_{i-1} < X(\omega) \leqslant x_i\}$$

$$= \sum_{i=1}^n \phi(x_i)(F_X(x_i) - F_X(x_{i-1}))$$

$$= \sum_{i=1}^n \phi(x_i)\left[\frac{F_X(x_i) - F_X(x_{i-1})}{x_i - x_{i-1}}\right](x_i - x_{i-1}).$$

Now if $X(\omega)$ is a continuous function, then we may approximate it by a sequence of step functions $X_n(\omega)$, and then take the limit $n \to \infty$. In this way we get

$$E(\phi(X)) = \lim_{n \to \infty} \sum_{i=1}^{n} \phi(x_i) \left[\frac{F_X(x_i) - F_X(x_{i-1})}{x_i - x_{i-1}} \right] (x_i - x_{i-1})$$

$$= \int_a^b \phi(x) \frac{dF_X(x)}{dx} dx$$

$$= \int_a^b \phi(x) f_X(x) dx,$$

as required. ∎

In the same way, we can show that if $X_1, X_2, \ldots, X_n$ are n bounded random variables on Ω with joint density function $f_{X_1 X_2 \ldots X_n}$, then

$$E(X_1 X_2 \ldots X_n)$$

$$= \int_{a_1}^{b_1} \int_{a_2}^{b_2} \ldots \int_{a_n}^{b_n} x_1 x_2 \ldots x_n f_{X_1 X_2 \ldots X_n} (x_1, x_2, \ldots, x_n) dx_1 dx_2 \ldots dx_n.$$

EXAMPLE 1

If $\Omega = [0,1]$ with uniform density $p(\omega) = 1$, and $X(\omega) = \omega$, then $E(X) = \int_0^1 \omega \cdot 1 \cdot d\omega = \frac{1}{2}$. It follows that if we choose a large number N of random numbers from $[0,1]$ and take the average, then we can expect that this average should be close to the expected value of $\frac{1}{2}$. For the variance of X we have

$$V(X) = \int_0^1 \left(\omega - \frac{1}{2} \right)^2 d\omega = \frac{1}{12}. \qquad \square$$

EXAMPLE 2

If Ω is the unit disc with uniform distribution, as in the dart game (Chapter 2, Section 2.2, Example 2), and $X(\omega) = (x^2 + y^2)^{1/2} = $ distance from the center, then by the definition of expected value,

$$E(X) = \int_\Omega X(\omega) p(\omega) d\omega = \int_0^{2\pi} \int_0^1 r \cdot \frac{1}{\pi} \cdot r \, dr \, d\theta = \frac{2}{3}.$$

We can also compute $E(X)$ by using the results of the preceding theorem. Here the density function $f_X(x) = 2x$, and so

$$E(X) = \int_0^1 x f_X(x) dx = \int_0^1 x(2x) dx = \frac{2}{3}. \qquad \square$$

EXAMPLE 3

In the example of the couple meeting at the Inn (Chapter 5, Section 5.2, Example 6), Ω is the unit square, $p(\omega) \equiv 1$, and $X(\omega) = |\omega_1 - \omega_2|$. Hence,

$$E(X) = \int_\Omega X(\omega)p(\omega)d\omega$$

$$= \int_0^1 \int_0^1 |\omega_1 - \omega_2| d\omega_2 d\omega_1$$

$$= 2\int_0^1 \int_0^{\omega_1} (\omega_1 - \omega_2)d\omega_2 d\omega_1 = \frac{1}{3}. \qquad \square$$

In general, it is not true that $E(XY) = E(X)E(Y)$, since the integral of a product is not the product of integrals. But it is true if X and Y are independent, as follows in Theorem 12.

Independence

THEOREM 12

Let X and Y be independent bounded random variables defined on Ω. Then we have

$$E(XY) = E(X)E(Y).$$

Proof.

$$E(XY) = \int X(\omega)Y(\omega)p(\omega)d\omega$$

$$= \int_a^b \int_c^d xy\, f_{XY}(x,y)dydx,$$

where f_{XY} is the joint density function for X and Y. But if X and Y are independent, then $f_{XY}(x,y) = f_X(x)f_Y(y)$. Hence,

$$E(XY) = \int_a^b \int_c^d xy\, f_X(x)f_Y(y)dydx$$

$$= \int_a^b x\, f_X(x)dx \int_c^d y\, f_Y(y)dy$$

$$= E(X)E(Y). \qquad \blacksquare$$

EXAMPLE 4

Let Ω be the unit square with uniform probability, and $X(\omega) = \omega_1^2$, $Y(\omega) = \omega_2^2$. Then X and Y are independent (cf. Chapter 5, Section 5.2, Example 11), and we have

$$E(XY) = \int_0^1 \int_0^1 \omega_1^2 \, \omega_2^2 \, d\omega_1 \, d\omega_2$$

$$= \left[\int_0^1 \omega_1^2 \, d\omega_1 \right] \left[\int_0^1 \omega_2^2 \, d\omega_2 \right]$$

$$= E(X)E(Y) = \frac{1}{9}. \qquad \square$$

EXAMPLE 5

Again let Ω be the unit square with uniform probability, $Y(\omega) = \omega_2$ and $Z(\omega) = \omega_1 + \omega_2$. Then Y and Z are not independent, and we have

$$E(Y) = \frac{1}{2},$$

$$E(Z) = 1,$$

$$E(YZ) = E(\omega_2(\omega_1 + \omega_2)) = \frac{1}{4} + \frac{1}{3} = \frac{7}{12} \neq E(Y)E(Z). \qquad \square$$

We turn now to the properties of $V(X)$.

Properties of Variance

THEOREM 13

If X is a bounded random variable defined on Ω and c is any constant, then (cf. Section 6.2, Theorem 6)

$$V(cX) = c^2 \, V(X),$$

$$V(X+c) = V(X).$$

Proof. Let $\mu = E(X)$. Then $E(cX) = c\mu$, $E(X + c) = \mu + c$, and

$$V(cX) = E\left[(cX - c\mu)^2\right]$$

$$= c^2 \, E(X - \mu)^2 = c^2 \, V(X),$$

$$V(X+c) = E[((X + c)-(\mu + c))^2]$$

$$= E\left[(X - \mu)^2\right] = V(X). \qquad \blacksquare$$

THEOREM 14

If X is a bounded random variable with $E(X) = \mu$, then (cf. Section 6.2, Theorem 7)

$$V(X) = E(X^2) - \mu^2.$$

Proof.

$$
\begin{aligned}
V(X) &= E((X - \mu)^2) \\
&= E(X^2 - 2\mu X + \mu^2) \\
&= E(X^2) - 2\mu E(X) + \mu^2 \\
&= E(X^2) - \mu^2.
\end{aligned}
$$
∎

THEOREM 15

If X and Y are independent bounded random variables on Ω, then

$$V(X + Y) = V(X) + V(Y).$$

Proof. Let $E(X) = \mu$ and $E(Y) = \nu$. Then

$$
\begin{aligned}
V(X + Y) &= E((X + Y)^2) - (\mu + \nu)^2 \\
&= E(X^2) + 2E(XY) + E(Y^2) - \mu^2 - 2\mu\nu - \nu^2.
\end{aligned}
$$

If X and Y are independent, then $E(XY) = E(X)E(Y) = \mu\nu$, and

$$V(X + Y) = E(X^2) - \mu^2 + E(Y^2) - \nu^2 = V(X) + V(Y).$$

More generally, if $X_1, X_2, \ldots, X_n$ are independent, then

$$V(c_1 X_1 + c_2 X_2 + \cdots + c_n X_n) = c_1^2 V(X_1) + c_2^2 V(X_2) + \cdots + c_n^2 V(X_n).$$
∎

Independent Trials

COROLLARY 15

If $X_1, X_2, \ldots, X_n$ is an independent trials process of bounded random variables, with $E(X_i) = \mu$ and $V(X_i) = \sigma^2$, and if

$$S_n = X_1 + X_2 + \cdots + X_n,$$

$$A_n = \frac{S_n}{n},$$

then

$$E(S_n) = n\mu , \qquad V(S_n) = n\sigma^2,$$

$$E(A_n) = \mu , \qquad V(A_n) = \frac{1}{n} \sigma^2.$$

It follows that if we set

$$S_n^* = \frac{S_n - \mu}{\sqrt{n\sigma^2}},$$

then

$$E(S_n^*) = 0 ; \qquad V(S_n^*) = 1.$$

We say that S_n^* is a *standardized version of S_n* (see Section 6.2, Exercise 13).

Unbounded Random Variables

So far, we have considered only bounded random variables. But all of our results concerning expected values and variances hold as well for unbounded random variables, provided that the expected values and variances in question are *finite*. The expected value will be finite if

$$\int_{-\infty}^{+\infty} |x| f_X(x) dx < \infty,$$

and the variance will be finite if, in addition,

$$\int_{-\infty}^{+\infty} x^2 f_X(x) dx < \infty.$$

When these conditions hold, then the proofs of our previous results involve only the additional care required to assure that the integrals in question are convergent, and we shall not take the time to consider them here. Let us look instead at a few examples involving unbounded random variables.

Exponential Density

EXAMPLE 6
Let X be a continuous random variable with range $[0,\infty]$ and density function

$$f_X(x) = \lambda e^{-\lambda x}$$

(exponential density with parameter λ, Example 6 of Chapter 2, Section 2.2). Then we have, by using Theorem 11 and integrating by parts,

$$E(X) = \int_0^\infty x f_X(x)dx$$

$$= \lambda \int_0^\infty x e^{-\lambda x}dx$$

$$= -xe^{-\lambda x}\Big|_0^\infty + \int_0^\infty e^{-\lambda x}dx$$

$$= 0 + \frac{e^{-\lambda x}}{-\lambda}\Big|_0^\infty = \frac{1}{\lambda}.$$

Similarly,

$$V(X) = \int_0^\infty x^2 f_X(x)dx - \frac{1}{\lambda^2}$$

$$= \lambda \int_0^\infty x^2 e^{-\lambda x}dx - \frac{1}{\lambda^2}$$

$$= -x^2 e^{-\lambda x}\Big|_0^\infty + 2\int_0^\infty x e^{-\lambda x}dx - \frac{1}{\lambda^2}$$

$$= -x^2 e^{-\lambda x}\Big|_0^\infty - \frac{2xe^{-\lambda x}}{\lambda}\Big|_0^\infty - \frac{2}{\lambda^2}e^{-\lambda x}\Big|_0^\infty - \frac{1}{\lambda^2} = \frac{2}{\lambda^2} - \frac{1}{\lambda^2} = \frac{1}{\lambda^2}.$$

In this case, both $E(X)$ and $V(X)$ are finite if $\lambda > 0$. $\square$

Normal Density

EXAMPLE 7
Let X^* be a continuous random variable with range $(-\infty, +\infty)$ and normal density function

$$f_{X^*}(x) = \frac{1}{\sqrt{2\pi}}e^{-x^2/2}$$

(standardized normal density, Example 7 of Chapter 2, Section 2.2). Then we have

$$E(X^*) = \int_{-\infty}^\infty x f_{X^*}(x)dx$$

$$= \frac{1}{\sqrt{2\pi}}\int_{-\infty}^\infty x e^{-x^2/2}dx$$

$$= \frac{1}{\sqrt{2\pi}}(-e^{-x^2/2})\Big|_{-\infty}^{+\infty} = 0,$$

$$V(X^*) = \int_{-\infty}^{+\infty} x^2 f_{X^*}(x)dx - 0$$

$$= \frac{1}{\sqrt{2\pi}} \int_{-\infty}^{+\infty} xxe^{-x^2/2}dx$$

$$= \frac{1}{\sqrt{2\pi}} (-xe^{-x^2/2}) \Big|_{-\infty}^{+\infty} + \frac{1}{\sqrt{2\pi}} \int_{-\infty}^{+\infty} e^{-x^2/2}dx = 0 + 1 = 1.$$

Again both $E(X^*)$ and $V(X^*)$ are finite.

Now let X be a continuous random variable with range $(-\infty, +\infty)$ and density function (general normal density)

$$f_X(x) = \frac{1}{\sqrt{2\pi a^2}} e^{-\frac{(x-c)^2}{2a^2}}.$$

Then we can write $X = aX^* + c$, where X^* has the standardized normal density function described above. Since $E(X^*) = 0$, $V(X^*) = 1$ by the calculation above, we must have by Theorem 13 that

$$\mu = E(X) = E(aX^* + c) = c,$$

$$\sigma^2 = V(X) = V(aX^* + c) = a^2.$$

Accordingly, in this case we shall write the density function $f_X(x)$ in the form

$$f_X(x) = \frac{1}{\sqrt{2\pi\sigma^2}} e^{-\frac{(x-\mu)^2}{2\sigma^2}},$$

knowing that the expected value and variance for this density are μ and σ^2, respectively. □

Cauchy Density

EXAMPLE 8

Let X be a continuous random variable with range $(-\infty, +\infty)$ and density function.

$$f_X(x) = \frac{a}{\pi} \frac{1}{a^2 + x^2}.$$

Such a density is called a *Cauchy density* with parameter a. Then we have

$$\frac{a}{\pi} \int_{-\infty}^{+\infty} \frac{|x|dx}{a^2 + x^2} = \infty,$$

so that *neither the expected value nor the variance is defined for the Cauchy density.*

Densities like the Cauchy density whose variance is not defined, behave quite differently from those whose variance is finite in a number of important respects. We shall see one instance of this difference in Chapter 8, Section 8.2. □

Queues

EXAMPLE 9
Let us consider again the queueing problem, that is, the problem of the customers waiting in a queue for service (see Chapter 5, Section 5.2, Example 12). We suppose again that customers join the queue in such a way that the time between arrivals is an exponentially distributed random variable X with density function

$$f_X(t) = \lambda e^{-\lambda t}.$$

Then the expected value of the time between arrivals is simply $\dfrac{1}{\lambda}$ (See Example 6). The reciprocal λ of this expected value is often referred to as the *arrival rate*. Similarly, we suppose again that the customers are served in such a way that the service time is another exponentially distributed random variable Y with density function

$$f_X(t) = \mu e^{-\mu t}.$$

Then the expected value of the service time is

$$E(X) = \int_0^\infty t f_X(t)dt = \frac{1}{\mu}.$$

The reciprocal μ of this expected value is often referred to as the *service rate*.

We expect on grounds of our everyday experience with queues that if the service rate is greater than the arrival rate, then the average queue size will tend to stabilize, but if the service rate is less than the arrival rate, then the queue will tend to increase in length without limit. The simulations in Example 12 of Chapter 5, Section 5.2, tend to bear out our everyday experience. We can make this conclusion more precise if we introduce the *traffic intensity* as the product

$$\rho = \text{(arrival rate)(average service time)} = \frac{\lambda}{\mu} = \frac{1/\mu}{1/\lambda}.$$

The traffic intensity is also the ratio of the average service time to the average time between arrivals. If the traffic intensity is less than 1 the queue will perform reasonably, but if it is greater than 1 the queue will grow indefinitely large. In the critical case of $\rho = 1$, it can be shown that the queue will become large but there will always be times at which the queue is empty.[16]

---

[16]See L. Kleinrock, *Queueing Systems*, vol. 2 (New York: John Wiley and Sons, 1975).

In the case that the traffic intensity is less than 1 we can consider the length of the queue as a random variable Z whose expected value is finite,

$$E(Z) = N.$$

The time spent in the queue by a single customer can be considered as a random variable W whose expected value is finite,

$$E(W) = T.$$

Then we can argue that, when a customer joins the queue, he expects to find N people ahead of him, and when he leaves the queue, he expects to find λT people behind him. Since, in equilibrium, these should be the same, we would expect to find that

$$N = \lambda T.$$

Little's Law

This is the content of *Little's law for queues*.[17] This is a quite general law, and the proof is an elaboration of our simple heuristic argument. Note that in this case we are counting the waiting time of all customers, even those that do not have to wait at all. In our simulation in Chapter 5, Section 5.2, we did not consider these customers.

If we knew the expected queue length then we could use Little's law to obtain the expected waiting time, since

$$T = \frac{N}{\lambda}.$$

The queue length is a random variable with a discrete density. We can estimate this density by simulation, keeping track of the queue lengths at the times at which a customer arrives. We show the result of this simulation (using the program **Queue Length Density**) in Figure 5.

We note that the density appears to be a geometric density. In the study of queueing theory it is shown that the density for the queue length in equilibrium is indeed a geometric density with

$$p_j = (1 - \rho)\rho^j \qquad j = 0,1,2, \ldots$$

The expected value of a random variable with this density is

$$N = \frac{\rho}{(1 - \rho)}.$$

(see Section 6.1, Example 8). Thus by Little's result the expected waiting time is

$$T = \frac{\rho}{\lambda(1 - \rho)} = \frac{1}{\mu - \lambda},$$

where μ is the service rate, λ the arrival rate, and p the traffic intensity.

[17]Ibid., p. 17.

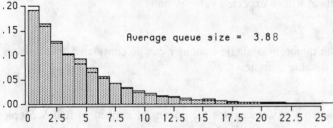

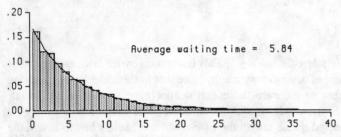

Figure 5 Queue size and waiting time densities.

In our simulation, the arrival rate was $^2/_3$ and the average service time was 1.2. Thus, the traffic intensity is $^2/_3 \cdot 1.2 = .8$, the expected queue size is

$$\frac{.8}{(1 - .8)} = 4,$$

and the expected waiting time is

$$\frac{1}{\dfrac{5}{6} - \dfrac{2}{3}} = 6.$$

In our simulation the average queue size was 3.88 and the average waiting time was 5.84, in reasonable agreement with the theoretical values. In Figure 5 we show the histogram for the waiting times. This histogram suggests that the density for the waiting times is exponential with parameter $\mu - \lambda$, and this is the case. □

Numerical Calculation

Of course, another way to compute the mean and variance for a continuous random variable is by numerical integration. It is a simple matter to provide subroutines to do this. We have put in **Lib.Cont** a function called **expectation_cont** and one called

variance_cont to compute the expected value and variance for a density function that the user specifies at the end of the program calling these subroutines. Here is an example showing the way that these subroutines can be used to compute the mean and variance of the exponential density.

```
! Continuous Mean & Variance   (CONIMVAR)
!
! Uses the functions 'expectation_cont' and 'variance_cont' in Lib.cont
! to evaluate the expected value and variance of a continuous random
! variable, whose density must be defined here as an external function
! called 'density'.  You need to give the endpoints a,b of the interval
! over which you want the integration carried out, and the number of
! subdivisions thereof.

library "Lib.cont*"
declare function expectation_cont, variance_cont

do

    input prompt "Endpoints & number of subdivisions: a, b, n = ": a,b,n
    if n = 0 then stop

    print "The expected value is"; round(expectation_cont(a,b,n),4)
    print "The variance is"; round(variance_cont(a,b,n),4)
    print

loop

end


function density(x)

    declare function exponential
    let lambda = 1/4
    let density = exponential(x,lambda)

end function
```

You are asked to use this program to check your calculations for these quantities in certain of the exercises.

Exercises

1. Let X be a random variable with range $[-1,1]$ and f_X its density function. Find $\mu(X)$ and $\sigma^2(X)$ if, for $|x| > 1$ $f_X(x) = 0$, and for $|x| < 1$,
   (a) $f_X(x) = \frac{1}{2}$.
   (b) $f_X(x) = |x|$.
   (c) $f_X(x) = 1 - |x|$.
   (d) $f_X(x) = \frac{3}{2} x^2$.

2. Check the computations in Exercise 1 by using the functions **expectation_cont** and **variance_cont** to compute the mean and variance numerically.

3. Let X be a random variable with range $[-1,1]$ and f_X its density function. Find $\mu(X)$ and $\sigma^2(X)$ if, for $|x| > 1$ $f_X(x) = 0$, and for $|x| < 1$,
   (a) $f_X(x) = \frac{3}{4}(1 - x^2)$.
   (b) $f_X(x) = \frac{\pi}{4} \cos\left(\frac{\pi x}{2}\right)$.
   (c) $f_X(x) = \frac{x + 1}{2}$.
   (d) $f_X(x) = \frac{3}{8}(x + 1)^2$.

4. Check the computations in Exercise 3 by using the functions **expectation_cont** and **variance_cont** to compute the mean and variance numerically.

5. The lifetime, measured in hours, of the ACME super light bulb is a random variable T with density function $f_T(t) = \lambda^2 t e^{-\lambda t}$, where $\lambda = .05$. What is the expected lifetime of this light bulb? What is its variance?

6. Let X be a random variable with range $[-1,1]$ and density function $f_X(x) = ax + b$ if $|x| < 1$ and 0 otherwise.
   (a) Show that if $\int_{-1}^{+1} f_X(x)dx = 1$, then $b = \frac{1}{2}$.
   (b) Show that if $f_X(x) \geqslant 0$, then $-\frac{1}{2} \leqslant a \leqslant \frac{1}{2}$.
   (c) Show that $\mu = \frac{2}{3}a$, and hence that $-\frac{1}{3} \leqslant \mu \leqslant \frac{1}{3}$.
   (d) Show that $\sigma^2(X) = \frac{2}{3}b = \frac{1}{3}$.

7. Let X be a random variable with range $[-1, +1]$ and density function $f_X(x) = ax^2 + bx + c$ if $|x| < 1$, and 0 otherwise.
   (a) Show that $\frac{2a}{3} + 2c = 1$ (see Exercise 6).
   (b) Show that $\frac{2b}{3} = \mu(X)$.
   (c) Show that $\frac{2a}{5} + \frac{2c}{3} = \sigma^2(X)$.
   (d) Find a, b, and c if $\mu(X) = 0$, $\sigma^2(X) = \frac{1}{15}$, and sketch the graph of f_X.
   (e) Find a, b, and c if $\mu(X) = 0$, $\sigma^2(X) = \frac{1}{2}$, and sketch the graph of f_X.

8. Let T be a random variable with range $[0,\infty]$ and f_T its density function. Find $\mu(T)$ and $\sigma^2(T)$ if, for $t < 0$, $f_T(t) = 0$, and for $t > 0$,
   (a) $f_T(t) = 3e^{-3\tau}$.
   (b) $f_T(t) = \frac{9te^{-3t}}{2}$.
   (c) $f_T(t) = \frac{3}{(1 + t)^4}$.

9. Let X be a random variable with density function f_X. Show, using elementary calculus, that the function

$$\phi(a) = E((X - a)^2)$$

takes its minimum value when $a = \mu(X)$, and in that case $\phi(a) = \sigma^2(X)$.

10. Let X be a random variable with mean μ and variance σ^2. Let $Y = aX^2 + bX + c$. Find the expected value of Y.

11. Let X, Y, and Z be independent random variables, each with mean μ and variance σ^2.
    (a) Find the expected value and variance of $S = X + Y + Z$.
    (b) Find the expected value and variance of $A = \frac{1}{3}(X + Y + Z)$.
    (c) Find the expected value of S^2 and A^2.

12. Let X and Y be independent random variables with uniform density functions on $[0,1]$. Find
    (a) $E(|X - Y|)$.
    (b) $E(\max(X,Y))$.
    (c) $E(\min(X,Y))$.
    (d) $E(X^2 + Y^2)$.
    (e) $E((X + Y)^2)$.

13. The Pilsdorff beer company runs a fleet of trucks along the 100 mile road from Hangtown to Dry Gulch. The trucks are old, and are apt to break down at any point along the road with equal probability. Where should the company locate a garage so as to minimize the expected distance from a typical breakdown to the garage? In other words, if X is a random variable giving the location of the breakdown, measured, say, from Hangtown, and b gives the location of the garage, what choice of b minimizes $E(|X - b|)$? Now suppose X is not distributed uniformly over $[0,100]$, but instead has density function $f_X(x) = \dfrac{2x}{10,000}$. Then what choice of b minimizes $E(|X - b|)$?

14. Find $E(\text{rnd}^{\text{rnd}})$. Then verify your answer by simulation.

15. Let X be a random variable that takes on nonnegative values and has distribution function $F(x)$. Show that

$$E(X) = \int_0^\infty (1 - F(x))dx.$$

    Hint: integrate by parts.
    Illustrate this result by calculating $E(X)$ by this method if X has an exponential distribution $F(x) = 1 - e^{-\lambda x}$ for $x \geq 0$, and $F(x) = 0$ otherwise.

16. Let X be a random variable distributed uniformly over $[0,20]$. Define a new random variable Y by $Y = \text{int}[X]$ (the greatest integer in X). Find the expected value and

variance for Y. Do the same for $Z = \text{int}[X + .5]$. (Note that Y is the value of X rounded off to the nearest smaller integer, while Z is the value of X rounded off to the nearest integer. Which method of rounding off is better? Why?)

17. Assume that the lifetime of a diesel engine part is a random variable X with density f_X. When the part wears out, it is replaced by another with the same density. Let $N(t)$ be the number of parts that are used in time t. We want to study the random variable $N(t)/t$. Since parts are replaced on the average every $E(X)$ time units, we expect about $t/E(X)$ parts to be used in time t. That is, we expect that

$$\lim_{t \to \infty} E\left(\frac{N(t)}{t}\right) = \frac{1}{E(X)}.$$

This result is correct but quite difficult to prove. Write a program that will allow you to specify the density f_X, and the time t, and simulate this experiment to find $N(t)/t$. Have your program repeat the experiment 500 times and plot a bar graph for the random outcomes of $N(t)/t$. From this data, estimate $E(N(t)/t)$ and compare this with $1/E(X)$. In particular, do this for $t = 100$ with the two densities

(a) $f_X = e^{-t}$

and

(b) $f_X = te^{-t}$.

18. Let X and Y be random variables. The *covariance* $\text{cov}(X,Y)$ is defined by (see Exercise 24 of Section 6.2)

$$\text{cov}(X,Y) = E((X - \mu(X))(Y - \mu(Y))).$$

(a) Show that $\text{cov}(X,Y) = E(XY) - E(X)E(Y)$.
(b) Using (a), show that $\text{cov}(X,Y) = 0$, if X and Y are independent. (Caution: the converse is *not* always true.)
(c) Show that $V(X + Y) = V(X) + V(Y) + 2\text{cov}(X,Y)$.

19. Let X and Y be random variables with positive variance. The *correlation* of X and Y is defined as

$$\rho(X,Y) = \frac{\text{cov}(X,Y)}{\sqrt{V(X)V(Y)}}.$$

(a) Using 18(c), show that

$$0 \le V\left(\frac{X}{\sigma(X)} + \frac{Y}{\sigma(Y)}\right) = 2(1 + \rho(X,Y)).$$

(b) Now show that

$$0 \le V\left(\frac{X}{\sigma(X)} - \frac{Y}{\sigma(Y)}\right) = 2(1 - \rho(X,Y)).$$

(c) Using **(a)** and **(b)**, show that

$$-1 \leq \rho(X,Y) \leq +1.$$

20. Let X and Y be independent random variables with uniform densities in $[0,1]$. Let $Z = X + Y$ and $W = X - Y$. Find
    (a) $\rho(X,Y)$ (see Exercise 19).
    (b) $\rho(X,Z)$.
    (c) $\rho(Y,W)$.
    (d) $\rho(Z,W)$.

21. When studying certain physiological data, such as heights of fathers and sons, it is often natural to assume that these data (e.g., the heights of the fathers and the heights of the sons) are described by random variables with normal densities. These random variables, however, are not independent but rather are correlated. For example, a two dimensional standard normal density for correlated random variables has the form

$$f_{X,Y}(x,y) = \frac{1}{2\pi\sqrt{1-\rho^2}} \cdot e^{-(x^2-2\rho xy+y^2)/2(1-\rho^2)}.$$

    (a) Show that X and Y each have standard normal densities.
    (b) Show that the correlation of X and Y (see Exercise 19) is ρ.

22. For correlated random variables X and Y it is natural to ask for the expected value for X given Y. For example, Galton calculated the expected value of the height of a son given the height of the father. He used this to show that tall men can be expected to have sons who are less tall on the average. Similarly, students who do very well on one exam can be expected to do less well on the next exam, and so forth. This is called *regression on the mean*. To define this conditional expected value, we first define a conditional density of X given $Y = y$ by

$$f_{X|Y}(x|y) = \frac{f_{X,Y}(x,y)}{f_Y(y)},$$

    where $f_{X,Y}(x,y)$ is the joint density of X and Y, and f_Y is the density for Y. Then the conditional expected value of X given $Y = y$ is

$$E(X|Y = y) = \int_a^b x f_{X|Y}(x|y)dx.$$

    For the normal density in Exercise 21, show that the conditional expectation of $f_{X|Y}(x|y)$ is normal with mean ρy and variance $1 - \rho^2$. From this we see that if X and Y are positively correlated $(0 < \rho \leq 1)$, then the expected value for X given $Y = y$ will be less than y (i.e., we have regression on the mean).

23. A point Y is chosen at random from $[0,1]$. A second point X is then chosen from the interval $[0,Y]$. Find the density for X. *Hint:* Calculate $f_{X|Y}$ as in Exercise 22 and then use

$$f_X(x) = \int_0^1 f_{X|Y}(x|y)f_Y(y)dy.$$

24. Let W and Z be two random numbers chosen from the unit interval. Then

$$X = \sqrt{-2\log(W)} \left[\frac{\cos(2\pi Z)}{\sqrt{2(1 - \rho)}} + \frac{\sin(2\pi Z)}{\sqrt{2(1 + \rho)}} \right],$$

$$Y = \sqrt{-2\log(W)} \left[\frac{\cos(2\pi Z)}{\sqrt{2(1 - \rho)}} - \frac{\sin(2\pi Z)}{\sqrt{2(1 + \rho)}} \right]$$

are *dependent* normally distributed random variables, both standardized to have mean 0 and standard deviation 1, with correlation ρ (see Exercise 19). Write a program to plot 1000 pairs X,Y for $\rho = -^1/_2, 0, ^1/_2$. For each choice of ρ, have your program plot the curve determined by the parametric equations

$$x = \frac{r\cos(\theta)}{\sqrt{2(1 - \rho)}} + \frac{r\sin(\theta)}{\sqrt{2(1 + \rho)}},$$

$$y = \frac{r\cos(\theta)}{\sqrt{2(1 - \rho)}} - \frac{r\sin(\theta)}{\sqrt{2(1 + \rho)}},$$

for $r = 1,2,3$. These curves are curves of constant density, and describe the shape of the region in the x-y plane where your outcomes tend to fall.

25. Following Galton, let us assume that the fathers and sons have heights that are dependent normal random variables. Assume that the average height is 68 inches, standard deviation is 2.7 inches, and the correlation coefficient is .5 (see Exercises 21 and 22). That is, assume that the heights of the fathers and sons have the form $2.7X + 68$ and $2.7Y + 68$, respectively, where X and Y are correlated standardized normal random variables, with correlation coefficient .5.

(a) What is the expected height for the son of a father whose height is 72 inches?

(b) Plot a scatter diagram of the heights of 1000 father and son pairs. *Hint:* you can choose standardized pairs as in Exercise 24 and then plot $(2.7X + 68, 2.7Y + 68)$.

26. When we have pairs of data (x_i, y_i) that are outcomes of the pairs of dependent random variables X, Y we can estimate the correlation coefficient ρ by

$$\bar{r} = \frac{\sum_i (x_i - \bar{x})(y_i - \bar{y})}{(n - 1)s_X s_Y},$$

where $\bar{x}$ and $\bar{y}$ are the sample means for X and Y, respectively, and s_X and s_Y are the sample standard deviations for X and Y (see Section 6.2, Exercise 19). Write a program to compute the sample means, variances, and correlation for such dependent data. Use your program to compute these quantities for Galton's data on heights of parents and children given in Appendix B.

Plot the equal density ellipses as defined in Exercise 24 for $r = 4, 6$, and 8, and on the same graph print the values that appear in the table at the appropriate points. For example, print 12 at the point (70.5,68.2), indicating that there were 12 cases where the parent's height was 70.5 and the child's was 68.2. See if Galton's data is consistent with the equal density ellipses.

Chapter 7

Sums of Independent Random Variables

7.1 SUMS OF DISCRETE RANDOM VARIABLES

In this chapter we turn to the important question of determining the distribution of a sum of independent random variables in terms of the distributions of the individual constituents. In this section we consider only sums of discrete random variables, reserving the case of continuous random variables for the next section.

We consider here only random variables whose values are integers, positive or negative. Their density functions are then defined on these integers. We shall find it convenient to assume here that these density functions are defined for *all* integers, by defining them to be 0 where they are not otherwise defined.

Thus, if X is a random variable describing the outcome of one toss of a fair coin, then the values of X are 0 and 1 and the density function for X is

$$p_X = \begin{pmatrix} 0 & 1 \\ {}^1/_2 & {}^1/_2 \end{pmatrix}.$$

(See Chapter 5, Section 5.1, Example 2.)

Convolutions

DEFINITION 1

Let p and q be two densities defined on the set of all integers, but > 0 for only a finite number of integers. Then the *convolution* of p and q is the density $r = p*q$ given by

$$r(j) = \sum_k p(k) \cdot q(j - k) \qquad j = \ldots, -2, -1, 0, 1, 2, \ldots.$$

(Since p and q are now defined for all integers, but > 0 for only a finite number of integers, the sum here is actually a finite sum of positive numbers.)

Sums

The next theorem shows that r is, in fact, a density.

THEOREM 1

Let X and Y be two independent random variables with densities p and q defined on the set of all integers. Then the density r for the sum $Z = X + Y$ is equal to the convolution of p and q.

Proof. Let $Z = X + Y$ and let $r(j) = P(Z = j)$. Then

$$r(j) = P(Z = j) = \sum_k P(X = k, \text{ and } Y = j - k).$$

Since X and Y are independent, we can write this as

$$r(j) = \sum_k P(X = k) \cdot P(Y = j - k) = \sum_k p(k) \cdot q(j - k),$$

and this last sum is the convolution of p and q. ∎

The equation for $r(j)$ has a simple probabilistic interpretation. In order for the sum Z to have value j, the variable X must have some value k and then Y must have the value $j - k$, and this happens with probability $p(k)q(j - k)$.

Now let $S_n = X_1 + X_2 + \cdots + X_n$ be the sum of n independent random variables of an independent trials process with common density p defined on the integers. Then the density of S_1 is p. We can write

$$S_n = S_{n-1} + X_n.$$

Thus, since we know the density of X_n is p, we can find the density of S_n by induction.

EXAMPLE 1

A die is rolled twice. Let X_1 and X_2 be the outcomes, and let $S_2 = X_1 + X_2$ be the sum of these outcomes. Then X_1 and X_2 have the common density:

$$p = \begin{pmatrix} 1 & 2 & 3 & 4 & 5 & 6 \\ \dfrac{1}{6} & \dfrac{1}{6} & \dfrac{1}{6} & \dfrac{1}{6} & \dfrac{1}{6} & \dfrac{1}{6} \end{pmatrix}.$$

The density for S_2 is then the convolution of this density with itself. Thus,

$$P(S_2 = 2) = p(1)p(1)$$

$$= \frac{1}{6} \cdot \frac{1}{6} = \frac{1}{36},$$

$$P(S_2 = 3) = p(1)p(2) + p(2)p(1)$$

$$= \frac{1}{6} \cdot \frac{1}{6} + \frac{1}{6} \cdot \frac{1}{6} = \frac{2}{36},$$

$$P(S_2 = 4) = p(1)p(3) + p(2)p(2) + p(3)p(1)$$

$$= \frac{1}{6} \cdot \frac{1}{6} + \frac{1}{6} \cdot \frac{1}{6} + \frac{1}{6} \cdot \frac{1}{6} = \frac{3}{36}.$$

Continuing in this way we would find $P(S_2 = 5) = {}^4/_{36}$, $P(S_2 = 6) = {}^5/_{36}$, $P(S_2 = 7) = {}^6/_{36}$, $P(S_2 = 8) = {}^5/_{36}$, $P(S_2 = 9) = {}^4/_{36}$, $P(S_2 = 10) = {}^3/_{36}$, $P(S_2 = 11) = {}^2/_{36}$, and $P(S_2 = 12) = {}^1/_{36}$.

The density for S_3 would then be the convolution of the density for S_2 with the density for X_3. Thus,

$$P(S_3 = 3) = P(S_2 = 2)P(X_3 = 1)$$

$$= \frac{1}{36} \cdot \frac{1}{6} = \frac{1}{216},$$

$$P(S_3 = 4) = P(S_2 = 3) P(X_3 = 1) + P(S_2 = 2) P(X_3 = 2)$$

$$= \frac{2}{36} \cdot \frac{1}{6} + \frac{1}{36} \cdot \frac{1}{6} = \frac{3}{216},$$

and so forth.

This is clearly a tedious job, and we should write a program to carry this calculation out for us. To do this we first write a subroutine to form the convolution of two densities p and q and return the density r, and put this in our library **Lib.Prob** (see top of facing page).

We can then use this subroutine to obtain a program **Sum** to find the density for the sum S_n of n independent random variables with a common density p (see bottom of facing page).

```
sub convolve(p(),q(),  r())

    let p_lower = lbound(p)
    let q_lower = lbound(q)
    let r_lower = p_lower + q_lower

    let p_upper = ubound(p)
    let q_upper = ubound(q)
    let r_upper = p_upper + q_upper

    mat r = zer(r_lower to r_upper)

    for j = r_lower to r_upper
        let sum = 0
        for k = p_lower to p_upper
            if q_lower <= j-k and j-k <= q_upper then
                let sum = sum + p(k) * q(j-k)
            end if
        next k
        let r(j) = sum
    next j

end sub


! Sum    (SUM)
!
! Computes the density of the sum of n independent random variables,
! each of which has the density
!
!                       p(1),...,p(size)
!
! on the integers 1 to 'size'.  This is done by
!
!    (1) setting q() = p() and convolving them to get r() = p() * q()
!    (2) setting q() = r(); r() = p() * q() = p() * p() * p()
!    (3) repeating (2)

library "Lib.prob*"
dim p(20), q(20), r(20)

read size
mat p = zer(size)
mat read p

data 6
data .166667,.166667,.1666667,.1666667,.1666667,.1666667

mat q = p

input prompt "Take n-fold sum for n = ": n

for convolution = 2 to n
    call convolve(p,q,r)
    mat q = zer(lbound(r) to ubound(r))
    mat q = r
next convolution

for k = n to n*size
    print  k , round(r(k),4)
next k

end
```

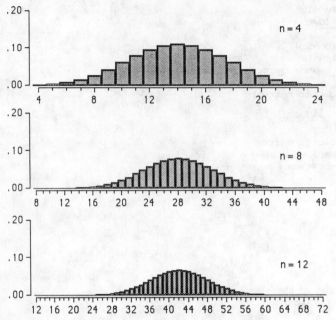

Figure 1 Densities of S_n for rolling a die n times.

This program can, in turn, be easily modified to obtain a program **Sum Plot** to plot the density for the n-fold convolution of a given density. Running **Sum Plot** for the example of rolling a die n times for $n = 4, 8, 12$ results in the densities shown in Figure 1.

We see that, as in the case of Bernoulli trials, the densities become bell-shaped, but the maximum values decrease and the curves flatten out. We shall discuss in Chapter 9 a very general theorem called the *Central Limit Theorem* that will explain this phenomenon.　　　　　　　　　　　　　　　　　　　　　　　　　　　　□

EXAMPLE 2

A well-known method for evaluating a bridge hand is: an ace is assigned a value of 4, a king 3, a queen 2, and a jack 1. All other cards are assigned a value of 0. The *point count* of the hand is then the sum of the values of the cards in the hand. (It is actually more complicated than this, taking into account voids in suits, and so forth, but we consider here this simplified form of the point count.) If a card is dealt at random to a player, then the point count for this card has density

$$p_X = \begin{pmatrix} 0 & 1 & 2 & 3 & 4 \\ 36/52 & 4/52 & 4/52 & 4/52 & 4/52 \end{pmatrix}.$$

Let us regard the total hand of 13 cards as 13 independent trials with this common distribution. (Again this is not quite correct because we assume here that we are always choosing a card from a full deck.) Then the density for the point count C for the hand can be found from the program **Sum** by using the density for a single card and choosing $n = 13$. A player with a point count of 13 or more is said to have an *opening bid*. The probability of having an opening bid is then

$P(C \geq 13)$.

We can easily modify the program **Sum** to find this probability after it has found the density for C. We have only to add the values for the density for point counts ≥ 13. Doing this we find that

$P(C \geq 13) = .2845$,

so that about one in four hands should be opening hands according to this simplified model. A more realistic discussion of this problem can be found in Epstein, *The Theory of Gambling and Statistical Logic*[1]: $\square$

For certain special distributions it is possible to find an expression for the density that results from convoluting the density with itself n times.

Sums of Bernoulli Trials

EXAMPLE 3

Let $X_1, X_2, \ldots, X_n$ be the outcomes of n Bernoulli trials with probability p for success. Let $X_{n+1}, X_{n+2}, \ldots, X_{n+m}$ be the result of another m independent trials with the same p. Here $X_j = 1$ if success occurs and 0 if failure occurs. Then the sum of the first n random variables has a binomial density $b(n,p,j)$, and the sum of the next m random variables has a binomial density $b(m,p,j)$. But the sum of the $n + m$ random variables has a binomial density $b(n + m,p,j)$, and so the convolution of the binomial density $b(n,p,j)$ with the binomial density $b(m,p,j)$ is the binomial density $b(n + m,p,j)$. Note that we have to have the same value for p in each case. $\square$

EXAMPLE 4

Consider a Bernoulli trials process with probability p for success. Let T_1 be the number of failures before the first success. Then the density for T_1 is:

$P(T_1 = i) = q^i p \qquad i = 0,1,2, \ldots .$

This is essentially the same as the geometric density, the only difference being that the values of i start with 0 and for a geometric density we assumed that they started with 1 (see Chapter 5, Section 5.1, Example 7). That is, $T_1 + 1$ has a geometric density. Now let T_r be the number of failures, before the rth success. Then T_r is the sum of r random variables each having the density of T_1. But we can compute the density for T_r as follows: In order for T_r to have the value k it must be the case that in the first $k + r - 1$ outcomes

[1]R.A. Epstein, *The Theory of Gambling and Statistical Logic*, rev. ed. (New York: Academic Press, 1977).

there have been exactly $r - 1$ successes and k failures, and then the next outcome must be a success. Thus, the density for T_r is

$$u(r,p,k) = P(T_r = k) = \binom{r + k - 1}{k} p^r q^k, \quad k = 0, 1, 2, \dots .$$

In this form the density is called the *negative binomial density*. ☐

EXAMPLE 5

A coin is tossed until the second time a head turns up. The density for the number of tails that turn up is $u(2,{}^1\!/_2,k)$. Thus the probability that k tails turn up before the second head does is

$$u\left(2,\frac{1}{2},k\right) = \binom{k + 1}{k}\frac{1}{2^{k+2}}, \quad k = 0,1,2, \dots .$$

In Figure 2 we give a graph of the density for $r = 2$ and $p = .25$ and for $r = 4$ and $p = .5$. Note that the density is quite asymmetric, having a long tail reflecting the fact that large values of k are possible. ☐

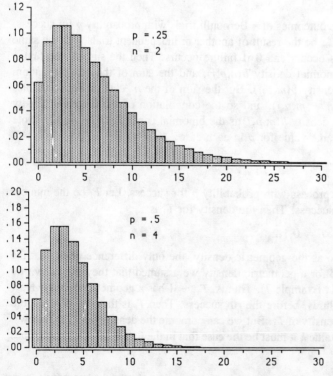

Figure 2 Negative binomial densities.

Exercises

1. A die is rolled three times. Find the probability that the sum of the outcomes is
   (a) greater than 9.
   (b) an odd number.

2. The price of a stock on a given trading day changes according to the density

$$p_X = \begin{pmatrix} -1 & 0 & 1 & 2 \\ 1/4 & 1/2 & 1/8 & 1/8 \end{pmatrix}.$$

   Find the density for the change in price after two (independent) trading days.

3. Let X_1 and X_2 be independent random variables with common density

$$p_X = \begin{pmatrix} 0 & 1 & 2 \\ 1/8 & 3/8 & 1/2 \end{pmatrix}.$$

   Find the density of the sum $X_1 + X_2$.

4. In one play of a certain game you win an amount X with density

$$p_X = \begin{pmatrix} 1 & 2 & 3 \\ 1/4 & 1/4 & 1/2 \end{pmatrix}.$$

   Using the program **Sum** find the density for your total winnings after ten (independent) plays. Plot this density.

5. Consider the following two experiments: the first has outcome X taking on the values 0, 1, and 2 with equal probabilities; the second results in an (independent) outcome Y taking on the value 3 with probability $1/4$ and 4 with probablity $3/4$. Find the density of
   (a) $Y + X$.
   (b) $Y - X$.

6. People arrive at a queue according to the following scheme: During each minute of time either 0 or 1 person arrives. The probability that 1 person arrives is p and that no person arrives is $q = 1 - p$. Let C_r be the number of customers arriving in the first r minutes. Consider a Bernoulli trials process with a success if a person arrives in a unit time and failure if no person arrives in a unit time. Let T_r be the number of failures before the rth success.
   (a) What is the density for T_r?
   (b) What is the density for C_r?
   (c) Find the mean and variance for the number of customers arriving in the first r minutes.

7. A die is rolled three times with outcomes X_1, X_2, and X_3. Let Y_3 be the maximum of the values obtained. Show that

$$P(Y_3 \le j) = P(X_1 \le j)^3.$$

   Use this to find the density of Y_3. Does Y_3 have a bell-shaped density?

8. Let q_{nj} be the probability that in n rolls of a die the maximum number that turns up is j. Show that

$$q_{nj} = \left(\frac{j}{6}\right)^n - \left(\frac{j-1}{6}\right)^n.$$

9. You are presented with four different dice. The first one has two sides marked 0 and four sides marked 4. The second one has a 3 on every side. The third one has a 2 on four sides and a 6 on two sides, and the fourth one has a 1 on three sides and a 5 on three sides. You allow your friend to pick any of the four dice he wishes. Then you pick one of the remaining three and you each roll your die. The person with the largest number showing wins a dollar. Show that you can choose your die so that you have probability $^2/_3$ of winning no matter which die your friend picks.

10. A baseball player is to play in the World Series. Based upon his season play, you estimate that if he comes to bat four times in a game the number of hits he will get has a density

$$p_X = \begin{pmatrix} 0 & 1 & 2 & 3 & 4 \\ .4 & .2 & .2 & .1 & .1 \end{pmatrix}.$$

Assume that the player comes to bat four times in each game of the series. Using the program **Sum,** find the probability that his batting average for the series exceeds .400 for each of the possible series lengths: four-game, five-game, six-game, seven-game. (The batting average is the number of hits divided by the number of times at bat.)

11. Prove that you cannot load two dice in such a way that the probabilities for any sum from 2 to 12 are the same. (Be sure to consider the case where one or more sides turn up with probability zero.)

12. (Lévy)[2] Assume that n is an integer, not prime. Show that you can find two densities a and b on the nonnegative integers such that the convolution of a and b is the equiprobable density on the set $0, 1, 2, \ldots, n - 1$. If n is prime this is not possible, but the proof is not so easy. (Note that Exercise 11 is of this form, with $n = 11$.)

13. Assume that you are playing craps with dice that are loaded in the following way: faces two, three, four, and five all come up with the same probability $^1/_6 + r$. Faces one and six come up with probability $^1/_6 - 2r$, with $0 < r < .02$. Write a computer program to find the probability of winning at craps with these dice, and using your program find which values of r make craps a favorable game for the player with these dice.

---

[2]See M. Krasner and B. Ranulae, "Sur une Proprieté des Polynomes de la Division du Circle"; and the following note by J. Hadamard, in *C.R. Acad. Sci.*, vol. 204 (1937), pp. 397–399.

7.2 SUMS OF CONTINUOUS RANDOM VARIABLES

In this section we consider the continuous version of the problem posed in the previous section: How are sums of independent random variables distributed?

Sums

Let X and Y be two random variables defined on a continuous probability space Ω with distribution functions $F_X(x)$ and $F_Y(y)$ and density functions $f_X(x)$ and $f_Y(y)$. Suppose, moreover, that X and Y are *independent*, so that the joint distribution functions $F_{XY}(x,y)$ can be written

$$F_{XY}(x,y) = F_X(x)F_Y(y).$$

Now let $Z = X + Y$. Then Z is also a random variable defined on Ω, with distribution function $F_Z(z)$, say, and density function $f_Z(z)$. How is f_Z related to f_X and f_Y?

To see how Z is distributed (i.e., to find the density function f_Z), we argue as follows: If the outcome of any experiment gives Z a value $\leq z$, say, then that outcome must give X a value x and Y a value y such that $x + y \leq z$. We calculate the probability of all such outcomes in two ways. On the one hand, from the definition of F_Z,

$$P(Z \leq z) = F_Z(z) = \int_{-\infty}^{z} f_Z(t)dt.$$

On the other hand,

$$P(X + Y \leq z) = \int\int_{x+y\leq z} f_X(x)f_Y(y)dxdy.$$

Here we can consider that the probability space Ω is the xy-plane, with probability density given by the function $f_{XY}(x,y) = f_X(x)f_Y(y)$; the event in question then is the subset of the plane determined by the condition $x + y \leq z$ (see Figure 3). If we define a new variable $t = x + y$, then $x = t - y$, and we get

$$P(X + Y \leq z) = \int_{-\infty}^{z} \int_{-\infty}^{+\infty} f_X(t - y)f_Y(y)dydt.$$

Comparing the two expressions for $P(X + Y \leq Z)$, we find that

$$F_Z(z) = \int_{-\infty}^{z} \int_{-\infty}^{+\infty} f_X(t - y)f_Y(y)dydt.$$

Hence,

$$f_Z(z) = \frac{d}{dz} F_Z(z) = \int_{-\infty}^{+\infty} f_X(z - y)f_Y(y)dy.$$

Thus, the density function $f_Z(z)$ is given in terms of the densities $f_X(x)$ and $f_Y(y)$ in this way. We call this combination of f_X and f_Y the *convolution* of f_X and f_Y, and note that it

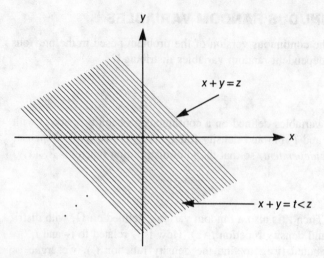

Figure 3 Calculation of $F_Z(z)$.

is the continuous analogue of the discrete version of convolution introduced in the previous section.

We can formalize these results as follows (cf. Definition 1 and Theorem 1 of Section 7.1).

Convolutions

DEFINITION 2

Let $f(x)$ and $g(x)$ be two density functions defined for all real numbers x. Then the *convolution* $f*g$ of f and g is the density function given by

$$(f*g)(z) = \int_{-\infty}^{+\infty} f(z - y)g(y)dy$$
$$= \int_{-\infty}^{+\infty} g(z - x) f(x)dx.$$

(Note that we assume here, as we did in Section 7.1, that the densities f and g are defined for *all* values of x; if not, we define them to be 0 where not otherwise defined.)

THEOREM 2

Let X and Y be two independent random variables with density functions $f_X(x)$ and $f_Y(x)$ defined for all x. Then the sum $Z = X + Y$ is a random variable with density function $f_Z(x)$, where f_Z is the convolution of f_X and f_Y.

To get a better understanding of this important result, we will look at some examples.

Uniform Case

EXAMPLE 1

Suppose we choose independently two numbers at random from the interval [0,1] with uniform probability distribution. What is the distribution of their sum?

Let X and Y be random variables describing our choices and $Z = X + Y$ their sum. Then we have

$$f_X(x) = f_Y(x) = \begin{cases} 1 & \text{if } 0 \leqslant x \leqslant 1, \\ 0 & \text{otherwise;} \end{cases}$$

and the density function for the sum is given by

$$f_Z(z) = \int_{-\infty}^{+\infty} f_X(z - y)f_Y(y)dy.$$

Since $f_Y(y) = 1$ if $0 \leqslant y \leqslant 1$ and 0 otherwise, this becomes

$$f_Z(z) = \int_0^1 f_X(z - y)dy.$$

Now the integrand is 0 unless $0 \leqslant z - y \leqslant 1$ (i.e., unless $z - 1 \leqslant y \leqslant z$) and then it is 1 (see Figure 4). So if $0 \leqslant z \leqslant 1$, we have

$$f_Z(z) = \int_0^z dy = z,$$

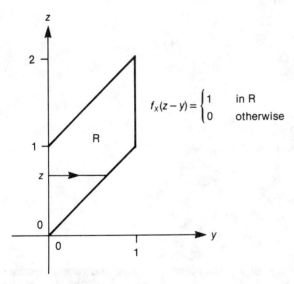

$$f_X(z-y) = \begin{cases} 1 & \text{in R} \\ 0 & \text{otherwise} \end{cases}$$

Figure 4 Calculation of f_Z.

while if $1 < z \leqslant 2$, we have

$$f_Z(z) = \int_{z-1}^1 dy = 2 - z,$$

and if $z < 0$ or $z > 2$ we have $f_Z(z) = 0$ (see Figure 5). Hence,

$$f_Z(z) = \begin{cases} z & \text{if } 0 \leqslant z \leqslant 1, \\ 2 - z & \text{if } 1 < z \leqslant 2, \\ 0 & \text{otherwise.} \end{cases}$$

Note that this result agrees with that of Example 4 of Chapter 5, Section 5.2   □

Exponential Case

EXAMPLE 2

Suppose we choose two numbers at random from the inverval $[0, \infty)$ with an *exponential* probability distribution with parameter λ. What is the distribution of their sum?

Let X, Y and $Z = X + Y$ denote the relevant random variables and f_X, f_Y, and f_Z their densities. Then (see Chapter 2, Section 2.2, Example 6)

$$f_X(x) = f_Y(x) = \begin{cases} \lambda e^{-\lambda x} & \text{if } 0 \leqslant x, \\ 0 & \text{if } x < 0; \end{cases}$$

and so, if $z > 0$,

$$f_Z(z) = \int_{-\infty}^{+\infty} f_X(z - y) f_y(y) dy$$

$$= \int_0^z \lambda e^{-\lambda(z-y)} \lambda e^{-\lambda y} dy$$

$$= \int_0^z \lambda^2 e^{-\lambda z} dy$$

$$= \lambda^2 z e^{-\lambda z},$$

while if $z < 0$, $f_Z(z) = 0$ (see Figure 6). Hence,

$$f_Z(z) = \begin{cases} \lambda^2 z e^{-\lambda z} & \text{if } z \geqslant 0, \\ 0 & \text{if } z < 0. \end{cases}$$ □

Gamma Density

The exponential density is a special case of a gamma density. The general *gamma density* is defined by

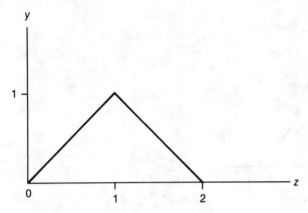

Figure 5 Graph of $f_Z(z)$, uniform case.

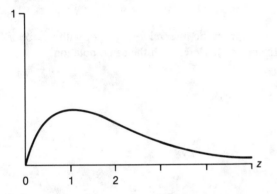

Figure 6 Graph of $f_Z(z)$, exponential case, with $\lambda = 1$.

$$f(x) = \begin{cases} \dfrac{\lambda e^{-\lambda x}(\lambda x)^{\beta - 1}}{\Gamma(\beta)} & \text{if } 0 \leqslant x \leqslant \infty, \\ 0 & \text{otherwise.} \end{cases}$$

Here λ and β are any positive numbers, and the gamma function $\Gamma(\beta)$ is given by

$$\Gamma(\beta) = \int_0^\infty \lambda e^{-\lambda x} (\lambda x)^{\beta - 1} \, dx.$$

The case $\beta = 1$ is the exponential density, while the case $\beta = 2$ is the density f_Z above. In general, the sum of n independent random variables each having an exponential density with parameter λ has a gamma density with parameters λ and $\beta = n$. We see here an example of the fact that the convolution of any gamma density with itself is another gamma density.

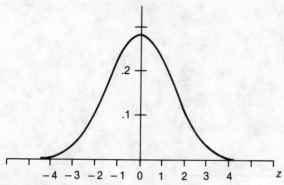

Figure 7 Graph of $f_Z(z)$, normal case.

Normal Case

EXAMPLE 3

Suppose we choose two numbers at random from the interval $(-\infty, +\infty)$ with a *normal* density (see Chapter 2, Section 2.2, Example 7). Here, with the same notation,

$$f_X(x) = f_Y(x) = \frac{1}{\sqrt{2\pi}} e^{-x^2/2},$$

and so (see Figure 7)

$$f_Z(z) = f_X * f_Y(z) = \frac{1}{2\pi} \int_{-\infty}^{+\infty} e^{-(z-y)^2/2} e^{-y^2/2} \, dy$$

$$= \frac{1}{2\pi} e^{-z^2/4} \int_{-\infty}^{+\infty} e^{-(y-z/2)^2} \, dy$$

$$= \frac{1}{\sqrt{4\pi}} e^{-z^2/4}. \qquad \square$$

We see here that if we add two independent normal random variables with mean 0 and variance 1, we obtain a new normal random variable with mean 0 and variance 2. More generally, the convolution of any two normal densities of means μ_1 and μ_2 and variances σ_1^2 and σ_2^2 is again a normal density, of mean $\mu_1 + \mu_2$ and variance $\sigma_1^2 + \sigma_2^2$.

Cauchy Case

EXAMPLE 4

Suppose we choose two numbers, X and Y, at random from the interval $(-\infty, \infty)$ with the *Cauchy* density with parameter $a = 1$ (see Chapter 6; Section 6.3, Example 8). Then

$$f_X(x) = f_Y(x) = \frac{1}{\pi(1+x^2)},$$

and $Z = X + Y$ has density

$$f_Z(z) = \frac{1}{\pi^2} \int_{-\infty}^{+\infty} \left(\frac{1}{1 + (z-y)^2} \right) \left(\frac{1}{1 + y^2} \right) dy.$$

This integral requires some effort, and we give here only the result:

$$f_Z(z) = \frac{2}{\pi(4 + z^2)}.$$

(See Chapter 10, Section 10.3, or Dwass, "On the Convolution of Cauchy Distributions."[3])

If, in this example, we ask for the density function of the *average* $A = \frac{1}{2}(X + Y)$ of X and Y, then by Corollary 1a of Chapter 5, Section 5.2,

$$f_A(z) = 2f_Z(2z) = \frac{1}{\pi(1 + z^2)}.$$

Hence, the density function for the average of two random variables, each having a Cauchy density, is again a random variable with a Cauchy density; this remarkable property is a peculiarity of the Cauchy density. One consequence of this is that, if the error in a certain measurement process had a Cauchy density and you averaged a number of measurements, the average could not be expected to be any more accurate than any one of your individual measurements! □

Maxwell Case

EXAMPLE 5

Suppose we choose independently two numbers, X and Y, at random from the interval $(-\infty, +\infty)$ with a normal density of mean 0 and variance 1. Now suppose we locate a point P in the xy-plane with coordinates (X, Y), and ask: What is the density of the square of the distance of P from the origin? (We have already simulated this problem in Example 9 of Chapter 5, Section 5.2.)

Here, with the preceding notation, we have

$$f_X(x) = f_Y(x) = \frac{1}{\sqrt{2\pi}} e^{-x^2/2}.$$

Moreover, if X^2 denotes the square of X, then (see Theorem 1 of Chapter 5 Section 5.2 and the discussion following)

$$f_{X^2}(r) = \begin{cases} \frac{1}{2\sqrt{r}} (f_X(\sqrt{r}) + f_X(-\sqrt{r})) & \text{if } r > 0, \\ 0 & \text{if } r \leq 0. \end{cases}$$

$$= \begin{cases} \frac{1}{\sqrt{2\pi r}} e^{-r/2} & \text{if } r > 0, \\ 0 & \text{if } r \leq 0. \end{cases}$$

This is a gamma density with $\lambda = \frac{1}{2}$, $\beta = \frac{1}{2}$ (see Example 2). Now let $R^2 = X^2 + Y^2$. Then

$$f_{R^2}(r) = \int_{-\infty}^{+\infty} f_{X^2}(r-s) f_{Y^2}(s) ds$$

$$= \frac{1}{4\pi} \int_{-\infty}^{+\infty} e^{-(r-s)/2} \left(\frac{r-s}{2}\right)^{-1/2} e^{-s} \left(\frac{s}{2}\right)^{-1/2} ds$$

$$= \begin{cases} \dfrac{1}{2} e^{-r/2} & \text{if } r \geq 0 \\ 0 & \text{if } r < 0. \end{cases}$$

Hence, R^2 has a gamma density with $\lambda = \frac{1}{2}$, $\beta = 1$. We can interpret this result as giving the density of the square of the distance of P from the center of a target if its coordinates are normally distributed.

The density of the random variable R is obtained from that of R^2 in the usual way (see Theorem 1 and Example 9 of Chapter 5, Section 5.2), and we find

$$f_R(r) = \begin{cases} \dfrac{1}{2} e^{-r^2/2} \cdot 2r = re^{-r^2/2} & \text{if } r \geq 0, \\ 0 & \text{if } r < 0. \end{cases}$$

Physicists will recognize this as a two-dimensional Maxwell density. Our result here agrees with our simulation in Example 9 of Chapter 5, Section 5.2. □

Chi-Squared Density

More generally, the same method shows that the sum of the squares of n independent normally distributed random variables with mean 0 and standard deviation 1 has a gamma density with $\gamma = \frac{1}{2}$ and $\beta = n/2$. Such a density is called a *chi-squared density* with n degrees of freedom. Sums of squares arise in all sorts of applications; we give only one more example.

EXAMPLE 6

Suppose we are given a single die that we suspect might be loaded. How can we test the die for fairness?

One standard test can be described as follows: If we roll a fair die a large number of times, then we expect that each face will turn up in roughly $\frac{1}{6}$ of the trials. If we let X_k be the number of trials in which the kth face turns up, then X_k should be approximately $n/6$, where n is the total number of trials.

If we form the quantity

$$Z = \sum_{i=1}^{6} \frac{(X_k - np_k)^2}{np_k},$$

then it can be shown that, for a fair die, Z has approximately a chi-squared density with

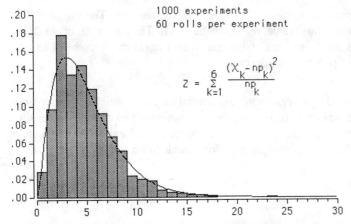

Figure 8   Result of running the program, **Die Test**.

$6 - 1 = 5$ degrees of freedom. The approximation improves as n is increased. We shall see why this result is true in Chapter 9. We can, as usual, illustrate this result by computer simulation. To do this we consider the experiment of rolling a die 60 times. Then we would expect each of the outcomes to occur about 10 times. The deviations from these expectations will contribute to the size of Z. We then repeat this experiment 1000 times, each time calculating the value of Z. We then plot a histogram of these 1000 values for Z and compare this with the theoretical chi-squared density. The program **Die Test** implements this simple test. The output is shown in Figure 8. We see that the results are quite consistent with the theoretical chi-squared distribution for Z.

We now ask how one would detect a bad die. We agree on the following procedure. We will roll the die 60 times and compute the value of Z. From the chi-squared density with 5 degrees of freedom we will find the number $z_{.95}$ such that

$$P(Z > z_{.95}) = .05.$$

Then if our value of Z is greater than $z_{.95}$ we will reject the hypothesis that the die is fair. Note that there is a 5 percent chance that we will reject a fair die. If $Z < z_{.95}$ it is tempting to accept the hypothesis that the die is fair, but the statistician would warn us to be careful here. Can you see why?

To illustrate this test we change our probabilities for the outcomes of the die to be .1 for all numbers other than six and .5 for a six. This is certainly a crooked die. We modify the program **Die Test** to roll this die 60 times and print out the value of

$$Z = \sum_{i=1}^{6} \frac{(X_i - np_i)^2}{np_i}.$$

We obtained the value 21.2. Is this a sufficiently large value of Z so that we would feel that it is very unlikely that the die is a fair die? To check this find the value $z_{.95}$ such that

$$P(Z > z_{.95}) = .05$$

when Z has a chi-squared distribution with 5 degrees of freedom. The program **Chi-Squared Confidence** finds this value for us to be 11.1. Thus a value of 21.2 is a surprisingly large value for Z, and the statistician would reject the hypothesis that the die is a fair die at the 95 percent confidence level. □

So far we have looked at several important special cases for which the convolution integral can be evaluated explicitly. In general, the convolution of two continuous densities cannot be evaluated explicitly, and we must resort to numerical methods. Fortunately, these prove to be remarkably effective, at least for bounded densities.

Independent Trials

We now consider briefly the distribution of the sum of n independent random variables, all having the same density function. If $X_1, \cdots, X_n$ are these variables and $S_n = X_1 + \cdots + X_n$ is their sum, then we will have

$$f_{S_n}(x) = \left(f_{X_1} * f_{X_2} * \cdots * f_{X_n} \right)(x),$$

where the right-hand side is an n-fold convolution. It is possible to calculate this density for general values of n in certain simple cases.

EXAMPLE 7

Suppose the X_i are uniformly distributed on the interval [0,1]. Then

$$f_X(x) = \begin{cases} 1 & \text{if } 0 \leq x \leq 1, \\ 0 & \text{otherwise;} \end{cases}$$

and $f_{S_n}(x)$ is given by the formula[4]

$$f_{S_n}(x) = \begin{cases} \dfrac{1}{(n-1)!} \sum_{j \leq x} (-1)^j \binom{n}{j} (x-j)^{n-1} & \text{if } 0 < x < n, \\ 0 & \text{otherwise.} \end{cases}$$

The density $f_{S_n}(x)$ for $n = 2,4,6,8,10$ is shown in Figure 9.

If the X_i are distributed normally, with mean 0 and variance 1, then (cf. Example 3)

$$f_X(x) = \frac{1}{\sqrt{2\pi}} e^{-x^2/2},$$

[4]See J.B. Uspensky, *Introduction to Mathematical Probability* (New York: McGraw-Hill, 1937), p. 277.

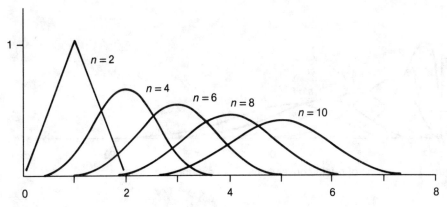

Figure 9 Graphs of *n*-fold convolutions of a uniform density.

and

$$f_{S_n}(x) = \frac{1}{\sqrt{2\pi n}} e^{-x^2/2n}.$$

Here the density f_{S_n} for $n = 2,4,6,8,10$ is shown in Figure 10.

Again, if the X_i are all *exponentially* distributed, with mean λ, then

$$f_{X_i}(x) = \lambda e^{-\lambda x}.$$

and

$$f_{S_n}(x) = \frac{\lambda e^{-\lambda x}(\lambda x)^{n-1}}{(n-1)!}.$$

In this case the density f_{S_n} for $n = 2,4,6,8,10$ is shown in Figure 11. $\qquad\square$

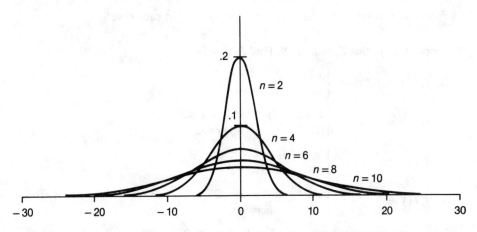

Figure 10 Graphs of *n*-fold convolutions of a normal density.

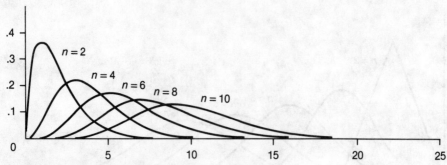

Figure 11 Graphs of *n*-fold convolutions of an exponential density with $\lambda = 1$.

Exercises

1. Let X and Y be independent random variables defined on the space Ω, with density functions f_X and f_Y, respectively. Suppose that $Z = X + Y$. Find the density f_Z of Z if

(a) $f_X(x) = f_Y(x) = \begin{cases} \frac{1}{2} & \text{if } -1 \leqslant x \leqslant +1, \\ 0 & \text{otherwise.} \end{cases}$

(b) $f_X(x) = f_Y(x) = \begin{cases} \frac{1}{2} & \text{if } 3 \leqslant x \leqslant 5, \\ 0 & \text{otherwise.} \end{cases}$

(c) $f_X(x) = \begin{cases} \frac{1}{2} & \text{if } -1 \leqslant x \leqslant +1, \\ 0 & \text{otherwise.} \end{cases}$

$ f_Y(x) = \begin{cases} \frac{1}{2} & \text{if } 3 \leqslant x \leqslant 5, \\ 0 & \text{otherwise.} \end{cases}$

What can you say about the set $E = \{z: f_Z(z) > 0\}$ in each case?

2. Suppose again that $Z = X + Y$. Find f_Z if

(a) $f_X(x) = f_Y(x) = \begin{cases} x/2 & \text{if } 0 < x < 2, \\ 0 & \text{otherwise.} \end{cases}$

(b) $f_X(x) = f_Y(x) = \begin{cases} (\frac{1}{2})(x-3) & \text{if } 3 < x < 5, \\ 0 & \text{otherwise.} \end{cases}$

(c) $f_X(x) = \begin{cases} \frac{1}{2} & \text{if } 0 < x < 2, \\ 0 & \text{otherwise.} \end{cases}$

$ f_Y(x) = \begin{cases} x/2 & \text{if } 0 < x < 2, \\ 0 & \text{otherwise.} \end{cases}$

What can you say about the set $E = \{z: f_Z(z) > 0\}$ in each case?

3. Let X, Y and Z be independent random variables with

$$f_X(x) = f_Y(x) = f_Z(x) = \begin{cases} 1 & \text{if } 0 < x < 1, \\ 0 & \text{otherwise.} \end{cases}$$

Suppose that $W = X + Y + Z$. Find F_W directly, and compare your answer with that given by the formula in Example 7. (*Hint:* see Example 1.)

4. Suppose that X and Y are independent and $Z = X + Y$. Find f_Z if

(a) $f_X(x) = \begin{cases} \lambda e^{-\lambda x} & \text{if } x < 0, \\ 0 & \text{otherwise.} \end{cases}$

$f_Y(x) = \begin{cases} \mu e^{-\mu x} & \text{if } x > 0, \\ 0 & \text{otherwise.} \end{cases}$

(b) $f_X(x) = \begin{cases} \lambda e^{-\lambda x} & \text{if } x > 0, \\ 0 & \text{otherwise.} \end{cases}$

$f_Y(x) = \begin{cases} 1 & \text{if } 0 < x < 1, \\ 0 & \text{otherwise.} \end{cases}$

(See Example 2.)

5. Suppose again that $Z = X + Y$. Find f_Z if

$$f_X(x) = \frac{1}{\sqrt{2\pi}\sigma_1} e^{-(x-\mu_1)^2/2\sigma_1^2}$$

$$f_Y(x) = \frac{1}{\sqrt{2\pi}\sigma_2} e^{-(x-\mu_2)^2/2\sigma_2^2}.$$

(See Example 3.)

6. Suppose that $R^2 = X^2 + Y^2$. Find f_{R^2} and f_R if

$$f_X(x) = \frac{1}{\sqrt{2\pi}\sigma_1} e^{-(x-\mu_1)^2/2\sigma_1^2},$$

$$f_Y(x) = \frac{1}{\sqrt{2\pi}\sigma_2} e^{-(x-\mu_2)^2/2\sigma_2^2}.$$

(See Example 5.)

7. Suppose that $R^2 = X^2 + Y^2$. Find f_{R^2} and f_R if

$$f_X(x) = f_Y(x) = \begin{cases} 1/2 & \text{if } -1 \leqslant x \leqslant +1, \\ 0 & \text{otherwise.} \end{cases}$$

8. Assume that the service time for a customer at a bank is exponentially distributed with mean service time 2 minutes. Let X be the total service time for 100 customers. Estimate the probability that $X > 220$ minutes.

9. Let $X_1, X_2, \ldots, X_n$ be n independent random variables each of which has an exponential density with mean μ. Let M be the *minimum* value of the X_j. Show that the density for M is exponential with mean μ/n.

10. A company buys 100 lightbulbs, each of which has an exponential lifetime of 1000 hours. What is the expected time for the first of these bulbs to burn out? (See Exercise 9.)

11. An insurance company assumes that the time between claims from each of its home-owners' policies is exponentially distributed with mean μ. It would like to estimate μ by averaging the times for a number of policies, but this is not very practical since the time between claims is typically about 30 years. At Galambos's[5] suggestion the company puts its customers in groups of 50 and observes the time of the first claim within each group. Show that this provides a practical way to estimate the value of μ.

12. Particles are subject to collisions that cause them to split into two parts with each part a fraction of the parent. Suppose that this fraction is uniformly distributed between 0 and 1. Following a single particle through several splittings we obtain a fraction of the original particle $Z_n = X_1 \cdot X_2 \cdot X_3 \cdot \cdots \cdot X_n$ where each X_j is uniformly distributed between 0 and 1. Show that the density for the random variable Z_n is

$$f_n(z) = \frac{1}{n!} \log\left(\frac{1}{z}\right)^{n-1}.$$

Hint: Show that $Y_k = -\log(X_k)$ is exponentially distributed. Use this to find the distribution function for $S_n = Y_1 + \cdots + Y_n$, and from this the distribution and density of $Z_n = e^{-S_n}$.

13. Assume that X_1 and X_2 are independent random variables, each having an exponential density with parameter λ. Show that $Z = X_1 - X_2$ has density

$$f_z(z) = (1/2\lambda)e^{-\lambda|z|}.$$

14. Suppose we want to test a coin for fairness. We flip the coin n times and record the number of times X_0 that the coin turns up tails and the number of times $X_1 = n - X_0$ that the coin turns up heads. Now we set

$$Z = \sum_{i=0}^{1} \frac{(X_i - n/2)^2}{n/2}.$$

Then for a fair coin Z has approximately a chi-squared distribution with $2 - 1 = 1$ degree of freedom. Try this by computer simulation first for a fair coin ($p = 1/2$) and then for a biased coin ($p = 1/3$).

15. Verify your answers in Exercise 1(a) by computer simulation: Choose X and Y from $[-1,1]$ with uniform density and calculate $Z = X + Y$. Repeat this experiment 500

---

[5]J. Galambos, *Introductory Probability Theory* (New York: Marcel Dekker, 1984).

times, recording the outcomes in a bar graph on $[-2,2]$ with 40 bars. Does the density f_Z calculated in 1(a) describe the shape of your bar graph? Try this for Exercises 1(b) and 1(c), too.

16. Verify your answers to Exercise 2 by computer simulation.

17. Verify your answer to Exercise 3 by computer simulation.

18. Let X and Y be independent random variables with densities f_X and f_Y, and let $Z = X + Y$, with density f_Z. Suppose $f_X(x) > 0$ if and only if $a < x < b$. (Then we say $[a,b]$ is the *support* of f_X.) Similarly, suppose $[c,d]$ is the support of f_Y. Using the convolution formula, find the support of f_Z if
(a) $[a,b] = [c,d] = [0,1]$.
(b) $[a,b] = [c,d] = [0,e]$.
(c) $[a,b] = [c,d]$.
(d) $0 < a < b < c < d$.
Now can you describe the support of f_Z in the general case?

19. Let $X_1, X_2, \ldots, X_n$ be a sequence of independent random variables, all having a common density function f_X with support $[a,b]$ (see Exercise 18). Let $S_n = X_1 + \cdots + X_n$, with density function f_{S_n}. Show that the support of f_{S_n} is the interval $[na, nb]$. *Hint:* Write $f_{S_n} = f_{S_{n-1}} * f_X$. Now use Exercise 18 to establish the desired result by induction.

20. Let $X_1, X_2, \ldots, X_n$ be a sequence of independent random variables, all having a common density function f_X. Let $A = \dfrac{S_n}{n}$ be their average. Find f_A if

(a) $f_X(x) = \dfrac{1}{\sqrt{2\pi}} e^{-x^2/2}$ (normal density).

(b) $f_X(x) = e^{-x}$ (exponential density).
Hint: Write $f_A(x)$ in terms of $f_{S_n}(x)$.

Chapter *8*

Law of Large Numbers

8.1 LAW OF LARGE NUMBERS FOR DISCRETE RANDOM VARIABLES

We are now in a position to prove our first fundamental theorem of probability. This theorem will justify our frequency interpretation of probabilities as well as our interpretation of the expected value as an average outcome. The theorem, called the *Law of Large Numbers*, is the mathematical version of the idea more often expressed as the *law of averages*.

Chebyshev Inequality

To discuss the law of large numbers, we first need an important inequality called the *Chebyshev Inequality*.

THEOREM I   Chebyshev Inequality

Let X be a random variable with expected value $\mu = E(X)$, and let $\varepsilon > 0$ be any positive real number. Then

$$P(|X - \mu| \geq \varepsilon) \leq \frac{V(X)}{\varepsilon^2}.$$

In words this says that X differs from $\mu = E(X)$ by more than ε with probability at most $\dfrac{V(X)}{\varepsilon^2}$. The larger ε is, the less likely that $|X - \mu| > \varepsilon$.

Proof.   Let A be the subset of the sample space Ω consisting of all outcomes ω such that $|X(\omega) - \mu| \geq \varepsilon$. Then

$$V(X) = \sum_{\omega \in \Omega} (X(\omega) - \mu)^2 \, p(\omega)$$

$$= \sum_{\omega \in A} (X(\omega) - \mu)^2 \, p(\omega) + \sum_{\omega \in \tilde{A}} (X(\omega) - \mu)^2 \, p(\omega)$$

$$\geq \sum_{\omega \in A} (X(\omega) - \mu)^2 \, p(\omega).$$

On the other hand, $(X(\omega) - \mu)^2 \geq \varepsilon^2$ for ω in A. Thus,

$$V(X) \geq \varepsilon^2 \sum_{\omega \in A} p(\omega) = \varepsilon^2 P(A).$$

Hence,

$$P(|X - \mu| \geq \varepsilon) = P(A) \leq \frac{V(X)}{\varepsilon^2}. \qquad \blacksquare$$

Note that X in the above theorem can be any discrete random variable, and ε any positive number.

EXAMPLE 1

Let X be any random variable with $E(X) = \mu$ and $V(X) = \sigma^2$. Then, if $\varepsilon = k\sigma$, Chebyshev's inequality states that

$$P(|X - \mu| \geq k\sigma) \leq \frac{\sigma^2}{k^2\sigma^2} = \frac{1}{k^2}.$$

Thus, for any random variable, the probability of a deviation from the mean of more than k standard deviations is $\leq \dfrac{1}{k^2}$. If, for example, $k = 5$, $\dfrac{1}{k^2} = .04$. $\qquad \square$

Chebyshev's inequality is the best possible inequality in the sense that, for any $\varepsilon > 0$, it is possible to give an example of a random variable for which Chebyshev's inequality is in fact an equality. To see this, given $\varepsilon > 0$, choose X with density

$$p_X = \begin{pmatrix} -\varepsilon & \varepsilon \\ \dfrac{1}{2} & \dfrac{1}{2} \end{pmatrix}.$$

Then $E(X) = 0$, $V(X) = \varepsilon^2$, and

$$P(|X - \mu| \geq \varepsilon) = \frac{V(X)}{\varepsilon^2} = 1.$$

We are now prepared to prove the law of large numbers.

Law of Large Numbers

THEOREM 2   Law of Large Numbers
Let $X_1, \cdots, X_n$ be an independent trials process, with $\mu = E(X_j)$ and $S_n = X_1 + \cdots + X_n$. Then for any $\varepsilon > 0$,

$$P\left(\left|\frac{S_n}{n} - \mu\right| \geq \varepsilon\right) \to 0 \qquad \text{as } n \to \infty.$$

Equivalently,

$$P\left(\left|\frac{S_n}{n} - \mu\right| < \varepsilon\right) \to 1 \qquad \text{as } n \to \infty.$$

In words: As n increases, the probability that the average of n independent trials will differ from μ, the expected value of a single trial, by more than any preassigned ε tends to zero.

Proof.   Since $X_1, \ldots, X_n$ are independent and have the same densities,

$$V(S_n) = nV(X_1) = n\sigma^2,$$

and

$$V\left(\frac{S_n}{n}\right) = \frac{V(S_n)}{n^2} = \frac{n\sigma^2}{n^2} = \frac{\sigma^2}{n}.$$

Also we know that

$$E\left(\frac{S_n}{n}\right) = \frac{nE(X_1)}{n} = \mu.$$

By Chebyshev's inequality, for any $\varepsilon > 0$,

$$P\left(\left|\frac{S_n}{n} - \mu\right| \geq \varepsilon\right) \leq \frac{\sigma^2}{n\varepsilon^2}.$$

Thus, for fixed ε,

$$P\left(\left|\frac{S_n}{n} - \mu\right| \geq \varepsilon\right) \to 0 \qquad \text{as } n \to \infty,$$

or equivalently,

$$P\left(\left|\frac{S_n}{n} - \mu\right| < \varepsilon\right) \to 1 \qquad \text{as } n \to \infty. \qquad \blacksquare$$

Law of Averages

Note that $\dfrac{S_n}{n}$ is an average of the individual outcomes, and one often calls the law of large numbers the "law of averages." It is a striking fact that we can start with a random experiment about which little can be predicted and, by taking averages, obtain an experiment in which the outcome can be predicted with a high degree of certainty. The law of large numbers, as we have stated it, is often called the "weak law of large numbers" to distinguish it from the "strong law of large numbers" described in Exercise 16.

Consider the important special case of Bernoulli trials with probability p for success. Let $X_j = 1$ if the jth outcome is a success and 0 if it is a failure. Then $S_n = X_1 + \cdots + X_n$ is the number of successes in n trials and $\mu = E(X_1) = p$. The law of large numbers states that for any $\varepsilon > 0$

$$P\left(\left|\frac{S_n}{n} - p\right| < \varepsilon\right) \to 1 \qquad \text{as } n \to \infty.$$

This, finally, justifies our frequency interpretation for the probability p that an event will occur. It says that, in a large number of repetitions of a Bernoulli experiment, we can expect the proportion of times the event will occur to be near p.

Coin Tossing

Let us consider the special case of tossing a coin n times with S_n the number of heads that turn up. Then the random variable $\dfrac{S_n}{n}$ represents the fraction of times heads turns up and will have values between 0 and 1. The law of large numbers predicts that the outcomes for this random variable will, for large n, be near $1/2$.

In Figure 1, we have plotted the density for this example and have shaded the area between .45 and .55 for increasing values of n. We see that as n increases the density

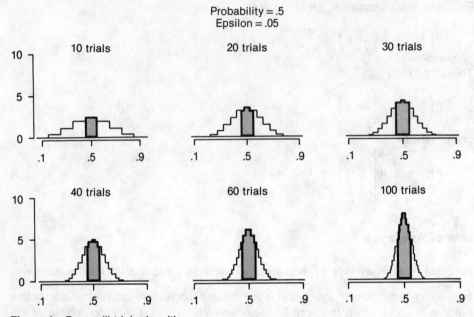

Figure 1 Bernoulli trials densities.

gets more and more concentrated around .5 and a larger and larger percentage of the total area is contained within the interval (.45, .55), as predicted by the law of large numbers.

Die Rolling

EXAMPLE 2

Consider n rolls of a die. Let X_j be the outcome of the jth roll. Then $S_n = X_1 + X_2 + \cdots + X_n$ is the sum of the first n rolls. This is an independent trials process with $E(X_j) = {}^7/_2$. Thus, by the law of large numbers, for any $\varepsilon > 0$

$$P\left(\left|\frac{S_n}{n} - \frac{7}{2}\right| \geq \varepsilon\right) \to 0 \qquad \text{as } n \to \infty.$$

An equivalent way to state this is that, for any $\varepsilon > 0$,

$$P\left(\left|\frac{S_n}{n} - \frac{7}{2}\right| < \varepsilon\right) \to 1 \qquad \text{as } n \to \infty. \qquad \square$$

Bernoulli Trials

EXAMPLE 3

Let $X_1, \ldots, X_n$ be a Bernoulli trials process with probability .3 for success and .7 for failure. Let $X_j = 1$ if the jth outcome is a success and 0 otherwise. Then, $E(X_j) = .3$ and $V(X_j) = (.3)(.7) = .21$. If

$$A_n = \frac{S_n}{n} = \frac{X_1 + X_2 + \cdots + X_n}{n}$$

is the *average* of the X_i, then $E(A_n) = .3$ and $V(A_n) = \frac{V(S_n)}{n^2} = \frac{.21}{n}$. Chebyshev's inequality states that if, for example, $\varepsilon = .1$,

$$P(|A_n - .3| \geq .1) \leq \frac{.21}{n(.1)^2} = \frac{21}{n}.$$

Thus, if $n = 100$,

$$P(|A_{100} - .3| \geq .1) \leq .21,$$

or if $n = 1000$,

$$P(|A_{1000} - .3| \geq .1) \leq .021.$$

These can be rewritten as

$$P(.2 < A_{100} < .4) \geq .79,$$
$$P(.2 < A_{1000} < .4) \geq .979.$$

□

Numerical Comparisons

It should be emphasized that, although Chebyshev's inequality proves the law of large numbers, it is actually a very crude inequality for the probabilities involved. However, its strength lies in the fact that it is true for any random variable at all, and it allows us to prove a very powerful theorem.

We can compare the estimates given by Chebyshev's inequality with the exact values in simple cases by using our program **Demo Binomial** (see Chapter 3). We choose instead to write a program **Law** which will handle larger values of n. The program **Law** computes the exact probability

$$P(|A_n - p| \geq \varepsilon),$$

where A_n is the average outcome of n Bernoulli trials with probability p for success, for $n = 50$ to 400 in steps of 50. It also computes the Chebyshev estimate $\frac{pq}{n\varepsilon^2}$ for comparison.

```
! Law     (LAW)
!
! Illustrates the law of large numbers for a Bernoulli trials process,
! and compares the exact probabilities with the Chebyshev estimates.
! Note that this computes 1 - P(np - n*epsilon < Sn < np + n*epsilon),
! which is, of course, the same as P(|An - p| ≥ epsilon).

library "Lib.prob*"
declare function binomial

input prompt "Probability, epsilon = " : p, epsilon
let q = 1 - p

print
print "  n", "P(|An-" &str$(p) & "|≥" & str$(epsilon) & ")",
print "Chebyshev bound"
print

for n = 50 to 400 step 50

    let mean = n * p
    let lower_bound = int(max(0,mean - n*epsilon)) + 1
    let upper_bound = -int(-min(n, mean + n*epsilon)) -1

    let sum = 0

    for k = lower_bound to upper_bound
        let sum = sum + binomial(n,p,k)
    next k

    let probability = 1 - sum
    let Chebyshev = p*q/(n*epsilon^2)

    print using$("###",n), using$(".#####", probability),
    print using$(".#####", Chebyshev)

next n

end
```

From the run of the program we note, for example, that

$$P(|A_{100} - .3| \geq .1) = .03745,$$

as compared to the conservative estimate of .21 given by Chebyshev's inequality.

Probability, epsilon = .3,.1

n	P(|An-.3|≥.1)	Chebyshev
50	.16365	.42000
100	.03745	.21000
150	.00955	.14000
200	.00257	.10500
250	.00071	.08400
300	.00020	.07000
350	.00006	.06000
400	.00002	.05250

Historical Remarks

The law of large numbers was first proved by the Swiss mathematician James Bernoulli in the fourth part of his work *Ars Conjectandi* published posthumously in 1713.[1] As often happens with a first proof, Bernoulli's proof was much more difficult than the proof we have presented using Chebyshev's inequality. Chebyshev developed his inequality to prove a general form of the law of large numbers (See Exercise 18). The inequality itself appeared much earlier in a work by Bienaymé, and in discussing its history Maistrov remarks that it was referred to as the Bienaymé-Chebyshev inequality for a long time.[2]

In *Ars Conjectandi* Bernoulli provides his reader with a long discussion of the meaning of his theorem with lots of examples. In modern notation he has an event that occurs with probability p but he does not know p. He wants to estimate p by the fraction $\bar{p}$ of the times the event occurs when the experiment is repeated a number of times. He discusses in detail the problem of estimating, by this method, the proportion of white balls in an urn that contains an unknown number of white and black balls. He would do this by drawing a sequence of balls from the urn, replacing the ball drawn after each draw, and estimating the unknown proportion of white balls in the urn by the proportion of the balls drawn that are white. He shows that, by choosing n large enough he can obtain any desired accuracy and reliability for the estimate. He also provides a lively discussion of the applicability of his theorem to estimating the probability of dying of a particular disease, of different kinds of weather occurring, and so forth.

In speaking of the number of trials necessary for making a judgement, Bernoulli observes that the "man on the street" believes the "law of averages."

> Further, it cannot escape anyone that for judging in this way about any event at all, it is not enough to use one or two trials, but rather a great number of trials is required. And sometimes the stupidest man—by some instinct of nature *per se* and by no previous instruction (this is truly amazing)—knows for sure that the more observations of this sort that are taken, the less the danger will be of straying from the mark.[3]

But he goes on to say that he must contemplate another possibility.

> Something further must be contemplated here which perhaps no one has thought about till now. It certainly remains to be inquired whether after the number of observations has been increased, the probability is increased of attaining the true ratio between the number of cases in which some event can happen and in which it cannot happen, so that this probability finally exceeds any given degree of certainty; or whether the problem has, so to speak, its own asymptote—that is, whether some degree of certainty is given which one can never exceed.[4]

[1] See J. Bernoulli, *The Art of Conjecturing IV*, trans. Bing Sung, Technical Report No. 2, Dept. of Statistics, Harvard Univ., 1966.

[2] L.E. Maistrov, *Probability Theory: A Historical Approach*, trans. and ed. Samuel Kotz, (New York: Academic Press, 1974), p. 202.

[3] Bernoulli, *The Art of Conjecturing IV*, p. 38.

[4] Ibid, p. 39.

Bernoulli recognized the importance of this theorem, writing:

> Therefore, this is the problem which I now set forth and make known after I have already pondered over it for twenty years. Both its novelty and its very great usefulness, coupled with its just as great difficulty, can exceed in weight and value all the remaining chapters of this thesis.[5]

Bernoulli concludes his long proof with the remark:

> Whence, finally, this one thing seems to follow: that if observations of all events were to be continued throughout all eternity, (and hence the ultimate probability would tend toward perfect certainty), everything in the world would be perceived to happen in fixed ratios and according to a constant law of alternation, so that even in the most accidental and fortuitous occurrences we would be bound to recognize, as it were, a certain necessity and, so to speak, a certain fate.
>
> I do not know whether Plato wished to aim at this in his doctrine of the universal return of things, according to which he predicted that all things will return to their original state after countless ages have past.[6]

Exercises

1. A fair coin is tossed 100 times. The expected number of heads is 50, and the standard deviation for the number of heads is $(100 \cdot {}^1/_2 \cdot {}^1/_2)^{1/2} = 5$. What does Chebyshev's inequality tell you about the probability that the number of heads that turn up deviates from the expected number 50 by three or more standard deviations (i.e., by at least 15)?

2. Write a program that uses the function **binomial** (n, p, x) to compute the exact probability that you estimated in Exercise 1. Compare the two results.

3. Write a program to toss a coin 10,000 times. Let S_n be the number of heads in the first n tosses. Have your program print out, after every 1000 tosses, $S_n - \dfrac{n}{2}$. On the basis of this simulation, is it correct to say that you can expect heads about half of the time when you toss a coin a large number of times?

4. A 1-dollar bet on craps has an expected winning of $-.0141$. What does the law of large numbers say about your winnings if you make a large number of 1-dollar bets at the craps table? Does it assure you that your losses will be small? Does it assure you that if n is very large you will lose?

5. Let X be a random variable with $E(X) = 0$ and $V(X) = 1$. What integer value k will assure us that $P(|X| \geqslant k) \leqslant .01$?

[5]Ibid, p. 42.
[6]Ibid, pp. 65–66.

6. Let S_n be the number of successes in n Bernoulli trials with probability p for success on each trial. Show, using Chebyshev's inequality, that for any $\varepsilon > 0$

$$P\left(\left|\frac{S_n}{n} - p\right| \geq \varepsilon\right) \leq \frac{p(1-p)}{n\varepsilon^2}.$$

7. Find the maximum possible value for $p(1-p)$ if $0 < p < 1$. Using this result and Exercise 6, show that the estimate

$$P\left(\left|\frac{S_n}{n} - p\right| \geq \varepsilon\right) \leq \frac{1}{4n\varepsilon^2}$$

is valid for any p.

8. In an opinion poll it is assumed that an unknown proportion p of the people are in favor of a proposed new law and a proportion $1 - p$ are against it. A sample of n people is taken to obtain their opinion. The proportion $\bar{p}$ in favor in the sample is taken as an estimate of p. Using Exercise 7, determine how large a sample will ensure that the estimate will, with probability .95, be correct to within .01.

9. A fair coin is tossed a large number of times. Does the law of large numbers assure us that, if n is large enough, with probability $>.99$ the number of heads that turn up will not deviate from $\frac{n}{2}$ by more than 100?

10. In Exercise 16 of Chapter 6, Section 6.2, you showed that, for the hat check problem, the number S_n of people who get their own hats back has $E(S_n) = V(S_n) = 1$. Using Chebyshev's inequality, show that $P(S_n \geq 11) \leq .01$ for any $n \geq 11$.

11. Let X be any random variable which takes on values $0, 1, 2, \ldots, n$ and has $E(X) = V(X) = 1$. Show that, for any integer k,

$$P(X \geq k + 1) \leq \frac{1}{k^2}.$$

12. We have two coins: one is a fair coin and the other is a coin that produces heads with probability $^3/_4$. One of the two coins is picked at random, and this coin is tossed n times. Let S_n be the number of heads that turns up in these n tosses. Does the law of large numbers allow us to predict the proportion of heads that will turn up in the long run? After we have observed a large number of tosses, can we tell which coin was chosen? How many tosses suffice to make us 95 percent sure?

13. (Chebyshev)[7] Assume that $X_1, X_2, \ldots$ are independent random variables with possibly different distributions. Let $m_k = E(X_k)$, $\sigma_k^2 = V(X_k)$ and $M_n = m_1 + m_2 + \cdots + m_n$. Assume that $\sigma_k^2 < R$ for all k. Prove that, for any $\varepsilon > 0$,

$$P\left(\left|\frac{S_n}{n} - \frac{M_n}{n}\right| < \varepsilon\right) \to 1 \qquad \text{as } n \to \infty.$$

[7]P.L. Chebyshev, "On Mean Values," *J. Math. Pure. Appl.*, vol. 12 (1867), pp. 177–184.

14. A stronger form of the law of large numbers (see Exercise 16) for coin tossing implies that you could not write a computer program to select a subsequence of the outcomes to make the proportion of heads approach a number bigger than $^1/_2$. Write a program to implement a method of selection that you or your friends think might give proportion of heads greater than $^1/_2$. Your program must decide whether to accept an outcome before the toss is made. For example, you might select only outcomes that come after there have been three tails in a row. See if you can get more than 50% heads by your "system."

*15. Prove the following analogue of Chebyshev's inequality:

$$P(|X - E(X)| \geq \varepsilon) \leq \frac{1}{\varepsilon} E(|X - E(X)|).$$

*16. We have proved a theorem often called the "weak law of large numbers." Most people's intuition and our computer simulations suggest that, if we toss a coin a sequence of times, the proportion of heads will really approach $^1/_2$; that is, if S_n is the number of heads in n times, then we will have

$$A_n = \frac{S_n}{n} \to \frac{1}{2}$$

as $n \to \infty$. Of course, we cannot be sure of this since we are not able to toss the coin an infinite number of times, and, if we could, the coin could come up heads every time. However, the "strong law of large numbers," proven in more advanced courses, states that

$$P\left(\frac{S_n}{n} \to \frac{1}{2}\right) = 1.$$

Describe a sample space Ω that would make it possible for us to talk about the event $E = \left\{ \omega : \dfrac{S_n(\omega)}{n} \to \dfrac{1}{2} \right\}$. Could we assign the equiprobable measure to this space? (See Chapter 2, Section 2.2, Example 9.)

*17. Let us toss a biased coin that comes up heads with probability p and assume the validity of the strong law of large numbers as described in Exercise 16. Then, with probability 1,

$$\frac{S_n}{n} \to p$$

as $n \to \infty$. If $f(x)$ is a continuous function on the unit interval, then we also have

$$f\left(\frac{S_n}{n}\right) \to f(p).$$

Finally, we could hope that

$$E\left(f\left(\frac{S_n}{n}\right)\right) \rightarrow E(f(p)) = f(p).$$

Show that, if all this is correct, as in fact it is, we would have proven that any continuous function on the unit interval is a limit of polynomial functions. This is a sketch of a probabilistic proof of an important theorem in mathematics called the *Weierstrass approximation theorem*.

8.2 LAW OF LARGE NUMBERS FOR CONTINUOUS RANDOM VARIABLES

In the previous section we discussed in some detail the law of large numbers for discrete probability distributions. This law has a natural analogue for continuous probability distributions, which we consider somewhat more briefly here.

Chebyshev Inequality

Just as in the discrete case, we begin our discussion with the Chebyshev inequality.

THEOREM 3 Chebyshev Inequality
Let X be a continuous random variable on the probability space Ω with probability density function $p(\omega)$. Suppose X has finite expected value $\mu = E(X)$ and finite variance $\sigma^2 = V(X)$. Then for any positive number $\varepsilon > 0$ we have

$$P(|X - \mu| \geq \varepsilon) \leq \frac{\sigma^2}{\varepsilon^2}.$$

Note that this theorem says nothing if $\sigma^2 = V(X)$ is infinite.

Proof.   (This is a transcription, word for word, of the proof in the discrete case.) Let A be the subset of the sample space Ω consisting of all outcomes ω such that $|X(\omega) - \mu| \geq \varepsilon$. Then

$$V(X) = \int_\Omega (X(\omega) - \mu)^2 p(\omega)d\omega$$

$$= \int_A (X(\omega) - \mu)^2 p(\omega)d\omega$$

$$+ \int_{\bar{A}} (X(\omega) - \mu)^2 p(\omega)d\omega$$

$$\geq \int_A (X(\omega) - \mu)^2 p(\omega)d\omega.$$

But $(X(\omega) - \mu)^2 \geqslant \varepsilon^2$ for $\omega \in A$. Thus,

$$V(X) \geqslant \int_A (X(\omega) - \mu)^2 \, p(\omega)d\omega$$

$$\geqslant \varepsilon^2 \int_A p(\omega)d\omega = \varepsilon^2 \cdot P(A).$$

Hence,

$$P(A) = P(|X - \mu| \geqslant \varepsilon) \leqslant \frac{\sigma^2}{\varepsilon^2},$$

as required. ∎

EXAMPLE 1

Let X be any continuous random variable with $E(X) = \mu$ and $V(X) = \sigma^2$. Then, if $\varepsilon = k\sigma = k$ standard deviations for some integer k, then

$$P(|X - \mu| \geqslant k\sigma) \leqslant \frac{\sigma^2}{k^2\sigma^2} = \frac{1}{k^2},$$

just as in the discrete case. □

Law of Large Numbers

With the Chebyshev inequality we can now state and prove the law of large numbers for the continuous case.

THEOREM 4   Law of Large Numbers

Let $X_1, \ldots, X_n$ be an independent trials process with a continuous density p, finite expected value μ, and finite variance σ^2. Let $S_n = X_1 + \cdots + X_n$ be the sum of the X_i. Then for any real number $\varepsilon > 0$ we have

$$\lim_{n \to \infty} P\left(\left| \frac{S_n}{n} - \mu \right| \geqslant \varepsilon \right) = 0,$$

or equivalently,

$$\lim_{n \to \infty} P\left(\left| \frac{S_n}{n} - \mu \right| < \varepsilon \right) = 1.$$

Note that this theorem is not necessarily true if σ^2 is infinite (see Example 5).

As in the discrete case, the law of large numbers says that the average value of n independent trials tends to the expected value as $n \to \infty$, in the precise sense that, given $\varepsilon > 0$, the probability that the average value and the expected value differ by more than ε tends to 0 as $n \to \infty$.

The law of large numbers stated here does *not* guarantee that, in any given sequence of independent trials, the average value tends to the expected value as $n \to \infty$. It guarantees only that if we repeat an independent trials experiment over and over again, then in most of the repetitions the average value will be found close to the expected value; and the law quantifies the terms *most* and *close* in this statement. All this will become clearer after looking at a few examples.

Proof. (Again this proof is transcribed directly from the discrete case.) Since the X_i are independent and have the same density, we have

$$E(S_n) = n\mu,$$

$$V(S_n) = n\sigma^2,$$

$$V\left(\frac{S_n}{n}\right) = \frac{n\sigma^2}{n^2} = \frac{\sigma^2}{n}.$$

By the Chebyshev inequality, for any $\varepsilon > 0$ and all n, we have

$$P\left(\left|\frac{S_n}{n} - \mu\right| \geq \varepsilon\right) \leq \frac{\sigma^2}{n\varepsilon}.$$

Hence, as $n \to \infty$,

$$0 \leq \lim_{n \to \infty} P\left(\left|\frac{S_n}{n} - \mu\right| \geq \varepsilon\right) \leq \lim_{n \to \infty} \frac{\sigma^2}{n\varepsilon} = 0. \qquad \blacksquare$$

Uniform Case

EXAMPLE 2
Suppose we choose at random n numbers from the interval $[0,1]$ with uniform distribution. Then if X_i describes the ith choice, we have

$$\mu = E(X_i) = \int_0^1 x\,dx = \frac{1}{2},$$

$$\sigma^2 = V(X_i) = \int_0^1 x^2\,dx - \mu^2$$

$$= \frac{1}{3} - \frac{1}{4} = \frac{1}{12}.$$

Hence,

$$E\left(\frac{S_n}{n}\right) = \frac{1}{2},$$

$$V\left(\frac{S_n}{n}\right) = \frac{1}{12n},$$

and for any $\varepsilon > 0$,

$$P\left(\left|\frac{S_n}{n} - \frac{1}{2}\right| \geq \varepsilon\right) \leq \frac{1}{12n\varepsilon^2}.$$

This says that if we choose n numbers at random from $[0,1]$, then the chances are better than $1 - \dfrac{1}{12n\varepsilon^2}$ that the difference $\left|\dfrac{S_n}{n} - \dfrac{1}{2}\right|$ is less than ε. Note that ε plays the role of the amount of error we are willing to tolerate: If we choose $\varepsilon = 0.1$, say, then the chances that $\left|\dfrac{S_n}{n} - \dfrac{1}{2}\right|$ is less than 0.1 are better than $1 - \dfrac{100}{12n}$. For $n = 100$, this

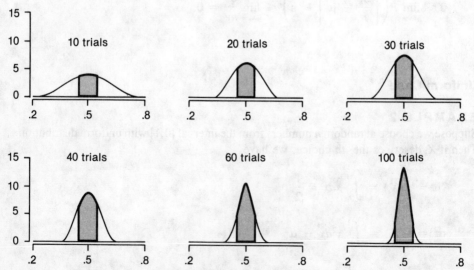

Figure 2 Illustration of law of large numbers—uniform case.

is about .92, but if $n = 1000$, this is better than .99 and if $n = 10,000$, this is better than .999.

We can illustrate what the law of large numbers says for this example graphically. The density for $A_n = \dfrac{S_n}{n}$ is determined by

$$f_{A_n}(x) = nf_{S_n}(nx).$$

We have seen in Chapter 7, Section 7.2, that we can compute the density $f_{S_n}(x)$ for the sum of n uniform random variables. In Figure 2 we have used this to plot the density for A_n for various values of n. We have shaded in the area for which A_n would lie between .4 and .6. We see that as we increase n, we obtain more and more of the total area inside the shaded region. The law of large numbers tells us that we can obtain as much of the total area as we please inside the shaded region by choosing n large enough (see also Figure 1). □

Normal Case

EXAMPLE 3
Suppose we choose n numbers at random from the interval $(-\infty, +\infty)$, using a normal distribution with mean 0 and variance 1. Then

$$\mu = E(X_i) = 0,$$

$$\sigma^2 = V(X_i) = 1.$$

Hence,

$$E\left(\frac{S_n}{n}\right) = 0,$$

$$V\left(\frac{S_n}{n}\right) = \frac{1}{n},$$

and, for any $\varepsilon > 0$,

$$P\left(\left|\frac{S_n}{n} - 0\right| \geq \varepsilon\right) \leq \frac{1}{n\varepsilon^2}.$$

In this case, it is possible to compare the Chebyshev estimate for $P\left(\left|\dfrac{S_n}{n} - \mu\right| \geq \varepsilon\right)$ in the law of large numbers with exact values, since we know the density function for $\dfrac{S_n}{n}$ exactly (see Example 3 of Chapter 7, Section 7.2). Here is what we find, using the program **Law Continuous**.

```
! Law Continuous   (LAWCONT)
!
! Illustrates the continuous version of the Law of Large Numbers for
! the sum of n random varibles identically distributed on (-∞,∞) with
! density the standard normal.  This is particularly easy because the
! convolution of the standard normal with itself n times is again a
! normal, with mean 0 and variance n.
!
! This calculates, for a given epsilon,
!
!               P(|Sn/n|> epsilon)
!
! and compares the Chebyshev estimate, doing this for n = 100 to 1000,
! step 100. The above probability is the same as the probability that
! Sn is outside of [-n*epsilon, n*epsilon], which is exactly the same
! as 1 - normal_area(-√(n)*epsilon,√(n)*epsilon)

library "Lib.cont*"
declare function normal_area

input prompt "Epsilon = " :epsilon


print
print "   n", "P(|Sn/n|≥" & str$(epsilon) & ")",
print "Chebyshev"
print

for n = 100 to 1000 step 100

    let deviations = sqr(n)* epsilon

    let probability = 1 - normal_area(-deviations,deviations)
    let Chebyshev = 1/(n*epsilon^2)

    print using$("####",n), using$(".#####", probability),
    print using$("#.#####", Chebyshev)

next n

end
```

Running this program, we get

```
Epsilon = .1

   n          P(|Sn/n|≥.1)      Chebyshev

  100           .31731          1.00000
  200           .15730           .50000
  300           .08326           .33333
  400           .04550           .25000
  500           .02535           .20000
  600           .01431           .16667
  700           .00815           .14286
  800           .00468           .12500
  900           .00270           .11111
 1000           .00157           .10000
```

We see here that the Chebyshev estimates are in general *not* very accurate.   □

Monte Carlo Method

Here is a somewhat more interesting example.

EXAMPLE 4
Let $g(x)$ be a continuous function defined for $x \in [0,1]$ with values in $[0,1]$. In Chapter 2, Section 2.1, we showed how to estimate the area of the region under the graph of $g(x)$ by the Monte Carlo method, that is, by choosing a large number of random values for x and y with uniform distribution and seeing what fraction of the points $P(x,y)$ fell inside the region under the graph (see Example 2, Chapter 2, Section 2.1).

Here is a better way to estimate the same area (see Figure 3). Let us choose a large number of independent values X_n at random from $[0,1]$ with uniform density, set $Y_n = g(X_n)$, and find the average value of the Y_n. Then this average is our estimate for the area. To see this, note that if the density function for X_n is uniform,

$$f_X(x) \equiv 1,$$

then the *expected value* for Y_n is (cf. Theorem 11 of Chapter 6, Section 6.3)

$$\mu = E(Y_n) = \int_0^1 g(x)\, f(x)\, dx$$

$$= \int_0^1 g(x)\, dx$$

$$= \text{average value of } g(x),$$

while the variance is

$$\sigma^2 = E((Y_n - \mu)^2) = \int_0^1 (g(x) - \mu)^2\, dx < 1.$$

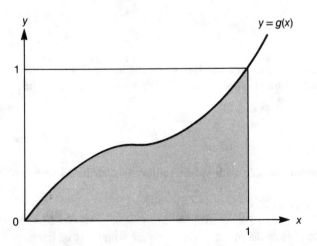

Figure 3 Area problem.

Now let $Z_n = 1/n \, (Y_1 + Y_2 + \cdots + Y_n)$. Then by Chebychev's inequality, we have

$$P(|Z_n - \mu| \geq \varepsilon) \leq \frac{\sigma^2}{n\varepsilon^2} < \frac{1}{n\varepsilon^2}.$$

This says that to get within ε of the true value for $\mu = \int_0^1 g(x)dx$ with probability at least p, we should choose n so that $1/n\varepsilon^2 \leq 1 - p$ (i.e., so that $n \geq 1/\varepsilon^2(1 - p)$). Note that this method tells us how large to take n to get a desired accuracy. □

The law of large numbers requires that the variance σ^2 of the original underlying density be finite: $\sigma^2 < \infty$. In cases where this fails to hold, the law of large numbers may fail, too. An example follows.

Cauchy Case

EXAMPLE 5
Suppose we choose n numbers from $(-\infty, +\infty)$ with a Cauchy density with parameter $a = 1$. We know that for the Cauchy density the expected value and variance are undefined (see Example 8 of Chapter 6, Section 6.3). In this case, the density function for

$$A_n = \frac{S_n}{n}$$

is given by (see Example 4 of Chapter 7, Section 7.2)

$$f_{A_n}(x) = \frac{1}{\pi(1 + x^2)},$$

that is, *the density function for A_n is the same for all n.* In this case, as n increases, the density function does not change at all, and the law of large numbers does not hold. □

Exercises

1. Let X be a continuous random variable with mean $\mu = 10$ and variance $\sigma^2 = 100/3$. Using Chebyshev's inequality, find an upper bound for the following probabilities
   (a) $P(|X - 10| \geq 2)$.
   (b) $P(|X - 10| \geq 5)$.
   (c) $P(|X - 10| \geq 9)$.
   (d) $P(|X - 10| \geq 20)$.

2. Let X be a continuous random variable with values uniformly distributed over the interval $[0,20]$.
   (a) Find the mean and variance of X.
   (b) Calculate $P(|X - 10| \geq 2)$, $P(|X - 10| \geq 5)$, $P(|X - 10| \geq 9)$, and $P(|X - 10| \geq 20)$ exactly. How do your answers compare with those of Exercise 1? How good is Chebyshev's inequality in this case?

3. Let X be the random variable of Exercise 2.
   (a) Calculate the function $f(x) = P(|X - 10| \geq x)$.
   (b) Now graph the function $f(x)$, and on the same axes, graph the Chebyshev function $g(x) = 100/3x^2$. Show that $f(x) \leq g(x)$ for all $x > 0$, but that $g(x)$ is not a very good approximation for $f(x)$.

4. Let X be a continuous random variable with values exponentially distributed over $[0,\infty)$ with parameter $\lambda = 0.1$.
   (a) Find the mean and variance of X.
   (b) Using Chebyshev's inequality, find an upper bound for the following probabilities: $P(|X - 10| \geq 2)$, $P(|X - 10| \geq 5)$, $P(|X - 10| \geq 9)$, and $P(|X - 10| \geq 20)$.
   (c) Calculate these probabilities exactly, and compare with the bounds in (b).

5. Let X be a continuous random variable with values normally distributed over $(-\infty, +\infty)$ with mean $\mu = 0$ and variance $\sigma^2 = 1$.
   (a) Using Chebyshev's inequality, find an upper bound for the following probabilities: $P(|X| \geq 1)$, $P(|X| \geq 2)$, and $P(|X| \geq 3)$.
   (b) The area under the normal curve between -1 and 1 is .6827, between -2 and 2 is .9545 and between -3 and 3 it is .9973 (see the table in Appendix A). Compare your bounds in (a) with these exact values. How good is Chebyshev's inequality in this case?

6. If X is normally distributed, with mean μ and variance σ^2, find an upper bound for the following probabilities, using Chebyshev's inequality.
   (a) $P(|X - \mu| \geq \sigma)$.
   (b) $P(|X - \mu| \geq 2\sigma)$.
   (c) $P(|X - \mu| \geq 3\sigma)$.
   (d) $P(|X - \mu| \geq 4\sigma)$.
   Now find the exact value using the program **Normal Area** or the normal table in Appendix A, and compare.

7. If X is a random variable with mean μ and variance σ^2, define the *relative deviation* D of X from its mean by

   $$D = \left| \frac{X - \mu}{\mu} \right|.$$

   (a) Show that $P(D \geq a) \leq \sigma^2/\mu^2 a^2$.
   (b) If X is the random variable of Exercise 1, find an upper bound for $P(D \geq .2)$, $P(D \geq .5)$, $P(D \geq .9)$, and $P(D \geq 2)$.

8. Let X be a continuous random variable and define the *standardized version* X^* of X by:

   $$X^* = \frac{X - \mu}{\sigma}.$$

   (a) Show that $P(|X^*| \geq a) \leq \frac{1}{a^2}$.

(b) If X the random variable of Exercise 1, find bounds for $P\left(|X^*| \geq \dfrac{2\sqrt{3}}{10}\right)$, $P\left(|X^*| \geq \dfrac{5\sqrt{3}}{10}\right)$, and $P\left(|X^*| \geq \dfrac{9\sqrt{3}}{10}\right)$.

9. (a) Suppose a number X is chosen at random from $[0,20]$ with uniform probability. Find a lower bound for the probability that X lies between 8 and 12, using Chebyshev's inequality.
   (b) Now suppose 20 real numbers are chosen independently from $[0,20]$ with uniform probability. Find a lower bound for the probability that their average lies between 8 and 12.
   (c) Now suppose 100 real numbers are chosen independently from $[0,20]$. Find a lower bound for the probability that their average lies between 8 and 12.

10. A student's score on a particular calculus final is a random variable with values of $[0,100]$, mean 70 and variance 25.
    (a) Find a lower bound for the probability that the student's score will fall between 65 and 75.
    (b) If 100 students take the final, find a lower bound for the probability that the class average will fall between 65 and 75.

11. The Pilsdorff beer company runs a fleet of trucks along the 100 mile road from Hangtown to Dry Gulch, and maintains a garage half way in between. Each of the trucks is apt to break down at a point X miles from Hangtown, where X is a random variable uniformly distributed over $[0,100]$.
    (a) Find a lower bound for the probability $P(|X - 50| \leq 10)$.
    (b) Suppose that in one bad week, 20 trucks break down. Find a lower bound for the probability $P(|A_{20} - 50| \leq 10)$, where A_{20} is the average of the distances from Hangtown at the time of breakdown.

12. A share of common stock in the Pilsdorff beer company has a price Y_n on the nth business day of the year. Finn observes that the price change $X_n = Y_{n+1} - Y_n$ appears to be a random variable with mean $\mu = 0$ and variance $\sigma^2 = 1/4$. If $Y_1 = 30$, find a lower bound for the following probabilities.
    (a) $P(25 \leq Y_2 \leq 35)$.
    (b) $P(25 \leq Y_{11} \leq 35)$.
    (c) $P(25 \leq Y_{101} \leq 35)$.

13. Suppose one hundred numbers $X_1, \ldots, X_{100}$ are chosen independently at random from $[0,20]$. Let $S = X_1 + \cdots + X_{100}$ be the sum, $A = 1/100\, S$ the average, and $S^* = \dfrac{S - 1000}{10/\sqrt{3}}$ the standardized sum. Find lower bounds for the probabilities
    (a) $P(|S - 1000| \leq 100)$.
    (b) $P(|A - 10| \leq 1)$.
    (c) $P(|S^*| \leq \sqrt{3})$.

14. Let X be a continuous random variable normally distributed on $(-\infty, +\infty)$ with mean 0 and variance 1. Using the normal table provided in Appendix A, or the program **Normal Area**, find values for the function $f(x) = P(|X| \geq x)$ as x increases from 0 to 4.0 in steps of .25. (Note that for $x \geq 0$ the table gives $NA(0,x) = P(0 \leq X \leq x)$ and thus $P(|X| \geq x) = 2(.5 - NA(0,x))$. Plot by hand the graph of $f(x)$ using these values, and the graph of the Chebyshev function $g(x) = \dfrac{1}{x^2}$, and compare (see Exercise 3).

15. Repeat Exercise 14, but this time with mean 10 and variance 3. (Note that the table in Appendix A presents values for a standard normal variable. Find the standardized version X^* for X, find values for $f^*(x) = P(|X^*| \geq x)$ as in Exercise 14, and then rescale these values for $f(x) = P(|X - 10| \geq x)$. Graph and compare this function with the Chebyshev function $g(x) = 3/x^2$.

16. Let $Z = \dfrac{X}{Y}$ where X and Y have normal densities with mean 0 and standard deviation 1. Then it can be shown that Z has a Cauchy density.
    (a) Write a program to illustrate this result by plotting a bar graph of 1000 samples obtained by forming the ratio of two standard normal outcomes. Compare your bar graph with the graph of the Cauchy density.
    (b) We have seen that the law of large numbers does not apply to the Cauchy density (see Example 5). Simulate a large number of experiments with Cauchy density and compute the average of your results. Do these averages seem to be approaching a limit? If so can you explain why this might be?

17. Show that, if $X \geq 0$, then $P(X \geq a) \leq \dfrac{E(X)}{a}$.

18. (D. Lamperti) Let X be a non-negative random variable. What is the best upper bound you can give for $P(X \geq a)$ if you know
    (a) $E(X) = 20$.
    (b) $E(X) = 20$ and $V(X) = 25$.
    (c) $E(X) = 20$, $V(X) = 25$, and X is symmetric about its mean.

Chapter 9

Central Limit Theorem

9.1 THE CENTRAL LIMIT THEOREM FOR BERNOULLI TRIALS

Normal Density

The second fundamental theorem of probability is the *Central Limit Theorem*. This theorem permits us to compute probabilities for the sum of independent random variables by relating these probabilities to the standard *normal probability measure* defined by the standard *normal density function*

$$n(x) = \frac{1}{\sqrt{2\pi}} \, e^{-x^2/2}.$$

The graph of this function is the familiar bell-shaped curve shown in Figure 1.

The central limit theorem is a theorem that tells us, quite generally, what happens when we have the sum of a large number of independent random variables each of which

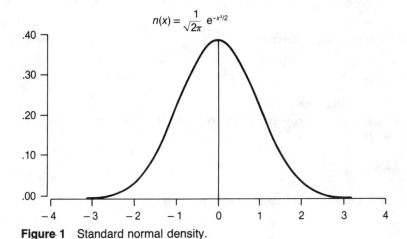

$$n(x) = \frac{1}{\sqrt{2\pi}} e^{-x^2/2}$$

Figure 1 Standard normal density.

contributes a small amount to the total. In this section we shall discuss this theorem as it applies to the Bernoulli trials and in the next section we shall consider more general processes.

Bernoulli Trials

Consider a Bernoulli trials process with probability p for success on each trial. Let $X_i = 1$ or 0 according as the ith outcome is a success or a failure, and let $S_n = X_1 + \cdots + X_n$. Then S_n is the number of successes in n trials. We know that S_n has as its density the binomial probabilities $b(n,p,j)$. In Chapter 3, Section 3.2, we plotted these densities for $p = .3$ and $p = .5$ for various values of n.

We noted that the maximum values of the densities appeared near the expected value np, which caused their bar graphs to drift off to the right as n increased. Moreover, these maximum values approached 0 as n increased, which caused the bar graphs to flatten out.

Standardized Sums

We can prevent the drifting of these bar graphs by subtracting the expected number of successes np from S_n, obtaining the new random variable $S_n - np$. Now the maximum values of the densities will always be near 0.

To prevent the spreading of these bar graphs, we can normalize $S_n - np$ to have variance 1 by dividing by its standard deviation $\sqrt{npq}$ (see Exercises 13 and 17 of Chapter 6, Section 6.2).

DEFINITION 1

The *standardized sum* of the S_n is given by

$$S_n^* = \frac{S_n - np}{\sqrt{npq}}.$$

S_n^* always has expected value 0 and variance 1.

Suppose we plot a bar graph with the bars centered at the possible values of S_n^*: $x_0, x_1, \ldots, x_n$, where

$$x_j = \frac{j - np}{\sqrt{npq}}. \tag{1}$$

We want to make the area of the bar centered at x_j equal to

$$P(S_n^* = x_j)$$

and the length b of the base of each bar equal to the distance between successive values of x_j:

$$b = \frac{1}{\sqrt{npq}}.$$

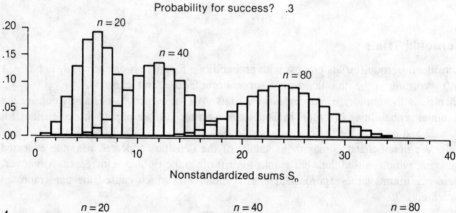

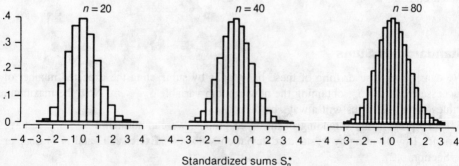

Figure 2 Graphs of nonstandardized sums S_n and standardized sums S_n^*.

In order to make the area of the bar equal to $P(S_n^* = x_j)$, we must choose the height of the bar at x_j to be

$$h(x_j) = \sqrt{npq}\, P(S_n^* = x_j).$$

In Figure 2 we show the resulting bar graphs for $p = .3$ and three increasing values of n, first without the standardization (S_n), and then with the standardization (S_n^*).

The standardized bar graphs are all quite similar and resemble the normal curve of Figure 1 for large n. The program **CLT Bernoulli Plot** examines this more closely by comparing the standardized bar graph with the normal curve.

```
! CLT Bernoulli Plot   (CLTBERP)
!
! Illustrates the Central Limit Theorem for Bernoulli trials.  Plots a
! histogram of the scaled binomial probabilities (within 4 standard
! deviations of the mean) and compares the approximating normal curve.

library  "Lib.cont*"
declare function standard_normal
library  "Lib.prob*"
declare function binomial

let deviations = 4
let xmin = -deviations
let xmax = deviations

input prompt "Number of trials, probability of success = ": n,p

let mean = n*p                    ! Mean of the binomial density
let sigma = sqr(n*p*(1-p))         ! Standard deviation
let kmin =  int(max(0, mean - deviations*sigma)) + 1
let kmax = -int(-min(n, mean + deviations*sigma)) -1
let dx = (xmax-xmin)/100
let ymin = 0
let ymax = 5/4 * standard_normal(0)


set window xmin,xmax,ymin,ymax
plot xmin,0; xmax,0
plot 0,ymin; 0,ymax

for k = kmin to kmax
    let x = (k-mean)/sigma                     ! Normalized value
    let height = binomial(n,p,k) * sigma       ! Height of normalized bar
    let width = 1/sigma                        ! Width of bar
    box lines x-width/2, x+width/2, 0, height
next k

for x = xmin to xmax step dx                   ! Compare normal curve
    plot x, standard_normal(x);
next x

end
```

We have run this program for $n = 100$ and $p = .4$ and the result is shown in Figure 3. We see that the normal curve does indeed very closely approximate the standardized bar graph.

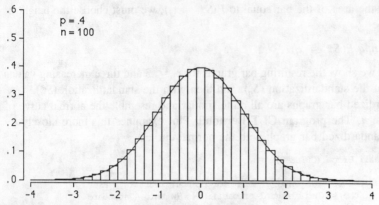

Figure 3 Standardized Bernoulli trials bar graphs.

Let us fix a value x on the x-axis. Then, as n increases, x will be contained in the bar centered at the point x_j closest to x. From Equation (1) we see that this point is given by

$$j = \langle np + x\sqrt{npq}\rangle,$$

where $\langle x \rangle$ means the integer nearest to x. Then the height of the bar containing x will be

$$h(x) = \sqrt{npq}\, b(n,p,j) = \sqrt{npq}\, b(n,p,\langle np + x\sqrt{npq}\rangle).$$

But these heights seem to be approaching the height of the normal curve at x. This suggest the following theorem.

Central Limit Theorem for Densities

THEOREM 1

For the binomial density $b(n,p,j)$ we have

$$\lim_{n\to\infty} \sqrt{npq}\, b(n,p,\langle np + x\sqrt{npq}\rangle) = n(x),$$

where $n(x)$ is the value of the normal density at x.

The proof of this theorem can be carried out using Stirling's approximation (see Chapter 3, Section 3.1). We indicate this method of proof by considering the case $x = 0$. In this case, the theorem states that

$$\lim_{n\to\infty} \sqrt{npq}\, b(n,p,\langle np \rangle) = \frac{1}{\sqrt{2\pi}} = .3989 \ldots$$

In order to simplify the calculation, we assume that np is an integer, so that $\langle np \rangle = np$. Then

$$\sqrt{npq}\, b(n,p,np) = \sqrt{npq}\, p^{np}q^{nq}\,\frac{n!}{(np)!(nq)!}.$$

Recall that Stirling's formula (see Theorem 2, Chapter 3, Section 3.1) states that

$$n! \sim \sqrt{2\pi n}\, n^n e^{-n} \quad \text{as } n \to \infty.$$

Using this, we have

$$\sqrt{npq}\, b(n,p,np) \sim \frac{\sqrt{npq}\, p^{np} q^{nq} \sqrt{2\pi n}\, n^n e^{-n}}{\sqrt{2\pi np} \sqrt{2\pi nq}\, (np)^{np} (nq)^{nq} e^{-np} e^{-nq}},$$

which simplifies to $1/\sqrt{2\pi}$.

The above theorem suggests the following approximation theorem for the individual probabilities of a binomial density.

Approximation Theorem for Densities

THEOREM 2   Approximation Theorem

If S_n is the number of successes in n Bernoulli trials with probability p for success, then

$$P(S_n = j) = b(n,p,j) \sim \frac{n(x_j)}{\sqrt{npq}}$$

where $x_j = (j - np)/\sqrt{npq}$.

EXAMPLE 1

Let us estimate the probability of exactly 55 heads in 100 tosses of a coin. For this case $np = 100 \cdot \frac{1}{2} = 50$ and $\sqrt{npq} = \sqrt{100 \cdot \frac{1}{2} \cdot \frac{1}{2}} = 5$. Thus $x_{55} = (55 - 50)/5 = 1$ and

$$P(S_{100} = 55) \sim \frac{n(1)}{5} = \frac{1}{5}\left(\frac{1}{\sqrt{2\pi}} e^{-1/2}\right)$$

$$= .0484.$$

To four decimal places, the exact value is actually .0485, and so the approximation is very good. □

The program **CLT Bernoulli Local** (see next page) illustrates this approximation for any choice of n, p, and j. This program uses the function **local_Bernoulli_approx**, which in turn uses **Bernoulli statistics**, both of which we also list here. These functions, along with several others relating to the central limit theorem, comprise the library **Lib.CLT**.

```
! CLT Bernoulli Local    (CLTBERL)
!
! Local version of the Central Limit Theorem for Bernoulli trials:
! Compares the exact calculation of binomial(n,p,k) with the normal
! approximation.

library "Lib.prob*"
library "Lib.cont*"
library "Lib.CLT*"
declare function binomial
declare function standard_normal
declare function local_Bernoulli_approx

do

    print  "Binomial(n,p,k) and normal approximation ";
    input prompt "for n,p,k = " : n, p, k
    print
    print " Exact"," Normal approximation"

    let exact = binomial(n,p,k)
    let approximation = local_Bernoulli_approx(n,p,k)

    print round(exact, 4),
    print round(approximation, 4)
    print
    print

loop

end


function local_Bernoulli_approx(n,p,k)

    library "Lib.cont*"
    declare function standard_normal

    call Bernoulli_statistics(n,p,  mean,std)

    let x = (k-mean)/std
    let local_Bernoulli_approx = standard_normal(x)/std

end function

sub Bernoulli_statistics(n,p,  mean,std)
    let q = 1-p
    let mean = n*p
    let std = sqr(n*p*q)
end sub
```

We have run this program for two examples. The first is the probability of exactly 50 heads in 100 tosses of a coin; here our estimate is correct to two decimal places. The second example is the probability of exactly eight sixes in 36 rolls of a die; here the estimate is good but not correct to two decimal places.

```
Binomial(n,p,k) and normal approximation for n,p,k = 100, .5, 50
```

```
Exact             Normal approximation
.0796             .0798
```

```
Binomial(n,p,k) and normal approximation for n,p,k = 36, .166667, 8
```

```
Exact             Normal approximation
.1093             .1196
```

The individual binomial probabilities tend to 0 as n tends to infinity. In most applications we are not interested in the probability that a specific outcome occurs, but rather in the probability that the outcome lies in a given interval, say from a to b. In order to find this probability, we add the areas of the bar graphs for values of j between a and b. But as n tends to infinity the sum of these areas could be expected to approach the area under the normal curve between a and b. The *Central Limit Theorem* states that this does indeed happen.

THEOREM 3   Central Limit Theorem for Bernoulli Trials

Let S_n be the number of successes in n Bernoulli trials with probability p for success. Then

$$\lim_{n\to\infty} P\left(a < \frac{S_n - np}{\sqrt{npq}} < b\right) = \frac{1}{\sqrt{2\pi}} \int_a^b e^{-x^2/2}dx.$$

Again, this theorem can be proven by using Stirling's formula, but the proof is rather complicated, and we shall not give it here (see Chapter 10, Section 10.3).

We know from calculus that the integral on the right side of this equation is equal to the area under the graph of the normal density function $n(x)$ between a and b. Unfortunately, there is no simple way to integrate the function $e^{-x^2/2}$, and so we must either use a table of values or else a numerical integration program, like **Normal Area**, which uses the function **normal_area** in **Lib.Cont**.

```
! Normal Area    (NORMAREA)
!
! Gets the area under the standard normal density on [a,b], using the
! function normal_area(a,b) in Lib.cont.  Normal_area uses Simpson's
! rule for the numerical integration.

library "Lib.cont*"
declare function normal_area

do

    input prompt "Endpoints a,b = " : a,b
    let area = normal_area(a,b)

    print "Area between "; a; "and"; b; "equals"; round(area,4)
    print

loop until a = b

end
```

We have run this program for $[a,b] = [-k,k]$, for $k = 1$ to 4:

```
Endpoints a,b = -1,1
Area between -1 and 1 equals .6827

Endpoints a,b = -2,2
Area between -2 and 2 equals .9545

Endpoints a,b = -3,3
Area between -3 and 3 equals .9973

Endpoints a,b = -4,4
Area between -4 and 4 equals .9999
```

From these values for S_n, the number of successes in n Bernoulli trials with probability p for success, we obtain approximations for

$$P\left(-k < \frac{S_n - np}{\sqrt{npq}} < k\right),$$

or, equivalently,

$$P(np - k\sqrt{npq} < S_n < np + k\sqrt{npq}).$$

For a large number of Bernoulli trials the probability of being within one standard deviation of the expected value is about .683; within two standard deviations, .954; and within three standard deviations, .997. The probability of being within four standard deviations is, for all practical purposes, 1 and that is why, in the program **CLT Bernoulli Plot**, we limited the calculations of the binomial probabilities to values which gave a standardized value between -4 and 4.

It is often convenient to use a table of areas under the normal curve (See Table 1. A more extensive table is given in Appendix A).

Table 1. Table of values of $NA(0,d)$, the normal area from 0 to d.

NA $(0,d)$ = area of shaded region

d	$NA(d)$	d	$NA(d)$	d	$NA(d)$	d	$NA(d)$
.0	.0000	1.0	.3413	2.0	.4772	3.0	.4987
.1	.0398	1.1	.3643	2.1	.4821	3.1	.4990
.2	.0793	1.2	.3849	2.2	.4861	3.2	.4993
.3	.1179	1.3	.4032	2.3	.4893	3.3	.4995
.4	.1554	1.4	.4192	2.4	.4918	3.4	.4997
.5	.1915	1.5	.4332	2.5	.4938	3.5	.4998
.6	.2257	1.6	.4452	2.6	.4953	3.6	.4998
.7	.2580	1.7	.4554	2.7	.4965	3.7	.4999
.8	.2881	1.8	.4641	2.8	.4974	3.8	.4999
.9	.3159	1.9	.4713	2.9	.4981	3.9	.5000

Normal Distribution Table

It is clear from the symmetry of the normal curve that areas such as that between -2 and 3 can be found from this table by adding the area from 0 to 2 (same as that from -2 to 0) to the area from 0 to 3.

We can now use the central limit theorem to solve various problems relating to Bernoulli trials.

Examples

EXAMPLE 2

A coin is tossed 100 times. Estimate the probability that the number of heads lies between 40 and 60. The expected number of heads is $100 \cdot {}^1/_2 = 50$, and the standard deviation for the number of heads is $\sqrt{100 \cdot {}^1/_2 \cdot {}^1/_2} = 5$. Thus, since $n = 100$ is reasonably large, we have

$$P(40 < S_n < 60) = P\left(\frac{40 - 50}{5} < S_n^* < \frac{60 - 50}{5}\right)$$
$$= P(-2 < S_n^* < 2) \sim NA(-2,2) = 2\, NA(0,2) = .9542$$

Note that in this case we are asking for the probability that the outcome will not deviate by more than two standard deviations from the expected value. Had we asked for the probability that the number of successes is between 35 and 65, this would have represented three standard deviations from the mean, and our estimate would be the area under the normal curve between -3 and 3, or $2\, NA(3) = .9974$. $\qquad\square$

The central limit theorem assumes that n tends to infinity, so, since individual probabilities tend to 0 as $n \to \infty$, it does not matter whether we use $<$ or $\leq$ in our inequalities. However, in applying the theorem as an approximation, it does make a significant difference when n is small.

For example, suppose that we want to estimate a probability of the form

$$P(i \leq S_n \leq j),$$

where i and j are integers with $i \leq j$. Then, as stated, the central limit theorem tells us to use the area under the normal curve between

$$\frac{i - np}{\sqrt{npq}} = x_i \quad \text{and} \quad \frac{j - np}{\sqrt{npq}} = x_j.$$

However, looking at the bar graphs we see that this cuts off the left half of the bar corresponding to i and the right half of the bar corresponding to j. We obtain a better approximation if we use the area between

$$\frac{i - \dfrac{1}{2} - np}{\sqrt{npq}} = x_i - 1/(2\sqrt{npq}) \quad \text{and} \quad \frac{j + \dfrac{1}{2} - np}{\sqrt{npq}} = x_j + 1/(2\sqrt{npq}).$$

As a special case of this correction we see that, if n is large,

$$P(S_n = j) = P(j \leq S_n \leq j) \simeq \frac{1}{\sqrt{2\pi}} \int_{x_j - 1/(2\sqrt{npq})}^{x_j + 1/(2\sqrt{npq})} e^{-x^2/2}dx$$

$$\simeq \frac{1}{\sqrt{npq}}\, n(x_j),$$

which was the approximation obtained earlier for the individual binomial probabilities (see Theorem 1).

It is important to work a few problems by hand to understand the conversion from a given inequality to an inequality relating to the standardized variable. After this, one can then use a computer program that carries out this conversion, including the $\frac{1}{2}$ correction. The program **CLT Bernoulli Global** is such a program for estimating probabilities of the form $P(a \leq S_n \leq b)$.

```
! CLT Bernoulli Global   (CLTBERG)
!
! Global version of the Central Limit Theorem for Bernoulli trials:
! Approximates the probability that a Bernoulli trials outcome Sn
! lies in [kmin,kmax], using the normal approximation, with 1/2
! correction. (The last parameter in global_bernoulli_approx is a flag;
! 0 means without 1/2 correction, 1 means with).
!

library "Lib.CLT*"
declare function global_bernoulli_approx
do

    print "Trials,success probability,lower k,upper k = ";
    input prompt "": n, p, kmin, kmax

    let approximation = global_bernoulli_approx(n,p,kmin,kmax,1)

    print "Approximation =";round(approximation,4)
    print

loop

end
```

EXAMPLE 2 (continued)
We have run the program **CLT Bernoulli Global** to estimate the probabilities $P(40 \leq S_{100} \leq 60)$ and $P(40 < S_{100} < 60) = P(41 \leq S_{100} \leq 59)$.

```
Trials,success probability,lower k,upper k = 100,.5,40,60
Approximation = .9643

Trials,success probability,lower k,upper k = 100,.5,41,59
Approximation = .9426
```

We see that when we include the endpoints the answers are both different from our simple approximation .954 without the $1/2$ correction, but the differences are small.

We have added to this program the function **binomial_sum** $(n,p,k\text{min},k\text{max})$, which gets the exact calculation of $P(k\text{min} \leq S_n \leq k\text{max})$, and compared this with the normal approximation, both with and without $1/2$ correction, for three examples:

Trials, success probability, lower k, upper k = 100, .5, 40, 60

Exact	Without 1/2 correction	With 1/2 correction
.9648	.9545	.9643

Trials, success probability, lower k, upper k = 100, .5, 0, 35

Exact	Without 1/2 correction	With 1/2 correction
.0018	.0013	.0019

Trials, success probability, lower k, upper k = 100, .2, 25, 30

Exact	Without 1/2 correction	With 1/2 correction
.1253	.0994	.126

We see that although the differences are not large they can be significant when the probabilities themselves are small. ☐

EXAMPLE 3

Dartmouth College would like to have 1050 freshmen. This college cannot accommodate more than 1060. Assume that each applicant accepts with probability .6 and that the acceptances can be modeled by Bernoulli trials. If the college accepts 1700, what is the probability that it will have too many acceptances?

If it accepts 1700 students, the expected number of students who matriculate is $.6 \cdot 1700 = 1020$. The standard deviation for the number that accept is $\sqrt{1700 \cdot .6 \cdot .4} \sim 20$. Thus we want to estimate the probability

$$P(S_{1700} > 1060)$$

$$= P\left(S_{1700}^* > \frac{1060 - 1020}{20}\right)$$

$$= P(S_{1700}^* > 2).$$

From Table 1 on page 322 we would estimate this probability to be $.5 - .4772 = .0228$. Thus, the college is fairly safe using this admission policy. ☐

EXAMPLE 4

A drug is believed to be effective a proportion p of the time. The drug is given to n patients and found to be effective a proportion $\bar{p} = S_n/n$ of the time. If we had to estimate p, we might well choose $\bar{p}$ for this estimate. However, we know that this quantity $\bar{p}$ will change if we were to run another experiment. The cental limit theorem states that

$$P\left(-2 < \frac{S_n - np}{\sqrt{npq}} < 2\right) \sim .954.$$

After some modest algebra, this states that

$$P\left(\bar{p} - \frac{2\sqrt{pq}}{\sqrt{n}} < p < \bar{p} + \frac{2\sqrt{pq}}{\sqrt{n}}\right) \sim .954.$$

We do not know the standard deviation $\sqrt{pq}$, but we can estimate it by $\sqrt{\bar{p}\bar{q}}$, where $\bar{q} = 1 - \bar{p}$. The resulting interval

$$\left(\bar{p} - \frac{2\sqrt{\bar{p}\bar{q}}}{\sqrt{n}}, \bar{p} + \frac{2\sqrt{\bar{p}\bar{q}}}{\sqrt{n}}\right)$$

is called the *95 percent confidence interval* for the unknown value of p. The name is suggested by the fact that if we use this method to estimate p in a large number of experiments we should expect that in about 95 percent of the cases the true value of p is contained in the confidence interval obtained from the data. In Exercise 11 you are asked to write a program to illustrate that this does indeed happen. □

Historical Remarks

The central limit theorem for Bernoulli trials was first proved by Abraham de Moivre and appeared in his book *The Doctrine of Chances*, first published in 1718.[1]

De Moivre spent his years from age 18 to 21 in prison in France because of his Protestant background. When he was released he left France for England, where he worked as a tutor to the sons of noblemen. Newton had presented a copy of his *Principia Mathematica* to the Earl of Devonshire. The story goes that, while de Moivre was tutoring at the earl's house, he came upon Newton's work and found that it was beyond him. It is said that he then bought a copy of his own and tore it into separate pages, learning it page by page as he walked around London to his tutoring jobs. De Moivre frequented the coffeehouses in London, where he started his probability work by calculating odds for gamblers. He also met Newton at such a coffeehouse and they became fast friends. De Moivre dedicated his book to Newton.

The Doctrine of Chances provides the techniques for solving a wide variety of gambling problems. In the midst of these gambling problems de Moivre rather modestly introduces his proof of the central limit theorem, writing

[1]A. de Moivre, *The Doctrine of Chances*, 3d ed. (London: Millar, 1756).

A Method of approximating the Sum of the Terms of the Binomial $(a + b)^n$ expanded into a Series, from whence are deduced some practical Rules to estimate the Degree of Assent which is to be given to Experiments.[2]

De Moivre's proof used the approximation to factorials that we now call Stirling's formula. De Moivre states that he had obtained this formula before Stirling but without determining the exact value of the constant $\sqrt{2\pi}$. While he says it is not really necessary to know this exact value, he concedes that knowing it "has spread a singular Elegancy on the Solution."

The complete proof and an interesting discussion of the life of de Moivre can be found in the book *Games, Gods and Gambling* by F. N. David.[3]

Exercises

1. Let S_{100} be the number of heads that turn up in 100 tosses of a fair coin. Use the central limit theorem to estimate
   (a) $P(S_{100} \leqslant 45)$.
   (b) $P(45 < S_{100} < 55)$.
   (c) $P(S_{100} > 63)$.

2. Let S_{200} be the number of heads that turn up in 200 tosses of a fair coin. Estimate
   (a) $P(S_{200} = 100)$.
   (b) $P(S_{200} = 90)$.
   (c) $P(S_{200} = 80)$.

3. A true-false examination has 48 questions. June has probability $^3/_4$ of answering a question correctly. April just guesses on each question. A passing score is 30 or more correct answers. Compare the probability that June passes the exam with the probability that April passes it.

4. Let S be the number of heads in 1,000,000 tosses of a balanced coin. Use **(a)** Chebyshev's inequality, and **(b)** the central limit theorem, to estimate the probability that S lies between 499,500 and 500,500. Use the same two methods to estimate the probability that S lies between 499,000 and 501,000, and the probability that S lies between 498,500 and 501,500.

5. A rookie is brought to a baseball club on the assumption that he will have a .300 batting average. (Batting average is the ratio of the number of hits to the number of times at bat.) In the first year, he comes to bat 300 times and his batting average is .267. Assume that his hits can be considered Bernoulli trials with probability .3 for success. Could such a low average be considered just bad luck or should he be sent back to the minor leagues? Comment on the assumption of Bernoulli trials in this situation.

[2]de Moivre, *The Doctrine of Chances*, p. 243.
[3]F.N. David, *Games, Gods, and Gambling* (London: Griffin, 1962).

6. Once upon a time, there were two railway trains competing for the passenger traffic of 1000 people leaving from Chicago at the same hour and going to Los Angeles. Assume that passengers are equally likely to choose each train. How many seats must a train have to assure a probability of .99 or better of having a seat for each passenger?

7. Assume that, as in Example 3, Dartmouth admits 1750 students. What is the probability of too many acceptances?

8. A club serves dinner to members only. They are seated at 12-seat tables. The manager observes over a long period of time that 95 percent of the time there are between six and nine full tables of members, and the remainder of the time the numbers are equally likely to fall above or below this range. Assume that each member decides to come with a given probability p, and that the decisions are independent. How many members are there? What is p?

9. Let S_n be the number of successes in n Bernoulli trials with probability .8 for success on each trial. Let $A_n = S_n/n$ be the average of the number of successes. In each case give the value for the limit, and give a reason for your answer.
   (a) $\lim_{n\to\infty} P(A_n = .8)$.
   (b) $\lim_{n\to\infty} P(.7n < S_n < .9n)$.
   (c) $\lim_{n\to\infty} P(S_n < .8n + .8\sqrt{n})$.
   (d) $\lim_{n\to\infty} P(.79 < A_n < .81)$.

10. Find the probability that among 10,000 random digits the digit 3 appears not more than 931 times.

11. Write a computer program to simulate 10,000 Bernoulli trials with probability .3 for success on each trial. Have the program compute the 95 percent confidence interval for the probability of success based on the proportion of successes. Repeat the experiment 20 times and see how many times the true value of .3 is included within the confidence limits.

12. A factory employs 100 workers who eat lunch at one of two diners, Joe's or Pete's. Assume that they choose their diner at random. How many seats should Joe's have to assure a probability of .95 of having seats for all the workers that choose his restaurant?

13. A balanced coin is flipped 400 times. Determine the number x such that the probability that the number of heads is between $200 - x$ and $200 + x$ is approximately .80.

14. A noodle machine in Spumoni's spaghetti factory makes about 5 percent defective noodles even when properly adjusted. The noodles are then packed in crates containing 1900 noodles each. A crate is examined and found to contain 115 defective noodles. What is the approximate probability of finding at least this many defective noodles if the machine is properly adjusted?

15. A restaurant feeds 400 customers per day. On the average 20 percent of the customers order apple pie.

    (a) Give a range (called a 95 percent confidence interval) for the number of pieces of apple pie ordered on a given day such that you can be 95 percent sure that the actual number will fall in this range.

    (b) How many customers must the restaurant have, on the average, to be at least 95 percent sure that the number of customers ordering pie on that day falls in the 19 to 21 percent range?

16. Recall that if X is a random variable, the *distribution* of X is the function $F(x)$ defined by

    $$F(x) = P(X \leq x).$$

    (a) Let S_n be the number of successes in n Bernoulli trials with probability p for success. Write a program to plot the distribution for S_n.

    (b) Modify your program in (a) to plot the distribution $F_n^*(x)$ of the standardized random variable

    $$S_n^* = \frac{S_n - np}{\sqrt{npq}}.$$

    (c) Define the *normal distribution* $N(x)$ to be the area under the normal curve up to the value x. Modify your program in (b) to plot the normal distribution as well, and compare it with the distribution of S_n^*.

17. In Example 5 of Chapter 3, Section 3.2, we were interested in testing the hypothesis that a new form of aspirin is effective 80 percent of the time rather than the 60 percent of the time as reported for standard aspirin. The new aspirin is given to n people. If it is effective in m or more cases, we accept the claim that the new drug is effective 80 percent of the time and if not we reject the claim. Using the central limit theorem, show that you can choose the number of trials n and the critical value m so that the probability that we reject the hypothesis when it is true is less than .01 and the probability that we accept it when it is false is also less than .01. Find the smallest value of n that will suffice for this.

18. Redo Exercise 8 of Chapter 8, Section 8.1, using the central limit theorem instead of Exercise 7 there.

9.2 POISSON APPROXIMATION

In this section we consider a second limit theorem, less general than the central limit theorem but of interest in a number of applications. Let S_n be the number of successes in n Bernoulli trials with probability p for success on each trial. Then $E(S_n) = np$. To obtain the central limit theorem, we changed the units to obtain a new random variable S_n^* which had, for all n, expected value 0 and variance 1. We now keep the same units but let n tend to infinity and p tend to 0 in such a way that the expected number of successes $m = np$ remains constant. Then we get the *Poisson Limit Theorem*.

Poisson Limit Theorem

THEOREM 4

Let $b(n,p,j)$ be the probability for exactly j successes for a Bernoulli trials process with probability p for success on each trial. Assume that n approaches infinity and p approaches 0 in such a way that $np = m$ remains constant. Then

$$b(n,p,j) \to \frac{m^j e^{-m}}{j!}.$$

Proof. Consider the case $j = 0$. For this case

$$b(n,p,0) = (1 - p)^n = \left(1 - \frac{m}{n}\right)^n. \tag{2}$$

It is shown in calculus that for any value a

$$\left(1 + \frac{a}{n}\right)^n \to e^a \tag{3}$$

as $n \to \infty$. Choosing $a = -m$ in Equation (3), we obtain

$$b(n,p,0) \to e^{-m}$$

as $n \to \infty$. This proves the theorem for $j = 0$. In general, for $j \geq 1$, let $q = 1 - p$. Then

$$\frac{b(n,p,j)}{b(n,p,j-1)} = \frac{\binom{n}{j} p^j q^{n-j}}{\binom{n}{j-1} p^{j-1} q^{n-j+1}}$$

$$= \frac{n - j + 1}{j} \cdot \frac{p}{q} = \frac{m - jp + p}{j(1 - p)}.$$

Since $p \to 0$ and m and j are fixed, we have

$$\frac{b(n,p,j)}{b(n,p,j-1)} \to \frac{m}{j} \text{ as } n \to \infty.$$

Thus, if $j = 1$,

$$b(n,p,1) = \frac{b(n,p,1)}{b(n,p,0)} \cdot b(n,p,0) \to me^{-m}.$$

Similarly,

$$b(n,p,2) \to \frac{m}{2}\, me^{-m} = \frac{m^2}{2!}\, e^{-m},$$

$$b(n,p,3) \to \frac{m}{3}\frac{m^2}{2!}\, e^{-m} = \frac{m^3}{3!}\, e^{-m},$$

and so forth. Continuing by induction, we obtain for all j

$$b(n,p,j) \to \frac{m^j}{j!}\, e^{-m}. \qquad \blacksquare$$

Examples

EXAMPLE 1

A typesetter makes, on the average, one mistake per 1000 words. Assume that he is setting a book with 100 words to a page. Let S_{100} be the number of mistakes that he makes on a single page. Then the exact probability density for S_{100} would be obtained by considering S_{100} as the result of 100 Bernoulli trials with $p = {}^1/_{1000}$. The expected value of S_{100} is $m = 100({}^1/_{1000}) = .1$. The exact probability that $S_n = j$ is $b(100, {}^1/_{1000}, j)$, and the Poisson approximation is

$$\frac{e^{-.1}(.1)^j}{j!}.$$

In Table 2 we give the exact values computed by the binomial density and the Poisson approximation. $\qquad \square$

Table 2. Poisson approximation for $b(100,.001,j)$.

j	Exact	Poisson
0	.90480	.90484
1	.09057	.09048
2	.00449	.00452
3	.00015	.00015
4	.00000	.00000

EXAMPLE 2

A number of applications of the Poisson approximation are equivalent to the following somewhat frivolous application. Assume that we are making raisin cookies. We put a box of 600 raisins into our dough mix, mix up the dough, then make from the dough 500 cookies. We then ask for the probability that a randomly chosen cookie will have

Table 3. Poisson approximation for $b(600,.002,d)$.

j	Exact probability	Poisson approximation
0	.3008	.3012
1	.3617	.3614
2	.2171	.2169
3	.0867	.0867
4	.0259	.0260
5	.0062	.0062
6	.0012	.0012
7	.0002	.0002
8	.0000	.0000

Table 4. Poisson approximation for $b(n,p,j)$.

j	Poisson $m = .1$	Binomial $n = 10$ $p = .01$	Poisson $m = 1$	Binomial $n = 100$ $p = .01$	Poisson $m = 10$	Binomial $n = 1000$ $p = .01$
0	.9048	.9044	.3679	.3660	.0000	.0000
1	.0905	.0914	.3679	.3697	.0005	.0004
2	.0045	.0042	.1839	.1849	.0023	.0022
3	.0002	.0001	.0613	.0610	.0076	.0074
4	.0000	.0000	.0153	.0149	.0189	.0186
5			.0031	.0029	.0378	.0374
6			.0005	.0005	.0631	.0627
7			.0001	.0001	.0901	.0900
8			.0000	.0000	.1126	.1128
9					.1251	.1256
10					.1251	.1257
11					.1137	.1143
12					.0948	.0952
13					.0729	.0731
14					.0521	.0520
15					.0347	.0345
16					.0217	.0215
17					.0128	.0126
18					.0071	.0069
19					.0037	.0036
20					.0019	.0018
21					.0009	.0009
22					.0004	.0004
23					.0002	.0002
24					.0001	.0001
25					.0000	.0000

0,1,2, . . . raisins. To compute this probability, we assume that each of the 600 raisins has an equal probability of being in a particular cookie. This probability would be $p = \frac{1}{500}$. Then we may regard the number of raisins in a cookie as the result of $n = 600$ independent trials with probability $p = \frac{1}{500}$ for success on each trial. Since n is large and p is small, we can use the Poisson approximation with $m = 600(\frac{1}{500}) = 1.2$. The exact probability densities and the Poisson approximations for the number of raisins in a given cookie are given in Table 3. We note that the model suggests that the raisins are not likely to cluster in a few cookies. It is extremely unlikely that any one cookie will have as many as five raisins. Examples similar to this, but relating to more serious matters such as blood counts, can be found in Feller's book.[4] $\qquad\square$

Table of Poisson Approximation

In using the Poisson approximation, we replace the density

$$b(n,p,j) = \binom{n}{j} p^j q^{n-j}, \qquad j = 0,1, \ldots , n \tag{4}$$

by the numbers

$$p_j = \frac{m^j e^{-m}}{j!}, \qquad j = 0,1,2, \ldots n, \tag{5}$$

where $m = np$. In Table 4 we give three comparisons of these approximations. We see that when p is small, they are quite good.

We now have two ways to approximate individual binomial probabilities: by the normal approximation and by the Poisson approximation. It is interesting to compare these approximations. We have only to add the Poisson approximation to the program **CLT Bernoulli Local** that we used in Chapter 9, Section 9.1. Doing this and running the program, we obtain the following results.

```
Exact Binomial(n,p,k) and Normal & Poisson approximations for :

n,p,k = 100,.01,1
Exact       Poisson       Normal
.3697       .3679         .401


n,p,k = 100,.1,10
Exact       Poisson       Normal
.1319       .1251         .133


n,p,k = 100,.5,50
Exact       Poisson       Normal
.0796       .0563         .0798
```

[4]W. Feller, *Introduction to Probability Theory and its Applications*, 3d ed., vol. 1 (New York: Wiley, 1968).

We have chosen $n = 100$ and several values for p and k. Note that, when $p = .01$, the estimate for the probability of exactly 1 success (the most probable value) is better by the Poisson approximation than by the normal approximation. As we increase p, the normal approximation improves, and when $p = .5$ it is much better than the Poisson. It is not possible to give simple rules that dictate with any accuracy when to use the Poisson and when to use the normal approximation. However, since the proof of the Poisson approximation assumes that p tends to 0 as n tends to infinity, we should use this approximation only for small p and large n.

Poisson Density

DEFINITION 2

The Poisson density with mean m is the density defined on the nonnegative integers $0, 1, 2, \ldots$ by the formula

$$p_j = \frac{e^{-m}m^j}{j!}.$$

To justify this definition as a density with mean m we must show that

$$\sum_{j=0}^{\infty} p_j = 1.$$

and

$$\sum_{j=0}^{\infty} jp_j = m.$$

We recall that

$$e^x = 1 + x + \frac{x^2}{2!} + \frac{x^3}{3!} + \cdots.$$

Thus,

$$\sum_{j=0}^{\infty} p_j = \sum_{j=0}^{\infty} e^{-m} \frac{m^j}{j!}$$

$$= e^{-m} \sum_{j=0}^{\infty} \frac{m^j}{j!}$$

$$= e^{-m}e^m = 1.$$

Moreover,

$$
\begin{aligned}
\sum_{j=0}^{\infty} jp_j &= \sum_{j=1}^{\infty} je^{-m} \frac{m^j}{j!} \\
&= me^{-m} \sum_{j=1}^{\infty} \frac{m^{j-1}}{(j-1)!} \\
&= me^{-m} \sum_{j=0}^{\infty} \frac{m^j}{j!} \\
&= me^{-m}e^{m} = m.
\end{aligned}
$$

In Exercise 13 you are asked to show that the variance of the Poisson density with mean m is also m.

EXAMPLE 3

In his book *Introduction to Probability with Applications*,[5] Feller discusses the statistics of flying bomb hits in the south of London during the Second World War.

Assume that you live in a district of size 10 blocks by 10 blocks so that the total district is divided into 100 small squares. How likely is it that the square in which you live will receive no hits if the total area is hit by 400 bombs?

We assume that a particular bomb will hit your square with probability $1/100$. Since there are 400 bombs, we can regard the number of hits that your square receives as the number of *successes* in a Bernoulli trials process with $n = 400$ and $p = 1/100$. Thus we can use the Poisson density with $m = 400 \cdot 1/100 = 4$ to approximate the probability that your square will receive j hits. This probability is $p(j) = e^{-4}4^j/j!$. The expected number of squares that receive exactly j hits is then $100 \cdot p(j)$. It is easy to write a program **London Bombs** to simulate this situation and compare the expected number of squares with j hits with the observed number. In Exercise 15 you are asked to compare the actual observed data with that predicted by the Poisson density.

From our simulation (see Figure 4) we see that your block is likely to be hit at least once but not more than seven times. $\qquad\Box$

Discussion

The above examples suggest that the Poisson density is reasonable when you have arrivals in a given time interval taking place *at random*. Thus the number of cars that go by your house during the noon hour might be regarded as having a Poisson density. You would have to estimate m by taking the average over a large number of days. You might ask: If the number going from east to west and the number going from west to east each have a Poisson density then does the total number of cars that pass your house in the noon

[5]Ibid., p. 161.

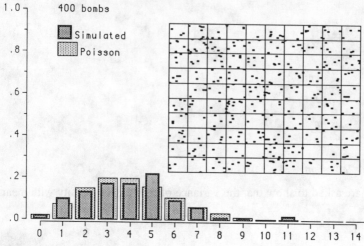

Figure 4 Flying bomb hits.

hour have a Poisson density? Exercise 21 asks you to answer this question, and Exercise 22 explores a related question.

The Poisson density is used, quite generally, to describe the number of occurrences of *rare* events in a fixed time period. For example, consider the number of hurricanes that hit the East Coast in one year. We can consider this as the result of a large number n of Bernoulli trials with a small probability p for success by taking $n = 365$ days and p the (small) probability of a hurricane on any one day. The classical data for the use of the Poisson density involved the number of deaths from mule kicks in the Prussian army corps (see Exercise 20). A more typical example of the use of the Poisson density is provided by the Bus Example (Example 4 of Chapter 2, Section 2.1). Recall that, in this example, the bus arrived in any 1 minute with a small probability of $^1/_{30}$. Then the number of times the bus arrives in a 30-minute time period should have a Poisson density with mean $m = 30(^1/_{30}) = 1$. This model suggests that, quite generally, the number of chance events in a fixed time interval, like the number of cars that arrive at an intersection, the number of breakdowns of a machine, or the number of particles emitted from a radioactive source, should have a Poisson density.

Exercises

1. The Poisson density with mean .3 has been assigned for the outcome of an experiment. Let X be the outcome function. Find $P(X = 0)$, $P(X = 1)$, and $P(X > 1)$.

2. On the average, only 1 person in 1000 has a particular rare blood type.
   (a) Find the probability that, in a city of 10,000 people, no one has this blood type.
   (b) How many people would have to be tested to give a probability greater than $^1/_2$ of finding at least one person with this blood type?

3. Write a program for the user to input n,p,j and have the program print out the Poisson approximation to binom(n,p,j).

4. Assume that, during each second, a Dartmouth switchboard receives one call with probability .01 and no calls with probability .99. Use the Poisson approximation to estimate the probability that the operator will miss at most one call if she takes a 5-minute coffee break.

5. The probability of a royal flush in a poker hand is $p = 1/649,740$. How large must n be to render the probability of having no royal flush in n hands smaller than $1/e$?

6. A baker blends 600 raisins and 400 chocolate chips into a dough mix and, from this, makes 500 cookies.
   (a) Find the probability that a randomly picked cookie will have no raisins.
   (b) Find the probability that a randomly picked cookie will have exactly two chocolate chips.
   (c) Find the probability that a randomly chosen cookie will have at least two bits (raisins or chips) in it.

7. In Example 1, assume that the book in question has 1000 pages. Let X be the number of pages with no mistakes. Show that $E(X) = 905$ and $V(X) = 86$. Using these results, show that the probability is $\leq .05$ that there will be more than 924 pages without errors or fewer than 886 pages without errors.

8. The probability that, in a bridge deal, one of the four hands has all hearts is approximately $(6.3)(10^{-12})$. In a small town with about 50,000 bridge players the resident probability expert is called on the average once a year (usually late at night) and told that the caller has just been dealt a hand of all hearts. Should she suspect that some of these callers are the victims of practical jokes?

9. An advertiser drops 10,000 leaflets on a city which has 2000 blocks. Assume that each leaflet has an equal chance of landing on each block. What is the probability that a particular block will receive no leaflets?

10. In a class of 80 students, the professor calls on 1 student chosen at random for a recitation in each class period. There are 32 class periods in a term.
    (a) Write a formula for the exact probability that a given student is called upon j times during the term.
    (b) Write a formula for the Poisson approximation for this probability. Using your formula estimate the probability that a given student is called upon more than twice.

11. For a certain experiment, the Poisson density with mean m has been assigned. Show that a most probable outcome for the experiment is the integer value k such that $m - 1 \leq k \leq m$. Under what conditions will there be two most probable values? *Hint:* Consider the ratio of successive probabilities.

12. John Kemeny receives an average of ten letters each day. On a certain weekday he receives no mail and wonders if it is a holiday. To decide this he computes the

probability that, in ten years, he would have at least 1 day without any mail. He assumes that the number of letters he receives on a given day has a Poisson density. What probability does he find? *Hint:* Apply the Poisson density twice. First, to find the probability that, on a given day, he receives no mail, and second, to find the probability that, in 3000 days, he will have at least 1 day without mail, assuming each year has about 300 days on which mail is delivered.

13. A Poisson density is assigned to the nonnegative integers by the formula $p_j = m^j e^{-m}/j!$. Prove that the variance $\sigma^2 = m$.

14. Reese Prosser never puts money in a 10-cent parking meter in Hanover. He assumes that there is a probability of .05 that he will be caught. The first offense costs nothing, the second costs 2 dollars, and subsequent offenses cost 5 dollars each. Under his assumptions, how does the expected cost of parking 100 times without paying the meter compare with the cost of paying the meter each time?

15. Feller[6] discusses the statistics of flying bomb hits in an area in the south of London during the Second World War. The area in question was divided into $24 \times 24 = 576$ small areas. The total number of hits was 537. There were 229 squares with 0 hits, 211 with 1 hit, 93 with 2 hits, 35 with 3 hits, 7 with 4 hits, and 1 with 5 or more. Assuming the hits were purely random, use the Poisson approximation to find the probability that a particular square would have exactly k hits. Compute the expected number of squares that would have 0, 1, 2, 3, 4, and 5 or more hits and compare this with the observed results.

16. Assume that the probability that there is a significant accident in a nuclear power plant during one year's time is .001. If a country has 100 nuclear plants, estimate the probability that there is at least one such accident during a given year.

17. An airline finds that 4 percent of the passengers that make reservations on a particular flight will not show up. Consequently, their policy is to sell 100 reserved seats on a plane that has only 98 seats. Find the probability that every person who shows up for the flight will find a seat available.

18. The king's coinmaster boxes his coins 500 to a box and puts 1 counterfeit coin in each box. The king is suspicious, but, instead of testing all the coins in 1 box, he tests 1 coin chosen at random out of each of 500 boxes. What is the probability that he finds at least one fake? What is it if the king tests 2 coins from each of 250 boxes?

19. (Kemeny).[7] Show that, if you make 100 bets on the number 17 at roulette at Monte Carlo (see Chapter 6, Section 6.1, Example 7), you will have a probability greater than $\frac{1}{2}$ of coming out ahead. What is your expected winning?

[6] Ibid., p. 161.
[7] Private communication.

20. In one of the first studies of the Poisson density, von Bortkiewicz[8] considered the frequency of deaths from mule kicks in the Prussian army corps. From the study of 200 corps he obtained the data

Number of deaths	Number of corps with x deaths
0	109
1	65
2	22
3	3
4	1

Fit a Poisson density to this data and see if you think that the Poisson density is appropriate.

21. It is often assumed that the auto traffic that arrives at the intersection during a unit time period has a Poisson density with expected value m. Assume that the number of cars X that arrive at an intersection from the north in unit time has a Poisson density with mean m and the number Y that arrive from the west in unit time has a Poisson density with mean $\overline{m}$. If X and Y are independent, show that the total number $X + Y$ that arrive at the intersection in unit time has a Poisson density with mean $m + \overline{m}$.

22. Cars coming along Magnolia Street come to a fork in the road and have to choose either Willow Street or Main Street to continue. Assume that the number of cars that arrive at the fork in unit time has a Poisson density with mean 4. A car arriving at the fork chooses Main Street with probability $^3/_4$ and Willow Street with probability $^1/_4$. What will be the density per unit time of the cars that pass by Joe's Barber Shop on Main Street?

23. In the appeal of the *People v. Collins* case (see Chapter 4, Section 4.1, Exercise 25), the counsel for the defense argued as follows: Suppose, for example, there are 5,000,000 couples in the Los Angeles area and the probability that a randomly chosen couple fits the witnesses' description is 1/12,000,000. Then the probability that there are two such couples given that there is at least one is not at all small. Find this probability. (The California Supreme Court overturned the initial guilty verdict.)

9.3 CENTRAL LIMIT THEOREM FOR DISCRETE INDEPENDENT TRIALS

We have illustrated the central limit theorem in terms of Bernoulli trials, but this theorem applies to a much more general class of chance processes. In particular, it applies to any independent trials processes with a finite number of outcomes for each experiment. For

[8]L. von Bortkiewicz, *Das Gesetz der Kleinen Zahlen* (Leipzig: Teubner, 1898).

such a process, both the normal approximation for individual terms and the central limit theorem are valid.

Let $S_n = X_1 + X_2 + \cdots + X_n$ be the sum of n independent random variables of an independent trials process with common density p defined on the integers with mean μ and variance σ^2. We have seen in Chapter 7, Section 7.1, that the densities for such independent sums have shapes resembling the normal curve, but the largest values drift to the right and the curves flatten out (see Chapter 7, Section 7.1, Figure 1). We can prevent this just as we did for Bernoulli trials.

Standardized Sums

Consider the standardized random variables

$$S_n^* = \frac{S_n - n\mu}{\sqrt{n\sigma^2}}.$$

This standardizes S_n to have expected value 0 and variance 1. Now when $S_n = j$, S_n^* has the value x_j with

$$x_j = \frac{j - n\mu}{\sqrt{n\sigma^2}}.$$

We construct a bar graph just as we did for Bernoulli trials. Each bar is centered at some x_j. The base of the bar has length

$$b = \frac{1}{\sqrt{n\sigma^2}},$$

and the height of the bar is

$$h = \sqrt{n\sigma^2}\, P(S_n = j).$$

Bernoulli trials is the special case for which $X_j = 1$ if the jth outcome is a success and 0 otherwise; then $\mu = p$ and $\sigma^2 = pq$.

The program **CLT Ind Trials Plot** (page 341) carries out these computations and plots the resulting bar graphs and the normal curve (see Figure 5, page 342).

The first run of this program is for the case where $n = 2$ or $n = 10$ independent trials, using the common density p given by

$$p_X = \begin{pmatrix} 1 & 2 & 3 & 4 & 5 \\ .2 & .2 & .2 & .2 & .2 \end{pmatrix}.$$

Even for $n = 2$ the approximation is surprisingly good.

The second run of the program is for $n = 3$ or $n = 10$ and common density

$$p_X = \begin{pmatrix} 1 & 2 & 3 & 4 & 5 \\ .3 & .2 & .1 & .1 & .3 \end{pmatrix}.$$

```
! CLT Ind Trials Plot    (CLTINDP)
!
! Illustrates the Central Limit Theorem for independent trials by
! plotting the density of the standardized sum Sn* of n identically
! distributed independent random variables Xk with common density
! p(lower),....,p(upper), and comparing this bar graph with the graph
! of the standard normal density.

library "Lib.prob*"
library "Lib.CLT*"
library "Lib.cont*"
declare function standard_normal

dim p(20)                           ! Common density of the X's
dim density(20)                     ! Density for Sn

open #1:screen .25,.75,.2,.8        ! Set up graph window

do

    clear
    input prompt "Lower, upper = ": lower, upper
    mat p = zer(lower to upper)
    let prompt$ = "p(" & str$(lower) & ") to p(" & str$(upper) & ") = "
    mat input prompt prompt$: p
    input prompt "n = ":n

    call density_statistics(p, mu,sigma)      ! Get mu, sigma
    let mean = n*mu                  ! Mean of Sn and ...
    let std = sqr(n * sigma^2)       ! standard deviation.
    let kmin = max( n*lower,int(mean - 4*std))    ! Bounds for bar graph
    let kmax = min( n*upper,int(mean + 4*std))

    call get_Sn_density(n,p,  density)

    call plot_standardized(density, 4)

    get key k

  loop

end
```

This density is quite unsymmetric and the approximation is not very good for $n = 3$, but by $n = 10$ we have again an excellent approximation.

Approximation Theorem

As for the case of Bernoulli trials, these graphs suggest the following approximation theorem for the individual probabilities.

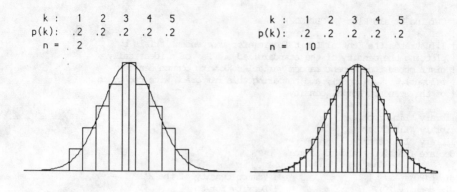

Uniform density.

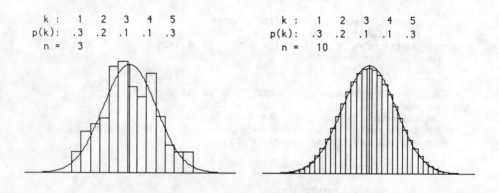

Non-uniform density

Figure 5 Density of standardized sums.

THEOREM 5

Let $X_1, X_2, \ldots, X_n$ be an independent trials process and let $S_n = X_1 + \cdots + X_n$. Assume that the greatest common divisor of the differences of all the values that the X_j can take on is 1. Let $E(X_j) = \mu$ and $V(X_j) = \sigma^2$. Then for n large

$$P(S_n = j) \sim \frac{n(x_j)}{\sqrt{n\sigma^2}},$$

where $x_j = (j - n\mu)/\sqrt{n\sigma^2}$, and $n(x)$ is the normal density.

The program **CLT Ind Trials Local** implements this approximation.

```
! CLT Ind Trials Local    (CLTINDL)
!
! Local version of the Central Limit Theorem for independent trials:
! Compares the exact calculation of P(Sn = k) with the normal
! approximation. The exact calculation is by get_Sn_density(n,p, sum)
! in Lib.CLT, which does the necessary convolution.The function
! local_ind_trials_approx(n,p,k), also in Lib.CLT, gets the approximation.

library "Lib.prob*"
library "Lib.CLT*"
declare function local_ind_trials_approx
clear

dim p(20), sum(20)

input prompt "Lower, upper = ": lower, upper
mat p = zer(lower, to upper)
let prompt$ = "p(" & str$(lower) & ") to p(" & str$(upper) & ") = "
mat input prompt prompt$: p
print

print
print "n, k", " Exact P(Sn=k)", " Normal approximation"
print "----", " -------------", " --------------------"

do

    input prompt "" : n, k

    call get_Sn_density(n,p, sum)
    print ,round(sum(k),4),

    let approximation = local_ind_trials_approx(n,p,k)
    print round(approximation,4)

loop

end
```

Running this program for rolling a die 6 times and 24 times gives:

```
Lower, upper = 1,6.
p(1) to p(6) = .166667,.166667,.166667,.166667,.166667,.166667
```

n, k	Exact P(Sn=k)	Normal approximation
6,21	.0929	.0954
24,84	.0474	.0477

These results show that the normal approximations are quite good.

Central Limit Theorem

The central limit theorem for an independent trials process is as follows.

THEOREM 6   Central Limit Theorem

Let $S_n = X_1 + X_2 + \cdots + X_n$ be the sum of n independent random variables with common density having expected value μ and variance σ^2. Then, for $a < b$,

$$\lim_{n \to \infty} P\left(a < \frac{S_n - n\mu}{\sqrt{n\sigma^2}} < b\right) = \frac{1}{\sqrt{2\pi}} \int_a^b e^{-x^2/2} dx.$$

We will discuss the proofs of Theorems 5 and 6 in Chapter 10, Section 10.3. Here we consider several examples.

Examples

EXAMPLE 1

A die is rolled 420 times. What is the probability that the sum of the rolls lies between 1400 and 1540?

The sum is a random variable

$$S_{420} = X_1 + X_2 + \cdots + X_{420},$$

where each X_j has density

$$p_X = \begin{pmatrix} 1 & 2 & 3 & 4 & 5 & 6 \\ 1/6 & 1/6 & 1/6 & 1/6 & 1/6 & 1/6 \end{pmatrix}.$$

We have seen that $\mu = E(X) = 7/2$ and $\sigma^2 = V(X) = 35/12$. Thus, $E(S_{420}) = 420 \cdot 7/2 = 1470$, $\sigma^2(S_{420}) = 420 \cdot 35/12 = 1225$, and $\sigma(S_{420}) = 35$. Therefore,

$$P(1400 \le S_{420} \le 1540)$$

$$= P\left(\frac{1400 - 1470}{35} \le S_{420}^* \le \frac{1540 - 1470}{35}\right)$$

$$= P\left(-2 \le S_{420}^* \le 2\right) \sim \mathrm{NA}(-2,2) = .9542. \qquad \square$$

EXAMPLE 2

A student's grade point average is the average of his grades in 30 courses. The grades are based on 100 possible points reported and are correct to two decimal places. Thus, a typical grade might be 87.65. Assume that, in each course, the instructor makes an error in grading of $.01k$ with probability $|p/k|$, where $k = \pm 1, \pm 2, \pm 3, \pm 4, \pm 5$. The probability of no error is then $1 - {}^{137}/_{30}\, p$. (The parameter p represents the accuracy of the instructor's grading.) For a grade point average to be accurate in the first decimal place, we require the average of the errors to be at most $\pm .05$.

Let us assume that $p = {}^1/_{20}$ and estimate the probability that the first decimal point is correct for a given student. We assume that the total error is the sum S_{30} of 30 independent random variables each with density

$$
p_X: \left\{ \begin{array}{ccccccccccc} -5 & -4 & -3 & -2 & -1 & 0 & 1 & 2 & 3 & 4 & 5 \\ \dfrac{1}{100} & \dfrac{1}{80} & \dfrac{1}{60} & \dfrac{1}{40} & \dfrac{1}{20} & \dfrac{463}{600} & \dfrac{1}{20} & \dfrac{1}{40} & \dfrac{1}{60} & \dfrac{1}{80} & \dfrac{1}{100} \end{array} \right\}.
$$

For this density, $E(X) = 0$ and $\sigma^2(X) = 1.5$. We want to find

$$
P\left(-.05 \leq \frac{S_{30}}{30} \leq .05 \right)
$$

$$
= P(-1.5 \leq S_{30} \leq 1.5)
$$

$$
= P\left(\frac{-1.5}{\sqrt{30 \cdot 1.5}} \leq S_{30}^{*} \leq \frac{1.5}{\sqrt{30 \cdot 1.5}} \right)
$$

$$
= P(-.224 \leq S_{30}^{*} \leq .224)
$$

$$
\sim NA\,(-.224, .224) = .1772.
$$

Therefore, if our model is reasonable, it is not likely that the student's grade point will be accurate to the first decimal place. For a further discussion of this example, see "Grade-Point Averages and the Central Limit Theorem," by R. M. Kozelka.[9] □

Just as in the calculations for Bernoulli trials, the $^1/_2$ correction is a significant improvement in our approximations. The program **CLT Ind Trials Global** (see page 346) computes the approximation with this correction.

We have run the program to find the probability that the sum of 16 rolls of a die lies between 42 and 70, and between 35 and 77—about two and three standard deviations, respectively, from the expected sum of 56 (see page 346).

Again the reader is encouraged to do some problems without using this program in order to be able to make these calculations on a desert island.

[9]R.M. Kozelka, "Grade-Point Averages and the Central Limit Theorem," *American Math. Monthly*, vol. 86 (Nov 1979), pp. 773–777.

```
! CLT Ind Trials Global   (CLTINDG)
!
! Global version of the Central Limit Theorem for independent trials:
! Approximates the  probability that Sn lies in [kmin,kmax] with the
! normal approximation with 1/2 correction.

library "Lib.CLT*"
declare function Sn_density_sum
declare function global_ind_trials_approx
dim p(20)

let flag = 1                        ! Signal for 1/2 correction

input prompt "Lower, upper = ": lower, upper
mat p = zer(lower to upper)
let prompt$ = "p(" & str$(lower) & ") to p(" & str$(upper) & ") = "
mat input prompt prompt$: p
print
input prompt "Number of summands: n = ": n
print
print "kmin, kmax", "Approximation for P(kmin ≤ Sn ≤ kmax)"
print

do

    input prompt "" :kmin,kmax

    let approximation = global_ind_trials_approx(n,p,kmin,kmax,flag)
    print ,round(approximation, 4)

loop

end
```

Running this program gives

```
Lower, upper = 1,6
p(1) to p(6) = .166667,.166667,.166667,.166667,.166667,.166667

Number of summands: n = 16

kmin, kmax     Approximation for P(kmin ≤ Sn ≤ kmax)

42,70          .9662

35,77          .9984
```

Discussion

So far, we have illustrated the central limit theorem in situations where we can compute the exact probability $P(S_n = j)$. But the normal curve is also found, quite generally, in the analysis of all sorts of empirical data, and so we might expect the central limit theorem to hold in more general situations. For example, assume that your height is the result of a large number of small random effects—whether you ate your Wheaties on your seventh

```
! CLT General    (CLTGEN)
!
! Illustrates our most general form of the Central Limit Theorem.

library "Lib.Prob*"
library "Lib.CLT*"
library "Lib.Cont*"
declare function rand
declare function normal

dim p(20), q(20), r(20), list(20), temp(20)

    input prompt "Maximum range [A,B] for A,B = ": A,B

        input prompt "Number of summands n = ": n

        mat p = zer(A to B]

        call make_density              ! Make a density p()
        mat q = p

        for k = 2 to n
            call make_density
            call convolve(p, q, r)
            mat q = zer(lbound(r) to ubound(r))
            mat q = r
        next k

        call plot_standardized(q, 5) ! Graph standardized density and
                                     ! normal on [-5, 5]

sub make_density

    let masses = rand(1,2,B-A+1)         ! Random number of points in [A,B]
    mat list = zer(1 to masses)
    call pick_distinct(masses,A,B,list) ! Pick the points in [A,B]

    mat temp = zer(1 to masses)
    call random_density(temp)            ! Assign Random density to the points.

    mat p = 0

    for mass = 1 to masses
        let p(list(mass)) = temp(mass)
    next mass

end sub


end
```

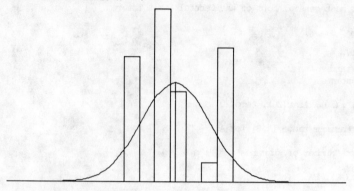

Maximum range [A,B] for A,B = -2,4
Number of summands n = 1

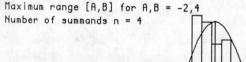

Maximum range [A,B] for A,B = -2,4
Number of summands n = 4

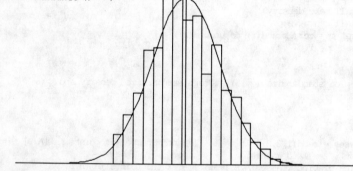

Maximum range [A,B] for A,B = -2,4
Number of summands n = 10

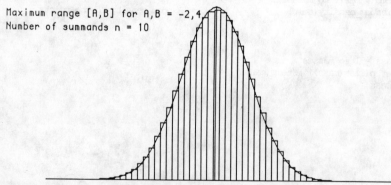

Figure 6 Sums of randomly chosen random variables.

birthday, and so forth. Should the total of all these small effects result in random heights approximated by the normal curve? There are very general forms of the central limit theorem that suggest that the answer is yes. For example, let

$$S_n = X_1 + \cdots + X_n$$

where $X_1, X_2, \ldots ,X_n$ are mutually independent random variables but not necessarily having the same density. If there is a constant K such that none of the individual random variables has a value greater in absolute value than K, and if the variance $V(S_n)$ tends to infinity as n tends to infinity, then the density of the normalized sums can be approximated by the normal curve.

We illustrate this theorem by generating a sequence of n random densities on the interval $[A,B]$. We then convolute these densities to find the density of the sum of n experiments governed by these densities. Finally, we standardized the density for the sum to have mean 0 and standard deviation 1 and compare it with the normal density. The program **CLT General** (see page 347) carries out this procedure.

In Figure 6 (see page 348) we show the result of running this program for $n = 1$, 4, and 10. We see that our first random density was on five of the seven points in the interval from -2 to 4 and was a quite unpleasant density. The sum of four experiments with random densities is already pretty nearly normal and by the time we choose the sum of ten such experiments we have a very good fit to the normal curve.

Exercises

1. A die is rolled 24 times. Use the central limit theorem to estimate the probability that
   (a) the sum is greater than 84.
   (b) the sum is equal to 84.

2. A random walker starts at 0 on the X-axis and at each time unit moves 1 step to the right or 1 step to the left with probability $1/2$. Estimate the probability that, after 100 steps, the walker is more than 10 steps from the starting position.

3. A piece of rope is made up of 100 strands. Assume that the breaking strength of the rope is the sum of the breaking strengths of the individual strands. Assume further that this sum may be considered to be the sum of an independent trials process with 100 experiments each having expected value of 10 pounds and standard deviation 1. Find the approximate probability that the rope will support a weight
   (a) of 1000 pounds.
   (b) of 970 pounds.

4. Write a program to find the average of 1000 random digits 0,1,2,3,4,5,6,7,8, or 9. Have the program test to see if the average lies within three standard deviations of the expected value of 4.5. Modify the program so that it repeats this simulation 100 times and keeps track of the number of times the test is passed. Does your outcome agree with the central limit theorem?

5. A die is thrown until the first time the total sum of the face values of the die is 700 or greater. Estimate the probability that, for this to happen,
   (a) more than 210 tosses are required.
   (b) less than 190 tosses are required.
   (c) between 180 and 210 tosses, inclusive, are required.

6. A bank accepts rolls of pennies and gives 50 cents credit to a customer without counting the contents. Assume that a roll contains 49 pennies 30 percent of the time, 50 pennies 60 percent of the time, and 51 pennies 10 percent of the time.
   (a) Find the expected value and the variance for the amount that the bank loses on a typical roll.
   (b) Estimate the probability that the bank will lose more than 25 cents in a hundred rolls.
   (c) Estimate the probability that the bank will lose exactly 20 cents in 100 rolls.

7. A surveying instrument makes an error of -2, -1, 0, 1, or 2 feet with equal probabilities when measuring the height of a 200-foot tower.
   (a) Find the expected value and the variance for the height obtained using this instrument once.
   (b) Estimate the probability that in 18 independent measurements of this tower, the average of the measurements is between 199 and 201, inclusive.

8. For Example 2 estimate $P(S_n = 0)$. That is, estimate the probability that the errors cancel out and the student's grade point average is correct.

9. Prove the law of large numbers using the central limit theorem.

10. Peter and Paul match pennies 10,000 times. Describe briefly what each of the following theorems tells you about Peter's fortune.
    (a) The law of large numbers.
    (b) The central limit theorem.

11. A tourist in Las Vegas was attracted by a certain gambling game in which the customer stakes 1 dollar on each play; a win then pays the customer 2 dollars plus the return of her stake, although a loss costs her only her stake. Las Vegas insiders, and alert students of probability theory, know that the probability of winning at this game is $^1/_4$. When driven from the tables by hunger, the tourist had played this game 240 times. Assuming that no near miracles happened, about how much poorer was the tourist upon leaving the casino?

12. We have seen that, in playing roulette at Monte Carlo (Chapter 6, Section 6.1, Example 7), betting 1 dollar on red or 1 dollar on 17 amounts to choosing between the densities

$$p_X = \begin{pmatrix} -1 & -\dfrac{1}{2} & 1 \\ \dfrac{18}{37} & \dfrac{1}{37} & \dfrac{18}{37} \end{pmatrix}$$

or

$$p_X = \begin{pmatrix} -1 & 35 \\ 36/37 & 1/37 \end{pmatrix}.$$

You plan to choose one of these methods and use it to make 100 1-dollar bets using the method chosen. Which gives you the higher probability of winning at least 20 dollars?

13. In Example 2 find the largest value of p that gives probability .954 that the first decimal place is correct.

9.4 CENTRAL LIMIT THEOREM FOR CONTINUOUS INDEPENDENT TRIALS

We have seen in Section 9.3 that the density function for the sum of a large number n of independent discrete random variables with mean μ and variance σ^2 tends to look like a normal density with mean $n\mu$ and variance $n\sigma^2$. The remarkable result holds true no matter what the common density function of the individual random variables may be.

We shall see in this section that this same result holds true also if the individual random variables are defined on a continuous probability space and have a continuous density function.

Let us begin by looking at some examples to see whether such a result is even plausible.

Standardized Sums

EXAMPLE 1
Suppose we choose n random numbers from the interval $[0,1]$ with uniform density. Let $X_1, X_2, \ldots, X_n$ denote these choices, and $S_n = X_1 + X_2 + \cdots + X_n$ their sum.

We saw in Chapter 7, Section 7.1, Example 7 that the density function for S_n tends to have a normal shape, but is centered at $^n/_2$ and flattened out. In order to compare the shapes of these density functions for different values of n, we proceed as in the previous section: we *standardize* S_n by defining

$$S_n^* = \frac{S_n - n\mu}{\sqrt{n}\sigma}.$$

Then we see that for all n we have

$$E(S_n^*) = 0,$$

$$V(S_n^*) = 1.$$

The density function for S_n^* is just a standardized version of the density function for S_n (see Figure 7). □

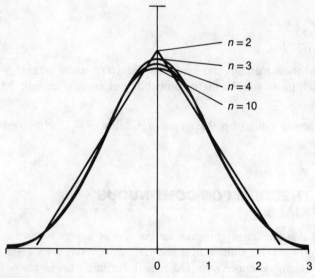

Figure 7 Density function for S_n^* (uniform case, $n = 2,3,4,10$).

EXAMPLE 2

Let us do the same thing, but this time choose numbers from the interval $[0,1]$ with a nonuniform density, say with density function $f(x) = 4x^3$. Then

$$\mu = E(X_i) = \int_0^1 4x^4 dx = \frac{4}{5},$$

$$\sigma^2 = V(X_i) = \int_0^1 4x^5 dx - \frac{16}{25} = \frac{2}{3} - \frac{16}{25} = \frac{2}{75}.$$

If we graph the density function for S_n^*, we get the graph shown in Figure 8. □

EXAMPLE 3

Let us do the same thing, but now choose numbers from the interval $[0, +\infty)$ with an exponential density with parameter λ. Then (see Chapter 6, Section 6.3, Example 6)

$$\mu = E(X_i) = \frac{1}{\lambda},$$

$$\sigma^2 = V(X_i) = \frac{1}{\lambda^2}.$$

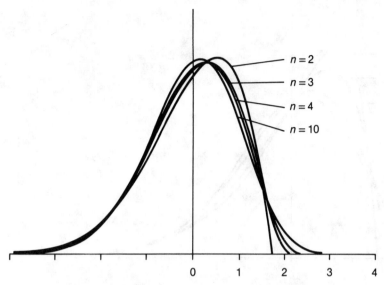

Figure 8 Densities for S_n^* (nonuniform case, $n = 2,3,4,10$).

Here we know the density function for S_n and S_n^* explicitly (see Chapter 7, Section 7.2)

$$f_{S_n}(x) = \frac{\lambda e^{-\lambda x}(\lambda x)^{n-1}}{(n-1)!},$$

$$f_{S_n^*}(x) = \frac{\sqrt{n}}{\lambda} f_{S_n}\left(\frac{\sqrt{n}x + n}{\lambda}\right).$$

If we graph the density function for S_n^* we get the graph shown in Figure 9. $\qquad \square$

These examples make it seem plausible that the density function for the normalized random variable S_n^* for large n will look very much like the normal density with mean 0 and variance 1 in the continuous case as well as in the discrete case. The central limit theorem makes this statement precise.

Central Limit Theorem

THEOREM 7

Let $S_n = X_1 + \cdots + X_n$ be the sum of n independent continuous random variables with common density function p having expected value μ and variance σ^2. Let $S_n^* = \frac{S_n - n\mu}{\sqrt{n}\,\sigma}$. Then we have, for all $a < b$,

$$\lim_{n \to \infty} P(a < S_n^* < b) = \frac{1}{\sqrt{2\pi}} \int_a^b e^{-x^2/2} \, dx.$$

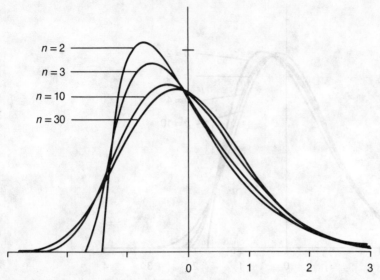

Figure 9 Density function for S_n^* (exponential case $n = 2,3,10,30$).

We shall sketch a proof of this theorem in a later section (Chapter 10, Section 10.3). Here we shall focus our attention on various interpretations of this theorem and their applications.

Discussion

First of all, the central limit theorem says, just as in the discrete case, that the *area* under the graph of the density function for S_n^*, from $x = a$ to $x = b$, will approach, as $n \to \infty$, the area under the normal density function from $x = a$ to $x = b$. If $a = -\infty$, then this says that the *distribution function* for S_n^* approaches the normal distribution function as $n \to \infty$. We shall see in our discussion of the proof that the same is true of their derivatives (i.e., that the density function for S_n^* approaches the normal density function). This is already apparent in each of the preceding examples.

Generally speaking, the central limit theorem contains more information than the law of large numbers, because it gives us detailed information about the *shape* of the density for S_n^*: for large n the shape is approximately normal.

This means that, to a good approximation, we can replace the density for S_n^*, and hence for S_n, by a normal density when n is large. Then we have a computable approximation for the density for S_n, which provides us with a powerful technique for generating answers for all sorts of questions about sums of independent random variables, no matter what their common density may be.

The empirical frequencies of many populations arising in nature seem to be distributed approximately normally (i.e., their densities are approximately normal in shape).

In many cases this empirical fact can be accounted for by assuming that the members of the population are independent, and that each is chosen from the same distribution.

Let us look at some examples.

Examples

EXAMPLE 4

Figure 10 gives empirical data in the form of a bar graph for the heights of a certain population sample (the 928 adult children in Galton's study of heights, see Appendix B).

We can see here that these heights are approximately normally distributed, with normal density as shown, having mean $\mu = 68.2$ inches and standard deviation $\sigma = 2.54$ inches.

We have suggested that the deviation from the average of an individual's height might be the cumulative result of a lot of small random experiments—whether you ate your Wheaties on your seventh birthday, and so forth. But, although you might have been asked to eat your Wheaties your sister might have been asked to eat her Bran Flakes. Thus, it is not enough to allow different densities for the individual effects that make up the height deviations, but we even have to allow different densities for different repetitions of the experiment. Now the mathematics is far beyond us here but, as usual, it is an easy matter to simulate this situation. We simply take the sum of n experiments, each of which is governed by a random density chosen from the interval $[a,b]$. We repeat this experiment a large number of times and see what fraction of these sums fall in each interval of a given size within the range of possible values for the sum. This gives us an *empirical density*. We then standardize this density to have mean 0 and standard deviation 1 and compare it with the normal density. The program **CLT Empirical** carries this out. We do not show the program but in Figure 11 we show the result of running the program

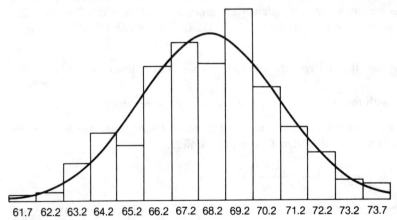

61.7 62.2 63.2 64.2 65.2 66.2 67.2 68.2 69.2 70.2 71.2 72.2 73.2 73.7

Figure 10 Heights from Galton Data.

```
Maximum range [A,B] for A,B = -6,6
Number of summands n = 20
Number of trials = 1000
```

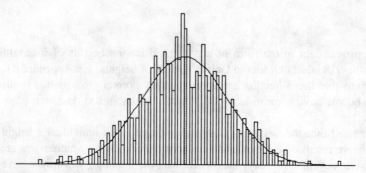

Figure 11 Computer simulated empirical density.

with $n = 20$ for 1000 experiments. This corresponds to the heights of 1000 people if the deviations of their heights from the average were the result of 20 different random effects, each falling in the interval $[-6, +6]$ inches. We see that the results fit the normal curve as well as those from the Galton data. □

EXAMPLE 5

Suppose a surveyor wants to measure a known distance, say of 1 mile, using a transit and some method of triangulation. He knows that because of possible motion of the transit, atmospheric distortions, and human error, any one measurement is apt to be slightly in error. He plans to make several measurements and take an average. If he assumes that his measurements are independent random variables with a common distribution of mean $\mu = 1$ and variance $\sigma^2 = .01$, then what can he say about their average?

He can say that if n is large, the average $\dfrac{S_n}{n}$ has a density function that is approximately normal, with mean $\mu = 1$ mile, and variance $\sigma^2 = \dfrac{.01}{n}$ miles.

How many measurements should he make to be reasonably sure that his average lies within .01 of the true value? The Chebyshev inequality says

$$P\left(\left| \frac{S_n}{n} - \mu \right| \geq .01 \right) \leq \frac{.01}{n(.0001)} = \frac{100}{n},$$

so that n must be ≥ 2000 before the probability that his error is less than .01 exceeds .95.

We have already noticed that the estimate in the Chebyshev inequality is not always a good one, and here is a case in point. If we assume that n is large enough so that the density for S_n is approximately normal, then we have

$$P\left(\left|\frac{S_n}{n} - \mu\right| < .01\right)$$

$$= P\left(-.1\sqrt{n} < S_n^* < +.1\sqrt{n}\right)$$

$$\sim \frac{1}{2\pi}\int_{-.1\sqrt{n}}^{+.1\sqrt{n}} e^{-x^2/2}\, dx$$

$$> .95 \text{ if } .1\sqrt{n} > 2.$$

This says that it suffices to take $n = 400$ measurements for the same results. This second calculation is stronger, but depends on the assumption that $n = 400$ is large enough to establish the normal density as a good approximation to S_n^*, and hence to S_n. The central limit theorem here says nothing about how large n has to be. A glance at our examples shows that, at least in these cases, we get a good approximation as soon as $n = 20$. Long experience with this problem has suggested that in most empirical application the normal approximation is good enough as soon as $n \geqslant 30$.

Estimating the Mean

Now suppose our surveyor is measuring an unknown distance with the same instruments under the same conditions. He takes 400 measurements and averages them. How sure can he be that his measurement lies within .01 of the true value?

Using again the normal approximation, we get

$$P\left(\left|\frac{S_n}{n} - \mu\right| < .01\right)$$

$$= P\left(|S_n^*| < .1\sqrt{n}\right)$$

$$\cong \frac{2}{\sqrt{2\pi}}\int_0^2 e^{-x^2/2}\, dx$$

$$\cong .95. \qquad \square$$

This means that the surveyor can be 95 percent sure that his average is within .01 of the true value. To improve his confidence, he can take more measurements, or require less accuracy, or improve the quality of his measurements (i.e., reduce the variance σ^2). In each case, the central limit theorem gives quantitative information about the confidence of a measurement process, assuming always that the normal approximation is valid.

Now suppose the surveyor does not know the error distribution of his measurements, but assumes that they are independent. How should he proceed?

Again, he makes several measurements of a known distance and averages them. As before, the average error is approximately normally distributed, but now with unknown mean and variance.

Sample Mean

If he knows the variance σ^2 of the error distribution is .01, then he can estimate the mean μ by taking the *average*, or *sample mean* of, say, 400 measurements:

$$\overline{\mu} = \frac{x_1 + \cdots + x_n}{n} \qquad \text{where } n = 400.$$

Then, as before, $E(\overline{\mu}) = \mu$. Moreover, the preceding argument shows that

$$P(|\overline{\mu} - \mu| < .01) \cong .95,$$

so that he can say with 95 percent confidence that $\overline{\mu}$ lies within .01 of the true value μ. The interval $(\overline{\mu} - .01, \overline{\mu} + .01)$ is called *the 95% confidence interval* for μ (see Chapter 9, Section 9.1, Example 4).

Sample Variance

If he does not know the variance σ^2 of the error distribution, then he can estimate σ^2 by the *sample variance:*

$$\overline{\sigma}^2 = \frac{(x_1 - \overline{\mu})^2 + \cdots + (x_n - \overline{\mu})^2}{n}, \qquad \text{where } n = 400.$$

The law of large numbers, applied to the random variables $(X_i - \overline{\mu})^2$, says that for large n, the sample variance $\overline{\sigma}^2$ lies close to the variance σ^2, so that the surveyor can use $\overline{\sigma}^2$ in place of σ^2 in the argument above.

Experience has shown that, in most practical problems of this type, the sample variance is a good estimate for the variance, and can be used in place of the variance to determine confidence levels for the sample mean. This means that we can rely on the law of large numbers for estimating the variance, and the central limit theorem for estimating the mean.

We can check this in some special cases. Suppose we know that the error distribution is *normal*, with unknown mean and variance. Then we can take a sample of n measurements, find the sample mean $\overline{\mu}$ and sample variance $\overline{\sigma}^2$, and form

$$T_n^* = \frac{S_n - n\overline{\mu}}{\sqrt{n}\,\overline{\sigma}}, \qquad \text{where } n = 400.$$

We expect T_n^* to be a good approximation for S_n^* for large n.

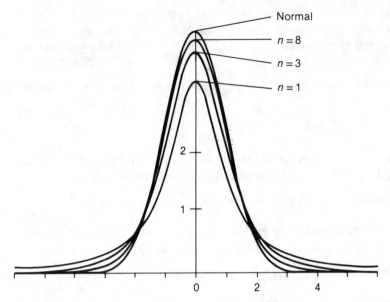

Figure 12 Graph of t-density for $n = 1,3,8$ and the normal density with $\mu = 0$, $\sigma = 1$.

t-Density

The statistician W.S. Gosset[10] has shown that in this case T_n^* has a density function that is not normal but rather a t-density with n degrees of freedom. In this case we can use the t-density in place of the normal density to determine confidence levels for μ. As n increases, the t-density approaches the normal density. Indeed, even for $n = 8$ the t-density and normal density are practically the same (see Figure 12).

Exercises

Notes on computer problems:

(a) Simulation: Recall (see Chapter 5, Section 5.2, Corollary 1b.) that

let $x = F^{-1}$ (rnd)

will simulate a random variable with density $f(x)$ and distribution

$$F(x) = \int_{-\infty}^{x} f(t)dt.$$

In the case $f(x) =$ normal (x,μ,σ), where neither F nor F^{-1} can be expressed in closed form, use instead

let $x = \sigma\sqrt{-2\log(\text{rnd})}\,\cos(2\pi\cdot\text{rnd}) + \mu$.

[10]W.S. Gosset discovered the distribution we now call the t-distribution while working for the Guinness Brewery in Dublin. He wrote under the pseudonym "Student." The results discussed here first appeared in Student, "The Probable Error of a Mean," *Biometrika*, vol. 6 (1908), pp. 1–24.

(b) Bar graphs: you should aim for about 20 to 30 bars (of equal width) in your graph. You can achieve this by a good choice of the range [xmin,xmax] and the number of bars (for instance, [$\mu - 3\sigma$, $\mu + 3\sigma$] with 30 bars will work in many cases). Experiment!

1. Let X be a continuous random variable with mean $\mu(X)$ and variance $\sigma^2(X)$, and let $X^* = \dfrac{X - \mu}{\sigma}$ be its standardized version. Verify directly that $\mu(X^*) = 0$ and $\sigma^2(X^*) = 1$.

2. Let X_k, $1 \leq k \leq n$, be a sequence of independent random variables, all with mean 0 and variance 1, and let S_n, S_n^*, and A_n be their sum, standardized sum, and average, respectively. Verify directly that $S_n^* = \dfrac{S_n}{\sqrt{n}} = \sqrt{n}\,A_n$.

3. Let X_k, $1 \leq k \leq n$, be a sequence of random variables, all with mean μ and variance σ^2, and let $Y_k = X_k^*$ be their standardized version. Let S_n and T_n be the sum of the X_k and Y_k, and S_n^* and T_n^* their standardized versions. Show that $S_n^* = T_n^* = \dfrac{T_n}{\sqrt{n}}$.

4. Suppose we choose independently 25 numbers at random (uniform density) from the interval [0,20]. Write the normal densities which approximate the densities of their sum S_{25}, their standardized sum S_{25}^*, and their average A_{25}.

5. Write a program to choose independently 25 numbers at random from [0,20], compute their sum S_{25}, and repeat this experiment 1000 times. Make a bar graph for the density of S_{25} and compare it with the normal approximation of Exercise 4. How good is the fit? Now do the same for the standardized sum S_{25}^* and the average A_{25}.

6. In general, the central limit theorem gives a better estimate than Chebyshev's inequality for the average of a sum. To see this, let A_{25} be the average calculated in Exercise 5, and let N be the normal approximation for A_{25}. Modify your program in Exercise 5 to provide a table of the function $F(x) = P(|A_{25} - 10| \geq x) =$ fraction of the total of 1000 trials for which $|A_{25} - 10| \geq x$. Do the same for the function $f(x) = P(|N - 10| \geq x)$. (You can use the normal table, Table 1, or the program **Normal Area** for this.) Now plot on the same axes the graphs of $F(x)$, $f(x)$, and the Chebyshev function $g(x) = \dfrac{4}{3x^2}$. How do $f(x)$ and $g(x)$ compare as estimates for $F(x)$?

7. The central limit theorem says the sums of independent random variables tend to look normal, no matter what crazy distribution the individual variables have. Let us test this by a computer simulation. Choose independently 25 numbers from the interval [0,1] with the probability density $f(x)$ given below, and compute their sum S_{25}. Repeat the experiment 1000 times, and make up a bar graph of the results. Now plot on the same graph the density $n(x) = $ normal $(x,\mu(S_{25}), \sigma(S_{25}))$. How well does the normal density fit your bar graph in each case?

(a) $f(x) = 1$.
(b) $f(x) = 2x$.
(c) $f(x) = 3x^2$.
(d) $f(x) = 4|x - 1/2|$.
(e) $f(x) = 2 - 4|x - 1/2|$.

8. Repeat the experiment described in Exercise 7 but now choose the 25 numbers in $[0, \infty)$, using $f(x) = e^{-x}$.

9. How large must n be before $S_n = X_1 + \cdots + X_n$ is approximately normal? This number is often surprisingly small. Let us explore this question with a computer simulation. Choose n numbers from $[0,1]$ with probability density $f(x)$, where $n = 3, 6, 12, 20$, and $f(x)$ is each of the densities in Exercise 7. Compute their sum S_n, repeat this experiment 1000 times, and make up a bar graph of 20 bars of the results. How large must n be before you get a good fit?

10. A surveyor is measuring the height of a cliff known to be about 1000 feet. He assumes his instrument is properly calibrated and that his measurement errors are independent, with mean $\mu = 0$ and variance $\sigma^2 = 10$. He plans to take n measurements and form the average. Estimate, using (a) Chebyshev's inequality and (b) the normal approximation, how large n should be if he wants to be 95 percent sure that his average falls within 1 foot of the true value. Now estimate, using (a) and (b), what value should σ^2 have if he wants to make only 10 measurements with the same confidence?

11. The price of one share of stock in the Pilsdorff Beer Company (see Chapter 8, Section 8.2, Exercise 12) is given by Y_n on the nth day of the year. Finn observes that the differences $X_n = Y_{n+1} - Y_n$ appear to be independent random variables with a common distribution having mean $\mu = 0$ and variance $\sigma^2 = 1/4$. If $Y_1 = 100$, estimate the probability that Y_{365} is
(a) ≥ 100.
(b) ≥ 110.
(c) ≥ 120.

12. Test your conclusions in Exercise 11 by computer simulation. First choose 364 numbers X_k with density $f(x) = \text{normal}(x, 0, 1/4)$. Now form the sum $Y_{365} = 100 + X_1 + \cdots + X_{364}$, and repeat this experiment 200 times. Make up a bar graph on $[50, 150]$ of the results, superimposing the graph of the approximating normal density. What does this graph say about your answers in Exercise 11?

13. Physicists say that particles in a long tube are constantly moving back and forth along the tube, each with a velocity V_k (in cm/sec) at any given moment that is normally distributed, with mean $\mu = 0$ and variance $\sigma^2 = 1$. Suppose there are 10^{20} particles in the tube.
(a) Find the mean and variance of the average velocity of the particles.
(b) What is the probability that the average velocity is $\geq 10^{-9}$ cm/sec?

14. A radioactive source is emitting particles in such a way that the time in seconds

between particles is distributed exponentially, with parameter $\lambda = .1$. Let T be the time it takes to emit 100 particles.

(a) Find the mean and variance of T.

(b) Find the probabilities $P(T \geq 1000)$, $P(T \geq 1200)$, and $P(T \geq 1500)$.

15. An astronomer makes n measurements of the distance between Jupiter and a particular one of its moons. Experience with the instruments used leads her to believe that for the proper units the measurements will be normally distributed with mean d, the true distance, and variance 16. She performs a series of n measurements. Let

$$A_n = \frac{X_1 + \cdots + X_n}{n}$$

be the average of these measurements. Show that

(a) $P\left(A_n - \frac{8}{\sqrt{n}} \leq d \leq A_n + \frac{8}{\sqrt{n}} \right) \sim .95.$

(b) When nine measurements were taken, the average of the distances turned out to be 23.2 units. Putting the observed values in (a) gives the *95 percent confidence interval* for the unknown distance d. Compute this interval.

(c) Why not say in (b) more simply that the probability is .95 that the value of d lies in the computed confidence interval?

(d) What changes would you make in the above procedure if you wanted to compute a 99 percent confidence interval?

16. Plot a bar graph similar to that in Figure 10 for the heights of the parents in Galton's data as given in Appendix B and compare this bar graph to the appropriate normal curve.

Chapter 10

Generating Functions

10.1 GENERATING FUNCTIONS FOR DISCRETE DENSITIES

So far we have considered in detail only the two most important attributes of a random variable, namely, the mean and the variance. We have seen how these attributes enter into the fundamental limit theorems of probability, as well as into all sorts of practical calculations. We have seen that the mean and variance of a random variable contain important information about the random variable, or, more precisely, about the density function of that variable.

Now we shall see that the mean and variance do *not* contain *all* the available information about the density function of a random variable. To begin with, it is easy to give examples of different density functions which have the same mean and the same variance. For instance, suppose X and Y are random variables, with densities

$$p_X = \begin{pmatrix} 1 & 2 & 3 & 4 & 5 \\ 0 & \dfrac{2}{3} & 0 & 0 & \dfrac{1}{3} \end{pmatrix},$$

$$p_Y = \begin{pmatrix} 1 & 2 & 3 & 4 & 5 \\ \dfrac{1}{3} & 0 & 0 & \dfrac{2}{3} & 0 \end{pmatrix}.$$

Then with these choices, we have $E(X) = E(Y) = 3$ and $V(X) = V(Y) = 2$, and yet certainly p_X and p_Y are quite different density functions.

This raises an interesting question: If X is a random variable with range $\{x_1, x_2, \ldots, x_n\}$ and density function $p = p_X$, and if we know its mean $\mu = E(X)$ and its variance $\sigma^2 = V(X)$, then what else do we need to know to determine p completely?

Moments

A nice answer to this question can be given in terms of the *moments* of X, which are numbers defined as follows:

$$\mu_k = k^{\text{th}} \text{ moment of } X$$

$$= E(X^k)$$

$$= \sum_{j=1}^{n} (x_j)^k p(x_j).$$

Here $p(x_j) = P(X = x_j)$.

In terms of these moments, the mean μ and variance σ^2 of X are given simply by

$$\mu = \mu_1,$$

$$\sigma^2 = \mu_2 - \mu_1^2,$$

so that a knowledge of the first two moments of X gives us its mean and variance. But a knowledge of *all* the moments of X determines its density function p completely.

Moment Generating Functions

To see how this comes about, we introduce a new variable t, and define a function $g(t)$ as follows:

$$g(t) = \sum_{k=0}^{\infty} \frac{\mu_k t^k}{k!}$$

$$= E\left(\sum_{k=0}^{\infty} \frac{X^k t^k}{k!} \right)$$

$$= E(e^{tX})$$

$$= \sum_{j=1}^{\infty} e^{tx_j} p x_j.$$

We call $g(t)$ the *moment generating function* for X, and think of it as a convenient bookkeeping device for describing the moments of X. Indeed, if we differentiate $g(t)$ n times and then set $t = 0$, we get μ_n:

$$\left. \frac{d^n}{dt^n} g(t) \right|_{t=0} = g^{(n)}(0)$$

$$= \left. \sum_{k=n}^{\infty} \frac{k! \mu_k t^{k-n}}{(k-n)! k!} \right|_{t=0}$$

$$= \mu_n.$$

It is easy to calculate the moment generating function for simple examples.

Examples

EXAMPLE 1
Suppose X has range $\{1,2,3, \ldots ,n\}$ and $p_X(j) = {}^1/_n$ for $1 \leqslant j \leqslant n$ (uniform density). Then

$$g(t) = \sum_{j=1}^{n} e^{tj} \frac{1}{n}$$

$$= \frac{1}{n} (e^t + e^{2t} + \cdots + e^{nt})$$

$$= \frac{e^t(e^{nt} - 1)}{n(e^t - 1)}.$$

Note that

$$\mu_1 = g'(0) = \frac{1}{n} (1 + 2 + 3 + \cdots + n) = \frac{n+1}{2},$$

$$\mu_2 = g''(0) = \frac{1}{n} (1 + 4 + 9 + \cdots + n^2) = \frac{(n+1)(2n+1)}{6},$$

and that $\mu = \mu_1 = \dfrac{n+1}{2}$ and $\sigma^2 = \mu_2 - \mu_1^2 = \dfrac{n^2-1}{12}$. $\qquad \Box$

EXAMPLE 2

Suppose now that X has range $\{0,1,2,3, \ldots ,n\}$ and $p(j) = \binom{n}{j} p^j q^{n-j}$ for $0 \leq j \leq n$

(binomial density). Then

$$g(t) = \sum_{j=0}^{n} e^{tj} \binom{n}{j} p^j q^{n-j}$$

$$= \sum_{j=0}^{n} \binom{n}{j} (pe^t)^j q^{n-j}$$

$$= (pe^t + q)^n.$$

Note that

$$\mu_1 = g'(0) = n(pe^t + q)^{n-1} pe^t \bigg|_{t=0} = np,$$

$$\mu_2 = g''(0) = n(n-1)p^2 + np,$$

so that $\mu_1 = np = \mu$, and $\mu_2 - \mu_1^2 = np(1-p) = \sigma^2$, as expected. □

EXAMPLE 3

Suppose X has range $\{1,2,3, \ldots \}$, and $p(j) = q^{j-1}p$ for all j (geometric density, see Chapter 5, Section 5.1, Example 7). Then

$$g(t) = \sum_{j=1}^{\infty} e^{tj} q^{j-1}p$$

$$= \frac{pe^t}{1 - qe^t}.$$

Here

$$\mu_1 = g'(0) = \frac{pe^t}{(1 - qe^t)^2} \bigg|_{t=0} = \frac{1}{p},$$

$$\mu_2 = g''(0) = \frac{pe^t + pqe^{2t}}{(1 - qe^t)^3} \bigg|_{t=0} = \frac{1+q}{p^2},$$

$\mu_1 = \dfrac{1}{p} = \mu$ and $\mu_2 - \mu_1^2 = \dfrac{q}{p^2} = \sigma^2$, as computed in Chapter 6, Section 6.2, Example 3. □

EXAMPLE 4

Let X have range $\{0,1,2,3, \ldots \}$ and let $p_X(j) = e^{-\lambda} \dfrac{\lambda^j}{j!}$ for all j (Poisson density with mean λ). Then

$$g(t) = \sum_{j=0}^{\infty} e^{tj} \frac{e^{-\lambda}\lambda^j}{j!}$$

$$= e^{-\lambda} \sum_{j=0}^{\infty} \frac{(\lambda e^t)^j}{j!}$$

$$= e^{-\lambda} e^{\lambda e^t} = e^{\lambda(e^t - 1)}.$$

Then

$$\mu_1 = g'(0) = e^{\lambda(e^t - 1)} \lambda e^t \bigg|_{t=0} = \lambda,$$

$$\mu_2 = g''(0) = e^{\lambda(e^t - 1)} (\lambda^2 e^{2t} + \lambda e^t) \bigg|_{t=0} = \lambda^2 + \lambda,$$

and $\mu_1 = \lambda = \mu$, and $\mu_2 - \mu_1^2 = \lambda = \sigma^2$. $\qquad\square$

Moment Problem

Using the moment generating function, we can now show, at least in the case of a discrete random variable with finite range, that its density function is completely determined by its moment generating function, which in turn is completely determined by its moments.

THEOREM 1

Let X be any discrete random variable with finite range $(x_1, x_2, \ldots, x_n)$, and moments $\mu_k = E(X^k)$. Then the moment series

$$g(t) = \sum_{k=0}^{\infty} \frac{\mu_k t^k}{k!}$$

converges for all t to an infinitely differentiable function $g(t)$.

Proof. We know that

$$\mu_k = \sum_{j=1}^{n} (x_j)^k p(x_j).$$

If we set $M = \max |x_j|$, then we have

$$|\mu_k| \leq \sum_{j=1}^{n} |x_j|^k p(x_j)$$

$$\leq M^k \cdot \sum_{j=1}^{n} p(x_j) = M^k.$$

Hence, for all N we have

$$\sum_{k=0}^{N} \left| \frac{\mu_k t^k}{k!} \right| \leq \sum_{k=0}^{N} \frac{(M|t|)^k}{k!} \leq e^{M|t|},$$

which shows that the moment series converges for all t. Since it is a power series, we know that its sum is infinitely differentiable.

This shows that the μ_k determine $g(t)$. Conversely, since $\mu_k = g^{(k)}(0)$, we see that $g(t)$ determines the μ_k. ∎

THEOREM 2

Let X be any discrete random variable with finite range $\{x_1, x_2, \ldots, x_n\}$, density function p, and moment generating function g. Then g is uniquely determined by p, and conversely.

Proof. We know that p determines g, since

$$g(t) = \sum_{j=1}^{n} e^{tx_j} p(x_j).$$

In this formula, we set $a_j = p(x_j)$ and, after choosing n convenient distinct values t_i of t, we set $b_i = g(t_i)$. Then we have

$$b_i = \sum_{j=1}^{n} e^{t_i x_j} a_j,$$

or, in matrix notation

$$\mathbf{B} = \mathbf{MA}.$$

Here $\mathbf{B} = (b_i)$ and $\mathbf{A} = (a_j)$ are column n-vectors, and $\mathbf{M} = \left(e^{t_i x_j} \right)$ is an $n \times n$ matrix.

We can solve this matrix equation for $\mathbf{A}$:

$$\mathbf{A} = \mathbf{M}^{-1}\mathbf{B},$$

provided only that the matrix **M** is *invertible* (i.e., provided that the determinant of **M** is different from 0). We can always arrange for this by choosing the values $t_i = i - 1$, since then the determinant of **M** is the *vandermonde determinant* of the e^{x_i}, with value $\prod_{i<j} (e^{x_i} - e^{x_j})$. This determinant is always different from 0 if the x_j are distinct. ∎

Ordinary Generating Functions

In the special but important case where the x_j are all nonnegative integers: $x_j = j$, we can prove this theorem in a simpler way.

In this case, we have

$$g(t) = \sum_{j=0}^{n} e^{tj}\, p(j),$$

and we see that $g(t)$ is a *polynomial* in e^t. If we write $z = e^t$, and define the function h by

$$h(z) = \sum_{j=0}^{n} z^j p(j),$$

then $h(z)$ is a polynomial in z containing the same information as $g(t)$, and in fact

$$h(z) = g(\log z),$$

$$g(t) = h(e^t).$$

The function $h(z)$ is often called the *ordinary generating function* for X. Note that $h(1) = g(0) = 1$, $h'(1) = g'(0) = \mu_1$, and $h''(1) = g''(0) - g'(0) = \mu_2 - \mu_1$. It follows from all this that if we know $g(t)$, then we know $h(z)$, and if we know $h(z)$, then we can find the $p(j)$ by Taylor's formula:

$$p(j) = \text{coefficient of } z^j \text{ in } h(z)$$

$$= \frac{h^{(j)}(0)}{j!}.$$

For example, suppose we know that the moments of a certain discrete random variable X are given by

$$\mu_0 = 1,$$

$$\mu_k = \frac{1}{2} + \frac{2^k}{4} \qquad \text{for } k \geq 1.$$

Then the moment generating function g of X is

$$g(t) = \sum_{k=0}^{\infty} \frac{\mu_k t^k}{k!}$$

$$= 1 + \frac{1}{2} \sum_{k=1}^{\infty} \frac{t^k}{k!} + \frac{1}{4} \sum_{k=1}^{\infty} \frac{(2t)^k}{k!}$$

$$= \frac{1}{4} + \frac{1}{2} e^t + \frac{1}{4} e^{2t}.$$

This is a polynomial in $z = e^t$, and

$$h(z) = \frac{1}{4} + \frac{1}{2} z + \frac{1}{4} z^2.$$

Hence, X must have range $\{0,1,2\}$, and p must have values $\{\frac{1}{4}, \frac{1}{2}, \frac{1}{4}\}$.

Properties

Both the moment generating function g and the ordinary generating function h have many properties useful in the study of random variables, of which we can consider only a few here. In particular, if X is any discrete random variable and $Y = X + a$, then

$$g_Y(t) = E(e^{tY})$$

$$= E(e^{t(X+a)})$$

$$= e^{ta} E(e^{tX})$$

$$= e^{ta} g_X(t),$$

while if $Y = bX$, then

$$g_Y(t) = E(e^{tY})$$

$$= E(e^{tbX})$$

$$= g_X(bt).$$

In particular, if

$$X^* = \frac{X - \mu}{\sigma},$$

then (see Exercise 14)

$$g_{X^*}(t) = e^{\frac{-\mu t}{\sigma}} g_X\left(\frac{t}{\sigma}\right).$$

If X and Y are *independent* random variables and $Z = X + Y$ is their sum, with p_X, p_Y, and p_Z the associated density functions, then we have seen in Chapter 7 that p_Z

is the *convolution* of p_X and p_Y, and we know that convolution involves a rather complicated calculation. But for the generating functions we have instead the simple relations

$$g_Z(t) = g_X(t)g_Y(t),$$

$$h_Z(z) = h_X(z)h_Y(z),$$

that is, g_Z is simply the *product* of g_X and g_Y, and similarly for h_Z.

To see this, first note that if X and Y are independent, then e^{tX} and e^{tY} are independent (see Exercise 38 of Chapter 5, Section 5.2), and hence

$$E(e^{tX}e^{tY}) = E(e^{tX})E(e^{tY}).$$

It follows that

$$g_Z(t) = E(e^{tZ}) = E(e^{t(X+Y)})$$

$$= E(e^{tX})E(e^{tY})$$

$$= g_X(t)g_Y(t),$$

and, replacing t by $\log z$, we also get

$$h_Z(z) = h_X(z)h_Y(z).$$

EXAMPLE 5

If X and Y are independent discrete random variables with range $\{0,1,2, \ldots ,n\}$ and binomial density

$$p_X(j) = p_Y(j) = \binom{n}{j} p^j q^{n-j},$$

and if $Z = X + Y$, then we know (cf. Chapter 7, Section 7.1) that Z has range $\{0,1,2,3, \ldots ,2n\}$ and binomial density

$$p_Z(j) = (p_X*p_Y)(j) = \binom{2n}{j} p^j q^{2n-j}.$$

Here we can easily verify this result by using generating functions. We know that

$$g_X(t) = g_Y(t) = \sum_{j=0}^{n} e^{tj} \binom{n}{j} p^j q^{n-j}$$

$$= (pe^t + q)^n,$$

$$h_X(z) = h_Y(z) = (pz + q)^n.$$

Hence, we have

$$g_Z(t) = g_X(t)g_Y(t) = (pe^t + q)^{2n},$$

or, what is the same,

$$h_Z(z) = h_X(z)h_Y(z) = (pz + q)^{2n}$$

$$= \sum_{j=0}^{2n} \binom{2n}{j} (pz)^j q^{2n-j},$$

from which we see that the coefficient of z^j is just $p_Z(j) = \binom{2n}{j} p^j q^{2n-j}$.   □

EXAMPLE 6

If X and Y are independent random variables with range $\{0,1,2,3,\ldots\}$ and geometric density function $p_X(j) = p_Y(j) = q^j p$ (see Chapter 6, Section 6.1, Exercise 4), then

$$g_X(t) = g_Y(t) = \frac{p}{1 - qe^t} \, ;$$

and if $Z = X + Y$, then

$$g_Z(t) = g_X(t)g_Y(t)$$

$$= \frac{p^2}{1 - 2qe^t + q^2 e^{2t}} \, .$$

If we replace e^t by z, we get

$$h_Z(z) = \frac{p^2}{(1 - qz)^2}$$

$$= p^2 \sum_{k=0}^{\infty} (k + 1) \, q^k z^k \, ,$$

and we can read off the values of $p_Z(j)$ as the coefficient of z^j in this expansion for $h(z)$, even though $h(z)$ is not a polynomial in this case. The density p_Z is a negative binomial density (see Chapter 7, Section 7.1, Example 4).   □

Here is a more interesting example of the power and scope of the method of generating functions.

Heads or Tails

EXAMPLE 7

In the coin-tossing game discussed in Chapter 1, Section 1.1, Example 3, we now consider the question: When is Peter first in the lead?

Let X_k describe the outcome of the kth trial in the game

$$X_k = \begin{cases} +1 & \text{if } k\text{th toss is heads,} \\ -1 & \text{if } k\text{th toss is tails.} \end{cases}$$

Then the X_k are independent random variables describing a Bernoulli process. Let

$$S_0 = 0,$$

$$S_n = X_1 + \cdots + X_n, \qquad n \geq 1.$$

Then S_n describes Peter's fortune after n trials, and Peter is first in the lead after n trials if $S_k \leq 0$ for $1 \leq k < n$ and $S_n = 1$.

Now this can happen when $n = 1$, in which case $S_1 = X_1 = 1$, or when $n > 1$, in which case $S_1 = X_1 = -1$. In the latter case, $S_k = 0$ for $k = n - 1$, and perhaps for other k between 1 and n. Let m be the *least* such value of k; then $S_m = 0$ and $S_k < 0$ for $1 \leq k < m$. In this case, then, Peter loses on the first trial, regains his initial position in the next $m - 1$ trials, and gains the lead in the next $n - m$ trials.

Let p_n be the probability that Peter is first in the lead after n trials. Then from the discussion above, we see that

$$p_n = 0 \qquad \text{if } n \text{ even,}$$

$$p_1 = p \qquad (= \text{probability of heads in a single toss}),$$

$$p_n = q(p_1 p_{n-2} + p_3 p_{n-4} + \cdots + p_{n-2} p_1)$$

(where $q = 1 - p$) if $n > 1$, n odd.

Now let T describe the time (that is, the number of trials) required for Peter to take the lead. Then T is a random variable, and since $P(T = n) = p_n$, p is the density function for T.

Introduce the generating function $h_T(z)$ for T:

$$h_T(z) = \sum_{n=0}^{\infty} p_n z^n.$$

Then, by using the relations above, we can verify the relation

$$h_T(z) = pz + qz h_T(z)^2.$$

If we solve this quadratic equation for $h_T(z)$, we get

$$h_T(z) = \frac{1 \pm \sqrt{1 - 4pqz^2}}{2qz} = \frac{2pz}{1 \mp \sqrt{1 - 4pqz^2}}.$$

Of these two solutions, we want the one that has a convergent power series in z (i.e., that is finite for $z = 0$). Hence we choose

$$h_T(z) = \frac{1 - \sqrt{1 - 4pqz^2}}{2qz} = \frac{2pz}{1 + \sqrt{1 - 4pqz^2}}.$$

Now we can ask: What is the probability that Peter is *ever* in the lead? This probability is given by (see Exercise 10)

$$\sum_{n=0}^{\infty} p_n = h_T(1) = \frac{1 - \sqrt{1 - 4pq}}{2q}$$

$$= \frac{1 - |p-q|}{2q}$$

$$= \begin{cases} p/q & \text{if } p < q \\ 1 & \text{if } p \geq q, \end{cases}$$

so that Peter is sure to be the lead eventually if $p \geq q$.

How long will it take? That is, what is the expected value of T? This value is given by

$$E(T) = h_T'(1) = \frac{1}{p - q} \qquad \text{if } p > q,$$

$$= \infty \qquad \text{if } p = q.$$

This says that if $p > q$, then Peter can expect to be in the lead by about $\dfrac{1}{p - q}$ trials, but if $p = q$, he can expect to wait a long time. $\square$

Exercises

1. Find the generating functions, both ordinary $h(z)$ and moment $g(t)$, for the following discrete probability densities.
   (a) The density describing a fair coin.
   (b) The density describing a fair die.
   (c) The density describing a die that always comes up 3.
   (d) The uniform density on the set $\{n, n+1, n+2, \ldots, n+k\}$.
   (e) The binomial density on $\{n, n+1, \ldots, n+k\}$.
   (f) The geometric density on $\{0,1,2, \ldots\}$ with $p(j) = \dfrac{2}{3^{j+1}}$.

2. For each of the densities (a) through (d) of Exercise 1 calculate the first and second moments, μ_1 and μ_2, directly from their definition, and verify that $h(1) = 1$, $h'(1) = \mu_1$ and $h''(1) = \mu_2 - \mu_1$.

3. Let p be a probability density on $\{0,1,2\}$ with moments $\mu_1 = 1$, $\mu_2 = 3/2$.
   (a) Find its ordinary generating function $h(z)$.
   (b) Using (a), find its moment generating function.
   (c) Using (b), find its first six moments.
   (d) Using (a), find p_0, p_1, and p_2.

4. In Exercise 3, the probability density is completely determined by its first two moments. Show that this is always true for any probability density on $\{0,1,2\}$. *Hint:* given μ_1 and μ_2, find $h(z)$ as in Exercise 3 and use $h(z)$ to determine p.

5. Let p and p' be the two densities

$$p = \begin{pmatrix} 1 & 2 & 3 & 4 & 5 \\ 1/3 & 0 & 0 & 2/3 & 0 \end{pmatrix},$$

$$p' = \begin{pmatrix} 1 & 2 & 3 & 4 & 5 \\ 0 & 2/3 & 0 & 0 & 1/3 \end{pmatrix}.$$

(a) Show that p and p' have the same first and second moments, but not the same third and fourth moments.

(b) Find the ordinary and moment generating functions for p and p'.

6. Let p be the probability density

$$p = \begin{pmatrix} 0 & 1 & 2 \\ 0 & 1/3 & 2/3 \end{pmatrix},$$

and let $p_n = p*p* \ldots *p$ be the n-fold convolution of p with itself.

(a) Find p_2 by direct calculation (see Chapter 7, Section 7.1, Definition 1).

(b) Find the ordinary generating functions $h(z)$ and $h_2(z)$ for p and p_2, and verify that $h_2(z) = (h(z))^2$.

(c) Find $h_n(z)$ from $h(z)$.

(d) Find the first two moments, and hence the mean and variance, of p_n from $h_n(z)$. Verify that the mean of p_n is n times the mean of p.

(e) Find those integers j for which $p_n(j) > 0$ from $h_n(z)$.

7. Let X be a discrete random variable with values in $\{0,1,2,\ldots,n\}$ and moment generating function $g(t)$. Find, in terms of $g(t)$, the generating functions for

(a) $-X$.

(b) $X + 1$.

(c) $3X$.

(d) $aX + b$.

8. Let $X_1, X_2, \ldots, X_n$ be an independent trials process, with values in $\{0,1\}$ and mean $\mu = 1/3$. Find the ordinary and moment generating functions for the density of

(a) $S_1 = X_1$ (*Hint:* first find X_1 explicitly).

(b) $S_2 = X_1 + X_2$.

(c) $S_n = X_1 + X_2 + \cdots + X_n$.

(d) $A_n = \dfrac{S_n}{n}$.

(e) $S_n^* = \dfrac{S_n - n\mu}{\sqrt{n\sigma^2}}$.

9. Let X and Y be random variables with values in $\{1,2,3,4,5,6\}$ with density functions p_X and p_Y given by

$$p_X(j) = a_j,$$
$$p_Y(j) = b_j.$$

(a) Find the ordinary generating functions $h_X(z)$ and $h_Y(z)$ for these densities.

(b) Find the ordinary generating function $h_Z(z)$ for the density $Z = X + Y$.

*(c) Show that $h_Z(z)$ cannot ever have the form

$$h_Z(z) = \frac{z^2 + z^3 + \cdots + z^{12}}{11}.$$

Hint: h_X and h_Y must have at least one nonzero root, but $h_Z(z)$ in the form given has no nonzero real roots.

It follows from this observation that there is no way to load two dice so that the probability that a given sum will turn up when they are tossed is the same for all sums (i.e., that all outcomes are equally likely).

10. Show that, if

$$h(z) = \frac{1 - \sqrt{1 - 4pqz^2}}{2qz},$$

then

$$h(1) = \begin{cases} \dfrac{p}{q} & \text{if } p \leqslant q, \\ 1 & \text{if } p \geqslant q, \end{cases}$$

and

$$h'(1) = \begin{cases} \dfrac{1}{p - q} & \text{if } p > q, \\ \infty & \text{if } p = q. \end{cases}$$

11. In the gambler's ruin problem the gambler's fortune is a random walk that moves on the integers. After each game the walk moves one step to the right with probability p and one step to the left with probability $q = 1 - p$. Assume that the gambler starts with 1 dollar and continues until he reaches 0 for the first time (if ever). Let T be the number of games until 0 is reached (the gambler is ruined). Using Example 7 show that the generating function for T is

$$h(z) = \frac{1 - \sqrt{1 - 4pqz^2}}{2pz},$$

and that

$$h(1) = \begin{cases} q/p, & \text{if } q \leqslant p \\ 1 & \text{if } q \geqslant p, \end{cases}$$

and

$$
h'(1) = \begin{cases} \dfrac{1}{q-p} & \text{if } q > p, \\[2mm] \infty & \text{if } q = p. \end{cases}
$$

Interpret your results in terms of the time T to reach 0.

12. Show that the Taylor's series expansion for $\sqrt{(1-x)}$ is

$$
\sqrt{(1 - x)} = \sum_{n=0}^{\infty} \binom{1/2}{n} x^n,
$$

where the *binomial coefficient* $\binom{1/2}{n}$ is

$$
\binom{1/2}{n} = \frac{{}^{1}/_{2}({}^{1}/_{2}-1) \,\cdots\, ({}^{1}/_{2}-n+1)}{n!}.
$$

Using this and the result of Exercise 11, show that the probability that the gambler is ruined on the nth step is

$$
p_T(n) = \begin{cases} \dfrac{(-1)^{k-1}}{2p} \binom{1/2}{k}(4pq)^k & \text{if } n = 2k - 1 = \text{odd}, \\[3mm] 0 & \text{if } n = 2k = \text{even}. \end{cases}
$$

13. For the gambler's ruin problem of Exercise 11, assume that the gambler starts with k dollars. Let T_k be the time to reach 0 for the first time. **(a)** Show that the generating function $h_k(z)$ for T_k is the kth power of the generating function for the time T to ruin starting at 1. *Hint:* Let $T_k = U_1 + U_2 + \cdots + U_k$, where U_j is the time for the walk starting at j to reach $j-1$ for the first time. **(b)** Find $h_k(1)$ and $h_k'(1)$ and interpret your results.

14. Show that if X is a random variable with mean μ and variance σ^2, and if $X^* = \dfrac{X - \mu}{\sigma}$ is the standardized version of X, then

$$
g_{X^*}(t) = e^{-\frac{\mu t}{\sigma}} g_X\left(\frac{t}{\sigma}\right).
$$

10.2 BRANCHING PROCESSES

Historical Background

In this section we apply the theory of generating functions to the study of an important chance process called a *branching process*.

Until recently it was thought that the theory of branching processes originated with the following problem posed by Francis Galton in the *Educational Times* in 1873.[1]

> Problem 4001: A large nation, of whom we will only concern ourselves with the adult males, N in number, and who each bear separate surnames, colonise a district. Their law of population is such that, in each generation, a_0 per cent of the adult males have no male children who reach adult life; a_1 have one such male child; a_2 have two; and so on up to a_5 who have five.
>
> Find (1) what proportion of the surnames will have become extinct after r generations; and (2) how many instances there will be of the same surname being held by m persons.

The first attempt at a solution was given by Reverend H. W. Watson. Because of a mistake in algebra, he incorrectly concluded that a family name would always die out with probability 1. However, the methods that he employed to solve the problem were, and still are, the basis for obtaining the correct solution.

Heyde and Seneta discovered an earlier communication by Bienaymé (1845) which anticipated Galton and Watson by 28 years. Bienaymé showed, in fact, that he was aware of the correct solution to Galton's problem. Heyde and Seneta in their book *I. J. Bienaymé: Statistical Theory Anticipated*,[2] give the following translation from Bienaymé's paper:

> If . . . the mean of the number of male children who replace the number of males of the preceding generation were less than unity, it would be easily realized that families are dying out due to the disappearance of the members of which they are composed. However, the analysis shows further that when this mean is equal to unity families tend to disappear, although less rapidly. . . .
>
> The analysis also shows clearly that if the mean ratio is greater than unity, the probability of the extinction of families with the passing of time no longer reduces to certainty. It only approaches a finite limit, which is fairly simple to calculate and which has the singular characteristic of being given by one of the roots of the equation (in which the number of generations is made infinite) which is not relevant to the question when the mean ratio is less than unity.[3]

Although Bienaymé does not give his reasoning for these results, he did indicate that he intended to publish a special paper on the problem. The paper was never written, or at least has never been found. In his communication Bienaymé indicated that he was motivated by the same problem that occurred to Galton. The opening paragraph of his paper as translated by Heyde and Seneta says,

> A great deal of consideration has been given to the possible multiplication of the numbers of mankind; and recently various very curious observations have been published on the fate which allegedly hangs over the aristocracy and middle classes; the families of famous men, etc. This fate, it is alleged, will inevitably bring about the disappearance of the so-called *families fermées*.[4]

[1] See D.G. Kendall, "Branching Processes Since 1873," *Journal of London Mathematics Society*, vol. 41 (1966), p. 386.

[2] C.C. Heyde and E. Senata, *I. J. Bienaymé: Statistical Theory Anticipated* (New York: Springer Verlag, 1977).

[3] Ibid., pp. 117–118.

[4] Ibid., p. 118.

A much more extensive discussion of the history of branching processes may be found in two papers by David G. Kendall.[5]

Branching processes have served not only as crude models for population growth but also as models for certain physical processes such as chemical and nuclear chain reactions.

Problem of Extinction

We turn now to the first problem posed by Galton (i.e., the problem of finding the probability of extinction for a branching process). As usual, we must choose an appropriate sample space and probability measure. We start in the 0th generation with 1 male parent. In the first generation we shall have $0, 1, 2, 3, \ldots$ male offspring with probabilities $p_0, p_1, p_2, p_3, \ldots$. If in the first generation there are k offspring, then in the second generation there will be $X_1 + \cdots + X_k$ offspring, where $X_1, X_2, \ldots, X_k$ are independent random variables, each with the common distribution $p_0, p_1, p_2, \ldots$. This description enables us to construct a tree, and a tree measure, for any number of generations.

Examples

EXAMPLE 1
Assume that $p_0 = 1/2$, $p_1 = 1/4$, and $p_2 = 1/4$. Then the tree measure for the first two generations is shown in Figure 1.

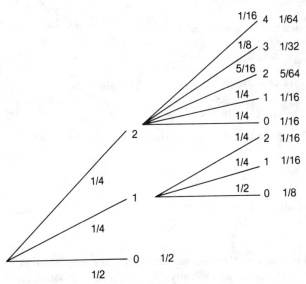

Figure 1 Tree diagram for Example 1.

[5]Kendall, "Branching Processes since 1873," pp. 385–406; and "The Genealogy of Genealogy: Branching Processes Before (and After) 1873," *Bulletin London Mathematics Society,* vol. 7 (1975), pp. 225–253.

Note that we use the theory of sums of independent random variables to assign branch probabilities. For example, if there are two offspring in the first generation, the probability that there will be two in the second generation is

$$P(X_1 + X_2 = 2) = p_0 p_2 + p_1 p_1 + p_2 p_0$$

$$= \frac{1}{2} \cdot \frac{1}{4} + \frac{1}{4} \cdot \frac{1}{4} + \frac{1}{4} \cdot \frac{1}{2} = \frac{5}{16}.$$

We shall now study the probability that our process dies out (i.e., that at some generation there are no offspring).

Let us denote by d_m the probability that the process dies out by the mth generation. Of course, $d_0 = 0$. In our example, $d_1 = 1/2$ and $d_2 = 1/2 + 1/8 + 1/16 = 11/16$ (see Figure 1). Note that we must add the probabilities for all paths that lead to 0 by the mth generation. It is clear from the definition that

$$0 = d_0 \leqslant d_1 \leqslant d_2 \leqslant \cdots \leqslant 1.$$

Hence, d_m converges to a limit d, $0 \leqslant d \leqslant 1$, and d is the probability that the process will ultimately die out. It is this value that we wish to determine. We begin by expressing the value d_m in terms of all possible outcomes on the first generation. If there are j offspring in the first generation, then to die out by the mth generation, each of these lines must die out in $m - 1$ generations. Since they proceed independently, this probability is $(d_{m-1})^j$. Therefore

$$d_m = p_0 + p_1 d_{m-1} + p_2 (d_{m-1})^2 + p_3 (d_{m-1})^3 + \cdots. \tag{1}$$

Let us define the generating function $h(z)$ for the p_i:

$$h(z) = p_0 + p_1 z + p_2 z^2 + \cdots.$$

Using the generating function, we can rewrite Equation (1) in the form

$$d_m = h(d_{m-1}). \tag{2}$$

Since $d_m \to d$, by Equation (2) we see that the value d that we are looking for satisfies the equation

$$d = h(d). \tag{3}$$

One solution of this equation is always $d = 1$, since

$$1 = p_0 + p_1 + p_2 + \cdots.$$

This is where Watson made his mistake. He assumed that 1 was the only solution to Equation (3). To examine this question more carefully, we first note that solutions to Equation (3) represent intersections of the graphs of

$$y = z$$

and

$$y = h(z) = p_0 + p_1 z + p_2 z^2 + \cdots.$$

Thus we need to study the graph of $y = h(z)$.

We note first that $h(0) = p_0$. Next,

$$h'(z) = p_1 + 2p_2 z + 3p_3 z^2 + \cdots, \tag{4}$$

and

$$h''(z) = 2p_2 + 3 \cdot 2p_3 z + 4 \cdot 3p_4 z^2 + \cdots.$$

From this we see that for $z \geq 0$, $h'(z) \geq 0$ and $h''(z) \geq 0$. Thus for nonnegative z, $h(z)$ is an increasing function and is concave upward. Therefore the graph of $y = h(z)$ can intersect the line $y = z$ in at most two points. Since we know it must intersect the line $y = z$ at $(1,1)$, we know that there are just three possibilities, as shown in Figure 2.

In case (a) the equation $d = h(d)$ has roots $\{d, 1\}$ with $0 \leq d < 1$. In the second case (b) it has only the one root $d = 1$. In case (c) it has two roots $\{1, d\}$ where $1 < d$. Since we are looking for a solution $0 \leq d \leq 1$, we see in cases (b) and (c) that our only solution is 1. In these cases we can conclude that the process will die out with probability 1. However in case (a) we are in doubt. We must study this case more carefully.

From Equation (4) we see that

$$h'(1) = p_1 + 2p_2 + 3p_3 + \cdots = m,$$

where m is the expected number of offspring produced by a single parent. In case (a) we have $h'(1) > 1$, in (b) $h'(1) = 1$, and in (c) $h'(1) < 1$. Thus our three cases correspond to $m > 1$, $m = 1$, and $m < 1$. We assume now that $m > 1$. Recall that $d_0 = 0$, $d_1 = h(d_0) = p_0$, $d_2 = h(d_1), \ldots$, and $d_n = h(d_{n-1})$. We can construct these values geometrically, as shown in Figure 3.

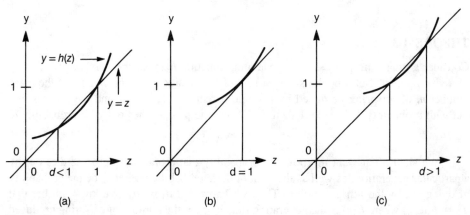

Figure 2 Graphs of $y = z$ and $y = h(z)$.

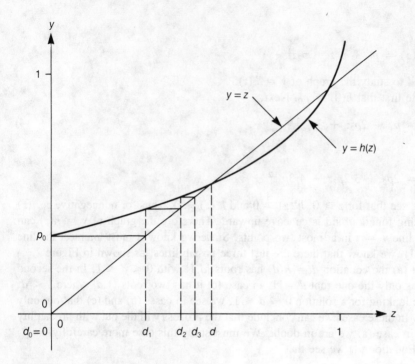

Figure 3 Geometric determination of d.

We can see geometrically, as indicated for d_0, d_1, d_2, and d_3 in Figure 3, that the points $(d_i, h(d_i))$ will always lie above the line $y = z$. Hence, they must converge to the first intersection of the curves $y = z$ and $y = h(z)$ (i.e., to the root $d < 1$). This leads us to the following theorem.

THEOREM 3

Consider a branching process with generating function $h(z)$ for the number of offspring of a given parent. Let d be the smallest root of the equation $z = h(z)$. Then if the mean number m of offspring produced by a single parent is ≤ 1, $d = 1$ and the process dies out with probability 1. If $m > 1$ then $d < 1$ and the process dies out with probability d.
∎

We shall often want to know the probability that a branching process dies out by a particular generation, as well as the limit of these probabilities. Let d_n be the probability of dying out by the nth generation. Then we know that $d_1 = p_0$. We know further that $d_n = h(d_{n-1})$ where $h(z)$ is the generating functions for the number of offspring produced by a single parent. This makes it easy to compute these probabilities. The program **Branch** calculates the mean number of offspring m and the values of d_n.

```
! Branch    (BRANCH)
!
! Computes the probability that a branching process will die out by all
! generations up to a given number of generations.

library "Lib.prob*"
declare function gen_function_discrete
dim p(20)

input prompt "Maximum number of offspring = ": max_offspring
mat p = zer(0 to max_offspring)
mat input prompt "Enter p(0) to p(" & str$(max_offspring) & "): ": p
input prompt "Maximum number of generations = ": max_generations

print
print "Generation","Probability of dying out"

let probability = 0
for generation = 1 to max_generations
    let probability = gen_function_discrete(p,probability)
    print generation,probability
next generation

end
```

We have run this program for 12 generations for the case that a parent can produce at most two offspring and the probabilities for the number produced are $p_0 = .2$, $p_1 = .5$, and $p_2 = .3$.

```
Maximum number of offspring = 2
Enter p(0) to p(2): .2,.5,.3
Maximum number of generations = 12
```

Generation	Probability of dying out
1	.2
2	.312
3	.385203
4	.437116
5	.475879
6	.505878
7	.529713
8	.549035
9	.564949
10	.578225
11	.589416
12	.598931

We see that the probability of dying out by 12 generations is about .6. We shall see in the next example that the probability of eventually dying out is 2/3, so that even 12 generations is not enough to give an accurate estimate for this probability. □

EXAMPLE 2

Assume that at most two offspring can be produced. Then

$$h(z) = p_0 + p_1 z + p_2 z^2.$$

In this simple case the condition $z = h(z)$ yields the equation

$$d = p_0 + p_1 d + p_2 d^2,$$

which is satisfied by $d = 1$ and $d = p_0/p_2$. Thus, in addition to the root $d = 1$ we have the second root $d = p_0/p_2$. The mean number m of offspring produced by a single parent is

$$m = p_1 + 2p_2 = 1 - p_0 - p_2 + 2p_2 = 1 - p_0 + p_2.$$

Thus, if $p_0 > p_2$, $m < 1$ and the second root is >1. If $p_0 = p_2$, we have a double root $d = 1$. If $p_0 < p_2$, $m > 1$ and the second root d is less than 1 and represents the probability that the process will die out. $\qquad\square$

EXAMPLE 3

Keyfitz[6] compiled and analyzed data on the continuation of the female family line among Japanese women. He estimates the basic probability distribution for the number of female children born to Japanese women of ages 45–49 in 1960 to be

$$p_0 = .20917$$
$$p_1 = .25838$$
$$p_2 = .23595$$
$$p_3 = .15933$$
$$p_4 = .08275$$
$$p_5 = .03567$$
$$p_6 = .01331$$
$$p_7 = .00420$$
$$p_8 = .00106$$
$$p_9 = .00016$$
$$p_{10} = .00002$$

The expected number of girls in a family is then 1.837 so the probability d of extinction is less than 1. Using the program **Branch** we find that d is in fact only .324. $\qquad\square$

Distribution of Offspring

So far we have considered only the first of the two problems raised by Galton, namely the probability of extinction. We now consider the second problem, that is, the distribution of the number Z_n of offspring in the nth generation. The exact form of the distribution is not known except in very special cases. We shall see, however, that we can describe the limiting behavior of Z_n as $n \to \infty$.

We first show that the generating function $h_n(z)$ of the distribution of Z_n can be obtained from $h(z)$ for any branching process.

[6]N. Keyfitz, *Introduction to the Mathematics of Population*, rev. ed. (Reading, PA: Addison Wesley, 1977).

We recall that the value of the generating function at the value z for any random variable X can be written as

$$h(z) = E(z^X) = p_0 + p_1 z + p_2 z^2 + \cdots.$$

That is, $h(z)$ is the expected value of an experiment which has outcome z^j with probability p_j.

We use this interpretation to derive the generating function for the sum of independent random variables. Let $S_n = X_1 + X_2 + \cdots + X_n$ where each X_j has the same integer valued distribution (p_j) with generating function $k(z) = p_0 + p_1 z + p_2 z^2 + \cdots$. Let $k_n(z)$ be the generating function of S_n. Then

$$\begin{aligned}
k_n(z) &= \sum_j P(S_n = j)z^j \\
&= E(z^{S_n}) \\
&= E(z^{X_1 + \cdots + X_n}) \\
&= E(z^{X_1} \cdot z^{X_2} \cdots z^{X_n}) \\
&= E(z^{X_1})E(z^{X_2}) \cdots E(z^{X_n}) \\
&= (k(z))^n,
\end{aligned}$$

since the X_j are independent and all have the same distribution.

Consider now the branching process Z_n. Let $h_n(z)$ be the generating function of Z_n. Then

$$\begin{aligned}
h_{n+1}(z) &= E(z^{Z_{n+1}}) \\
&= \sum_k E(z^{Z_{n+1}} \mid Z_n = k)P(Z_n = k).
\end{aligned}$$

If $Z_n = k$, then $Z_{n+1} = X_1 + \cdots + X_k$ where $X_1, X_2, \ldots, X_k$ are independent random variables with common generating function $h(z)$. Thus

$$E(z^{Z_{n+1}} \mid Z_n = k) = E(z^{X_1 + \cdots + X_k}) = (h(z))^k,$$

and

$$h_{n+1}(z) = \sum_k (h(z))^k P(Z_n = k).$$

But

$$h_n(z) = \sum_k P(Z_n = k)z^k.$$

Thus,

$$h_{n+1}(z) = h_n(h(z)). \tag{5}$$

Hence the generating function for Z_2 is $h_2(z) = h(h(z))$, $h_3(z) = h(h(h(z)))$, and so forth. From this we see also that

$$h_{n+1}(z) = h(h_n(z)). \tag{6}$$

If we differentiate Equation (6) and use the chain rule we have

$$h'_{n+1}(z) = h'(h_n(z))h'_n(z).$$

Putting $z = 1$ and using the fact that $h_n(1) = 1$ and $h'_n(1) = m_n =$ the mean number of offspring in the nth generation, we have

$$m_{n+1} = m \cdot m_n.$$

Thus, $m_2 = m \cdot m = m^2$, $m_3 = m \cdot m^2 = m^3$, and in general

$$m_n = m^n.$$

Thus, for a branching process with $m > 1$ the mean number of offspring grows exponentially at a rate m.

Examples

EXAMPLE 1 (continued)
For the branching process of Example 1 we have

$$h(z) = 1/2 + 1/4z + 1/4z^2,$$

$$h_2(z) = h(h(z)) = 1/2 + 1/4(1/2 + 1/4z + 1/4z^2)$$

$$+ 1/4(1/2 + 1/4z + 1/4z^2)^2$$

$$= 11/16 + 1/8z + 9/64z^2 + 1/32z^3 + 1/64z^4.$$

The probabilities for the number of offspring in the second generation agree with those obtained directly from the tree measure (see Figure 1). ☐

It is clear that even in the simple case of at most two offspring, we cannot easily carry out the calculation of $h_n(z)$ by this method. However, there is one special case in which this can be done.

EXAMPLE 4
Assume that the probabilities p_1, p_2, . . . form a geometric series: $p_k = bc^{k-1}$, $k = 1$, 2, . . . , with $0 < b \leqslant 1 - c$ and

$$p_0 = 1 - p_1 - p_2 - \cdots$$

$$= 1 - b - bc - bc^2 - \cdots$$

$$= 1 - \frac{b}{1-c}.$$

Then the generating function $h(z)$ for this distribution is

$$h(z) = p_0 + p_1 z + p_2 z^2 + \cdots$$

$$= 1 - \frac{b}{1-c} + bz + bcz^2 + bc^2 z^3 + \cdots$$

$$= 1 - \frac{b}{1-c} + \frac{bz}{(1-cz)}.$$

From this we find

$$h'(z) = \frac{bcz}{(1-cz)^2} + \frac{b}{1-cz} = \frac{b}{(1-cz)^2}$$

and

$$m = h'(1) = \frac{b}{(1-c)^2}.$$

We know that if $m \leq 1$ the process will surely die out and $d = 1$. To find the probability d when $m > 1$ we must find a root $d < 1$ of the equation

$$z = h(z),$$

or

$$z = 1 - \frac{b}{1-c} + \frac{bz}{1-cz}.$$

This leads to a quadratic equation. We know that $z = 1$ is one solution. The other is found to be

$$d = \frac{1-b-c}{c(1-c)}.$$

It is easy to verify that $d < 1$ just when $m > 1$.

It is possible in this case to find the distribution of Z_n. This is done by first finding the generating function $h_n(z)$.[7] The result for $m \neq 1$ is:

$$h_n(z) = 1 - m'' \left[\frac{1-d}{m''-d} \right] + \frac{m'' \left[\dfrac{1-d}{m''-d} \right]^2 z}{1 - \left[\dfrac{m''-1}{m''-d} \right] z}.$$

[7] See T.E. Harris, *The Theory of Branching Processes* (Berlin: Springer, 1963), p. 9.

The coefficients of the powers of z give the density for Z_n:

$$p(Z_n = 0) = 1 - m^n \frac{(1-d)}{(m^n-d)} = \frac{d(m^n - 1)}{(m^n - d)},$$

$$P(Z_n = j) = m^n \frac{(1-d)^2}{(m^n-d)^2} \cdot \frac{(m^n-1)^{j-1}}{(m^n-d)^{j-1}}, \qquad j \geq 1.$$

$\square$

EXAMPLE 3 (continued)

Let us re-examine the Keyfitz data to see if a distribution of the type considered in Example 4 could reasonably be used as a model for this population. We would have to estimate from the data the parameters b and c for the formula $p_k = bc^{k-1}$. Recall that

$$m = \frac{b}{(1-c)^2} \tag{7}$$

and the probability d that the process dies out is

$$d = \frac{1-b-c}{c(1-c)}. \tag{8}$$

Solving Equation (7) and Equation (8) for b and c gives

$$c = \frac{m-1}{m-d}$$

and

$$b = m\left(\frac{1-d}{m-d}\right)^2.$$

We shall use the value 1.837 for m and .324 for d that we found in the Keyfitz example. Using these values, we obtain $b = .3666$ and $c = .5533$. Note that $(1-c)^2 < b < 1 - c$, as required. In Table 1 we give for comparison the probabilities p_0 through p_8 as calculated by the geometric distribution versus the empirical values.

The geometric model tends to favor the larger numbers of offspring but is similar enough to show that this modified geometric density might be appropriate to use for studies of this kind.

Recall that if $S_n = X_1 + X_2 + \cdots + X_n$ is the sum of independent random variables with the same density then the law of large numbers states that S_n/n converges to a constant, namely $E(X_1)$. It is natural to ask if there is a similar limiting theorem for branching processes.

Consider a branching process with Z_n representing the number of offspring after n

Table 1 Theoretical versus empirical probabilities.

p_j	Data	Geometric Model
0	.2092	.1816
1	.2584	.3666
2	.2360	.2028
3	.1593	.1122
4	.0828	.0621
5	.0357	.0344
6	.0133	.0190
7	.0042	.0105
8	.0011	.0058
9	.0002	.0032
10	.0002	.0018

generations. Then we have seen that the expected value of Z_n is m^n. Thus we can scale the random variable Z_n to have expected value 1 by considering the random variable

$$W_n = \frac{Z_n}{m^n}.$$

In the theory of branching process it is proved that this random variable W_n will tend to a limit as n tends to infinity. However, unlike the case of the law of large numbers where this limit is a constant, for a branching process the limiting value of the random variables W_n is itself a random variable.

Although we cannot prove this theorem here we can illustrate it by simulation. This requires a little care. When a branching process survives, the number of offspring is apt to get very large. If in a given generation there are 1000 offspring, the offspring of the next generation are the result of 1000 chance events, and it will take a while to simulate these 1000 experiments. However, since the final result is the sum of 1000 independent experiments we can use the central limit theorem to replace these 1000 experiments by a single experiment with normal density having the appropriate mean and variance. The program **Branching Simulation** (see next page) carries out this process.

We have run this program for the Keyfitz example, carrying out 10 simulations and graphing the results in Figure 4.

The expected number of female offspring per female is 1.1, so that we are graphing the outcome for the random variables $W_n = \dfrac{Z_n}{(1.1)^n}$. For three of the simulations the process died out, which is consistent with the value $d = .3$ that we found for this example. For the other seven simulations the value of W_n tends to a limiting value which is different for each simulation. ☐

```
! Branching Simulation  (BRANSIM)
!
! Simulates a branching process.  When the size of a generation becomes
! greater than 500, the size of the next generation is determined by the
! normal density.

library "Lib.cont*"
library "Lib.prob*"
library "Lib.CLT*"
declare function simulate_discrete_X
declare function sample_normal
declare function expectation_discrete
declare function variance_discrete

dim p(20)

let max_offspring  = 9
let change_point = 500
let generations = 25
mat p = zer(0 to max_offspring)
mat read p
data .2767,.3289,.1949,.0862,.0509
data .0329,.0183,.0080,.0026,.0006

let mean = expectation_discrete(p)
let variance = variance_discrete(p)

set window 0, generations, 0, 10

for experiment = 1 to 10

    let generation = 0
    let generation_size = 1

    do
        plot generation, generation_size/mean^generation;

        let generation = generation + 1

        if generation_size < change_point then
            let offspring = 0
            for parent = 1 to generation_size
                let offspring = offspring + simulate_discrete_X(p)
            next parent
            let generation_size = offspring
        else
            let generation_mean = generation_size * mean
            let generation_std = sqr(generation_size * variance)
            let generation_size = sample_normal(generation_mean,generation_std)
        end if

    loop until generation_size = 0 or generation = generations

    plot generation, generation_size/mean^generation

next experiment

end
```

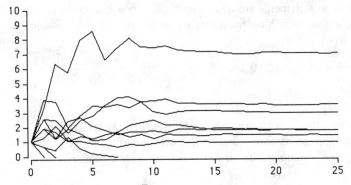

Figure 4   Simulation of $\dfrac{Z_n}{m^n}$ for the Keyfitz example.

EXAMPLE 4 (continued)

We now examine the random variable Z_n more closely for the case $m < 1$ (see Example 4). Fix a value $t > 0$; let $[tm^n]$ be the integer part of tm^n. Then

$$P(Z_n = [tm^n])$$

$$= m^n \left(\frac{1-d}{m^n-d} \right)^2 \left(\frac{m^n-1}{m^n-d} \right)^{[tm^n]-1}$$

$$= \frac{1}{m^n} \left(\frac{1-d}{1-\dfrac{d}{m^n}} \right)^2 \left(\frac{1-\dfrac{1}{m^n}}{1-\dfrac{d}{m^n}} \right)^{tm^n+a}$$

where $|a| \leq 2$. Thus, as $n \to \infty$,

$$m^n P(Z_n = [tm^n]) \to (1-d)^2 \frac{e^{-t}}{e^{-td}}$$

$$= (1-d)^2 e^{-t(1-d)}.$$

For $t = 0$,

$$P(Z_n = 0) \to d.$$

We can compare this result with the central limit theorem for sums S_n of integer-valued independent random variables (see Chapter 9, Section 9.3, Theorem 5), which states that if t is an integer and $u = \dfrac{t - n\mu}{(\sigma^2 n)^{1/2}}$, then as $n \to \infty$,

$$(\sigma^2 n)^{1/2} P(S_n = u(\sigma^2 n)^{1/2} + \mu n) \to \frac{1}{(2\pi)^{1/2}} e^{-u^2/2}.$$

We see that the form of these statements are quite similar. It is possible to prove a limit theorem for a general class of branching processes that states that under suitable hypotheses, as $n \to \infty$,

$$m^n P(Z_n = [tm^n]) \to k(t), \qquad t > 0,$$

$$P(Z_n = 0) \to d.$$

However, unlike the central limit theorem for sums of independent random variables, the function $k(t)$ will depend upon the basic distribution that determines the process. Its form is known for only a very few examples similar to the one we have considered here. □

Chain Letter Problem

EXAMPLE 5

An interesting example of branching process was suggested by Free Huizinga.[8] In 1978, a chain letter called the "Circle of Gold," believed to have started in California, found its way across the country to the theatre district of New York. The chain required a participant to buy a letter containing a list of 12 names for 100 dollars. The buyer gives 50 dollars to the person from whom the letter was purchased and then sends 50 dollars to the person whose name is at the top of the list. The buyer then crosses off the name at the top of the list and adds her own name at the bottom in each letter before it is sold again.

Let us first assume that the buyer may sell the letter only to a single person. If you buy the letter you will want to compute your expected winnings. (We are ignoring here the fact that the passing on of chain letters through the mail is a federal offense with certain obvious resulting penalties.) Assume that each person involved has a probability p of selling the letter. Then you will receive 50 dollars with probability p and another 50 dollars if the letter is sold to 12 people, since then your name would have risen to the top of the list. This occurs with probability p^{12}, and so your expected winnings are $-100 + 50p + 50p^{12}$. Thus the chain is in this situation a highly unfavorable game.

It would be more reasonable to allow each person involved to make a copy of the list and try to sell the letter to at least 2 other people. Then you would have a chance of recovering your 100 dollars on these sales, and if any of the letters is sold 12 times you will receive a bonus of 50 dollars for each of these cases. We can consider this as a branching process with 12 generations. The members of the first generation are the letters you sell. The second generation consists of the letters sold by members of the first generation, and so forth.

Let us assume that the probabilities that each individual sells letters to 0, 1, or 2 others are p_0, p_1, and p_2, respectively. Let $Z_1, Z_2, \ldots, Z_{12}$ be the number of letters in the first 12 generations of this branching process. Then your expected winnings are

$$50(E(Z_1) + E(Z_{12})) = 50m + 50m^{12},$$

[8]Private communication.

where $m = p_1 + 2p_2$ is the expected number of letters you sold. Thus to be favorable we must have

$$50m + 50m^{12} > 100,$$

or

$$m + m^{12} > 2.$$

But this will be true if and only if $m > 1$. We have seen that this will occur in the quadratic case if and only if $p_2 > p_0$. Let us assume for example that $p_0 = .2$, $p_1 = .5$, and $p_2 = .3$. Then $m = 1.1$ and the chain would be a favorable game. Your expected profit would be

$$50(1.1 + 1.1^{12}) - 100 \cong 112.$$

The probability that you receive at least one payment from the 12th generation is $1 - d_{12}$. We find from our program **Branch** that $d_{12} = .599$. Thus, $1 - d_{12} = .401$ is the probability that you receive some bonus. The maximum that you could receive from the chain would be $50 (2 + 2^{12}) = 204900$ if everyone were to sell successfully two letters. Of course you can not always expect to be so lucky. (What is the probability of this happening?)

To simulate this game, we need only simulate a branching process for 12 generations. Using a slightly modified version of our program **Branching Simulation** we carried out twenty such simulations, giving the following results.

```
Finite density (0) or Poisson (1): 0
Enter density p1, p2,..., pn: .2,.5,.3
Mean:  1.1
```

Z1	Z2	Z3	Z4	Z5	Z6	Z7	Z8	Z9	Z10	Z11	Z12	Profit
1	0	0	0	0	0	0	0	0	0	0	0	-50
1	1	2	3	2	3	2	1	2	3	3	6	250
0	0	0	0	0	0	0	0	0	0	0	0	-100
2	4	4	2	3	4	4	3	2	2	1	1	50
1	2	3	5	4	3	3	3	5	8	6	6	250
0	0	0	0	0	0	0	0	0	0	0	0	-100
2	3	2	2	2	1	2	3	3	3	4	6	300
1	2	1	1	1	1	2	1	0	0	0	0	-50
0	0	0	0	0	0	0	0	0	0	0	0	-100
1	0	0	0	0	0	0	0	0	0	0	0	-50
2	3	2	3	3	3	5	9	12	12	13	15	750
1	1	1	0	0	0	0	0	0	0	0	0	-50
1	2	2	3	3	0	0	0	0	0	0	0	-50
1	1	1	1	2	2	3	4	4	6	4	5	200
1	1	0	0	0	0	0	0	0	0	0	0	-50
1	0	0	0	0	0	0	0	0	0	0	0	-50
1	0	0	0	0	0	0	0	0	0	0	0	-50
1	1	2	3	3	4	2	3	3	3	3	2	50
1	2	4	6	6	9	10	13	16	17	15	18	850
1	0	0	0	0	0	0	0	0	0	0	0	-50

Note that we were quite lucky on a few runs, but we came out ahead only a little less than half the time. The process died out by the twelfth generation in 12 out of the

20 experiments, in good agreement with the probability $d_{12} = .599$ that we calculated using the program **Branch**.

Let us modify the assumptions about our chain letter to let the buyer sell the letter to as many people as she can instead of to a maximum of two. We shall assume, in fact, that a person has a large number N of acquaintances and a small probability p of persuading any one of them to buy the letter. Then the distribution for the number of letters that she sells will be a binomial distribution with mean $m = Np$. Since N is large and p is small, we can assume that the probability p_j that an individual sells the letter to j people is given by the Poisson density

$$p_j = \frac{e^{-m} m^j}{j!}.$$

The generating function for the Poisson distribution is

$$
\begin{aligned}
h(z) &= \sum_{j=0}^{\infty} \frac{e^{-m} m^j z^j}{j!} \\
&= e^{-m} \sum_{j=0}^{\infty} \frac{m^j z^j}{j!} \\
&= e^{-m} e^{mz} = e^{m(z-1)}.
\end{aligned}
$$

The expected number of letters that an individual passes on is m, and again to be favorable we must have $m > 1$. Let us assume again that $m = 1.1$. Then we can find again the probability $1 - d_{12}$ of a bonus from **Branch**. The result is .232. Although the expected winnings are the same, the variance is larger in this case, and the buyer has a better chance for a reasonably large profit. We again carried out 20 simulations using the Poisson density with mean 1.1. The results were:

```
Finite density (0) or Poisson (1): 1
Mean = 1.1
```

Z1	Z2	Z3	Z4	Z5	Z6	Z7	Z8	Z9	Z10	Z11	Z12	Profit
1	2	6	7	7	8	11	9	7	6	6	5	200
1	0	0	0	0	0	0	0	0	0	0	0	-50
1	0	0	0	0	0	0	0	0	0	0	0	-50
1	1	1	0	0	0	0	0	0	0	0	0	-50
0	0	0	0	0	0	0	0	0	0	0	0	-100
1	1	1	1	1	1	2	4	9	7	9	7	300
2	3	3	4	2	0	0	0	0	0	0	0	0
1	0	0	0	0	0	0	0	0	0	0	0	-50
2	1	0	0	0	0	0	0	0	0	0	0	0
3	3	4	7	11	17	14	11	11	10	16	25	1300
0	0	0	0	0	0	0	0	0	0	0	0	-100
1	2	2	1	1	3	1	0	0	0	0	0	-50
0	0	0	0	0	0	0	0	0	0	0	0	-100
2	3	1	0	0	0	0	0	0	0	0	0	0
3	1	0	0	0	0	0	0	0	0	0	0	50
1	0	0	0	0	0	0	0	0	0	0	0	-50
3	4	4	7	10	11	9	11	12	14	13	10	550
1	3	3	4	9	5	7	9	8	8	6	3	100
1	0	0	0	0	0	0	0	0	0	0	0	-50
1	0	0	0	0	0	0	0	0	0	0	0	-50

We note that, as before, we came out ahead less than half the time, but we also had one large profit. In only 6 of the 20 cases did we receive any profit. This is again in reasonable agreement with our calculation of a probability 232 for this happening. □

Exercises

1. Let $Z_1, Z_2, \ldots, Z_N$ describe a branching process in which each parent has j offspring with probability p_j. Find the probability d that the process eventually dies out if
   (a) $p_0 = {}^1/_2$, $p_1 = {}^1/_4$, and $p_2 = {}^1/_4$.
   (b) $p_0 = {}^1/_3$, $p_1 = {}^1/_3$, and $p_2 = {}^1/_3$.
   (c) $p_0 = {}^1/_3$, $p_1 = 0$, and $p_2 = {}^2/_3$.
   (d) $p_j = \dfrac{1}{2^{j+1}}$, $j = 0, 1, 2, \ldots$.
   (e) $p_j = {}^1/_3 ({}^2/_3)^j$, $j = 0, 1, 2, \ldots$.
   (f) $p_j = (e^{-2}) \dfrac{2^j}{j!}$, $j = 0, 1, 2 \ldots$ (estimate d numerically).

2. Let $Z_1, Z_2, \ldots, Z_N$ describe a branching process in which each parent has j offspring with probability p_j. Find the probability d that the process dies out if
   (a) $p_0 = {}^1/_2$, $p_1 = p_2 = 0$, and $p_3 = {}^1/_2$.
   (b) $p_0 = p_1 = p_2 = p_3 = {}^1/_4$.
   (c) $p_0 = t$, $p_1 = 1 - 2t$, $p_2 = 0$, and $p_3 = t$, where $t \leqslant {}^1/_2$.

3. In the chain letter problem (see Example 5) find your expected profit if
   (a) $p_0 = {}^1/_2$, $p_1 = 0$, and $p_2 = {}^1/_2$.
   (b) $p_0 = {}^1/_6$, $p_1 = {}^1/_2$, and $p_2 = {}^1/_3$.
   Show that if $p_0 > {}^1/_2$, you cannot expect to make a profit.

4. Let $S_N = X_1 + X_2 + \cdots + X_N$, where $X_1, X_2, \ldots, X_N$ are independent random variables with common density having generating function $f(z)$. Assume that N is an integer valued random variable independent of all of the X_j and having generating function $g(z)$. Show that the generating function for S_N is $h(z) = g(f(z))$. *Hint:* Use the fact that

$$h(z) = E(z^{S_N}) = \sum_k E(z^{S_k} \mid N = k) P(N = k).$$

5. We have seen that if the generating function for the offspring of a single parent is $f(z)$, then the generating function for the number of offspring after two generations is given by $h(z) = f(f(z))$. Explain how this follows from the result of Exercise 4.

6. Consider a queueing process (see Chapter 5, Section 5.2, Example 12) such that in each minute either 0 or 1 customers arrive with probabilities p or $q = 1 - p$, respectively. When a customer starts service he finishes in the next minute with probability r. Thus when a customer begins being served she will finish being served in j minutes with probability $(1 - r)^{j-1} r$ for $j = 1, 2, 3, \ldots$

(a) Find the generating function $f(z)$ for the number of customers who arrive in one minute and the generating function $g(z)$ for the length of time that a person spends in service once she begins service.

(b) Consider a *customer branching process* by considering the offspring of a customer to be the customers who arrive while she is being served. Using Exercise 4, show that the generating function for our customer branching process is $h(z) = g(f(z))$.

(c) If we start the branching process with the arrival of the first customer, then the length of time until the branching process dies out will be the *busy period* for the server. Find a condition in terms of the mean arrival rate and mean service time that will assure that the server will ultimately have a time when he is not busy.

7. Let N be the expected total number of offspring in a branching process. Let m be the mean number of offspring of a single parent. Show that

$$N = 1 + \left(\sum p_k \cdot k \right) N = 1 + mN$$

and hence that N is finite if and only if $m < 1$ and in that case $N = 1/(1-m)$.

8. Consider a branching process such that the number of offspring of a parent is j with probability $1/2^{j+1}$ for $j = 0,1,2, \ldots$

(a) Using the results of Example 4 show that the probability that there are j offspring in the nth generation is

$$p_j^{(n)} = \begin{cases} \dfrac{1}{n(n+1)} \left(\dfrac{n}{n+1} \right)^j & \text{if } j \geq 1, \\[3mm] \dfrac{n}{n+1} & \text{if } j = 0. \end{cases}$$

(b) Show that the probability that the process dies out exactly at the nth generation is $1/(n(n+1))$.

*(c) Show that the expected lifetime is infinite even though $d = 1$.

10.3 GENERATING FUNCTIONS FOR CONTINUOUS DENSITIES

In the previous section, we introduced the concepts of moments and moment generating functions for discrete random variables. These concepts have natural analogues for continuous random variables, provided some care is taken in arguments involving convergence.

Moments

If X is a continuous random variable defined on the probability space Ω, with density function f_X, then we define the nth moment μ_n of X by the formula

$$\mu_n = E(X^n)$$

$$= \int_{-\infty}^{+\infty} x^n f_X(x)\,dx,$$

provided this integral converges. Then, just as in the discrete case, we see that $\mu_0 = 1$, $\mu_1 = \mu$, and $\mu_2 - \mu_1^2 = \sigma^2$.

Moment Generating Functions

Now we define the *moment generating function $g(t)$* for X by the formula

$$g(t) = \sum_{k=0}^{\infty} \frac{\mu_k t^k}{k!}$$

$$= \sum_{k=0}^{\infty} \frac{E(X^k) t^k}{k!}$$

$$= E(e^{tX})$$

$$= \int_{-\infty}^{+\infty} e^{tx} f_X(x)\,dx,$$

provided this series converges. Then, as before, we have

$$\mu_n = g^{(n)}(0).$$

Examples

EXAMPLE 1
Let X be a continuous random variable with range $[0,1]$ and density function $f_X(x) \equiv 1$ for $0 \leq x \leq 1$ (uniform density). Then

$$\mu_n = \int_0^k x^n\,dx = \frac{1}{n+1},$$

and

$$g(t) = \sum_{k=0}^{\infty} \frac{t^k}{(k+1)!}$$

$$= \frac{e^t - 1}{t}.$$

Here the series converges for all t. Alternatively, we have

$$g(t) = \int_{-\infty}^{+\infty} e^{tx} f_X(x) dx$$

$$= \int_0^1 e^{tx} dx = \frac{e^t - 1}{t}.$$

Then (by L'Hôpital's rule)

$$\mu_0 = g(0) = \lim_{t \to 0} \frac{e^t - 1}{t} = 1,$$

$$\mu_1 = g'(0) = \lim_{t \to 0} \frac{te^t - e^t + 1}{t^2} = \frac{1}{2},$$

$$\mu_2 = g''(0) = \lim_{t \to 0} \frac{t^3 e^t - 2t^2 e^t + 2te^t - 2t}{t^4} = \frac{1}{3}.$$

In particular, we verify that $\mu = g'(0) = 1/2$ and

$$\sigma^2 = g''(0) - g'(0)^2 = \frac{1}{3} - \frac{1}{4} = \frac{1}{12}$$

as before (see Example 1 of Chapter 6, Section 6.3). □

EXAMPLE 2

Let X have range $[0, \infty)$ and density function $f_X(x) = \lambda e^{-\lambda x}$ (exponential density with parameter λ). In this case

$$\mu_n = \int_0^\infty x^n \lambda e^{-\lambda x} dx = \lambda(-1)^n \frac{d^n}{d\lambda^n} \int_0^\infty e^{-\lambda x} dx$$

$$= \lambda(-1)^n \frac{d^n}{d\lambda^n} \left[\frac{1}{\lambda} \right] = \frac{n!}{\lambda^n},$$

and

$$g(t) = \sum_{k=0}^\infty \frac{\mu_k t^k}{k!}$$

$$= \sum_{k=0}^\infty \left[\frac{t}{\lambda} \right]^k$$

$$= \frac{\lambda}{\lambda - t}.$$

Here the series converges only for $|t| < \lambda$. Alternatively, we have

$$g(t) = \int_0^\infty e^{tx} (\lambda e^{-\lambda x}) dx$$

$$= \frac{\lambda e^{(t-\lambda)x}}{t-\lambda} \Big|_0^\infty = \frac{\lambda}{\lambda - t}.$$

Now we can verify directly that

$$\mu_n = g^{(n)}(0) = \frac{\lambda n!}{(\lambda - t)^{n+1}} \Big|_{t=0} = \frac{n!}{\lambda^n}. \qquad \square$$

EXAMPLE 3

Let X have range $(-\infty, +\infty)$ and density function

$$f_X(x) = \frac{1}{\sqrt{2\pi}} e^{-x^2/2}$$

(normal density). In this case we have

$$\mu_n = \frac{1}{\sqrt{2\pi}} \int_{-\infty}^\infty x^n e^{-x^2/2} \, dx$$

$$= \begin{cases} 0 & \text{if } n \text{ is odd,} \\ \dfrac{(2m)!}{2^m m!} & \text{if } n = 2m \text{ is even.} \end{cases}$$

(These moments are calculated by integrating once by parts to show that $\mu_n = (n-1)\mu_{n-2}$, and observing that $\mu_0 = 1$ and $\mu_1 = 0$.) Hence,

$$g(t) = \sum_{n=0}^\infty \frac{\mu_n t^n}{n!}$$

$$= \sum_{m=0}^\infty \frac{t^{2m}}{2^m m!}$$

$$= e^{t^2/2}$$

This series converges for all values of t. Again we can verify that $g^{(n)}(0) = \mu_n$. $\quad\square$

In general, the series defining $g(t)$ will not converge for all t. But in the important special case where X is bounded (i.e., where the range of X is contained in a finite interval), we can show that the series does converge for all t.

THEOREM 4

Suppose X is a continuous random variable with range contained in the interval $[-M, M]$. Then the series

$$g(t) = \sum_{k=0}^{\infty} \frac{\mu_k t^k}{k!}$$

converges for all t to an infinitely differentiable function $g(t)$, and $g^{(n)}(0) = \mu_n$.

Proof. We have

$$\mu_k = \int_{-M}^{M} x^k f_X(x) dx,$$

so

$$|\mu_k| \leq \int_{-M}^{M} |x|^k f_X(x) dx$$

$$\leq M^k \int_{-M}^{M} f_X(x) dx$$

$$= M^k.$$

Hence, for all N we have

$$\sum_{k=0}^{N} \left| \frac{\mu_k t^k}{k!} \right| \leq \sum_{k=0}^{N} \frac{(M|t|)^k}{k!}$$

$$\leq e^{M|t|},$$

which shows that the power series converges for all t. We know that the sum of a convergent power series is always infinitely differentiable. ∎

Moment Problem

THEOREM 5

If x is a bounded random variable, then the moment generating function $g_X(t)$ of x determines the density function $f_X(x)$ uniquely.

Sketch of the Proof. We know that

$$g_X(t) = \sum_{k=0}^{\infty} \frac{\mu_k t^k}{k!}$$

$$= \int_{-\infty}^{+\infty} e^{tx} f(x) dx.$$

Characteristic Functions

If we replace t by $i\tau$, where τ is real and $i = \sqrt{-1}$, then the series converges for all τ, and we can define the function

$$k_X(\tau) = g_X(i\tau) = \int_{-\infty}^{+\infty} e^{i\tau x} f_X(x)dx.$$

The function $k_X(\tau)$ is called the *characteristic function* of X, and is defined by the above equation even when the series for g_X does not converge. This equation says that k_X is the *Fourier transform* of f_X. It is known that the Fourier transform has an inverse, given by the formula

$$f_X(x) = \frac{1}{2\pi} \int_{-\infty}^{+\infty} e^{-i\tau x} k_X(\tau)d\tau,$$

suitably interpreted.[9] Here we see that the characteristic function k_X, and hence the moment generating function g_X, determines the density function f_X uniquely under our hypotheses.   ■

Proof of Central Limit Theorem.   With this result in mind, we can now sketch a proof of the central limit theorem for bounded continuous random variables (see Theorem 7 of Chapter 9, Section 9.4). To this end, let X be a continuous random variable with density function f_X, mean $\mu = 0$ and variance $\sigma^2 = 1$, and moment generating function $g(t)$ defined by its series for all t. Let $X_1, X_2, \ldots,$ be an independent trials process with each X_i having density f_X, and let $S_n = X_1 + \cdots + X_n$, and $S_n^* = \dfrac{S_n - n\mu}{\sqrt{n\sigma^2}} = \dfrac{S_n}{\sqrt{n}}$. Then each X_i has moment generating function $g(t)$, and since the X_i are independent, the sum S_n, just as in the discrete case (see Section 10.1), has moment generating function

$$g_n(t) = (g(t))^n,$$

and the standardized sum S_n^* has moment generating function

$$g_n^*(t) = \left(g\left(\frac{t}{\sqrt{n}} \right) \right)^n.$$

We now show that, as $n \to \infty$, $g_n^*(t) \to e^{t^2/2}$, where $e^{t^2/2}$ is the moment generating function of the normal density $n(x) = \dfrac{1}{\sqrt{2\pi}} e^{-x^2/2}$ (see Example 3).

To show this, we set $u(t) = \log g(t)$, and

$$u_n^*(t) = \log g_n^*(t)$$

$$= n \log g\left(\frac{t}{\sqrt{n}} \right) = nu\left(\frac{t}{\sqrt{n}} \right),$$

---

[9]H. Dym and H.P. McKean, *Fourier Series and Integrals* (New York: Academic Press, 1972).

and show that $u_n^*(t) \to t^2/2$ as $n \to \infty$. First we note that

$$u(0) = \log(g_n(0)) = 0,$$

$$u'(0) = \frac{g'(0)}{g(0)} = \frac{\mu_1}{1} = 0,$$

$$u''(0) = \frac{g''(0)g(0) - g'(0)^2}{g(0)^2}$$

$$= \frac{\mu_2 - \mu_1^2}{1} = \sigma^2 = 1.$$

Now by using L 'Hôpital's rule twice, we get

$$\lim_{n \to \infty} u_n^*(t) = \lim_{s \to \infty} \frac{u\left(\dfrac{t}{\sqrt{s}}\right)}{s^{-1}}$$

$$= \lim_{s \to \infty} \frac{u'\left(\dfrac{t}{\sqrt{s}}\right)t}{2s^{-1/2}}$$

$$= \lim_{s \to \infty} u''\left(\frac{t}{\sqrt{s}}\right)\frac{t^2}{2} = \sigma^2 \frac{t^2}{2} = \frac{t^2}{2}.$$

Hence, $g_n^*(t) \to e^{t^2/2}$ as $n \to \infty$. Now to complete the proof of the central limit theorem, we must show that if $g_n^*(t) \to e^{t^2/2}$, then under our hypotheses the distribution functions $F_n^*(x)$ of the S_n^* must converge to the distribution function $F_N^*(x)$ of the normal variable N; that is, that

$$F_n^*(a) = P[S_n^* \le a] \to \frac{1}{\sqrt{2\pi}} \int_{-\infty}^{a} e^{-x^2/2} dx,$$

and furthermore, that the density functions $f_n^*(x)$ of the S_n^* must converge to the density function for N, that is, that

$$f_n^*(x) \to \frac{1}{\sqrt{2\pi}} e^{-x^2/2} \qquad \text{as } n \to \infty.$$

Since the densities, and hence the distributions, of the S_n^* are determined uniquely by their moment generating functions under our hypotheses, these conclusions are certainly plausible, but their proofs involve a detailed examination of characteristic functions and Fourier transforms, and we shall not attempt them here.

In the same way, we can prove the central limit theorem for bounded discrete random variables with integer values (see Theorem 6 of Chapter 9, Section 9.3). Let X be a discrete random variable with density function $p(j)$, mean $\mu = 0$ and variance $\sigma^2 = 1$, and moment generating function $g(t)$, and let $X_1, X_2, X_3, \cdots$, form an independent trials process with common density p. Let $S_n = X_1 + \cdots + X_n$ and $S_n^* = \dfrac{S_n}{\sqrt{n}}$, with densities p_n and p_n^*, and moment generating functions $g_n(t)$ and $g_n^*(t) = \left(g\left(\dfrac{t}{\sqrt{n}}\right)\right)^n$. Then we have

$$g_n^*(t) \to e^{t^2/2},$$

just as in the continuous case, and this implies in the same way that the distribution functions $F_n^*(x)$ converge to the normal distribution; that is, that

$$F_n^*(a) = P[S_n^* \leqslant a] \to \frac{1}{\sqrt{2\pi}} \int_{-\infty}^{a} e^{-x^2/2} dx \qquad \text{as } n \to \infty.$$

The corresponding statement about the density functions p_n^*, however, requires a little extra care (See Theorem 5 of Chapter 9, Section 9.3). The trouble arises because the density $p(x)$ is not defined for all x, but only for integer x. It follows that the density $p_n^*(x)$ is defined only for x of the form $\dfrac{j}{\sqrt{n}}$, and these values change as n changes.

We can fix this, however, by introducing the function $\bar{p}(x)$, defined by the formula

$$\bar{p}(x) = \begin{cases} p(j) & \text{if } j - 1/2 \leqslant x < j + 1/2, \\ 0 & \text{otherwise.} \end{cases}$$

Then $\bar{p}(x)$ is defined for all x, $\bar{p}(j) = p(j)$, and the graph of $\bar{p}(x)$ is the bar graph for the density $p(j)$ (see Figure 3 of Chapter 9, Section 9.1).

In the same way we introduce the bar graph functions $\bar{p}_n(x)$ and $\bar{p}_n^*(x)$ associated with the densities p_n and p_n^*, and their moment generating functions $\bar{g}_n(t)$ and $\bar{g}_n^*(t)$. If we can show that $\bar{g}_n^*(t) \to e^{t^2}/2$, then we can conclude that

$$\bar{p}_n^*(x) \to \frac{1}{\sqrt{2\pi}} e^{t^2/2} \qquad \text{as } n \to \infty$$

for all x, a conclusion strongly suggested by Figure 3 of Chapter 9, Section 9.1.

Now $\bar{g}(t)$ is given by

$$\bar{g}(t) = \int_{-\infty}^{+\infty} e^{tx} \bar{p}(x) dx$$

$$= \sum_{j=-N}^{+N} \int_{j-1/2}^{j+1/2} e^{tx} p(j) dx$$

$$= \sum_{j=-N}^{+N} p(j) e^{tj} \left(\frac{e^{t/2} - e^{-t/2}}{2t/2}\right)$$

$$= g(t) \frac{\sinh (t/2)}{t/2},$$

where we have put

$$\sinh (t/2) = \frac{e^{t/2} - e^{-t/2}}{2}.$$

In the same way, we find that

$$\bar{g}_n(t) = g_n(t) \cdot \frac{\sinh (t/2)}{t/2},$$

$$\bar{g}_n^*(t) = g_n^*(t) \frac{\sinh (t/2\sqrt{n})}{t/2\sqrt{n}}.$$

Now, as $n \to \infty$, we know that $g_n^*(t) \to e^{t^2/2}$, and, by L 'Hôpital's Rule,

$$\lim_{n \to \infty} \frac{\sinh (t/2\sqrt{n})}{t/2\sqrt{n}} = 1.$$

It follows that

$$\bar{g}_n^*(t) \to e^{t^2/2},$$

and hence that

$$\bar{p}_n^*(x) \to \frac{1}{\sqrt{2\pi}} e^{-x^2/2} \qquad \text{as } n \to \infty.$$

This last conclusion holds if and only if the greatest common divisor of the differences of all the values that the X_j can take on is 1 (cf. Theorem 5 of Chapter 9, Section 9.3).[10] ∎

Cauchy Density

The characteristic function of a continuous density is a useful tool even in cases when the moment series does not converge, or even in cases when the moments themselves are not finite. As an example, consider the Cauchy density with parameter $a = 1$ (see Example 8 of Chapter 6, Section 6.3)

$$f(x) = \frac{1}{\pi(1+x^2)}.$$

If X and Y are independent random variables with Cauchy density $f(x)$, then the average $Z = \dfrac{X + Y}{2}$ also has Cauchy density $f(x)$, that is,

$$f_Z(x) = f(x).$$

---

[10]B.V. Gnedenko and A.N. Kolomogorov, *Limit Distributions for Sums of Independent Random Variables* (Reading: Addison-Wesley, 1968), p. 233.

This is hard to check directly, but easy to check by using characteristic functions. Note first that

$$\mu_2 = E(X^2) = \int_{-\infty}^{+\infty} \frac{x^2}{\pi(1+x^2)} dx = \infty$$

so that μ_2 is infinite. Nevertheless, we can define the characteristic function $k_X(\tau)$ of x by the formula

$$k_X(\tau) = \int_{-\infty}^{+\infty} e^{i\tau x} \frac{1}{\pi(1+x^2)} dx.$$

This integral is easy to do by contour methods, and gives us

$$k_X(\tau) = k_Y(\tau) = e^{-|\tau|}.$$

Hence,

$$k_{X+Y}(\tau) = (e^{-|\tau|})^2 = e^{-2|\tau|},$$

and since

$$k_Z(\tau) = k_{X+Y}\left(\frac{\tau}{2}\right),$$

we have

$$k_Z(\tau) = e^{-2|\tau/2|} = e^{-|\tau|}.$$

This shows that $k_Z = k_X = k_Y$, and leads to the conclusion that $f_Z = f_X = f_Y$.

It follows from this that if $X_1, X_2, X_3, \ldots, X_n$ is an independent trials process with common Cauchy density, and if

$$A_n = \frac{X_1 + \cdots + X_n}{n}$$

is the average of the X_i, then A_n has the same density as do the X_i. This means that the law of large numbers fails for this process; the distribution of the average A_n is exactly the same as for the individual terms. Our proof of the law of large numbers fails in this case because the variance of X_i is not finite.

Exercises

1. Let X be a continuous random variable with values in $[0,2]$ and density f_X. Find the moment generating function $g(t)$ for X if
   (a) $f_X(x) = (1/2)$.
   (b) $f_X(x) = (1/2)x$.
   (c) $f_X(x) = 1 - (1/2)x$.

(d) $f_X(x) = |1 - x|$.
(e) $f_X(x) = 3/8x^2$.
Hint: Use the integral definition, as in Examples 1 and 2.

2. For each of the densities in Exercise 1 calculate the first and second moments, μ_1 and μ_2, directly from their definition and verify that $g(0) = 1$, $g'(0) = \mu_1$, and $g''(0) = \mu_2$.

3. Let X be a continuous random variable with values in $[0, \infty)$ and density f_X. Find the moment generating function for X if
   (a) $f_X(x) = 2e^{-2x}$.
   (b) $f_X(x) = e^{-2x} + \frac{1}{2}e^{-x}$.
   (c) $f_X(x) = 4xe^{-2x}$.
   (d) $f_X(x) = \lambda(\lambda x)^{n-1} e^{-\lambda x}$.

4. For each of the densities of Exercise 3, calculate the first and second moments, μ_1 and μ_2, directly from their definition and verify that $g(0) = 1$, $g'(0) = \mu_1$, and $g''(0) = \mu_2$.

5. Find the characteristic function $k_X(\tau)$ for each of the random variables X of Exercise 1.

6. Let X be a continuous random variable whose characteristic function $k_X(\tau)$ is

   $$k_X(\tau) = e^{-|\tau|} \qquad -\infty < \tau < +\infty.$$

   Show directly that the density f_X of X is

   $$f_X(x) = \frac{1}{\pi(1 + x^2)}.$$

7. Let X be a continuous random variable with values in $[0,1]$, uniform density function $f_X(x) \equiv 1$ and moment generating function $g(t) = \dfrac{e^t - 1}{t}$. Find in terms of $g(t)$ the moment generating function for
   (a) $-X$.
   (b) $1 + X$.
   (c) $3X$.
   (d) $aX + b$.

8. Let $X_1, X_2, \ldots, X_n$ be an independent trials process with uniform density. Find the moment generating function for
   (a) X_1.
   (b) $S_2 = X_1 + X_2$.
   (c) $S_n = X_1 + X_2 + \cdots + X_n$.
   (d) $A_n = \dfrac{S_n}{n}$.
   (e) $S_n^* = \dfrac{S_n - n\mu}{\sqrt{n\sigma^2}}$.

9. Let $X_1, X_2, \ldots, X_n$ be an independent trials process with normal density of mean 1 and variance 2. Find the moment generating function for

(a) X_1.

(b) $S_2 = X_1 + X_2$.

(c) $S_n = X_1 + X_2 + \cdots + X_n$.

(d) $A_n = \dfrac{S_n}{n}$.

(e) $S_n^* = \dfrac{S_n - n\mu}{\sqrt{n\sigma^2}}$.

What can you say about the moment generating function for S_n^* as $n \to \infty$?

10. Let $X_1, X_2, \ldots, X_n$ be an independent trials process with density

$$f(x) = \frac{1}{2}e^{-|x|}, \qquad -\infty < x < +\infty.$$

(a) Find the mean and variance of $f(x)$.

(b) Find the moment generating function for X_1, S_n, A_n, and S_n^*.

(c) What can you say about the moment generating function of S_n^* as $n \to \infty$?

(d) What can you say about the moment generating function of A_n as $n \to \infty$?

Chapter *11*

Markov Chains

11.1 INTRODUCTION

Most of our study of probability has dealt with independent trials processes. These processes are the basis of classical probability theory and much of statistics. We have discussed two of the principal theorems for these processes: the law of large numbers and the central limit theorem.

We have seen that when a sequence of chance experiments forms an independent trials process, the possible outcomes for each experiment are the same and occur with the same probability. Further, knowledge of the outcomes of previous experiments does not influence our predictions for the outcomes of the next experiment. The density for the outcomes of a single experiment is sufficient to construct a tree and a tree measure for a sequence of *n* experiments, and we can answer any probability question about these *n* experiments by using this tree measure.

Modern probability theory studies chance processes for which the knowledge of previous outcomes influences predictions for future experiments. In principle, when we observe a sequence of chance experiments, all of the past outcomes could influence our predictions for the next experiment. For example, this should be the case in predicting a student's grades on a sequence of exams in a course. But to allow this much generality would make it very difficult to prove general results.

Markov Chains

In an independent trials process, the knowledge of each outcome is irrelevant in predicting future outcomes. In 1907, A. A. Markov began the study of chance processes for which the knowledge of each outcome is relevant only in predicting the next outcome. The processes he studied have come to be called *Markov chains* and have found a large number of applications.

States

We can describe a Markov chain as follows: We have a set of *states*, $S = \{s_1, s_2, \ldots, s_r\}$. The process starts in one of these states at time 0 and moves successively from one state to another at unit time intervals. Each move is called a *step*. The probability p_{ij} that the process moves from state s_i to state s_j depends only on the state s_i occupied before the step.

Transition Probabilities

The probabilities p_{ij} are called *transition probabilities*. The process can remain in the state it is in; and this occurs with probability p_{ii}. An initial probability density, defined on S, specifies the starting state. Usually this is done by specifying a particular state as the starting state.

 R. A. Howard[1] provides us with a picturesque description of a Markov chain as a frog jumping around on a set of lily pads. The frog starts on one of the pads and then jumps around from lily pad to lily pad with the appropriate transition probabilities.

 To calculate probabilities relating to a Markov chain, we construct a tree and a tree measure which corresponds to the above description.

EXAMPLE 1

According to Kemeny, Snell, and Thompson,[2] the Land of Oz is blessed by many things, but not by good weather. They never have two nice days in a row. If they have a nice day, they are just as likely to have snow as rain the next day. If they have snow or rain, they have an even chance of having the same the next day. If there is change from snow or rain, only half of the time is this a change to a nice day. Let us suppose that it is a nice day today in the Land of Oz. With this information we form a Markov chain as follows. We take as states the kinds of weather R, N, and S. From the above information

---

[1]R.A. Howard, *Dynamic Probabilistic Systems*, vol. 1 (New York: John Wiley and Sons, 1971).

[2]J.G. Kemeny, J.L. Snell, G.L. Thompson, *Introduction to Finite Mathematics*, 3rd ed. (Englewood Cliffs, NJ: Prentice-Hall, 1974).

we determine the transition probabilities. These are most conveniently represented in a square array as

$$\mathbf{P} = \begin{array}{c} \\ R \\ N \\ S \end{array} \begin{array}{ccc} R & N & S \\ \begin{pmatrix} 1/2 & 1/4 & 1/4 \\ 1/2 & 0 & 1/2 \\ 1/4 & 1/4 & 1/2 \end{pmatrix}. \end{array}$$

Transition Matrix

The entries in the first row represent the probabilities for the various kinds of weather following a rainy day, those in the second row the weather following a nice day, and in the third row following a snowy day. Such a square array is called the *matrix of transition probabilities*. From this, we determine a tree and a tree measure for the next three days' weather as indicated in Figure 1.

The sample space Ω consists of the paths of the tree. The tree measure $p(\omega)$ is assigned in the usual manner. The random variables X_0, X_1, X_2, X_3 give the weather today and for the next three days.

From the tree measure, we can find the densities of these four random variables:

$$p_{X_0} = \begin{pmatrix} R & N & S \\ 0 & 1 & 0 \end{pmatrix},$$

$$p_{X_1} = \begin{pmatrix} R & N & S \\ 1/2 & 0 & 1/2 \end{pmatrix},$$

$$p_{X_2} = \begin{pmatrix} R & N & S \\ 3/8 & 2/8 & 3/8 \end{pmatrix},$$

$$p_{X_3} = \begin{pmatrix} R & N & S \\ 13/32 & 6/32 & 13/32 \end{pmatrix}.$$

For example, the value of the density of X_2 for R was obtained from the tree measure adding the weights for all paths that have R at the second stage:

$$\frac{1}{8} + \frac{1}{16} + \frac{1}{16} + \frac{1}{16} + \frac{1}{32} + \frac{1}{32} = \frac{12}{32} = \frac{3}{8}. \qquad \square$$

Since the range of these random variables is always the same, it is more convenient to write the densities without their ranges as row vectors:

$$\mathbf{w}^{(n)} = (w_1^{(n)}, w_2^{(n)}, \ldots, w_r^{(n)}),$$

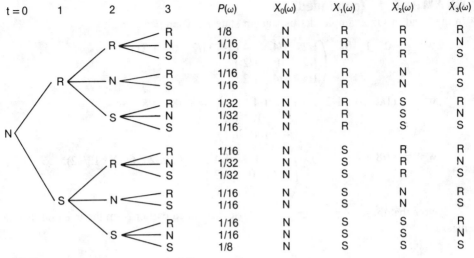

Figure 1   Weather in the Land of Oz.

where the jth component refers to state s_j. The first four densities are:

$$\mathbf{w}^{(0)} = (0 \quad 1 \quad 0),$$

$$\mathbf{w}^{(1)} = (1/2 \quad 0 \quad 1/2),$$

$$\mathbf{w}^{(2)} = (3/8 \quad 2/8 \quad 3/8),$$

$$\mathbf{w}^{(3)} = (13/32 \quad 6/32 \quad 13/32).$$

In studying independent processes, we found it necessary to develop methods for computing properties of the process without resorting to the tree and the tree measures. The same is true for the case of Markov chains. In particular, we shall now show how to obtain the vectors $\mathbf{w}^{(n)}$ directly from the transition matrix. The key to our method is the following simple observation

$$\mathbf{w}_j^{(n+1)} = \mathbf{P}(X_{n+1} = s_j)$$

$$= \sum_k \mathbf{P}(X_n = s_k \text{ and } X_{n+1} = s_j)$$

$$= \sum_k \mathbf{P}(X_n = s_k)\mathbf{P}(X_{n+1} = s_j | X_n = s_k).$$

But we have assumed that any time the chain is in state s_k it moves to state s_j with probability p_{kj}. Therefore

$$\mathbf{w}_j^{(n+1)} = \sum_k \mathbf{w}_k^{(n)} p_{kj}.$$

In matrix language this is

$$\mathbf{w}^{(n+1)} = \mathbf{w}^{(n)}\mathbf{P},$$

where $\mathbf{P}$ is the matrix (p_{kj}).

EXAMPLE 1 (continued)

In the Land of Oz example, let us start in state N. Then

$$\mathbf{w}^{(1)} = (0 \quad 1 \quad 0) \begin{pmatrix} 1/2 & 1/4 & 1/4 \\ 1/2 & 0 & 1/2 \\ 1/4 & 1/4 & 1/2 \end{pmatrix} = (1/2 \quad 0 \quad 1/2),$$

$$\mathbf{w}^{(2)} = (1/2 \quad 0 \quad 1/2) \begin{pmatrix} 1/2 & 1/4 & 1/4 \\ 1/2 & 0 & 1/2 \\ 1/4 & 1/4 & 1/2 \end{pmatrix} = (3/8 \quad 2/8 \quad 3/8),$$

$$\mathbf{w}^{(3)} = (3/8 \quad 2/8 \quad 3/8) \begin{pmatrix} 1/2 & 1/4 & 1/4 \\ 1/2 & 0 & 1/2 \\ 1/4 & 1/4 & 1/2 \end{pmatrix} = (13/32 \quad 6/32 \quad 13/32).$$

Note that these vectors agree with those calculated earlier from the tree and its tree measure. □

DEFINITION 1

A *probability vector* $\mathbf{p} = \{p_j\}$ is a row vector with nonnegative entries and components that sum to 1.

DEFINITION 2

A *transition matrix* $\mathbf{P} = \{p_{ij}\}$ is a square matrix with nonnegative entries and row sums equal to 1.

DEFINITION 3

Given an r component probability vector $\mathbf{w}^{(0)}$ and an $r \times r$ transition matrix $\mathbf{P}$, the n step *Markov chain* with starting vector $\mathbf{w}^{(0)}$ and transition matrix $\mathbf{P}$ is the tree measure with levels 0 to n, with branch weights at level zero determined by $\mathbf{w}^{(0)}$ and at other levels by p_{ij}.

The important connection between matrix theory and Markov chains is given by the following theorem.

THEOREM 1

Let $\mathbf{P}$ be the transition matrix of a Markov chain. The ijth entry $p_{ij}^{(n)}$ of the nth power $\mathbf{P}^n$ of $\mathbf{P}$ gives the probability that the Markov chain, started in state s_i, will be in state s_j after n steps.

Proof.   To start in state s_i, we choose $\mathbf{w}^{(0)}$ to be the probability vector with 1 in the ith component and 0 in all other components. Then

$$\mathbf{w}^{(1)} = \mathbf{w}^{(0)}\mathbf{P},$$

$$\mathbf{w}^{(2)} = \mathbf{w}^{(1)}\mathbf{P} = \mathbf{w}^{(0)}\mathbf{P}\mathbf{P} = \mathbf{w}^{(0)}\mathbf{P}^2,$$

$$\mathbf{w}^{(3)} = \mathbf{w}^{(2)}\mathbf{P} = \mathbf{w}^{(0)}\mathbf{P}^3,$$

.

.

.

$$\mathbf{w}^{(n)} = \mathbf{w}^{(0)}\mathbf{P}^n.$$

Now $w_j^{(n)}$ is the probability, starting in state s_i, of being in state s_j after n steps. Since $\mathbf{w}^{(0)}\mathbf{P}^n$ is the ith row of $\mathbf{P}^n$, $w_j^{(n)} = \mathbf{p}_{ij}^{(n)}$. ∎

EXAMPLE 1   (continued)

Let us consider again the Land of Oz example. We know that the powers of the transition matrix give us interesting information about the process as it evolves. We shall be particularly interested in the state of the chain after a large number of steps. The program **Matrix Powers** computes the powers of **P**.

```
! Matrix Powers    (MATPOWER)
!
! Computes the powers of a (transition) matrix.

library "Lib.Markov*"

dim P(10,10), Q(10,10)
dim label$(10)

read states                       ! Number of states
data 3
mat read label$(states)           ! Read labels
data Rain, Nice, Snow
mat read P(states,states)         ! Transition matrix
data .5,.25,.25
data .5,.0,.5
data .25,.25,.5

input prompt "Raise P to powers up to n = ": n
print

mat Q = P

for power = 1 to n
    print "P^" & str$(power) & ":"
    call matrix_labels(Q, label$, label$, "###.###")
    print
    mat Q = P * Q
next power

end
```

We have run the program **Matrix Powers** for the Land of Oz example to compute the successive powers of **P** from 1 to 6.

```
Raise P to powers up to n = 6

P^1:
        Rain    Nice    Snow
Rain    .500    .250    .250
Nice    .500    .000    .500
Snow    .250    .250    .500

P^2:
        Rain    Nice    Snow
Rain    .438    .188    .375
Nice    .375    .250    .375
Snow    .375    .188    .438

P^3:
        Rain    Nice    Snow
Rain    .406    .203    .391
Nice    .406    .188    .406
Snow    .391    .203    .406

P^4:
        Rain    Nice    Snow
Rain    .402    .199    .398
Nice    .398    .203    .398
Snow    .398    .199    .402

P^5:
        Rain    Nice    Snow
Rain    .400    .200    .399
Nice    .400    .199    .400
Snow    .399    .200    .400

P^6:
        Rain    Nice    Snow
Rain    .400    .200    .400
Nice    .400    .200    .400
Snow    .400    .200    .400
```

$\square$

We note that after six days our weather predictions are, to three decimal place accuracy, independent of today's weather. The probabilities for the three types of weather, R, N, and S, are .4, .2, and .4 for each of the possible starting states. This is an example of a type of Markov chain called a *regular* Markov chain. For this type of chain, it is true that long-range predictions are independent of the starting state. Not all chains are regular, but this is an important class of chains that we shall study in detail later.

The following examples of Markov chains will be used throughout the chapter for exercises.

Examples

EXAMPLE 2
The president of the United States tells person A his intention either to run or not to run in the next election. Then A relays the news to B, who in turn relays the message to C, and so forth, always to some new person. We assume that there is a probability a that a person will change the answer from yes to no when transmitting it to the next person and a probability b that he will change it from no to yes. We choose as states the message, either yes or no. The transition matrix is then

$$\mathbf{P} = \begin{matrix} \text{yes} \\ \text{no} \end{matrix} \begin{pmatrix} \overset{\text{yes}}{1-a} & \overset{\text{no}}{a} \\ b & 1-b \end{pmatrix}.$$

The initial state represents the president's choice. ☐

EXAMPLE 3
Each time a certain horse runs in a three-horse race, he has probability $^2/_5$ of winning, $^1/_5$ of placing, and $^2/_5$ of showing, independent of the outcome of any previous race. We have an independent trials process, but it can also be considered from the point of view of Markov chain theory. The transition matrix is

$$\mathbf{P} = \begin{matrix} \text{W} \\ \text{P} \\ \text{S} \end{matrix} \begin{pmatrix} \overset{\text{W}}{.4} & \overset{\text{P}}{.2} & \overset{\text{S}}{.4} \\ .4 & .2 & .4 \\ .4 & .2 & .4 \end{pmatrix}.$$

☐

EXAMPLE 4
In the dark ages, Harvard, Dartmouth, and Yale admitted only male students. Assume that, at that time, 80 percent of the sons of Harvard men went to Harvard and the rest went to Yale, 40 percent of the sons of Yale men went to Yale, and the rest split evenly between Harvard and Dartmouth; and of the sons of Dartmouth men, 70 percent went to Dartmouth, 20 percent to Harvard, and 10 percent to Yale. We form a Markov chain with transition matrix,

$$\mathbf{P} = \begin{matrix} \text{H} \\ \text{Y} \\ \text{D} \end{matrix} \begin{pmatrix} \overset{\text{H}}{.8} & \overset{\text{Y}}{.2} & \overset{\text{D}}{0} \\ .3 & .4 & .3 \\ .2 & .1 & .7 \end{pmatrix}.$$

☐

EXAMPLE 5

Modify Example 4 by assuming that the son of a Harvard man always went to Harvard. The transition matrix is now

$$
\mathbf{P} = \begin{array}{c} \\ \text{H} \\ \text{Y} \\ \text{D} \end{array} \begin{array}{ccc} \text{H} & \text{Y} & \text{D} \\ \left(\begin{array}{ccc} 1 & 0 & 0 \\ .3 & .4 & .3 \\ .2 & .1 & .7 \end{array} \right). \end{array}
$$

□

Ehrenfest Model

EXAMPLE 6

The following is a special case of a model, called the Ehrenfest model, that has been used to explain diffusion of gases. The general model will be discussed in detail in section 11.5. We have two urns that between them contain four balls. Each second, one of the four balls is chosen at random and moved from the urn that it is in into the other urn. We choose, as state, the number of balls in the first urn. The transition matrix is then

$$
\mathbf{P} = \begin{array}{c} \\ 0 \\ 1 \\ 2 \\ 3 \\ 4 \end{array} \begin{array}{ccccc} 0 & 1 & 2 & 3 & 4 \\ \left(\begin{array}{ccccc} 0 & 1 & 0 & 0 & 0 \\ 1/4 & 0 & 3/4 & 0 & 0 \\ 0 & 1/2 & 0 & 1/2 & 0 \\ 0 & 0 & 3/4 & 0 & 1/4 \\ 0 & 0 & 0 & 1 & 0 \end{array} \right). \end{array}
$$

□

Gene Model

EXAMPLE 7

The simplest type of inheritance of traits in animals occurs when a trait is governed by a pair of genes, each of which may be of two types, say G and g. An individual may have a GG combination or Gg (which is genetically the same as gG) or gg. Very often the GG and Gg types are indistinguishable in appearance, and then we say that the G gene dominates the g gene. An individual is called *dominant* if he or she has GG genes, *recessive* if he or she has gg, and *hybrid* with a Gg mixture.

In the mating of two animals, the offspring inherits one gene of the pair from each parent, and the basic assumption of genetics is that these genes are selected at random, independently of each other. This assumption determines the probability of occurrence of each type of offspring. The offspring of two purely dominant parents must be dominant, of two recessive parents must be recessive, and of one dominant and one recessive parent must be hybrid.

In the mating of a dominant and a hybrid animal, each offspring must get a G gene from the former and has an equal chance of getting G or g from the latter; hence there is an equal probability for getting a dominant or a hybrid offspring. Again, in the mating of a recessive and a hybrid, there is an even chance for getting either a recessive or a hybrid. In the mating of two hybrids, the offspring has an equal chance of getting G or g from each parent. Hence the probabilities are $1/4$ for GG, $1/2$ for Gg, and $1/4$ for gg.

Let us consider a process of continued matings. We start with an individual of known genetic character and mate it with a hybrid. We assume that there is one offspring. This offspring is then mated with a hybrid and this process repeated through a number of generations. The genetic type of the offspring in successive generations can be represented by a Markov chain. The states are dominant, hybrid, and recessive, and indicated by GG, Gg, and gg respectively.

The transition probabilities are

$$\mathbf{P} = \begin{array}{c} \\ GG \\ Gg \\ gg \end{array} \begin{array}{ccc} GG & Gg & gg \\ \left(\begin{array}{ccc} .5 & .5 & 0 \\ .25 & .5 & .25 \\ 0 & .5 & .5 \end{array}\right). \end{array}$$

$\square$

EXAMPLE 8

Modify Example 7 by continuing to mate the offspring with a dominant animal. The transition matrix is

$$\mathbf{P} = \begin{array}{c} \\ GG \\ Gg \\ gg \end{array} \begin{array}{ccc} GG & Gg & gg \\ \left(\begin{array}{ccc} 1 & 0 & 0 \\ .5 & .5 & 0 \\ 0 & 1 & 0 \end{array}\right). \end{array}$$

$\square$

EXAMPLE 9

We start with two animals of opposite sex, mate them, select two of their offspring of opposite sex, and mate those, and so forth. To simplify the example, we will assume that the trait under consideration is independent of sex.

Here a state is determined by a pair of animals. Hence, the states of our process will be: $s_1 = (GG,GG)$, $s_2 = (GG,Gg)$, $s_3 = (GG,gg)$, $s_4 = (Gg,Gg)$, $s_5 = (Gg,gg)$, and $s_6 = (gg,gg)$.

We illustrate the calculation of transition probabilities in terms of the state s_2. When the process is in this state, one parent has GG genes, the other Gg. Hence, the probability of a dominant offspring is $1/2$. Then the probability of transition to s_1 (selection of two dominants) is $1/4$, transition to s_2 is $1/2$, and to s_4 is $1/4$. The other states are treated the same way. The transition matrix of this chain and the powers $\mathbf{P}^2$ to $\mathbf{P}^6$ are then given by the following run of the program **Matrix Powers** for this example.

$\square$

Raise P to powers up to n = 1

P^1:

	GG,GG	GG,Gg	GG,gg	Gg,Gg	Gg,gg	gg,gg
GG,GG	1.0000	.0000	.0000	.0000	.0000	.0000
GG,Gg	.2500	.5000	.0000	.2500	.0000	.0000
GG,gg	.0000	.0000	.0000	1.0000	.0000	.0000
Gg,Gg	.0625	.2500	.1250	.2500	.2500	.0625
Gg,gg	.0000	.0000	.0000	.2500	.5000	.2500
gg,gg	.0000	.0000	.0000	.0000	.0000	1.0000

P^2:

	GG,GG	GG,Gg	GG,gg	Gg,Gg	Gg,gg	gg,gg
GG,GG	1.0000	.0000	.0000	.0000	.0000	.0000
GG,Gg	.3906	.3125	.0313	.1875	.0625	.0156
GG,gg	.0625	.2500	.1250	.2500	.2500	.0625
Gg,Gg	.1406	.1875	.0313	.3125	.1875	.1406
Gg,gg	.0156	.0625	.0313	.1875	.3125	.3906
gg,gg	.0000	.0000	.0000	.0000	.0000	1.0000

P^3:

	GG,GG	GG,Gg	GG,gg	Gg,Gg	Gg,gg	gg,gg
GG,GG	1.0000	.0000	.0000	.0000	.0000	.0000
GG,Gg	.4805	.2031	.0234	.1719	.0781	.0430
GG,gg	.1406	.1875	.0313	.3125	.1875	.1406
Gg,Gg	.2070	.1719	.0391	.2031	.1719	.2070
Gg,gg	.0430	.0781	.0234	.1719	.2031	.4805
gg,gg	.0000	.0000	.0000	.0000	.0000	1.0000

P^4:

	GG,GG	GG,Gg	GG,gg	Gg,Gg	Gg,gg	gg,gg
GG,GG	1.0000	.0000	.0000	.0000	.0000	.0000
GG,Gg	.5420	.1445	.0215	.1367	.0820	.0732
GG,gg	.2070	.1719	.0391	.2031	.1719	.2070
Gg,Gg	.2627	.1367	.0254	.1758	.1367	.2627
Gg,gg	.0732	.0820	.0215	.1367	.1445	.5420
gg,gg	.0000	.0000	.0000	.0000	.0000	1.0000

P^5:

	GG,GG	GG,Gg	GG,gg	Gg,Gg	Gg,gg	gg,gg
GG,GG	1.0000	.0000	.0000	.0000	.0000	.0000
GG,Gg	.5867	.1064	.0171	.1123	.0752	.1023
GG,gg	.2627	.1367	.0254	.1758	.1367	.2627
Gg,Gg	.3079	.1123	.0220	.1377	.1123	.3079
Gg,gg	.1023	.0752	.0171	.1123	.1064	.5867
gg,gg	.0000	.0000	.0000	.0000	.0000	1.0000

P^6:

	GG,GG	GG,Gg	GG,gg	Gg,Gg	Gg,gg	gg,gg
GG,GG	1.0000	.0000	.0000	.0000	.0000	.0000
GG,Gg	.6203	.0813	.0140	.0906	.0657	.1281
GG,gg	.3079	.1123	.0220	.1377	.1123	.3079
Gg,Gg	.3445	.0906	.0172	.1125	.0906	.3445
Gg,gg	.1281	.0657	.0140	.0906	.0813	.6203
gg,gg	.0000	.0000	.0000	.0000	.0000	1.0000

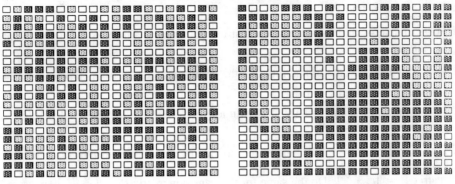

| Initial Configuration | Configuration after 10,000 seconds |

Figure 2 Simulation of the stepping stone model.

Stepping Stone Model

EXAMPLE 10

Our final example is another example that has been used in the study of genetics. It is called the *stepping stone* model.[3] In this model we have an n-by-n array of squares, and each square is initially any one of k different colors. Each second, a square is chosen at random. This square then chooses one of its eight neighbors at random and assumes the color of that neighbor. (To avoid boundary problems we imagine the squares placed on a doughnut). A state in this Markov chain is a description of the color of each square. For this Markov chain the number of states is k^{n^2}, which for even a small array of squares is enormous. This is an example of a Markov chain that is easy to simulate but difficult to analyze in terms of its transition matrix. The program **Stepping Stone** simulates this chain. We have started with a random initial configuration of three colors with $n = 20$ and show the result after the process has run for some time in Figure 2.

By watching the program run you can see that territories are established and a battle develops to see which color survives. At any time the probability that a particular color will win out is equal to the proportion of the squares of this color. You are asked to prove this in Exercise 31 of Section 11.2 of this chapter. □

Exercises

1. It is raining in the Land of Oz. Determine a tree and tree measure for the next three days' weather. Find $\mathbf{w}^{(1)}$, $\mathbf{w}^{(2)}$, and $\mathbf{w}^{(3)}$ and compare with the results obtained from $\mathbf{P}$, $\mathbf{P}^2$, and $\mathbf{P}^3$.

2. In Example 2, let $a = 0$ and $b = \frac{1}{2}$. Find $\mathbf{P}$, $\mathbf{P}^2$ and $\mathbf{P}^3$. What would $\mathbf{P}^n$ be? What happens to $\mathbf{P}^n$ as n tends to infinity? Interpret this result.

[3]See S. Sawyer, "Results for The Stepping Stone Model for Migration in Population Genetics," *Annals of Probability*, vol. 4 (1979), pp. 699–728.

3. In Example 3, find $\mathbf{P}^2$, and $\mathbf{P}^3$. What is $\mathbf{P}^n$?

4. For Example 4, find the probability that the grandson of a man from Harvard went to Harvard.

5. In Example 5, find the probability that the grandson of a man from Harvard went to Harvard.

6. In Example 7, assume that we start with a hybrid bred to a hybrid. Find $\mathbf{w}^{(1)}$, $\mathbf{w}^{(2)}$, $\mathbf{w}^{(3)}$. What would $\mathbf{w}^{(n)}$ be?

7. Find the matrices $\mathbf{P}^2$, $\mathbf{P}^3$, $\mathbf{P}^4$, and $\mathbf{P}^n$ for the Markov chain determined by the transition matrix $\mathbf{P} = \begin{pmatrix} 1 & 0 \\ 0 & 1 \end{pmatrix}$. Do the same for the transition matrix $\mathbf{P} = \begin{pmatrix} 0 & 1 \\ 1 & 0 \end{pmatrix}$. Interpret what happens in each of these processes.

8. A certain calculating machine uses only the digits 0 and 1. It is supposed to transmit one of these digits through several stages. However, at every stage, there is a probability p that the digit that enters this stage will be changed when it leaves and a probability $q = 1 - p$ that it won't. Form a Markov chain to represent the process of transmission by taking as states the digits 0 and 1. What is the matrix of transition probabilities?

9. For the Markov chain in Exercise 8, draw a tree and assign a tree measure assuming that the process begins in state 0 and moves through two stages of transmission. What is the probability that the machine, after two stages, produces the digit 0 (i.e., the correct digit)? What is the probability that the machine never changed the digit from 0?

10. Modify the program **Matrix Powers** so that it prints out the average $\mathbf{A}_n$ of the powers of $\mathbf{P}$ from 1 to N. Try your program on the Land of Oz example and compare $\mathbf{A}_n$ and $\mathbf{P}^n$.

11. Assume that a man's profession can be classified as professional, skilled laborer, or unskilled laborer. Assume that, of the sons of professional men, 80 percent are professional, 10 percent are skilled laborers, and 10 percent are unskilled laborers. In the case of sons of skilled laborers, 60 percent are skilled laborers, 20 percent are professional, and 20 percent are unskilled. Finally, in the case of unskilled laborers, 50 percent of the sons are unskilled laborers, and 25 percent each are in the other two categories. Assume that every man has a son, and form a Markov chain by following the profession of the youngest son of a given family through several generations. Set up the matrix of transition probabilities. Find the probability that the grandson of an unskilled laborer is a professional man.

12. In Exercise 11, we assumed that every man has a son. Assume instead that the probability a man has at least one son is .8. Form a Markov chain with four states. If a man has a son, the probability that this son is in a particular profession is the same as in Exercise 11. If there is no son, the process moves to state four which represents families whose male line has died out. Find the matrix of transition prob-

abilities and find the probability that an unskilled laborer has a grandson who is a professional man.

13. Explain why the transition probabilities given in Example 6 are correct.

14. Write a program to compute $\mathbf{w}^{(n)}$ given $\mathbf{w}^{(0)}$ and $\mathbf{P}$. Use this program to compute $\mathbf{w}^{(10)}$ for the Land of Oz example, with $\mathbf{w}^{(0)} = (0, 1, 0)$, and with $\mathbf{w}^{(0)} = (\frac{1}{3}\ \frac{1}{3}\ \frac{1}{3})$.

15. Using the program **Matrix Powers**, find $\mathbf{P}^1$ through $\mathbf{P}^6$ for Examples 7 and 8. See if you can predict the long-range probability of finding the process in each of the states for these examples.

16. Write a program to simulate the outcomes of a Markov chain after n steps, given the initial starting state and the transition matrix $\mathbf{P}$ as data (see Example 10). Keep this program for use in later problems.

17. Modify the program of Exercise 16 so that it keeps track of the proportion of times in each state in n steps. Run the modified program for different starting states for Example 1 and Example 6. Does the initial state affect the proportion of time spent in each of the states if n is large?

11.2 ABSORBING MARKOV CHAINS

The subject of Markov chains is best studied by considering special types of Markov chains. The first type that we shall study is called an *absorbing Markov chain*.

Absorbing States

DEFINITION 4

A state s_i of a Markov chain is called *absorbing* if it is impossible to leave it (i.e., $p_{ii} = 1$). A Markov chain is *absorbing* if it has at least one absorbing state, and if from every state it is possible to go to an absorbing state (not necessarily in one step).

Transient States

DEFINITION 5

In an absorbing Markov chain, a state which is not absorbing is called *transient*.

Drunkard's Walk

EXAMPLE 1   Drunkard's Walk

A man walks along a four-block stretch of Park Avenue. He starts at corner x and, with probability $\frac{1}{2}$, walks one block to the right and, with probability $\frac{1}{2}$, walks one block

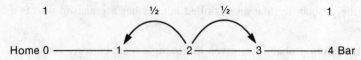

Figure 3 Drunkard's walk.

to the left; when he comes to the next corner he again randomly chooses his direction. He continues until he reaches corner 4, which is a bar, or corner 0, which is a home (see Figure 3). If he reaches either home or the bar, he stays there.

We form a Markov chain with states 0, 1, 2, 3, and 4. States 0 and 4 are absorbing states. The transition matrix is then

$$
\mathbf{P} = \begin{array}{c} 0 \\ 1 \\ 2 \\ 3 \\ 4 \end{array} \begin{pmatrix} \begin{array}{ccccc} 0 & 1 & 2 & 3 & 4 \\ 1 & 0 & 0 & 0 & 0 \\ 1/2 & 0 & 1/2 & 0 & 0 \\ 0 & 1/2 & 0 & 1/2 & 0 \\ 0 & 0 & 1/2 & 0 & 1/2 \\ 0 & 0 & 0 & 0 & 1 \end{array} \end{pmatrix}.
$$

The states 1, 2, and 3 are transient states, and from any of these it is possible to reach the absorbing states 0 and 4. Hence the chain is an absorbing chain. When a process reaches an absorbing state, we shall say that it is absorbed. ☐

For an absorbing Markov chain, we consider three interesting questions: (a) What is the probability that the process will end up in a given absorbing state? (b) On the average, how long will it take for the process to be absorbed? (c) On the average, how many times will the process be in each transient state? The answers to all these questions depend, in general, on the state from which the process starts as well as the transition probabilities.

Canonical Form

Consider an arbitrary absorbing Markov chain; renumber the states so that the transient states come first. If there are r absorbing states and s transient states, the transition matrix will have the following canonical (or standard) form

$$
\mathbf{P} = \begin{array}{c} \\ \text{TR.} \\ \text{ABS.} \end{array} \begin{array}{c} \text{TR.} \quad\;\; \text{ABS.} \\ \left(\begin{array}{c|c} \mathbf{Q} & \mathbf{R} \\ \hline \mathbf{0} & \mathbf{I} \end{array} \right). \end{array}
$$

Here $\mathbf{I}$ is an r-by-r identity matrix, $\mathbf{0}$ is an r-by-s zero matrix, $\mathbf{R}$ is a nonzero s-by-r matrix, and $\mathbf{Q}$ is an s-by-s matrix. The first s states are transient and the last r states are absorbing.

In Section 11.1, we saw that the entry $p_{ij}^{(n)}$ of the matrix $\mathbf{P}^n$ is the probability of being in the state s_j, after n steps, when the chain is started in state s_i. $\mathbf{P}^n$ is of the form

$$\mathbf{P}^n = \left(\begin{array}{c|c} \mathbf{Q}^n & * \\ \hline \mathbf{0} & \mathbf{I} \end{array}\right),$$

where the asterisk $*$ stands for the s-by-r matrix in the upper right-hand corner of $\mathbf{P}^n$. The form of $\mathbf{P}^n$ shows that the entries of $\mathbf{Q}^n$ give the probabilities for being in each of the transient states after n steps for each possible transient starting state. (After zero steps, the process must be in the same state in which it started. Hence $\mathbf{Q}^0 = \mathbf{I}$.) For our first theorem we prove that the probability of being in the transient states after n steps approaches zero. Thus every entry of $\mathbf{Q}^n$ must approach zero as n approaches infinity (i.e., $\mathbf{Q}^n \to \mathbf{0}$).

In the following, if $\mathbf{u}$ and $\mathbf{v}$ are two vectors we say that $\mathbf{u} \leq \mathbf{v}$ if all components of $\mathbf{u}$ are less than or equal to the corresponding components of $\mathbf{v}$. Similarly, if $\mathbf{A}$ and $\mathbf{B}$ are matrices then $\mathbf{A} \leq \mathbf{B}$ if each entry of $\mathbf{A}$ is less than or equal to the corresponding entry of $\mathbf{B}$.

Probability of Absorption

THEOREM 2

In an absorbing Markov chain, the probability that the process will be absorbed is 1 (i.e., $\mathbf{Q}^n \to \mathbf{0}$ as $n \to \infty$).

Proof. Assume first that from any transient state it is possible to move to an absorbing state in one step. Then the row sums of $\mathbf{Q}$ are all less than one. Let t be the largest of these row sums. Then if $\mathbf{c}$ is a column vector of all entries 1,

$$\mathbf{Q}\mathbf{c} \leq t\mathbf{c},$$

$$\mathbf{Q}^n\mathbf{c} = \mathbf{Q}^{n-1}\mathbf{Q}\mathbf{c} \leq t\mathbf{Q}^{n-1}\mathbf{c},$$

and so

$$\mathbf{Q}^n\mathbf{c} \leq t^n\mathbf{c}.$$

Since $t < 1$, $\mathbf{Q}^n\mathbf{c} \to \mathbf{0}$; and $\mathbf{Q} \geq \mathbf{0}$ assures that $\mathbf{Q}^n \to \mathbf{0}$.

Consider now the general case. Since $\mathbf{Q}\mathbf{c} \leq \mathbf{c}$ and $\mathbf{Q} \geq \mathbf{0}$, $\mathbf{Q}^2\mathbf{c} \leq \mathbf{Q}\mathbf{c}$, and

$$\mathbf{Q}^n\mathbf{c} = \mathbf{Q}^{n-1}\mathbf{Q}\mathbf{c} \leq \mathbf{Q}^{n-1}\mathbf{c},$$

and so $\mathbf{Q}^n\mathbf{c}$ is a monotone decreasing sequence of vectors. The fact that $\mathbf{P}$ is absorbing means that, from any transient state, it is possible to reach an absorbing state. Thus, for every such state s_i, there is an n_i such that the row sum of the ith row of $\mathbf{Q}^{n_i}$ is less than one. Let N be the largest of these n_i. Then all row sums of $\mathbf{Q}^N$ are less than 1, and by the first part of the proof $(\mathbf{Q}^N)^m\mathbf{c} \to \mathbf{0}$ as $m \to \infty$. But since $\mathbf{Q}^n\mathbf{c}$ is a monotone decreasing sequence of vectors, $\mathbf{Q}^n\mathbf{c} \to \mathbf{0}$ as $n \to \infty$. ∎

Since we now know that an absorbing Markov chain, started in a transient state, will end up in an absorbing state, we can turn to the questions of how long this will take and in which absorbing state it will end up.

Consider the set of paths for the first n steps of an absorbing chain that starts in state s_i. Let $X_j^{(k)}$ be a random variable which is 1 if the chain is in state s_j after k steps and 0 otherwise. Then

$$P(X_j^{(k)} = 1) = q_{ij}^{(k)},$$

and

$$P(X_j^{(k)} = 0) = 1 - q_{ij}^{(k)},$$

where $q_{ij}^{(k)}$ is the ijth entry of $\mathbf{Q}^k$. This equation holds for $k = 0$ if we define $\mathbf{Q}^0 = \mathbf{I}$. Then $E(X_j^{(k)}) = q_{ij}^{(k)}$. Let T_n be a random variable whose value is the total number of times in the first n steps that the chain is in state s_j. Then

$$T_n = X_j^{(0)} + X_j^{(1)} + \cdots + X_j^{(n)},$$

and

$$E(T_n) = E(X_j^{(0)}) + E(X_j^{(1)}) + \cdots + E(X_j^{(n)}).$$
$$= q_{ij}^{(0)} + q_{ij}^{(1)} + \cdots + q_{ij}^{(n)}.$$

This is the ijth entry of the sum

$$\mathbf{Q}^0 + \mathbf{Q}^1 + \cdots + \mathbf{Q}^n.$$

Let us define n_{ij} to be the limit of $E(T_n)$ as n tends to infinity. The quantity n_{ij} may be interpreted as "the expected number of times the chain is in s_j if it starts in s_i and proceeds until it is absorbed." We see from above that n_{ij} is the ijth entry of the matrix

$$\mathbf{N} = \mathbf{I} + \mathbf{Q} + \mathbf{Q}^2 + \cdots.$$

We prove now that this sum is finite and is given by the *inverse* of the matrix $\mathbf{I} - \mathbf{Q}$.

THEOREM 3

For an absorbing Markov chain, the matrix $\mathbf{I} - \mathbf{Q}$ has an inverse $\mathbf{N}$, and

$$\mathbf{N} = (\mathbf{I} - \mathbf{Q})^{-1} = \mathbf{I} + \mathbf{Q} + \mathbf{Q}^2 + \mathbf{Q}^3 + \cdots.$$

Proof. To show $\mathbf{N} = (\mathbf{I} - \mathbf{Q})^{-1}$ exists, it is enough to show that if $(\mathbf{I} - \mathbf{Q})\mathbf{x} = \mathbf{0}$, then $\mathbf{x} = \mathbf{0}$. But if

$$(\mathbf{I} - \mathbf{Q})\mathbf{x} = \mathbf{0},$$

then

$$\mathbf{Q}\mathbf{x} = \mathbf{x},$$

$$\mathbf{Q}^2\mathbf{x} = \mathbf{x},$$

$$\cdots$$

$$\mathbf{Q}^n\mathbf{x} = \mathbf{x},$$

and

$$\lim_{n \to \infty} \mathbf{Q}^n\mathbf{x} = \mathbf{x}.$$

But

$$\lim_{n \to \infty} \mathbf{Q}^n\mathbf{x} = \mathbf{0},$$

and so $\mathbf{x} = \mathbf{0}$. This proves that the inverse $\mathbf{N} = (\mathbf{I} - \mathbf{Q})^{-1}$ exits.
To show that

$$\mathbf{N} = \mathbf{I} + \mathbf{Q} + \mathbf{Q}^2 + \cdots,$$

consider the identity

$$(\mathbf{I} - \mathbf{Q})(\mathbf{I} + \mathbf{Q} + \mathbf{Q}^2 + \cdots + \mathbf{Q}^n) = \mathbf{I} - \mathbf{Q}^{n+1}.$$

Multiplying both sides by $(\mathbf{I} - \mathbf{Q})^{-1}$ gives

$$\mathbf{I} + \mathbf{Q} + \mathbf{Q}^2 + \cdots + \mathbf{Q}^n = (\mathbf{I} - \mathbf{Q})^{-1} (\mathbf{I} - \mathbf{Q}^{n+1}).$$

This holds for all n. Now let $n \to \infty$ and use the fact that $\mathbf{Q}^n \to 0$. ∎

Fundamental Matrix

DEFINITION 6

For an absorbing Markov chain $\mathbf{P}$, the matrix $\mathbf{N} = (\mathbf{I} - \mathbf{Q})^{-1}$ is called the *fundamental matrix* for $\mathbf{P}$. The entry n_{ij} of $\mathbf{N}$ gives the expected number of times in the transient state s_j when the process is started in the transient state s_i.

EXAMPLE 1 (continued)

In our drunkard's walk example, the transition matrix in canonical form is

$$\mathbf{P} = \begin{array}{c} \\ 1 \\ 2 \\ 3 \\ 0 \\ 4 \end{array} \begin{pmatrix} 1 & 2 & 3 & 0 & 4 \\ 0 & 1/2 & 0 & 1/2 & 0 \\ 1/2 & 0 & 1/2 & 0 & 0 \\ 0 & 1/2 & 0 & 0 & 1/2 \\ 0 & 0 & 0 & 1 & 0 \\ 0 & 0 & 0 & 0 & 1 \end{pmatrix}.$$

From this we see that the matrix $\mathbf{Q}$ is

$$\mathbf{Q} = \begin{pmatrix} 0 & 1/2 & 0 \\ 1/2 & 0 & 1/2 \\ 0 & 1/2 & 0 \end{pmatrix},$$

and

$$\mathbf{I} - \mathbf{Q} = \begin{pmatrix} 1 & -1/2 & 0 \\ -1/2 & 1 & -1/2 \\ 0 & -1/2 & 1 \end{pmatrix}.$$

Computing $(\mathbf{I} - \mathbf{Q})^{-1}$, we find

$$\mathbf{N} = (\mathbf{I} - \mathbf{Q})^{-1} = \begin{matrix} & \begin{matrix} 1 & \quad 2 & \quad 3 \end{matrix} \\ \begin{matrix} 1 \\ 2 \\ 3 \end{matrix} & \begin{pmatrix} 3/2 & 1 & 1/2 \\ 1 & 2 & 1 \\ 1/2 & 1 & 3/2 \end{pmatrix} \end{matrix}.$$

From the middle row of $\mathbf{N}$, we see, for example, that, starting at state 2, the expected number of times in state 1 before absorption is 1, in state 2 is 2, and in state 3 is 1. □

Times in Transient State

We turn next to question (b). That is, starting in a transient state, how long will it take, on the average, before reaching an absorbing state? If we add all the entries in the ith row, we will have the expected number of times in any of the transient states for a given starting state s_i, that is, the expected time required before being absorbed. This is described in Theorem 4.

Time to Absorption

THEOREM 4

Consider an absorbing Markov chain with s transient states. Let $\mathbf{c}$ be an s-component column vector with all entries 1. Then the vector $\mathbf{t} = \mathbf{Nc}$ has as the jth component the expected number of steps before being absorbed, starting in the state s_j. ∎

Absorption Probabilities

THEOREM 5

Let b_{ij} be the probability that an absorbing chain will be absorbed in the absorbing state s_j if it starts in the transient state s_i. Let $\mathbf{B}$ be the matrix with entries b_{ij}. Then $\mathbf{B}$ is an s-by-r matrix, and

$$\mathbf{B} = \mathbf{NR},$$

where $\mathbf{N}$ is the fundamental matrix and $\mathbf{R}$ is as in the canonical form.

Proof. Let s_i be a transient state and s_j be an absorbing state. If we compute b_{ij} in terms of the possibilities on the outcome of the first step, then we have the equation

$$b_{ij} = p_{ij} + \sum_k p_{ik}b_{kj},$$

where the summation is carried out over all transient states k. Writing this in matrix form gives

$$\mathbf{B} = \mathbf{R} + \mathbf{QB},$$

or

$$(\mathbf{I} - \mathbf{Q})\mathbf{B} = \mathbf{R},$$

and hence,

$$\mathbf{B} = (\mathbf{I} - \mathbf{Q})^{-1}\mathbf{R} = \mathbf{NR}. \qquad \blacksquare$$

EXAMPLE 1 (continued)

In the drunkard's walk example, we found that

$$
\mathbf{N} = \begin{array}{c} 1 \\ 2 \\ 3 \end{array}
\begin{array}{ccc} 1 & 2 & 3 \end{array}
\left(\begin{array}{ccc}
3/2 & 1 & 1/2 \\
1 & 2 & 1 \\
1/2 & 1 & 3/2
\end{array}\right).
$$

From the canonical form

$$
\mathbf{R} = \begin{array}{c} 1 \\ 2 \\ 3 \end{array}
\begin{array}{cc} 0 & 4 \end{array}
\left(\begin{array}{cc}
1/2 & 0 \\
0 & 0 \\
0 & 1/2
\end{array}\right).
$$

Hence,

$$
\mathbf{B} = \mathbf{NR} = \left(\begin{array}{ccc}
3/2 & 1 & 1/2 \\
1 & 2 & 1 \\
1/2 & 1 & 3/2
\end{array}\right) \cdot \left(\begin{array}{cc}
1/2 & 0 \\
0 & 0 \\
0 & 1/2
\end{array}\right).
$$

$$
= \begin{array}{c} 1 \\ 2 \\ 3 \end{array}
\begin{array}{cc} 0 & 4 \end{array}
\left(\begin{array}{cc}
3/4 & 1/4 \\
1/2 & 1/2 \\
1/4 & 3/4
\end{array}\right).
$$

Here the first row tells us that, starting from s_1, there is probability $3/4$ of absorption in s_0 and $1/4$ for absorption in s_4. $\qquad \square$

Let us summarize our results. We have shown that the answers to questions (a), (b), and (c) can all be given in terms of the fundamental matrix $\mathbf{N} = (\mathbf{I} - \mathbf{Q})^{-1}$. The matrix **N** itself gives us the expected number of times in each transient state before absorption, depending upon the starting state. The column vector $t = Nc$ gives us the expected number of steps before absorption, depending upon the starting state. The matrix $B = NR$ gives us the probability of absorption for each of the absorbing states, depending upon the starting state.

Computation

The fact that we have been able to obtain these three descriptive quantities in matrix form makes it very easy to write a computer program that determines these quantities for a given absorbing chain matrix. We first write a subroutine **absorb** to carry out the basic matrix operations.

```
sub absorb(Q(,), R(,), N(,), B(,), t())

    dim I(8,8),X(8,8),c(8)          ! Auxillary matrices

    let transient = size(Q,1)
    mat I = Idn(transient,transient)
    mat X = I - Q
    mat N = Inv(X)                   ! Fundamental matrix
    mat c = con(transient)          ! Vector of all 1's
    mat t = N * c                   ! Times to absorption
    mat B = N*R                     ! Absorption probabilities

end sub
```

We have put this subroutine, and others related to Markov chains, in a library called **Lib. Markov**. We use it in the program **Absorbing Chain** to calculate the basic descriptive quantities of an absorbing Markov chain.

```
! Absorbing Chain     (ABSCHAIN)
!
! Gets the descriptive quantities for an absorbing Markov chain.
!

dim  Q(10,10), R(10,5)              ! Transition matrix
dim  N(10,10), t(10), B(10,5)       ! Key quantities
dim abs_labels$(10), trans_labels$(5)

library "Lib.Markov*"
read absorbing, transient           ! Number of states of each kind.
data 2 , 4

mat read Q(transient,transient), R(transient,absorbing)
```

```
data 0,.5,0,0                      ! Q
data .5,0,.5,0
data 0,.5,0,.5
data 0,0,.5,0

data .5, 0                         ! R
data 0, 0
data 0, 0
data 0,.5

mat read abs_labels$(absorbing)
data 0, 5

mat read trans_labels$(transient)
data 1,2,3,4

print "Matrix Q:"
call matrix_labels(Q, trans_labels$, trans_labels$, " ##.##")

print
print "Matrix R:"
call matrix_labels(R, trans_labels$, abs_labels$, "##.##")

call absorb(Q, R, N, B, t)

print
print "Fundamental matrix N:"
call matrix_labels(N, trans_labels$, trans_labels$, "##.##")

print
print "Times to absorption t:"
call vector_labels(t, trans_labels$,  "##.##")

print
print "Absorption probabilities B:"
call matrix_labels(B, trans_labels$, abs_labels$, "##.##")

end
```

We have run the program **Absorbing Chain** for the example of the drunkard's walk (Example 1) with 5 blocks:

```
Matrix Q:
        1     2     3     4
1     .00   .50   .00   .00
2     .50   .00   .50   .00
3     .00   .50   .00   .50
4     .00   .00   .50   .00

Matrix R:
        0     5
1     .50   .00
2     .00   .00
3     .00   .00
4     .00   .50
```

```
Fundamental matrix N:
        1    2    3    4
1   1.60 1.20  .80  .40
2   1.20 2.40 1.60  .80
3    .80 1.60 2.40 1.20
4    .40  .80 1.20 1.60

Times to absorption t:
        1    2    3    4
     .4.00 6.00 6.00 4.00

Absorption probabilities B:
        0    5
1     .80  .20
2     .60  .40
3     .40  .60
4     .20  .80
```

Note that the probability of reaching the bar before reaching home, starting at x, is $x/5$ (i.e., proportional to the distance of home from the starting point).

Exercises

1. In Example 2 of Section 11.1, for what values of a and b do we obtain an absorbing Markov chain?

2. Show that Example 5 of Section 11.1 is an absorbing Markov chain.

3. Which of the genetics examples (Examples 7, 8, and 9 of Section 11.1) are absorbing?

4. Find the fundamental matrix N for Example 8 of Section 11.1.

5. For Example 9 of Section 11.1, verify that the following matrix is the inverse of $I - Q$, and hence is the fundamental matrix N.

$$N = \begin{pmatrix} 8/2 & 1/6 & 4/3 & 2/3 \\ 4/3 & 4/3 & 8/3 & 4/3 \\ 4/3 & 1/3 & 8/3 & 4/3 \\ 2/3 & 1/6 & 4/3 & 8/3 \end{pmatrix}.$$

Find Nc and NR.

6. In the Land of Oz example (Example 1 of Section 11.1), change the transition matrix by making R an absorbing state. This gives

$$\begin{array}{c} \\ R \\ N \\ S \end{array} \begin{array}{c} R \\ \begin{pmatrix} 1 \\ 1/2 \\ 1/4 \end{pmatrix} \end{array} \begin{array}{c} N \\ 0 \\ 0 \\ 1/4 \end{array} \begin{array}{c} S \\ 0 \\ 1/2 \\ 1/2 \end{array}.$$

Find the fundamental matrix N, and also Nc and NR. Give the interpretation of each quantity.

7. In Example 6 of Section 11.1, make states 0 and 4 into absorbing states. Find the fundamental matrix **N**, and also **Nc** and **NR**, for the resulting absorbing chain. Interpret the results.

8. In Example 1 (drunkard's walk) of this section, assume that the probability of a step to the right is $^2/_3$, and a step to the left is $^1/_3$. Find **N**, **Nc**, and **NR**. Compare these with the results of Example 1.

9. A process moves on the integers 1, 2, 3, 4, and 5. It starts at 1 and, on each successive step, moves to an integer greater than its present position, moving with equal probabilities to each of the remaining larger integers. State five is an absorbing state. Find the expected number of steps to reach state five.

10. Using the result of Exercise 9, make a conjecture for the form of the fundamental matrix if the process moves as in that exercise, except that it now moves on the integers from 1 to n. Assume that $n = 10$. What is the expected number of steps required to reach state 10 when the process is started in state 1?

11. Three tanks fight a three-way dual. Tank A has probability $^1/_2$ of destroying the tank at which it fires. Tank B has probability $^1/_3$ of destroying the tank at which it fires, and tank C has probability $^1/_6$ of destroying the tank at which it fires. The tanks fire together and each tank fires at the strongest opponent not yet destroyed. Form a Markov chain by taking as states the subsets of the set of tanks. Find **N**, **Nc**, **NR**, and interpret your results. *Hint:* take as states ABC, AC, BC, A, B, C, and none, indicating the tanks that could survive starting in state ABC. You can omit AB because this state cannot be reached from ABC.

12. Smith is in jail and has 1 dollar; he can get out on bail if he has 8 dollars. A guard agrees to make a series of bets with him. If Smith bets A dollars, he wins A dollars with probability .4 and loses A dollars with probability .6. Find the probability that he wins 8 dollars before losing all his money if
    (a) he bets 1 dollar each time (timid strategy).
    (b) he bets, each time, as much as possible but not more than necessary to bring his fortune up to 8 dollars (bold strategy).
    (c) Which strategy gives Smith the best chance of getting out of jail?

13. With the situation in Exercise 12, consider the strategy such that for $i < 4$ Smith bets $\min(i, 4 - i)$, and for $i \geq 4$ he bets according to the bold strategy, where i is his current fortune. Find the probability that he gets out of jail using this strategy. How does this probability compare with that obtained for the bold strategy?

14. Consider the game of tennis when *deuce* is reached. If a player wins the next point, he has *advantage*. On the following point, he either wins the game or the game returns to *deuce*. Assume that, at *deuce*, player A has probability $^1/_3$ and player B has probability $^2/_3$ of winning the point; and at *advantage*, the player with the advantage has probability $^1/_3$ of winning.
    (a) Set this up as a Markov chain with state 1: A wins; 2: B wins; 3: advantage A; 4: deuce; 5: advantage B.

(b) Find the absorption probabilities.

(c) At deuce, find the expected duration of the game and the probability that B will win.

Exercises 15 and 16 concern the inheritance of color-blindness, which is a sex-linked characteristic. There is a pair of genes, g and G, of which the former tends to produce color-blindness, the latter normal vision. The G gene is dominant. But a man has only one gene, and if this is g, he is color-blind. A man inherits one of his mother's two genes, while a woman inherits one gene from each parent. Thus a man may be of type G or g, while a woman may be type GG or Gg or gg. We will study a process of inbreeding similar to that of Example 9 of Section 11.1 by constructing a Markov chain.

15. List the states of the chain. *Hint:* There are six. Compute the transition probabilities. Find the fundamental matrix **N** and the vectors **Nc** and **NR**.

16. Show that, in both Example 9 of Section 11.1 and the example just given, the probability of absorption in a state having genes of a particular type is equal to the proportion of genes of that type in the starting state. Show that this can be explained by the fact that a game in which your fortune is the number of genes of a particular type in the state of the Markov chain is a fair game (Harry Gonshor, "An Application of Random Walk to a Problem in Population Genetics," *American Math Monthly*, vol. 94 (1987), pp. 668–671).

17. Assume that a student going to a certain four-year medical school in northern New England has, each year, a probability q of flunking out, a probability r of having to repeat the year, and a probability p of moving on to the next year (in the fourth year, moving on means graduating).

(a) Form a transition matrix for this process taking as states F, 1, 2, 3, 4, and G where F stands for flunking out and G for graduating and the other states represent the year of study.

(b) For the case $q = .1$, $r = .2$, and $p = .7$ find the time a beginning student can expect to be in the second year. How long should this student expect to be in medical school?

(c) Find the probability that this beginning student will graduate.

18. Mary and John are playing the following game: They have a three-card deck marked with the numbers 1, 2, and 3; they have a spinner with the numbers 1, 2, and 3 on it. The game begins by dealing the cards out so that the dealer gets one card and the other person gets two. A move in the game consists of a spin of the spinner; the person having the card with the number that comes up on the spinner hands that card to the other person. The game ends when someone has all the cards. After each move of the game let the state be the number of cards that Mary has.

(a) Set up the transition matrix for this absorbing Markov chain.

(b) Find the fundamental matrix.

(c) On the average, how many moves will the game last?

(d) If Mary deals, what is the probability that John will win the game?

19. Assume that an experiment has m equally probable outcomes. Show that the expected number of independent trials before the first occurrence of k consecutive occurrences of one of these outcomes is $(m^k - 1)/(m - 1)$. *Hint:* Form an absorbing Markov chain with states $1, 2, \ldots, k$ with state i representing the length of the current run. The expected time until a run of k is 1 more than the expected time until absorption for the chain started in state 1. It has been found that, in the decimal expansion of pi, starting with the 24,658,601st digit, there is a run of nine 7s. What would your result say about the expected number of digits necessary to find such a run if the digits are produced randomly?

20. (Roberts)[4] A city is divided into 3 areas 1, 2, and 3. It is estimated that, amounts u_1, u_2, and u_3 of pollution are emitted each day from these three areas. A fraction q_{ij} of the pollution from region i ends up the next day at region j. A fraction $q_i = \sum_j q_{ij} > 0$ goes into the atmosphere and escapes. Let $w_i^{(n)}$ be the amount of pollution in area i after m days.
   (a) Show that $\mathbf{w}^{(n)} = \mathbf{u} + \mathbf{u}Q + \cdots + \mathbf{u}Q^{n-1}$.
   (b) Show that $\mathbf{w}^{(n)} \to \mathbf{w}$ and show how to compute $\mathbf{w}$ from $\mathbf{u}$.
   (c) The government wants to limit pollution levels to a prescribed level by prescribing $\mathbf{w}$. Show how to determine the levels of pollution $\mathbf{u}$ which would result in a prescribed limiting value $\mathbf{w}$.

21. In the Leontief economic model,[5] there are n industries $1, 2, \ldots, n$. The ith industry requires an amount $0 \leq q_{ij} \leq 1$ of goods (in dollar value) from company j to produce 1 dollar's worth of goods. The outside demand on the industries, in dollar value, is given by the vector $\mathbf{d} = (d_1, d_2, \ldots, d_n)$. Let Q be the matrix with entries q_{ij}.
   (a) Show that if the industries produce total amounts given by the vector $\mathbf{x} = (x_1, x_2, \ldots, x_n)$ then the amounts of their goods that the industries will need just to meet their internal demands is given by the vector $\mathbf{x}Q$.
   (b) Show that to meet the outside demand $\mathbf{d}$ and the internal demands the industries must produce total amounts given by a vector $\mathbf{x} = (x_1, \ldots, x_n)$ which satisfies the equation $\mathbf{x} = \mathbf{x}Q + \mathbf{d}$.
   (c) Show that, if Q is the Q-matrix for an absorbing Markov chain then it is possible to meet any outside demand $\mathbf{d}$.
   (d) Assume that the row sums of Q are less than or equal to 1. Give an economic interpretation of this condition. Form a Markov chain by taking the states to be the industries and the transition probabilities to be the q_{ij}. Add one absorbing state 0. Define

$$q_{i0} = 1 - \sum_j q_{ij}.$$

   Show that this chain will be absorbing if every company is either making a profit or ultimately depends upon a profit-making company.

---

[4]F. Roberts, *Discrete Mathematical Models* (Englewood Cliffs, NJ: Prentice Hall, 1976).

[5]W.W. Leontief, *Input-Output Economics* (Oxford: Oxford University Press, 1966).

(e) Define **xc** to be the gross national product. Find an expression for the gross national product in terms of the demand vector **d** and the vector **t** giving the expected time to absorption.

22. A gambler plays a game in which on each play he wins one dollar with probability p and loses one dollar with probability $q = 1 - p$. The *Gambler's Ruin Problem* is the problem of finding the probability w_x of winning an amount T before losing everything, starting with a stake x. Show that this problem may be considered to be an absorbing Markov chain with state $0, 1, 2, \ldots, T$ with 0 and T absorbing states. Simulate a game in which the gambler has probability $p = .48$ of winning on each play, starts with 50 dollars, and $T = 100$ dollars. Repeat this simulation 100 times and see how often the gambler is ruined. (This estimates w_{50}.)

23. Show that w_x of Exercise 22 satisfies the following conditions:
    (a) $w_x = pw_{x+1} + qw_{x-1}$ for $x = 1, 2, \ldots, T - 1$
    (b) $w_0 = 0$
    (c) $w_T = 1$.
    Show that these conditions determine w_x. Show that, if $p = q = \frac{1}{2}$, then

    $$w_x = \frac{x}{T}$$

    satisfies (a), (b), and (c) and hence is the solution. If $p \neq q$, show that

    $$w_x = \frac{\left(\dfrac{q}{p}\right)^x - 1}{\left(\dfrac{q}{p}\right)^T - 1}$$

    satisfies these conditions and hence gives the probability of the gambler winning.

24. Write a program to compute the probability w_x of Exercise 23 for given values of x, p, and T. Study the probability that in a game that is only slightly unfavorable, say $p = .49$, that the gambler will ruin the bank if the bank has significantly more money than the gambler.

25. We considered the two examples of the drunkard's walk corresponding to the cases $n = 4$ and $n = 5$ blocks (see Example 1). Verify that in these two examples the expected time to absorption, starting at x, is equal to $x(n - x)$. See if you can prove this is true in general. *Hint:* show that if $f(x)$ is the expected time to absorption then

    (a) $f(0) = f(n) = 0$

    and

    (b) $f(x) = (1/2)f(x - 1) + (1/2)f(x + 1) + 1$ for $0 < x < n$.

    Then prove that there is a unique function which satisfies (a) and (b).

26. A coin is tossed a sequence of times. We are interested in finding the expected number of tosses until a particular pattern, say HTH, occurs for the first time. If, for example, the outcomes of the tosses are HHTTHTH we say that the pattern occurred, for the first time, after 7 tosses. Let T be the time to obtain this pattern for the first time. Li[6] gives the following method for determining the expected value $E(T)$ of T. We are in a casino and, before each toss of the coin, a gambler enters, pays 1 dollar to play, and bets that the sequence HTH will occur on the next three tosses. If H occurs, he wins 2 dollars and bets this amount that the next outcome will be T. If he wins, he wins 4 dollars and bets this amount that H will come up next time. If he wins, he wins 8 dollars and the pattern has occurred. If, at any time he loses, he leaves with no winnings. Under this scheme, the casino takes in 1 dollar for each gambler that arrives. That is, it takes in T dollars. How much does it pay out? For a pattern of length three the casino has to pay out money to at most three gamblers: the gambler who arrived at the beginning of the pattern was paid 8 dollars, the next gambler bet on H and lost, the next gambler bet on H and won 2 dollars. Thus the casino paid out $8 + $2 = $10. Since each gambler is playing a fair game, if fairness is preserved, we would have to have the expected amount paid out by the casino equal to the expected amount that it takes in, that is, $E(T) = 10$. Notice that if we had been trying to get the pattern HHH, this argument would show that $E(T) = 8 + 4 + 2 = 14$ since all the last three gamblers are paid off in this case. To justify this argument, Li used a theorem from the theory of martingales (fair games).

We can obtain these expectations by considering a Markov chain with states being all the possible initial segments of the sequence we are trying to get. For our example, the state space would be HTH, HT, H, and Ø, where Ø is the empty set. Then, for this example, the transition matrix would be

$$
\begin{array}{c c}
 & \begin{array}{cccc} \text{HTH} & \text{HT} & \text{H} & \text{Ø} \end{array} \\
\begin{array}{c} \text{HTH} \\ \text{HT} \\ \text{H} \\ \text{Ø} \end{array} &
\left(\begin{array}{cccc}
1 & 0 & 0 & 0 \\
.5 & 0 & 0 & .5 \\
0 & .5 & .5 & 0 \\
0 & 0 & .5 & .5
\end{array} \right),
\end{array}
$$

and $E(T)$ will be the expected time to absorption for this chain started in state Ø.

Show, using the associated Markov chain, that the values $E(T) = 10$ and $E(T) = 14$ are correct for the expected time to reach the patterns HTH and HHH, respectively.

27. In the gambling interpretation (see Exercise 26), we can conjecture, by the fairness argument, that the expected time to absorption for any starting state will be the expected time for the state Ø minus the expected winnings for the players in the initial segment. For example, starting in state HT, the first player will win 8 dollars with probability $^1/_2$ and the second player has already lost. Thus the expected time, starting in state HT is $10 - 4 = 6$. Verify that this gambling interpretation leads to

[6] S-Y.R. Li, "A Martingale Approach to the Study of Occurrence of Sequence Patterns in Repeated Experiments," *Annals of Probability*, vol. 8 (1980), pp. 1171–1176.

the correct answers for all starting states in the examples that you worked in Exercise 26.

28. Here is an elegant method due to Guibas and Odlyzko[7] to obtain the expected time to reach a pattern, say HTH, for the first time. Let $f(n)$ be the number of sequences of length n which do not have the pattern HTH. Let $f_p(n)$ be the number of sequences that have the pattern for the first time after n tosses. To each element of $f(n)$, add the pattern HTH. Then divide the resulting sequences into three subsets: the set where HTH occurs for the first time at time $n + 1$ (for this, the original sequence must have ended with HT); the set where HTH occurs for the first time at time $n + 2$ (cannot happen for this pattern); and the set where the sequence HTH occurs for the first time at time $n + 3$ (the original sequence ended with anything except HT). Doing this, we have

$$f(n) = f_p(n + 1) + f_p(n + 3).$$

Thus,

$$\frac{f(n)}{2^n} = \frac{2f_p(n + 1)}{2^{n+1}} + \frac{2^3 f_p(n + 3)}{2^{n+3}}.$$

If T is the time that the pattern occurs for the first time, this equality states that

$$P(T > n) = 2P(T = n + 1) + 8P(T = n + 3).$$

Show that if you sum this equality over all n you obtain

$$\sum_{n=0}^{\infty} P(T > n) = 2 + 8 = 10.$$

Show that for any integer-valued random variable

$$E(T) = \sum_{n=0}^{\infty} P(T > n),$$

and conclude that $E(T) = 10$. Note that this method of proof makes very clear that $E(T)$ is, in general, equal to the expected amount the casino pays out and avoids the martingale system theorem used by Li.

29. Consider an absorbing Markov chain with state space S. Let f be a function defined on S with the property that

$$f(i) = \sum_{j \in S} p_{ij} f(j),$$

or in vector form

$$\mathbf{f} = \mathbf{Pf}.$$

---

[7] L.J. Guibas and A.M. Odlysko, "String Overlaps, Pattern Matching, and Non-transitive Games," *Journal of Combinatorial Theory*, Series A, vol. 30 (1981), pp. 183–208.

Then f is called a *harmonic function* for **P**. If you imagine a game in which your fortune is $f(i)$ when you are in state i, then the harmonic condition means that the game is *fair* in the sense that your expected winning after one step is the same as it was before the step.

(a) Show that for f harmonic

$$\mathbf{f} = \mathbf{P}^n \mathbf{f}$$

for all n

(b) Show, using (a), that for f harmonic

$$\mathbf{f} = \mathbf{P}^{\times} \mathbf{f},$$

where

$$\mathbf{P}^{\times} = \lim_{n \to \times} \mathbf{P}^n = \left(\begin{array}{c|c} \mathbf{0} & \mathbf{B} \\ \hline \mathbf{0} & \mathbf{I} \end{array} \right).$$

(c) Using (b), prove that when you start in a transient state i your expected final fortune

$$\sum_k b_{ik} f(k)$$

is equal to your starting fortune $f(i)$. In other words, a fair game on a finite state space remains fair to the end. (Fair games in general are called *martingales*. Fair games on infinite state spaces need not remain fair with an unlimited number of plays allowed. For example, consider the game of Heads and Tails (see Example 3 of Chapter 1 Section 1.1). Let Peter start with 1 penny and play until he has 2. Then Peter will be sure to end up 1 penny ahead.)

30. In Example 9 of Section 11.1, define $f(i)$ to be the proportion of G genes in state i. Show that f is a harmonic function (see Exercise 29). Why does this show that the probability of being absorbed in state GG,GG is equal to the proportion of G genes in the starting state? (See Exercise 16.)

31. Show that the stepping stone model (Example 10 of Section 11.1) is an absorbing Markov chain. Assume that you are playing a game in which your fortune at any time is equal to the proportion of red squares at that time. Give an argument to show that this is a fair game in the sense that your expected winning after each step is just what it was before this step. *Hint:* Show that for every possible outcome in which your fortune will decrease by one there is another outcome of exactly the same probability where it will increase by one.

Use this fact and the results of Exercise 29 to show that the probability that a particular color wins out is equal to the proportion of the squares that are initially of this color.

32. Consider a random walker who moves on the integers $0,1, \ldots, N$, moving one step to the right with probability p and one step to the left with probability $q = 1 - p$.

If the walker ever reaches 0 or N he stays there. (This is the gambler's ruin of Exercises 22 to 24). If $p = q$ show that the function

$$f(i) = i$$

is a harmonic function, and if $p \neq q$ then

$$f(i) = \left(\frac{q}{p}\right)^i$$

is a harmonic function. Use this and the result of Exercise 29 to show that the probability b_{iN} of being absorbed in state N starting in state i is

$$b_{iN} = \begin{cases} \dfrac{i}{N} & \text{if } p = q, \\[2ex] \dfrac{\left(\dfrac{q}{p}\right)^i - 1}{\left(\dfrac{q}{p}\right)^N - 1} & \text{if } p \neq q. \end{cases}$$

For an alternative derivation of these results see Exercise 23.

11.3 ERGODIC MARKOV CHAINS

A second important kind of Markov chain that we shall study in detail is a *regular Markov chain,* defined as follows in Definition 7.

Regular Markov Chains

DEFINITION 7

A Markov chain is called a *regular* chain if some power of the transition matrix has only positive elements.

Of course, any transition matrix that has no zeros determines a regular Markov chain. The transition matrix of the Land of Oz example of Section 11.1 had $p_{NN} = 0$ but the second power $\mathbf{P}^2$ has no zeros, so this too is a regular Markov chain. An example of a nonregular Markov chain is an absorbing chain; for example, with transition matrix

$$\mathbf{P} = \begin{pmatrix} 1 & 0 \\ 1/2 & 1/2 \end{pmatrix}.$$

All powers of $\mathbf{P}$ will have a 0 in the upper right-hand corner.

The probabilistic interpretation of regularity is the following: A Markov chain is regular if there is some time at which it is possible to be in any of the states regardless of the starting state (i.e., all transitions are ultimately possible).

We shall now discuss two important theorems relating to regular chains. Before doing this, we introduce some useful matrix notation. We shall often want to refer to a matrix with all rows the same vector **w**. Using the column vector **c** with all 1s, we can write such a matrix in the form **cw**. For example, if **w** = (.4 .2 .4), then

$$\mathbf{cw} = \begin{pmatrix} 1 \\ 1 \\ 1 \end{pmatrix} \begin{matrix} (.4 & .2 & .4) \end{matrix} = \begin{pmatrix} .4 & .2 & .4 \\ .4 & .2 & .4 \\ .4 & .2 & .4 \end{pmatrix}.$$

If we compute **wc**, we obtain a number equal to the sum of the components of **w**. For example,

$$(.4, .2, .4) \begin{pmatrix} 1 \\ 1 \\ 1 \end{pmatrix} = 1.$$

THEOREM 6

Let **P** be the transition matrix for a regular chain. Then, as $n \to \infty$, the powers $\mathbf{P}^n$ approach a limiting matrix **cw** with all rows a strictly positive probability vector **w**.

We shall prove this theorem in the next section.

The ijth entry of $\mathbf{P}^n$, $p_{ij}^{(n)}$, is the probability that the process will be in state s_j after n steps if it starts in state s_i. Theorem 1 states that the probability of being in s_j in the long run is approximately w_j, the jth entry of **w**, and is independent of the starting state.

EXAMPLE 1

Recall that for the Land of Oz example of Section 11.1, the sixth power of the transition matrix **P** was, to three decimal places,

$$\mathbf{P}^6 = \begin{matrix} R \\ N \\ S \end{matrix} \begin{pmatrix} .4 & .2 & .4 \\ .4 & .2 & .4 \\ .4 & .2 & .4 \end{pmatrix}.$$

with columns R N S.

Thus, to this degree of accuracy, the probability of rain six days after a rainy day is the same as the probability of rain six days after a nice day, or six days after a snowy day. Theorem 1 predicts that, for large n, the rows of **P** approach a common vector. It is interesting that this occurs so soon in our example. The next theorem gives a method for determining vector **w** and, hence, the limiting matrix **cw**. □

THEOREM 7

Let **P** be a regular transition matrix. Then $\mathbf{P}^n \to \mathbf{cw}$ and $\mathbf{wP} = \mathbf{w}$.

Proof. By Theorem 6,

$$\mathbf{P}^n \to \mathbf{cw}.$$

Thus,

$$\mathbf{P}^{n+1} = \mathbf{P}^n \cdot \mathbf{P} \to \mathbf{cwP}.$$

But $\mathbf{P}^{n+1} \to \mathbf{cw}$, and so $\mathbf{cw} = \mathbf{cwP}$, and $\mathbf{w} = \mathbf{wP}$. ∎

THEOREM 8

Let $\mathbf{P}$ be a regular transition matrix. There is a unique probability row vector $\mathbf{w}$ such that $\mathbf{wP} = \mathbf{w}$, and any row vector $\mathbf{v}$ such that $\mathbf{vP} = \mathbf{v}$ is a constant multiple of $\mathbf{w}$. Moreover, if $\mathbf{c}$ is a constant column vector then $\mathbf{Pc} = \mathbf{c}$, and any column vector $\mathbf{x}$ such that $\mathbf{Px} = \mathbf{x}$ is a constant multiple of $\mathbf{c}$.

Proof. We know by Theorems 6 and 7 that there is a vector $\mathbf{w}$ with $\mathbf{w} = \mathbf{wP}$. Let $\mathbf{v}$ be any other vector with $\mathbf{vP} = \mathbf{v}$. Then $\mathbf{v} = \mathbf{vP}^n$, and passing to the limit, $\mathbf{v} = \mathbf{vcw}$. Hence, $\mathbf{v} = (\mathbf{vc})\mathbf{w} = \mathbf{w}$.

Assume next that $\mathbf{x} = \mathbf{Px}$. Then $\mathbf{x} = \mathbf{P}^n\mathbf{x} \to \mathbf{cwx}$, and so $\mathbf{x} = (\mathbf{wx})\mathbf{c}$. ∎

Fixed Vector

A row vector $\mathbf{w}$ with the property $\mathbf{wP} = \mathbf{w}$ or a column vector $\mathbf{x}$ such that $\mathbf{Px} = \mathbf{x}$ will be called a *fixed vector* for $\mathbf{P}$. Thus, the common row of $\mathbf{cw}$ is the unique vector $\mathbf{w}$ which is both a fixed row vector for $\mathbf{P}$ and a probability vector. Theorem 8 shows that any fixed row vector for $\mathbf{P}$ is a multiple of $\mathbf{w}$ and any fixed column vector for $\mathbf{P}$ is a constant vector.

EXAMPLE 1 (continued)

By Theorem 6 we can find the limiting vector $\mathbf{w}$ for the Land of Oz from the fact that

$$w_1 + w_2 + w_3 = 1$$

and

$$(w_1 \quad w_2 \quad w_3)\begin{pmatrix} 1/2 & 1/4 & 1/4 \\ 1/2 & 0 & 1/2 \\ 1/4 & 1/4 & 1/2 \end{pmatrix} = (w_1 \quad w_2 \quad w_3).$$

These relations lead to the following four equations in three unknowns.

$$w_1 + w_2 + w_3 = 1,$$

$$1/2w_1 + 1/2w_2 + 1/4w_3 = w_1,$$

$$1/4w_1 + 1/4w_3 = w_2,$$

$$1/4w_1 + 1/2w_2 + 1/2w_3 = w_3.$$

Our theorem guarantees that these equations have a unique solution. If the equations are solved, we obtain the solution

$$\mathbf{w} = (.4 \quad .2 \quad .4),$$

in agreement with that predicted from $\mathbf{P}^6$. $\quad\square$

To calculate the fixed vector, we can assume that the value at a particular state, say state one, is 1, and then use $r - 1$ of the equations from $\mathbf{wP} = \mathbf{w}$. This set of equations will have a unique solution and we can obtain $\mathbf{w}$ from this solution by dividing each of its entries by their sum to give the probability vector $\mathbf{w}$. In the above example, this would have required that we solve only two equations in two unknowns.

So far we have always assumed that we started in a specific state. The following theorem generalizes Theorem 6 to the case where the starting state is itself the result of a random choice.

THEOREM 9

Let $\mathbf{P}$ be the transition matrix for a regular chain and $\mathbf{v}$ an arbitrary probability vector. Then

$$\lim_{n \to \infty} \mathbf{vP}^n = \mathbf{w},$$

where $\mathbf{w}$ is the unique fixed probability vector for $\mathbf{P}$.

Proof. By Theorem 6,

$$\lim_{n \to \infty} \mathbf{P}^n = \mathbf{cw}.$$

Hence, since $\mathbf{vc} = 1$,

$$\lim_{n \to \infty} \mathbf{vP}^n = \mathbf{vcw} = \mathbf{w}. \quad\blacksquare$$

If we start a Markov chain with initial probabilities given by $\mathbf{v}$, then $\mathbf{vP}^n$ gives the probabilities of being in various states after n steps. Theorem 9 then establishes the fact that, even in this more general class of processes, the probability of being in s_j approaches w_j.

Equilibrium

We also obtain a new interpretation for $\mathbf{w}$. Suppose that our random starting choice picks state s_i as a starting state with probability w_i, for all i. Then the probability of being in the various states after n steps is given by $\mathbf{wP}^n = \mathbf{w}$, and is the same on all steps. Hence, this method of starting provides us with a process that is stationary (or in *equilibrium*). The fact that $\mathbf{w}$ is the only probability vector for which $\mathbf{wP} = \mathbf{w}$ shows that we must have a random starting device of exactly the kind described to obtain a stationary process.

Many interesting results concerning regular Markov chains depend only on the fact that the chain has a unique fixed probability vector which is positive. This property holds for a wider class of Markov chains.

Ergodic Chains

DEFINITION 8

A Markov chain is called an *ergodic chain* if it is possible to go from every state to every other state (i.e., if all transitions are ultimately possible).

Obviously, a regular chain is ergodic, because, if the nth power of the transition matrix is positive, it is possible to go from every state to every other state in n steps. On the other hand, an ergodic chain is not necessarily regular. For example, if, from a given state, we can only go to certain states in an even number of steps and to the others in an odd number of steps, then all powers of the transition matrix will have 0s, but the chain may still be ergodic.

EXAMPLE 2

An example of an ergodic Markov chain which is not regular is provided by the Ehrenfest urn model (Example 6 of Section 11.1). Recall that the transition matrix for this example was

$$
\mathbf{P} = \begin{array}{c} \\ 0 \\ 1 \\ 2 \\ 3 \\ 4 \end{array} \begin{array}{ccccc} 0 & 1 & 2 & 3 & 4 \\ \left(\begin{array}{ccccc} 0 & 1 & 0 & 0 & 0 \\ 1/4 & 0 & 3/4 & 0 & 0 \\ 0 & 1/2 & 0 & 1/2 & 0 \\ 0 & 0 & 3/4 & 0 & 1/4 \\ 0 & 0 & 0 & 1 & 0 \end{array} \right) \end{array}.
$$

In this example, if we start in state 0 we will, after any even numbers of steps, be in either state 0 or 2 or 4, and after any odd numbered steps we will be in states 1 or 3.

□

THEOREM 10

For an ergodic Markov chain, there is a unique probability vector $\mathbf{w}$ such that $\mathbf{wP} = \mathbf{w}$ and $\mathbf{w}$ is strictly positive. Any row vector such that $\mathbf{vP} = \mathbf{v}$ is a multiple of $\mathbf{w}$. Any column vector $\mathbf{x}$ such that $\mathbf{Px} = \mathbf{x}$ is a constant vector. ■

This theorem states that Theorem 8 is true for ergodic chains, and its proof follows easily from the fact that, if $\mathbf{P}$ is an ergodic transition matrix, then $\overline{\mathbf{P}} = \frac{1}{2}\mathbf{I} + \frac{1}{2}\mathbf{P}$ is a regular transition matrix with the same fixed vectors (see Exercises 24–27).

For ergodic chains, the fixed probability vector has a slightly different interpretation. The following two theorems, which we will not prove here, furnish an interpretation for this fixed vector.

THEOREM 11

Let $\mathbf{P}$ be the transition matrix for an ergodic chain. Let $\mathbf{A}_n$ be the matrix defined by

$$\mathbf{A}_n = \frac{\mathbf{I} + \mathbf{P} + \mathbf{P}^2 + \cdots + \mathbf{P}^n}{n + 1}.$$

Then $\mathbf{A}_n \to \mathbf{cw}$ where $\mathbf{w}$ is the unique fixed probability vector for $\mathbf{P}$. ∎

To interpret this theorem, let us assume that we have an ergodic chain that starts in state i. Let $X_m = 1$ if the mth step is to state j and 0 otherwise. Then the average number of times in state j in the first n steps is given by

$$H_j^{(n)} = \frac{X_0 + X_1 + X_2 + \cdots + X_n}{n + 1}.$$

But X_m takes on the value 1 with probability $p_{ij}^{(m)}$ and 0 otherwise. Thus $E(X_m) = p_{ij}^{(m)}$, and the ijth entry of $\mathbf{A}_n$ give the expected value of $H_j^{(n)}$, that is, the expected proportion of times in state j in the first n steps if the chain starts in state i.

If we call being in state j *success* and any other state *failure*, we could ask if a theorem analogous to the law of large numbers for independent trials holds. The answer is yes and is given by the following theorem.

Law of Large Numbers for Ergodic Chains

THEOREM 12

Let $H_j^{(n)}$ be the proportion of times in n steps that an ergodic chain is in state s_j. Then for any $\varepsilon > 0$,

$$\mathbf{P}(|H_j^{(n)} - w_j| > \varepsilon) \to 0,$$

independent of the starting state i.

We have observed that every regular Markov chain is also an ergodic chain. Hence, Theorems 11 and 12 apply also for regular chains. For example, this gives us a new interpretation for the fixed vector $\mathbf{w} = (.4 \quad .2 \quad .4)$ in the Land of Oz example. Theorem 11 predicts that, in the long run, it will rain 40 percent of the time in the Land of Oz, be nice 20 percent of the time, and snow 40 percent of the time.

Simulation

We illustrate this by writing a program to simulate the behavior of a Markov chain. **Simulate Chain** is such a program.

```
! Simulate Chain   (SIMCHAIN)
!
! Simulates a Markov chain
!

randomize
dim p(20,20), count(20), state$(20)

read n                          ! Number of states.
mat read p(n,n)                 ! Facts about Land of Oz.
data 3
data  .5, .25, .25
data  .5,  0,  .5
data  .25, .25, .5

mat read state$(n)              ! Different states.
data R, N, S

read start, steps               ! Starting state, number of steps.
data 1, 525

let state = start

for simulation = 1 to steps

    let r = rnd                 ! Select a random number.

    for j = 1 to n              ! For the number of states, ...
        let r = r - p(state,j)  ! check the probability.
        if r < 0  then
           let state = j
           print state$(state);
           exit for
        end if
    next j

    let count(state) = count(state) + 1    ! Keep count.

next simulation

print
print
print "State", "Times", "Fraction"
print

for state = 1 to n
    print state$(state), count(state), round(count(state)/steps, 3)
next state
print

end
```

Simulating the weather for one year in the Land of Oz example, this program gives:

```
RRRNRRRRRRRRRSRRNRRSSSRNSSSSSNRRNSNSSSSRNRSSRRNSSSSRSSRRSNSSSRRRNRRSNSRNRSSSNSR
RRNRRRRRRSRNRRNSSNRSSRNSNRNSSNSSSSRSSSNRSSRSRNRRRNRRRNSSNRRRRRRNSSSSNSSRRRSSSRRR
NSSSSSSSNRNRRSSNSNSSSSSRRNSSNSSSSNRSRRRSSSSSRNRRRRNSRNSSNRRRNSRSNRRRSRRNRSSSSSS
SRRRRSSSSRRRRNSRNRRRNRSSSSRRRRRRSRRRNRSSRRRRSSSSRRRSNSNRRNRRSSRNSSNSSNSSSRNSSSSS
SSNSSRSSNRSRNRRNRSSRNRRRRSRSNSNSSRNSSSSSSSSSSRRRRNRRRRRNRSRRRNSSSNSNRSSSSNRRRRRS
NSSNSSNRRRNSNSSNSRRRRRNRSSNSRRRSSSRRRRRSRRSSNRRRNRNSSSRRRRRNSSSNSNRSRNSNRRRRRNS
NSRSNRRNRSRSNSRNSNRNRRNSSSSNRNRRRSRRRRNSRRRNRSS
```

State	Times	Fraction
R	221	.421
N	96	.183
S	208	.396

(Recall that in the Land of Oz there are 525 days in a year; see Chapter 3, Section 3.1, Exercise 20.)

We note that the simulation gives a proportion of times in each of the states not too different from the long run predictions of .4, .2, and .4 assured by Theorem 6. To get better results we have to simulate our chain for a longer time. We do this for 10,000 days without printing out each day's weather.

State	Times	Fraction
R	3970	.397
N	2010	.201
S	4020	.402

We see that the results are now quite close to the theoretical values of .4, .2, and .4.

The computation of the fixed vector **w** may be very difficult if the transition matrix is large. It is sometimes possible to guess the fixed vector on purely intuitive grounds. Here is a simple example to illustrate this kind of situation.

EXAMPLE 3

A white rat is put into the maze of Figure 4. There are nine compartments with connections between the compartments as indicated. The rat moves through the compartments at random. That is, if there are k ways to leave a compartment, it chooses each of these with equal probability. We can represent the travels of the rat by a Markov chain process with transition matrix given by

$$
\mathbf{P} = \begin{array}{c} \\ 1 \\ 2 \\ 3 \\ 4 \\ 5 \\ 6 \\ 7 \\ 8 \\ 9 \end{array}
\begin{array}{c}
\begin{array}{ccccccccc} 1 & 2 & 3 & 4 & 5 & 6 & 7 & 8 & 9 \end{array} \\
\left(\begin{array}{ccccccccc}
0 & 1/2 & 0 & 0 & 0 & 1/2 & 0 & 0 & 0 \\
1/3 & 0 & 1/3 & 0 & 1/3 & 0 & 0 & 0 & 0 \\
0 & 1/2 & 0 & 1/2 & 0 & 0 & 0 & 0 & 0 \\
0 & 0 & 1/3 & 0 & 1/3 & 0 & 0 & 0 & 1/3 \\
0 & 1/4 & 0 & 1/4 & 0 & 1/4 & 0 & 1/4 & 0 \\
1/3 & 0 & 0 & 0 & 1/3 & 0 & 1/3 & 0 & 0 \\
0 & 0 & 0 & 0 & 0 & 1/2 & 0 & 1/2 & 0 \\
0 & 0 & 0 & 0 & 1/3 & 0 & 1/3 & 0 & 1/3 \\
0 & 0 & 0 & 1/2 & 0 & 0 & 0 & 1/2 & 0
\end{array} \right)
\end{array} .
$$

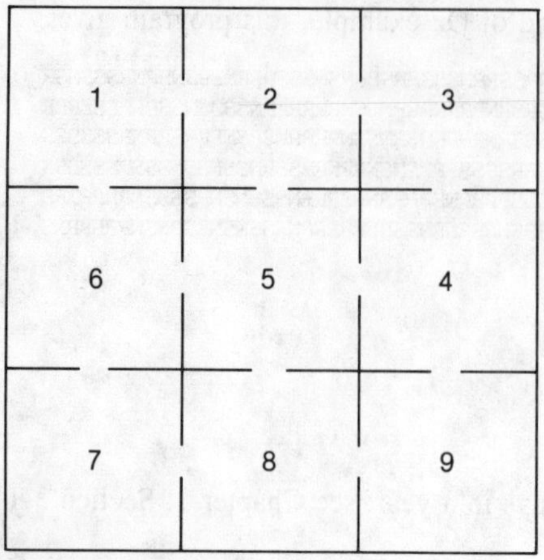

Figure 4 The maze problem.

That this chain is not regular can be seen as follows: From an odd numbered state the process can go only to an even numbered state, and from an even numbered state it can go only to an odd number. Hence, starting in s_1 the process will be alternately in even and odd numbered states. Therefore, odd powers of **P** will have 0s for the odd numbered entries in row 1. On the other hand, a glance at the maze shows that it is possible to go from every state to every other state, so that the chain is ergodic.

To find the fixed probability vector for this matrix, we would have to solve ten equations in nine unknowns. However, it would seem reasonable that the times spent in each compartment should, in the long run, be proportional to the number of entries to each compartment. Thus, we try the vector whose jth component is the number of entries to the jth compartment:

$$\mathbf{x} = (2 \quad 3 \quad 2 \quad 3 \quad 4 \quad 3 \quad 2 \quad 3 \quad 2).$$

It is easy to check that this vector is indeed a fixed vector so that the unique probability vector is this vector normalized to have sum 1:

$$\mathbf{w} = \left(\frac{1}{12} \quad \frac{1}{8} \quad \frac{1}{12} \quad \frac{1}{8} \quad \frac{1}{6} \quad \frac{1}{8} \quad \frac{1}{12} \quad \frac{1}{8} \quad \frac{1}{12} \right). \qquad \square$$

Fundamental Matrix

As we know, $\mathbf{w} = (w_1, \ldots, w_r)$ is the unique solution to

$$\mathbf{w} = \mathbf{w}\mathbf{P}$$

and

$$\sum_i w_i = 1.$$

We could use this fact to compute **w**. However, we shall develop instead a fundamental matrix for ergodic chains that will play a role similar to that of the fundamental matrix $\mathbf{N} = (\mathbf{I} - \mathbf{Q})^{-1}$ for absorbing chains.

Since there are no absorbing states, we might be tempted to try $\mathbf{Z} = (\mathbf{I} - \mathbf{P})^{-1}$ for a fundamental matrix. However $\mathbf{I} - \mathbf{P}$ does not have an inverse. To see this, recall that a matrix $\mathbf{R}$ has an inverse if and only if $\mathbf{Rx} = \mathbf{0}$ implies $\mathbf{x} = \mathbf{0}$, But since $\mathbf{Pc} = \mathbf{c}$ we have $(\mathbf{I} - \mathbf{P})\mathbf{c} = \mathbf{0}$, and so $\mathbf{I} - \mathbf{P}$ does not have an inverse. However, it turns out that we need only add to $\mathbf{I} - \mathbf{P}$ any matrix with all rows the same vector $\mathbf{b}$, where $\mathbf{bc} \neq 0$, and the resulting matrix will have an inverse that will serve as a fundamental matrix for ergodic chains.

Thus we begin by choosing any row vector

$$\mathbf{b} = (b_1, b_2, \ldots, b_r)$$

with $\mathbf{bc} \neq 0$. (Recall that $\mathbf{c}$ is a column vector with all components equal to 1.)

DEFINITION 9

The fundamental matrix $\mathbf{Z}$ determined by $\mathbf{b}$ for an ergodic chain is

$$\mathbf{Z} = (\mathbf{I} - \mathbf{P} + \mathbf{cb})^{-1}.$$

PROPOSITION

This inverse exists and

$$\mathbf{w} = \mathbf{bZ}.$$

Proof. Let $\mathbf{x}$ be a column vector such that

$$(\mathbf{I} - \mathbf{P} + \mathbf{cb})\mathbf{x} = \mathbf{0}.$$

Multiplying this equation by $\mathbf{w}$ and using the fact that $\mathbf{w}(\mathbf{I} - \mathbf{P}) = \mathbf{0}$ and $\mathbf{wc} = 1$, we have

$$\mathbf{w}(\mathbf{I} - \mathbf{P} + \mathbf{cb})\mathbf{x} = \mathbf{wcbx} = \mathbf{bx} = \mathbf{0}.$$

Therefore,

$$(\mathbf{I} - \mathbf{P})\mathbf{x} = \mathbf{0}.$$

But this means that $\mathbf{x} = \mathbf{Px}$ is a fixed column vector for $\mathbf{P}$. By Theorem 10, this can only happen if $\mathbf{x}$ is a constant vector. But now we know that $\mathbf{bx} = 0$ and $\mathbf{x}$ is a constant multiple of $\mathbf{c}$. Since we assumed that $\mathbf{bc} \neq 0$, $\mathbf{x}$ must be the zero vector. This means that $\mathbf{Z} = (\mathbf{I} - \mathbf{P} + \mathbf{cb})^{-1}$ exists and

$$(\mathbf{I} - \mathbf{P} + \mathbf{cb})\mathbf{Z} = \mathbf{I}.$$

If we multiply both sides of this equation by $\mathbf{w}$ and use the fact that $\mathbf{wP} = \mathbf{w}$ and $\mathbf{wc} = 1$, we obtain

$$\mathbf{bZ} = \mathbf{w}. \qquad \blacksquare$$

In their previous work on ergodic Markov chains, Kemeny and Snell[8] defined $\mathbf{Z}$ by choosing $\mathbf{b} = \mathbf{w}$. This had the defect that $\mathbf{w}$ was needed to define $\mathbf{Z}$. Kemeny observed that there is a large class of fundamental matrices which can be used to study ergodic chains. This class is a larger class than the one we have defined above. For the general class, see Exercise 21 of Section 11.5. A particularly simple choice for $\mathbf{b}$ is the vector $\mathbf{b} = (1,1,1, \ldots ,1)$. We shall make this choice here. With this choice, since $\mathbf{w} = \mathbf{bZ}$, we see that $\mathbf{w}$ will be the vector of column sums of $\mathbf{Z}$.

EXAMPLE 4

Let $\mathbf{P}$ be the transition matrix for the weather in the Land of Oz. Then choosing $\mathbf{b} = (1,1,1)$ we obtain

$$
\mathbf{I} - \mathbf{P} + \mathbf{cb} = \begin{pmatrix} 1 & 0 & 0 \\ 0 & 1 & 0 \\ 0 & 0 & 1 \end{pmatrix} - \begin{pmatrix} 1/2 & 1/4 & 1/4 \\ 1/2 & 0 & 1/2 \\ 1/4 & 1/4 & 1/2 \end{pmatrix} + \begin{pmatrix} 1 & 1 & 1 \\ 1 & 1 & 1 \\ 1 & 1 & 1 \end{pmatrix}
$$

$$
= \begin{pmatrix} 3/2 & 3/4 & 3/4 \\ 1/2 & 2 & 1/2 \\ 3/4 & 3/4 & 3/2 \end{pmatrix},
$$

and

$$
\mathbf{Z} = (\mathbf{I} - \mathbf{P} + \mathbf{cb})^{-1} = \begin{pmatrix} 14/15 & -1/5 & -2/5 \\ -2/15 & 3/5 & -2/15 \\ -2/5 & -1/5 & 14/15 \end{pmatrix}.
$$

For the choice of $\mathbf{b}$ that we have made, $\mathbf{bZ}$ consists of the column sums of $\mathbf{Z}$ and we note that this is indeed the fixed vector $\mathbf{w} = (2/5 \quad 1/5 \quad 2/5)$ for the Land of Oz example. □

The subroutine **get_fixed_vector** computes the fixed vector for an ergodic Markov chain:

```
sub get_fixed_vector(P(,), w())

    dim Z(8,8), I(8,8), X(8,8), E(8,8), c(8)

    let n = ubound(P,1)

    mat I = Idn(n,n)
    mat X = I - P
    mat E = con(n,n)
    mat X = X + E
    mat Z = inv(X)              ! Fundamental matrix
    mat c = con(n)
    mat w = c * Z               ! Fixed vector

end sub
```

[8]J.G. Kemeny and J.L. Snell, *Finite Markov Chains* (New York: Springer-Verlag, 1976).

The program **Limit Vector** uses this subroutine to compute the fixed vector.

```
! Limit Vector   (LIMVEC)
!
! Calculates the fixed vector for a regular Markov chain.

library "lib.Markov*"
dim P(0 to 8,8)                    ! Transition matrix
dim Z(8,8), w(8)                   ! Key quantities
dim label$(8)

read n                             ! Number of states
data 5
mat read label$(n)
data 0,1,2,3,4

mat read P(n,n)
data  0,1,0,0,0
data  .25,0,.75,0,0
data  0,.5,0,.5,0
data  0,0,.75,0,.25
data  0,0,0,1,0

print "Transition matrix P ="
call matrix_labels(P, label$, label$, " #.###")

call get_fixed_vector(P,w)         ! Compute key quantities

print
print "Fixed vector w ="
call vector_labels(w, label$, " #.####")

end
```

We have run this program for the ergodic chain obtained by considering the Ehrenfest urn model of Example 6 in Section 11.1.

```
Transition matrix P =

        0      1      2      3      4
0    .000  1.000   .000   .000   .000
1    .250   .000   .750   .000   .000
2    .000   .500   .000   .500   .000
3    .000   .000   .750   .000   .250
4    .000   .000   .000  1.000   .000

Fixed vector w =

        0      1      2      3      4
    .0625  .2500  .3750  .2500  .0625
```

By Theorem 10, we can interpret these values for w_i as the proportion of times the process is in each of the states in the long run. For example, the proportion of times in state 0 is .0625 and the proportion of times in state 2 is .375. The astute reader will note that these numbers are the binomial distribution 1/16, 4/16, 6/16, 4/16, 1/16. We could have guessed this answer as follows: If we consider a particular ball, it simply moves randomly back and forth between the two urns. This suggests that the equilibrium state should be just as if we randomly distributed the four balls in the two urns. If we did this, the probability that there would be exactly j balls in one urn would be given by the binomial distribution $b(n, p, j)$ with $n = 4$ and $p = 1/2$.

Exercises

1. Which of the following matrices are transition matrices for regular Markov chains?

(a) $\mathbf{P} = \begin{pmatrix} .5 & .5 \\ .5 & .5 \end{pmatrix}$.

(b) $\mathbf{P} = \begin{pmatrix} .5 & .5 \\ 1 & 0 \end{pmatrix}$.

(c) $\mathbf{P} = \begin{pmatrix} 1 & 0 \\ 0 & 1 \end{pmatrix}$.

(d) $\mathbf{P} = \begin{pmatrix} 1/3 & 0 & 2/3 \\ 0 & 1 & 0 \\ 0 & 1/5 & 4/5 \end{pmatrix}$.

(e) $\mathbf{P} = \begin{pmatrix} 0 & 1 \\ 1 & 0 \end{pmatrix}$.

(f) $\mathbf{P} = \begin{pmatrix} 1/2 & 1/2 & 0 \\ 0 & 1/2 & 1/2 \\ 1/3 & 1/3 & 1/3 \end{pmatrix}$.

2. Consider the transition matrix:

$$\mathbf{P} = \begin{pmatrix} 1/2 & 1/3 & 1/6 \\ 3/4 & 0 & 1/4 \\ 0 & 1 & 0 \end{pmatrix}.$$

(a) Show that this is a regular Markov chain.
(b) The process is started in state 1; find the probability that it is in state 3 after two steps.
(c) Find the limiting probability vector $\mathbf{w}$.

3. Consider the general 2×2 transition matrix

$$\mathbf{P} = \begin{pmatrix} 1 - a & a \\ b & 1 - b \end{pmatrix}.$$

(a) Under what conditions is $\mathbf{P}$ absorbing?
(b) Under what conditions is $\mathbf{P}$ ergodic but not regular?
(c) Under what conditions is $\mathbf{P}$ regular?

4. Find the fixed probability vector $\mathbf{w}$ for the matrices in Exercise 3 that are regular.

5. Find the fixed probability vector **w** for each of the following regular matrices.

   (a) $\mathbf{P} = \begin{pmatrix} .75 & .25 \\ .5 & .5 \end{pmatrix}$.

   (b) $\mathbf{P} = \begin{pmatrix} .9 & .1 \\ .1 & .9 \end{pmatrix}$.

   (c) $\mathbf{P} = \begin{pmatrix} 3/4 & 1/4 & 0 \\ 0 & 2/3 & 1/3 \\ 1/4 & 1/4 & 1/2 \end{pmatrix}$.

6. Consider the transition matrix in Exercise 3 with $a = b = 1$. Show that this chain is ergodic but not regular. Find the fixed probability vector and interpret it. Show that $\mathbf{P}^n$ does not tend to a limit, but that $\mathbf{A}_n = (\mathbf{I} + \mathbf{P} + \mathbf{P}^2 + \cdots + \mathbf{P}^n)/(n + 1)$ does.

7. Consider the transition matrix of Exercise 3 with $a = 0$ and $b = 1/2$. Compute directly the unique fixed probability vector, and use your result to prove that the chain is not ergodic.

8. Show that the matrix

$$\mathbf{P} = \begin{pmatrix} 1 & 0 & 0 \\ 1/4 & 1/2 & 1/4 \\ 0 & 0 & 1 \end{pmatrix}$$

has more than one fixed probability vector. Find the matrix that $\mathbf{P}^n$ approaches as $n \to \infty$, and verify that it is not a matrix all of whose rows are the same.

9. Prove that, if a 3-by-3 transition matrix has the property that its *column* sums are 1, then (1/3 1/3 1/3) is a fixed probability vector. State a similar result for n-by-n transition matrices. Interpret these results for ergodic chains.

10. Show that Examples 8 and 9 of Section 11.1 are not ergodic chains.

11. Consider Example 1 (drunkard's walk) of Section 11.2. Assume that if the walker reaches state 0, he turns around and returns to state 1 on the next step and, similarly, if he reaches 4 he returns on the next step to state 3. Is this new chain ergodic? Is it regular?

12. For Example 2 of Section 11.1 when **P** is ergodic, what is the proportion of people who are told that the president will run? Interpret the fact that this proportion is independent of the starting state.

13. Consider an independent trials process to be a Markov chain which states the possible outcomes of the experiment. What is its fixed probability vector? Is the chain always regular? Illustrate this for Example 3 of Section 11.1.

14. Show that Example 6 of Section 11.1 is an ergodic chain, but not a regular chain. Show that its fixed probability vector **w** is a binomial distribution.

15. Show that Example 7 of Section 11.1 is regular and find the limiting vector.

16. Toss a fair die repeatedly. Let S_n denote the total of the outcomes through the nth toss. Show that there is a limiting value for the proportion of the first n values of S_n that are divisible by 7, and compute the value for this limit. *Hint:* the desired limit is an equilibrium probability vector for an appropriate seven state Markov chain.

17. Let **P** be the transition matrix of a regular Markov chain. Assume that there are r states and let $N(r)$ be the smallest integer n such that **P** is regular if and only if $\mathbf{P}^{N(r)}$ has no zero entries. Find a finite upper bound for $N(r)$. See if you can determine $N(3)$ exactly.

18. It is natural to ask: What is the smallest power that we must check to see if a matrix with r states is regular? It has been shown that the answer is $r^2 - 2r + 2$. The following example shows that this number can, in fact, be required: for states $i = 1$, $2, \ldots, r - 2$, $\mathbf{P}(i, i + 1) = 1$, $\mathbf{P}(r - 1, r) = 1/2$, $\mathbf{P}(r - 1,1) = 1/2$, and $\mathbf{P}(r,1) = 1$.
    (a) Show that this is a regular Markov chain.
    (b) For $r = 3$, verify that the fifth power is the first power that has no zeros.

19. A discrete time queuing system of capacity n consists of the person being served and those waiting to be served. The queue length x is observed each second. If $0 < x < n$, then with probability p, the queue size is increased by one by an arrival and, independently, with probability r, it is decreased by one because the person being served finishes service. If $x = 0$, only an arrival (with probability p) is possible. If $x = n$, an arrival will depart without waiting for service, and so only the departure (with probability r) of the person being served is possible. Form a Markov chain with states given by the number of customers in the queue. Modify the program **Limit** so that you can input n, p, and r, and the program will construct the transition matrix and compute the fixed vector. The quantity $s = p/r$ is called the *traffic intensity*. Describe the differences in the fixed vectors according as $s < 1$, $s = 1$, or $s > 1$.

20. Write a computer program to simulate the queue in Exercise 19. Have your program keep track of the proportion of the time that the queue length is j for $j = 0, \ldots, n$ and the average queue length. Show that the behavior of the queue length is very different depending upon whether the traffic intensity s has the property $s < 1, s = 1$, or $s > 1$.

21. In the queueing problem of Exercise 19, let S be the total service time required by a customer and T the time between arrivals of the customers.
    (a) Show that $P(S = j) = (1 - r)^{j-1}r$ and $P(T = j) = (1 - p)^{j-1}p, j > 0$.
    (b) Show that $E(S) = 1/r$ and $E(T) = 1/p$.
    (c) Interpret the condition $s < 1, s. = 1$, and $s > 1$ in terms of these expected values.

22. In Exercise 19 the service time S has a geometric distribution with $E(S) = 1/r$. Assume that the service time is, instead, a constant time of t seconds. Modify your computer program of Exercise 20 so that it simulates a constant time service distri-

bution. Compare the average queue length for the two types of distributions when they have the same expected service time (i.e., take $t = 1/r$). Which distribution leads to the longer queues on the average?

23. A certain experiment is believed to be described by a two-state Markov chain with the transition matrix **P**, where

$$\mathbf{P} = \begin{pmatrix} .5 & .5 \\ p & 1 - p \end{pmatrix}$$

and the parameter p is not known. When the experiment is performed many times, the chain ends in state one approximately 20 percent of the time and in state two approximately 80 percent of the time. Compute a sensible estimate for the unknown parameter p and explain how you found it.

24. Prove that, in an r state ergodic chain, it is possible to go from any state to any other state in at most $r - 1$ steps.

25. Let **P** be the transition matrix of an r state ergodic chain. Prove that, if the diagonal entries p_{ii} are positive, then the chain is regular.

26. Prove that if **P** is the transition matrix of an ergodic chain, then $^1/_2 (\mathbf{I} + \mathbf{P})$ is the transition matrix of a regular chain. *Hint:* Use Exercise 25.

27. Prove that **P** and $^1/_2 (\mathbf{I} + \mathbf{P})$ have the same fixed vectors.

28. In his book, *Wahrscheinlichkeitsrechnung und Statistik,*[9] A. Engle proposes an algorithm for finding the fixed vector for an ergodic Markov chain when the transition probabilities are rational numbers. Here is his algorithm: For each state i, let a_i be the least common multiple of the nonzero entries in the ith row. Engle describes his algorithm in terms of moving chips around on the states—indeed, for small examples, he recommends implementing the algorithm this way. Start by putting a_i chips on state i for all i. Then, at each state, redistribute the a_i chips, sending $a_i p_{ij}$ to state j. The number of chips at state i after this redistribution need not be a multiple of a_i. For each state i, add just enough chips to bring the number of chips at state i up to a multiple of a_i. Then redistribute the chips in the same manner. This process will eventually reach a point where the number of chips at each state, after the redistribution, is the same as before redistribution. At this point, we have found a fixed vector. Here is an example:

$$\mathbf{P} = \begin{matrix} 1 \\ 2 \\ 3 \end{matrix} \begin{pmatrix} 1/2 & 1/4 & 1/4 \\ 1/2 & 0 & 1/2 \\ 1/2 & 1/4 & 1/4 \end{pmatrix}.$$

with column labels $1 \quad 2 \quad 3$

We start with **a** = (4 2 4). The chips after successive redistributions are

$$
\begin{array}{rrr}
(4 & 2 & 4) \\
(5 & 2 & 3) \\
(8 & 2 & 4) \\
(7 & 3 & 4) \\
(8 & 4 & 4) \\
(8 & 3 & 5) \\
(8 & 4 & 8) \\
(10 & 4 & 6) \\
(12 & 4 & 8) \\
(12 & 5 & 7) \\
(12 & 6 & 8) \\
(13 & 5 & 8) \\
(16 & 6 & 8) \\
(15 & 6 & 9) \\
(16 & 6 & 12) \\
(17 & 7 & 10) \\
(20 & 8 & 12) \\
(20 & 8 & 12),
\end{array}
$$

and we find that **a** = (20 8 12) is a fixed vector.

(a) Write a computer program to implement this algorithm.

(b) Prove that the algorithm will stop. *Hint:* Let **b** be a vector with integer coordinates that is a fixed vector for **P** and such that each coordinate of the starting vector **a** is less than or equal to the corresponding component of **b**. Show that, in the iteration, the components of the vectors are always increasing, and always less than or equal to the corresponding component of **b**.

29. (Shepp)[10] A computing center keeps information on a tape in positions of unit length. During each time unit there is one request to occupy a unit of the tape. When this arrives the first free unit is used. Also, during each second, each of the units that are occupied is vacated with probability p. Simulate this process, starting with an empty tape. Estimate the expected number of sites occupied for a given value of p. If p is small, can you choose the tape long enough so that there is a small probability that a new job will have to be turned away (i.e., that all the sites are occupied)? Form a Markov chain with states the number of sites occupied. Modify the program **Limit Vector** to compute the fixed vector. Use this to check your conjecture by simulation.

30. Let **P** be the transition matrix of an ergodic Markov chain. Let **x** be any column vector such that **Px** = **x**. Let M be the maximum value of the components of **x**. Assume that $x_i = M$. Show that if $p_{ij} > 0$ then $x_j = M$. Use this to prove that **x** must be a constant vector.

[10]E.G. Coffman, J.T. Kaduta, and L.A. Shepp, "On the Asymptotic Optimality of First-Storage Allocation," *IEEE Trans. Software Engineering*, vol. 11 (1985), pp. 235–239.

31. Let P be the transition matrix of an ergodic Markov chain. Let $\mathbf{w}$ be a fixed probability vector (i.e., $\mathbf{w}$ is a row vector with $\mathbf{w}P = \mathbf{w}$). Show that if $w_i = 0$ and $p_{ji} > 0$ then $w_j = 0$. Use this to show that the fixed probability vector for an ergodic chain cannot have any 0 entries.

11.4 THE FUNDAMENTAL LIMIT THEOREM FOR REGULAR MARKOV CHAINS

The fundamental limit theorem for regular Markov chains states that if P is a regular transition matrix then

$$\lim_{n \to \infty} P^n = \mathbf{cw},$$

where $\mathbf{w}$ is a unique probability vector. In this section we shall give two very different proofs of this theorem.

Averaging Theorem

THEOREM 13

If P is an r-by-r regular transition matrix and $\mathbf{y}$ is any r-component column vector, then

$$P^n\mathbf{y} \to k\mathbf{c}$$

where $k\mathbf{c}$ is the constant column vector with components k depending on $\mathbf{y}$.

Proof. This theorem has a simple interpretation as an averaging process. Consider the result of multiplying a column vector $\mathbf{y}$ on the left by a probability matrix P. Since the row sums of P are one, each component of the vector $P\mathbf{y}$ is an average of the components of the vector $\mathbf{y}$. The components of $P^2\mathbf{y}$ are an average of the components of the vector $P\mathbf{y}$. In general, the vector $P^n\mathbf{y}$ is the result of n such averaging operations. It seems reasonable that this averaging process should, for suitable P, smooth out the differences that may originally have existed in the components of the first vector. We shall first prove a lemma which shows that this *smoothing* does take place and then use this result to prove the theorem.

Smoothing Lemma

LEMMA 14

Let P be an r-by-r transition matrix with no zero entries. Let d be the smallest entry of the matrix. Let $\mathbf{y}$ be a column vector with r components, the largest of which is M_0 and the smallest m_0. Let M_1 and m_1 be the largest and smallest component, respectively, of the vector $P\mathbf{y}$. Then

$$M_1 - m_1 \leq (1 - 2d)(M_0 - m_0).$$

Proof. The component m_1 of $\mathbf{Py}$ is an average of the components of $\mathbf{y}$. This average assigns weight at least d to the maximum component M_0 of $\mathbf{y}$. The result is surely greater than or equal to the average which would be obtained by assigning weight d to the component M_0 and all the rest of the weight to the minimum component m_0. That is,

$$m_1 \geq dM_0 + (1 - d)m_0. \tag{1}$$

The same argument shows that

$$M_1 \leq dm_0 + (1 - d)M_0. \tag{2}$$

Multiplying Equation (1) by -1, we have

$$-m_1 \leq -dM_0 - (1 - d)m_0. \tag{3}$$

Adding Equation (2) and Equation (3), we have

$$M_1 - m_1 \leq d(m_0 - M_0) + (1 - d)(M_0 - m_0)$$

$$= (1 - 2d)(M_0 - m_0).$$

This completes the proof of the lemma. ∎

We return now to the proof of Theorem 13. We prove this theorem for the special case that $\mathbf{P}$ has no 0 entries, so that $d > 0$. The extension to the general case is indicated in Exercise 6.

Let $\mathbf{y}$ be any r-component column vector. Let M_n and m_n be, respectively, the maximum and minimum components of the vector $\mathbf{P}^n\mathbf{y}$. The vector $\mathbf{P}^n\mathbf{y}$ is obtained from the vector $\mathbf{P}^{n-1}\mathbf{y}$ by multiplying on the left by the matrix $\mathbf{P}$. Hence each component of $\mathbf{P}^n\mathbf{y}$ is an average of the components of $\mathbf{P}^{n-1}\mathbf{y}$. Thus

$$M_0 \geq M_1 \geq M_2 \geq \ldots$$

and

$$m_0 \leq m_1 \leq m_2 \leq \ldots$$

Each sequence is monotone and bounded:

$$m_0 \leq m_n \leq M_n \leq M_0.$$

Hence, each of these sequences will have a limit as n tends to infinity.

Let M be the limit of M_n and m the limit of m_n. We know that $m \leq M$. We shall prove that $M - m = 0$. This will be the case if $M_n - m_n$ tends to 0. Let d be the smallest element of $\mathbf{P}$. By our lemma

$$M_n - m_n \leq (1 - 2d)(M_{n-1} - m_{n-1}).$$

From this we see that

$$M_n - m_n \leq (1 - 2d)^n(M_0 - m_0).$$

Since $0 < d \leq \frac{1}{2}$ (see Exercise 5), $0 \leq 1 - 2d < 1$, so the difference $M_n - m_n$ tends to 0 as n tends to infinity. Since every component of $\mathbf{P}^n\mathbf{y}$ lies between m_n and M_n, each component must approach the same number $k = M = m$. This proves Theorem 13. ∎

Fundamental Limit Theorem

THEOREM 15   Fundamental Limit Theorem for Regular Chains

If **P** is the transition matrix for a regular Markov chain, then

$$\lim_{n \to \infty} \mathbf{P}^n = \mathbf{cw},$$

where **w** is a probability vector.

Proof.   Apply Theorem 13 for **y**, a vector with value 1 in the jth component and 0 in all other components. Theorem 13 states that

$$\lim_{n \to \infty} \mathbf{P}^n \mathbf{y} = k\mathbf{c}, \tag{4}$$

where $k\mathbf{c}$ is a constant column vector. But $\mathbf{P}^n \mathbf{y}$ is the jth column of $\mathbf{P}^n$. Doing this for each j proves that the columns of $\mathbf{P}^n$ approach constant column vectors. That is, the rows of $\mathbf{P}^n$ approach a common row vector **w**, or,

$$\lim_{n \to \infty} \mathbf{P}^n = \mathbf{cw}. \tag{5}$$

To show that **w** is a probability vector, note that $\mathbf{P}^n \mathbf{c} = \mathbf{c}$ and so

$$\lim_{n \to \infty} \mathbf{P}^n \mathbf{c} = \mathbf{c},$$

and from Equation (5)

$$\lim_{n \to \infty} \mathbf{P}^n \mathbf{c} = \mathbf{cwc},$$

which shows that $\mathbf{wc} = 1$. ∎

Doeblin's Proof

We give now a very different proof of the fundamental limit theorem for regular Markov chains. This proof was first given by Doeblin,[11] a brilliant young Belgian mathematician who was killed in his twenties in the Second World War.

Proof.   Consider a regular Markov chain with transition matrix **P** and with states $S = (1, 2, \ldots, r)$. Form a new Markov chain called a *coupled chain* as follows: Start a Markov chain in state i with transition matrix **P** and a Markov chain in state $j \neq i$ with the same transition matrix **P**. Let these processes move independently until the first time they are in the same state. When this happens, glue them together and have them proceed, from this time on, together as a single chain with transition matrix **P**. Let $X_0, X_1, X_2, \ldots$ be

---

[11] W. Doeblin, "Exposé de la Théorie des Chaines Simple Constantes de Markov à un Nombre Fini d'Etats," *Rev. Mach. de l'Union Interbalkanique*, vol. 2 (1937), pp. 77–105.

the outcomes for the process started in state i and $Y_0, Y_1, Y_2, \ldots$ the outcomes for the process started at j. If we watch only the X process, we have an ordinary Markov chain with transition matrix $\mathbf{P}$ started at state i. If we watch only the Y process, we have an ordinary Markov chain started at j.

For example, consider the weather in the Land of Oz. Start the first process in state R and the second in state S. Then a possible history of the coupled process is

X: R N S N R R S N R N S R N
Y: S R N S S R S N R N S R N

The two processes became glued together on the fifth day.

We first show that the two processes will eventually become glued together. To see this, make the states of the form (k,k) absorbing states for the coupled process. Then the coupled process becomes an absorbing Markov chain with states pairs (r,s) and transition matrix $\mathbf{P}_{rs,uv} = \mathbf{P}_{ru}\mathbf{P}_{sv}$ if $r \neq s$ and $\mathbf{P}_{rr,rr} = 1$. Since an absorbing chain eventually reaches an absorbing state, the coupled process will eventually become glued together.

Now for the original coupled process,

$$\mathbf{P}(X_n = k, Y_n = k) \leq \mathbf{P}(X_n = k) = p_{ik}^{(n)}$$

and

$$\mathbf{P}(X_n = k, Y_n = k) \leq \mathbf{P}(Y_n = k) = p_{jk}^{(n)},$$

so

$$\mathbf{P}(X_n = k, Y_n = k) \leq \min(p_{ik}^{(n)}, p_{jk}^{(n)}).$$

Thus,

$$\sum_k \mathbf{P}(X_n = k, Y_n = k) \leq \sum_k \min(p_{ik}^{(n)}, p_{jk}^{(n)}).$$

As n tends to infinity, the left side of this equation approaches 1 since the coupled chain will eventually become glued together. The right side has values ≤ 1 and hence it must also approach 1. But for any two numbers a, b

$$\min(a,b) = \frac{1}{2}(a + b - |a - b|).$$

Thus,

$$\lim_{n \to \infty} \sum_k \frac{1}{2}(p_{ik}^{(n)} + p_{jk}^{(n)} - |p_{ik}^{(n)} - p_{jk}^{(n)}|)$$

$$= \lim_{n \to \infty} 1 - \frac{1}{2}\sum_k |p_{ik}^{(n)} - p_{jk}^{(n)}| = 1,$$

and so

$$\lim_{n \to \infty} \sum_k \lceil p_{ik}^{(n)} - p_{jk}^{(n)} \rceil = 0.$$

But this states that the columns of $\mathbf{P}^n$ tend to constant vectors, or that the rows of $\mathbf{P}^n$ tend to the same vector $\mathbf{w}$, as was to be proved. The proof that $\mathbf{w}$ is a probability vector is the same as in the previous proof. ■

The fact that the entries of the limiting vector are strictly positive will follow from Corollary 17 in the next section (see also Exercise 7 or Exercise 31 of Section 11.2).

Exercises

1. Define $\mathbf{P}$ and $\mathbf{y}$ by

$$\mathbf{P} = \begin{pmatrix} .5 & .5 \\ .25 & .75 \end{pmatrix}, \qquad \mathbf{y} = \begin{pmatrix} 1 \\ 0 \end{pmatrix}.$$

Compute $\mathbf{Py}$, $\mathbf{P}^2\mathbf{y}$, and $\mathbf{P}^4\mathbf{y}$ and show that the results are approaching a constant vector. What is this vector?

2. Let $\mathbf{P}$ be a regular $r \times r$ transition matrix and $\mathbf{y}$ any r-component column vector. Show that the value of the limiting constant vector for $\mathbf{P}^n\mathbf{y}$ is $\mathbf{wy}$.

3. Show that if

$$\mathbf{P} = \begin{pmatrix} 1 & 0 & 0 \\ .25 & 0 & .75 \\ 0 & 0 & 1 \end{pmatrix}, \qquad \mathbf{y} = \begin{pmatrix} 1 \\ .25 \\ 0 \end{pmatrix}, \qquad \mathbf{z} = \begin{pmatrix} 0 \\ .75 \\ 1 \end{pmatrix},$$

then $\mathbf{Py} = \mathbf{y}$ and $\mathbf{Pz} = \mathbf{z}$. Does this show that the Markov chain with $\mathbf{P}$ as transition matrix is not regular?

4. Describe the set of all fixed column vectors for the chain given in Exercise 3.

5. Let $\mathbf{P}$ be the transition matrix for a Markov chain with at least two states, and assume that $\mathbf{P}$ has all entries positive. Let d be the minimum entry in the matrix. Show that d is at most $1/2$.

6. The theorem that $\mathbf{P}^n \to \mathbf{W} = \mathbf{cw}$ was proved only for the case that $\mathbf{P}$ has no zero entries. Fill in the details of the following extension to the case that $\mathbf{P}$ is regular. Since $\mathbf{P}$ is regular, for some N, $\mathbf{P}^N$ has no zeros. Thus, the proof given shows that $M_{nN} - m_{nN}$ approaches 0 as n tends to infinity. However, the difference $M_n - m_n$ can never increase. (Why?) Hence, if we know that the differences obtained by looking at every Nth time tend to 0, then the entire sequence must also tend to 0.

7. Let $\mathbf{P}$ be a regular transition matrix and $\mathbf{y}$ be a column that has a 1 in the jth component and 0 in all other components. Then

$$\lim_{n \to \infty} \mathbf{P}^n\mathbf{y} = w_j\mathbf{c}.$$

Prove that w_j is not 0. *Hint:* Let N be such that $\mathbf{P}^N$ has no zeros. Let m_N be the minimum component of $\mathbf{P}^N\mathbf{y}$. Show that $0 < m_N \leqslant w_j$.

This proves that the limiting vector $\mathbf{w}$ for a regular Markov chain has all positive components.

8. Here is a trick to try on your friends. Shuffle a deck of cards and deal them out one at a time. Count the face cards each as ten. Ask your friend to look at one of the first ten cards; if this card is a six, she is to look at the card that turns up six cards later; if this card is a three, she is to look at the card that turns up three cards later, and so forth. Eventually she will reach a point where she is to look at a card that turns up x cards later but there are not x cards left. You then tell her the last card that she looked at even though you did not know her starting point. You tell her you do this by watching her, and she cannot disguise the times that she looks at the cards. In fact you just do the same procedure and, even though you do not start at the same point as she does, you will most likely end at the same point. Why?

9. Write a program to play the game in Exercise 8.

11.5 MEAN FIRST PASSAGE TIMES FOR ERGODIC CHAINS

In this section we consider two closely related descriptive quantities of interest for ergodic chains: the mean time to return to a state and the mean time to go from one state to another state.

Let $\mathbf{P}$ be the transition matrix of an ergodic chain with states $s_1, s_2, \ldots, s_r$. Let $\mathbf{w} = (w_1, w_2, \ldots, w_r)$ be the unique probability vector such that $\mathbf{w}\mathbf{P} = \mathbf{w}$. Then, by the law of large numbers for Markov chains, in the long run the process will spend a fraction w_j of the time in state s_j. Thus, if we start in state s_i the chain will eventually reach state s_j; in fact, it will be in this state infinitely often.

Another way to see this is the following: Form a new Markov chain by making s_j an absorbing state, that is, define $p_{jj} = 1$. If we start at any state other than s_j, this new process will behave exactly like the original chain up to the first time that state s_j is reached. Since the original chain was an ergodic chain, it was possible to reach s_j from any other state. Thus the new chain is an absorbing chain with a single absorbing state s_j that will eventually be reached. And so, if we start the original chain at a state s_i with $i \neq j$, we will eventually reach the state s_j.

Let $\mathbf{N}$ be the fundamental matrix for the new chain. The entries of $\mathbf{N}$ give the expected number of times in each state before absorption. In terms of the original chain, these quantities give the expected number of times in each of the states before reaching state s_j for the first time. The ith component of the vector $\mathbf{N}\mathbf{c}$ gives the expected number of steps before absorption in the new chain, starting in state s_i. In terms of the old chain, this is the expected number of steps required to reach state s_j for the first time starting at state s_i.

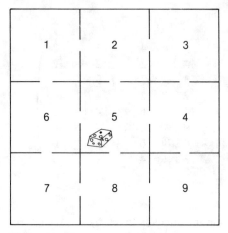

Figure 5 The maze problem.

Mean First Passage Time

DEFINITION 10

If an ergodic Markov chain is started in state s_i, the expected number of steps to reach state s_j for the first time is called the *mean first passage time* from s_i to s_j. It is denoted by m_{ij}. By convention $m_{ii} = 0$.

EXAMPLE 1

Let us return to the maze example (Example 3 of Section 11.3). We shall make this ergodic chain into an absorbing chain by making state 5 an absorbing state. For example, we might assume that food is placed in the center of the maze and once the rat finds the food, he stays to enjoy it (see Figure 5).

The new transition matrix in canonical form is

$$
\mathbf{P} = \begin{array}{c} \\ 1 \\ 2 \\ 3 \\ 4 \\ 6 \\ 7 \\ 8 \\ 9 \\ 5 \end{array}
\begin{array}{c} \begin{array}{cccccccc} 1 & 2 & 3 & 4 & 6 & 7 & 8 & 9 \end{array} \hspace{0.5em} 5 \\
\left(\begin{array}{cccccccc|c}
0 & 1/2 & 0 & 0 & 1/2 & 0 & 0 & 0 & 0 \\
1/3 & 0 & 1/3 & 0 & 0 & 0 & 0 & 0 & 1/3 \\
0 & 1/2 & 0 & 1/2 & 0 & 0 & 0 & 0 & 0 \\
0 & 0 & 1/3 & 0 & 0 & 0 & 0 & 1/3 & 1/3 \\
1/3 & 0 & 0 & 0 & 0 & 1/3 & 0 & 0 & 1/3 \\
0 & 0 & 0 & 0 & 1/2 & 0 & 1/2 & 0 & 0 \\
0 & 0 & 0 & 0 & 0 & 1/3 & 0 & 1/3 & 1/3 \\
0 & 0 & 0 & 1/2 & 0 & 0 & 1/2 & 0 & 0 \\
\hline
0 & 0 & 0 & 0 & 0 & 0 & 0 & 0 & 1
\end{array}\right)
\end{array} .
$$

If we compute the fundamental matrix $\mathbf{N}$, we obtain

$$
\mathbf{N} = \frac{1}{8}
\begin{pmatrix}
14 & 9 & 4 & 3 & 9 & 4 & 3 & 2 \\
6 & 14 & 6 & 4 & 4 & 2 & 2 & 2 \\
4 & 9 & 14 & 9 & 3 & 2 & 3 & 4 \\
2 & 4 & 6 & 14 & 2 & 2 & 4 & 6 \\
6 & 4 & 2 & 2 & 14 & 6 & 4 & 2 \\
4 & 3 & 2 & 3 & 9 & 14 & 9 & 4 \\
2 & 2 & 2 & 4 & 4 & 6 & 14 & 6 \\
2 & 3 & 4 & 9 & 3 & 4 & 9 & 14
\end{pmatrix}.
$$

The expected time to absorption for different starting states is given by the vector $\mathbf{Nc}$, where

$$
\mathbf{Nc} =
\begin{pmatrix}
6 \\
5 \\
6 \\
5 \\
5 \\
6 \\
5 \\
6
\end{pmatrix}.
$$

We see that, starting from compartment 1, it will take on the average six steps to reach food. It is clear from symmetry that we should get the same answer for starting at state 3, 7, or 9. It is also clear that it should take one more step, starting at one of these states, than it would starting at 2, 4, 6, or 8. Some of the results obtained from $\mathbf{N}$ are not so obvious. For instance, we note that the expected number of times in the starting state is 14/8 regardless of the state in which we start. $\qquad\square$

Mean Recurrence Time

A quantity that is closely related to the mean first passage time is the *mean recurrence time*, defined as follows. Assume that we start in state s_i; consider the length of time before we return to s_i for the first time. It is clear that we must return, since we either stay at s_i the first step or go to some other state s_j, and from any other state s_j, we will eventually reach s_i.

DEFINITION 11

If an ergodic Markov chain is started in state s_i, the expected number of steps to return to s_i for the first time is the *mean recurrence time* for s_i. It is denoted by r_i.

We shall need to develop some basic properties of the mean first passage times.

Consider the mean first passage time from s_i to s_j; assume that $i \neq j$. This may be computed as follows: take the expected number of steps required given the outcome of the first step, multiply by the probability that this outcome occurs, and add. If the first step is to s_j, the expected number of steps required is 1; if it is to some other state s_k, the expected number of steps required is m_{kj} plus 1 for the step already taken. Thus,

$$m_{ij} = p_{ij} + \sum_{k \neq j} p_{ik}(m_{kj} + 1),$$

or, since

$$\sum_k p_{ik} = 1,$$

$$m_{ij} = \sum_{k \neq j} p_{ik} m_{kj} + 1. \tag{1}$$

Similarly, starting in s_i, it must take at least one step to return. Considering all possible first steps gives us

$$r_i = \sum_k p_{ik}(m_{ki} + 1)$$

$$= \sum_k p_{ik} m_{ki} + 1. \tag{2}$$

Mean First Passage Matrix and Mean Recurrence Matrix

Let us now define two matrices $\mathbf{M}$ and $\mathbf{D}$. The ij entry m_{ij} of $\mathbf{M}$ is the mean first passage time to go from s_i to s_j if $i \neq j$; the diagonal entries are zero. $\mathbf{M}$ is called the *mean first passage matrix*. $\mathbf{D}$ is the matrix with all entries zero except the diagonal entries $d_{ii} = r_i$. $\mathbf{D}$ is called the *mean recurrence matrix*. Then if $\mathbf{C}$ is an $r \times r$ matrix with all entries 1, we can write Equation (1) and Equation (2) in matrix form as

$$\mathbf{M} = \mathbf{PM} + \mathbf{C} - \mathbf{D}, \tag{3}$$

or

$$(\mathbf{I} - \mathbf{P})\mathbf{M} = \mathbf{C} - \mathbf{D}. \tag{4}$$

Equation (4) with $m_{ii} = 0$ implies Equation (1) and Equation (2). We are now in a position to prove our first basic theorem.

THEOREM 16

For an ergodic Markov chain, the mean recurrence time for state s_i is $r_i = 1/w_i$, where w_i is the ith component of the fixed probability vector for the transition matrix.

Proof. Multiplying both sides of Equation (4) by $\mathbf{w}$ and using the fact that $\mathbf{w}(\mathbf{I} - \mathbf{P}) = \mathbf{0}$ gives

$$\mathbf{wC} - \mathbf{wD} = \mathbf{0}.$$

Here $\mathbf{wC}$ is a row vector with all entries 1 and $\mathbf{wD}$ is a row vector with ith entry $w_i r_i$. Thus

$$(1,1, \ldots ,1) = (w_1 r_1, w_2 r_2, \ldots ,w_n r_n)$$

and

$$r_i = 1/w_i,$$

as was to be proved. ∎

COROLLARY 17

For an ergodic Markov chain, the components of the fixed probability vector $\mathbf{w}$ are strictly positive.

Proof. We know that the values of r_i are finite and so $w_i = \dfrac{1}{r_i}$ cannot be 0. ∎

EXAMPLE 1 (continued)

In Example 3 of Section 11.3 we found the fixed probability vector for the maze example to be

$$\mathbf{w} = \left(\frac{1}{12} \quad \frac{1}{8} \quad \frac{1}{12} \quad \frac{1}{8} \quad \frac{1}{6} \quad \frac{1}{8} \quad \frac{1}{12} \quad \frac{1}{8} \quad \frac{1}{12} \right).$$

Hence, the mean recurrence times are given by the reciprocals of these probabilities. That is,

$$\mathbf{r} = (12 \quad 8 \quad 12 \quad 8 \quad 6 \quad 8 \quad 12 \quad 8 \quad 12). \qquad \square$$

Returning to the Land of Oz, we found that the weather in the Land of Oz could be represented by a Markov chain with states rain, nice, and snow. In Section 11.3 we found that the limiting vector was $\mathbf{w} = (2/5 \ 1/5 \ 2/5)$. From this we see that the mean number of days between rainy days is 5/2, between nice days is 5, and between snowy days is 5/2.

We have seen that the fixed vector $\mathbf{w}$ for an ergodic chain can be obtained from a fundamental matrix $\mathbf{Z} = (\mathbf{I} - \mathbf{P} + \mathbf{cb})^{-1}$ by $\mathbf{w} = \mathbf{bZ}$. Then we can obtain the mean recurrence times r_i by $r_i = 1/w_i$.

We shall now prove that, for an ergodic Markov chain, we can obtain the mean first passage matrix $\mathbf{M}$ from a fundamental matrix $\mathbf{Z}$. Recall that we defined $\mathbf{Z}$ by $\mathbf{Z} = (\mathbf{I} - \mathbf{P} + \mathbf{cb})^{-1}$, where

$$\mathbf{b} = (b_1, b_2, \ldots ,b_r)$$

is any vector with $\mathbf{bc} \neq 0$ with $\mathbf{c}$ a column vector of all ones.

We need some additional facts about $\mathbf{Z}$.

THEOREM 18

Let $\mathbf{Z} = (\mathbf{I} - \mathbf{P} + \mathbf{cb})^{-1}$. Then if $k = 1/(\mathbf{bc})$,

   (a) $\mathbf{Zc} = k\mathbf{c}$,

   (b) $\mathbf{Z}(\mathbf{I} - \mathbf{P}) = \mathbf{I} - k\mathbf{cb}$.

Proof. From the definition of $\mathbf{Z}$

$$\mathbf{Z}(\mathbf{I} - \mathbf{P} + \mathbf{cb}) = \mathbf{I}. \tag{5}$$

Multiplying by $\mathbf{c}$.

$$\mathbf{Z}(\mathbf{I} - \mathbf{P} + \mathbf{cb})\mathbf{c} = \mathbf{c}.$$

Since $\mathbf{c} = \mathbf{Pc}$, we have $\mathbf{Zcbc} = \mathbf{c}$ and $\mathbf{Zc} = 1/(\mathbf{bc})\, \mathbf{c} = k\mathbf{c}$.
(b) follows from Equation (5) and (a). ∎

THEOREM 19

The mean first passage matrix $\mathbf{M}$ is determined from $\mathbf{Z}$ by

$$m_{jj} = \frac{(z_{jj} - z_{ij})}{w_j}.$$

Proof. We showed in Equation (4) that

$$(\mathbf{I} - \mathbf{P})\mathbf{M} = \mathbf{C} - \mathbf{D}.$$

Thus,

$$\mathbf{Z}(\mathbf{I} - \mathbf{P})\mathbf{M} = \mathbf{ZC} - \mathbf{ZD},$$

and from (a) of Theorem 18,

$$\mathbf{Z}(\mathbf{I} - \mathbf{P})\mathbf{M} = k\mathbf{C} - \mathbf{ZD}.$$

Using (b) of Theorem 18,

$$\mathbf{M} - k\mathbf{cbM} = k\mathbf{C} - \mathbf{ZD}$$

or

$$\mathbf{M} = k\mathbf{C} - \mathbf{ZD} + k\mathbf{cbM},$$

and

$$m_{ij} = k - z_{ij}r_j + k(\mathbf{bM})_j. \tag{6}$$

But $m_{jj} = 0$, and so

$$k - z_{jj}\mathbf{r}_j + k(\mathbf{bM})_j = \mathbf{0},$$

or

$$k(\mathbf{bM})_j = z_{jj}r_j - k,$$

and from Equation (6),

$$m_{ij} = (z_{jj} - z_{ij}) \cdot r_j.$$

Since $r_j = 1/w_j$

$$m_{ij} = \frac{(z_{jj} - z_{ij})}{w_j}.$$ ∎

EXAMPLE 2

In Section 11.3 we found the fundamental matrix $\mathbf{Z}$ for $\mathbf{b} = (1,1,1)$ for the Land of Oz example to be

$$\mathbf{Z} = \begin{pmatrix} 14/15 & -1/5 & -2/5 \\ -2/15 & 3/5 & -2/15 \\ -2/5 & -1/5 & 14/15 \end{pmatrix}.$$

We have also seen that $\mathbf{w} = (2/5\ 1/5\ 2/5)$. From these we can now find $\mathbf{M}$ to be

$$\mathbf{M} = \begin{pmatrix} 0 & 4 & 10/3 \\ 8/3 & 0 & 8/3 \\ 10/3 & 4 & 0 \end{pmatrix}.$$

For example, from our theorem

$$m_{12} = \frac{(z_{22} - z_{12})}{w_2}$$

$$= \frac{(3/5 - (-1/5))}{(1/5)}$$

$$= 4.$$ □

Computation

The subroutine **ergodic** (in **Lib.Markov**) calculates the fundamental matrix, the fixed vector, the mean recurrence matrix $\mathbf{D}$, and the mean first passage matrix $\mathbf{M}$ (see top of facing page).

The program **Ergodic Chain** calls this subroutine to carry out the calculations for specific examples (see bottom of facing page). We have run the program for the Ehrenfest urn model (Example 6 of Section 11.1). (See top of page 468.)

From the mean first passage matrix, we see that the mean time to go from 0 balls in urn 1 to 2 balls in urn 1 is 2.6667 steps while the mean time to go from 2 balls in urn 1 to 0 balls in this urn is 18.6667. This reflects the fact that the model exhibits a central tendancy. Of course, the physicist is interested in the case of a large number of molecules, or balls, and so we should consider this example for n so large that we cannot compute it even with a computer.

```
sub ergodic(P(,),  w(),  r(),  M(,),  Z(,))

    dim I(8,8), X(8,8), E(8,8), c(8)

    let n = ubound(P,1)

    mat I = Idn(n,n)
    mat X = I - P
    mat E = con(n,n)
    mat X = X + E
    mat Z = inv(X)                    ! Fundamental matrix
    mat c = con(n)
    mat w = c*Z                       ! Fixed vector
    mat M = zer(n,n)
    mat r = zer(n)
    for k = 1 to n                    ! Compute mean first passage times
        for j = 1 to n
            let M(k,j) = (Z(j,j) - Z(k,j)) / w(j)
        next j
        let r(k) = 1/w(k)             ! mean recurrence times
    next k

end sub


! Ergodic Chain   (ECHAIN)
!
! Uses the subroutine ergodic in Lib.Markov to compute the descriptive
! quantities for an ergodic Markov chain.

library "Lib.Markov*"
dim P(6,6)                           ! Transition matrix.
dim Z(6,6), w(6), r(6),  M(6,6)    ! Key quantities.
dim label$(6)

read n                               ! Number of states.
data 5
mat read label$(n)
data 0,1,2,3,4

mat read P(n,n)
data  0,1,0,0,0
data  .25,0,.75,0,0
data  0,.5,0,.5,0
data  0,0,.75,0,.25
data  0,0,0,1,0

print "Transition matrix P:"
call matrix_labels(P, label$, label$, "##.####")

call ergodic(P,w,r,M,Z)

print
print "Fixed vector w:"
call vector_labels(w, label$, "##.####")

print
print "Mean recurrence times r:"
call vector_labels(r, label$, "####.####")

print
print "Mean first passage matrix M:"
call matrix_labels(M, label$, label$, "####.####")

end
```

```
Transition matrix P:
        0      1      2      3      4
0   .0000 1.0000  .0000  .0000  .0000
1   .2500  .0000  .7500  .0000  .0000
2   .0000  .5000  .0000  .5000  .0000
3   .0000  .0000  .7500  .0000  .2500
4   .0000  .0000  .0000 1.0000  .0000

Fixed vector w:
        0      1      2      3      4
    .0625  .2500  .3750  .2500  .0625

Mean recurrence times r:
        0      1       2        3       4
   16.0000 4.0000  2.6667   4.0000  16.0000

Mean first passage matrix M:
         0       1       2        3        4
0    .0000  1.0000  2.6667   6.3333  21.3333
1  15.0000   .0000  1.6667   5.3333  20.3333
2  18.6667  3.6667   .0000   3.6667  18.6667
3  20.3333  5.3333  1.6667    .0000  15.0000
4  21.3333  6.3333  2.6667   1.0000    .0000
```

Ehrenfest Model

EXAMPLE 3

Let us consider the Ehrenfest model[12] for gas diffusion for the general case of $2n$ balls. Every second, one of the $2n$ balls is chosen at random and moved from the urn it was in to the other urn. If there are i balls in the first urn, then with probability $\dfrac{i}{2n}$ we take one of them out and put it in the second urn, and with probability $\dfrac{(2n - i)}{2n}$ we take a ball from the second urn and put it in the first urn. At each second we let the number i of balls in the first urn be the state of the system. Then from state i we can pass only to state $i - 1$ and $i + 1$, and the transition probabilities are given by

$$p_{i,i-1} = \frac{i}{2n},$$

$$p_{i,i+1} = \frac{(2n - i)}{2n},$$

$p_{ik} = 0$, otherwise.

This defines the transition matrix of an ergodic but not regular Markov chain (see Exercise 14 of Section 11.3). Here the physicist is interested in long-term predictions about the state occupied. Our intuition can be used to guess the average number of times the system is in state s_i in the long run. We reason as follows: After watching many

[12]W. Feller, *Introduction to Probability and Its Applications*, 3d ed., (New York: John Wiley and Sons, 1957).

repetitions of the above mixing process and knowing nothing about how the process started we would expect any one ball to have probability $1/2$ of being in either urn. The probability then that we would have i balls in the first urn would be

$$w_i = \frac{\binom{2n}{i}}{2^{2n}},$$

that is, the same as the distribution of the number of heads in $2n$ tosses of a fair coin. Thus the mean recurrence time for state i is

$$r_i = \frac{2^{2n}}{\binom{2n}{i}}.$$

Consider in particular the central term $i = n$. We have seen that in $2n$ tosses of a fair coin the probability of exactly n heads is approximately $1/\sqrt{\pi n}$. Thus we may approximate r_n by $\sqrt{\pi n}$.

This model was used to explain a concept of reversibility in physical systems. Assume that we let our system run until it is in equilibrium. A graph is handed to you, and you are asked to tell if the outcomes were graphed in the natural order of time or with time reversed. It would seem that there should always be a tendency to move toward an equal proportion of balls so that the correct order of time should be the one with the most transition from i to $i - 1$ if $i > n$ and i to $i + 1$ if $i < n$.

In Figure 6 we show the results of simulating the Ehrenfest urn model for the case of $n = 50$ balls and 1000 time units, using the program **Ehrenfest Urn**. The top graph

```
Number of balls = 100
Number of seconds to elapse = 500
```

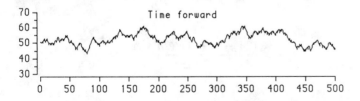

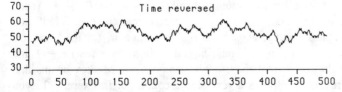

Figure 6 Simulation of the Ehrenfest urn model.

shows these results graphed in the order in which they occurred and the bottom graph shows the same results but with time reversed. There is no apparent difference. ☐

Reversibility

There is no apparent time direction in the Ehrenfest model. The reason for this is that this process has a property called *reversibility*. Let us calculate, for a general ergodic chain, the reverse transition probability:

$$P(X_{n-1} = j | X_n = i) = \frac{P(X_{n-1} = j, X_n = i)}{P(X_n = i)}$$

$$= \frac{P(X_{n-1} = j)P(X_n = i | X_{n-1} = j)}{P(X_n = i)}$$

$$= \frac{P(X_{n-1} = j)p_{ji}}{P(X_n = i)}.$$

In general, this will depend upon n, since $P(X_n = i)$ and also $P(X_{n-1} = j)$ change with n. However, if we start with the vector $\mathbf{w}$ or wait until equilibrium is reached, this will not be the case. Then we can define

$$p^*_{ij} = \frac{w_j p_{ji}}{w_i}$$

as a transition matrix for the process watched with time reversed.

Let us calculate a typical transition probability for the reverse chain $\mathbf{P}^* = \{p^*_{ij}\}$ in the Ehrenfest model. For example,

$$p^*_{i,i-1} = \frac{w_{i-1} p_{i-1,i}}{w_i} = \frac{\binom{2n}{i-1}}{2^{2n}} \times \frac{2n - i + 1}{2n} \times \frac{2^{2n}}{\binom{2n}{i}}$$

$$= \frac{(2n)!}{(i-1)!(2n-i+1)!} \times \frac{(2n-i+1)i!(2n-i)!}{2n(2n)!} = \frac{i}{2n}$$

$$= p_{i,i-1}$$

Similar calculations for the other transition probabilities show that $\mathbf{P}^* = \mathbf{P}$. When this occurs the process is called *reversible*. Clearly, an ergodic chain is reversible if, and only if, for every pair of states i and j, $w_i p_{ij} = w_j p_{ji}$. In particular, for the Ehrenfest model this means that $w_i p_{i,i-1} = w_{i-1} p_{i-1,i}$. Thus, in equilibrium, the pairs $i,i-1$ and $i-1,i$ should occur with the same frequency. While many of the Markov chains that occur in applications are reversible, this is a very strong condition. In Exercise 12 you are asked to· find an example of a Markov chain which is not reversible.

Exercises

1. Consider the Markov chain with transition matrix

$$\mathbf{P} = \begin{pmatrix} 1/2 & 1/2 \\ 1/4 & 3/4 \end{pmatrix}$$

Find the fundamental matrix $\mathbf{Z}$ for this chain, first by choosing $\mathbf{b} = (1,1)$, and then by choosing $\mathbf{b} = \mathbf{w}$, the fixed vector for $\mathbf{P}$. Compute the mean first passage matrix using each $\mathbf{Z}$ and verify that you get the same results.

2. A study of the strengths of Ivy League football teams shows that if a school has a strong team one year it is equally likely to have a strong or average team next year; if it has an average team, half the time it is average next year, and if it changes it is just as likely to become strong as weak; if it is weak it has $2/3$ probability of remaining so and $1/3$ of becoming average.

  (a) Find $\mathbf{Z}$ and use this to find $\mathbf{w}$.

  (b) A school has a strong team. On the average, how long will it be before it has another strong team?

  (c) A school has a weak team; how long (on the average) must the alumni wait for a strong team?

3. Consider Example 2 of Section 11.1 with $a = .5$ and $b = .75$. Assume that the president says that he will run. Find the expected length of time before the first time the answer is passed on incorrectly.

4. Find the mean recurrence time for each state for Example 2 of Section 11.1 for $a = .5$ and $b = .75$. Do the same for general a and b.

5. A die is rolled repeatedly. Show by the results of this Section that the mean time between occurrences of a given number is 6.

6. For the Land of Oz example, make rain into an absorbing state and find the fundamental matrix $\mathbf{N}$. Interpret the results obtained from this chain in terms of the original chain.

7. A rat runs through the maze shown below.

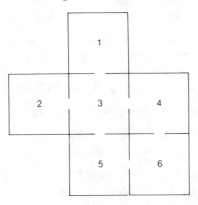

At each step it leaves the room it is in by choosing at random one of the doors out of the room.

(a) Give the transition matrix **P** for this Markov chain.

(b) Show that it is an ergodic chain but not a regular chain.

(c) Find the fixed vector.

(d) Find the expected number of steps before reaching Room 5 for the first time, starting in Room 1.

8. Modify the program **Ergodic Chain** so that you can compute the basic quantities for the queueing example of Exercise 19 of Section 11.3. Interpret the mean recurrence time for state 0.

9. Consider a random walk on a circle of circumference n (radius $n/2\pi$).

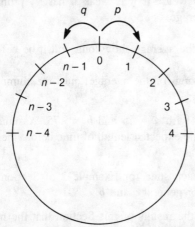

The walker takes one unit step clockwise with probability p and one unit counterclockwise with probability $q = 1 - p$. Modify the program **Ergodic Chain** to allow you to input n and p and compute the basic quantities for this chain.

(a) For which values of n is this chain regular? ergodic?

(b) What is the limiting vector **w**?

(c) Find the mean first passage matrix for $n = 5$ and $p = .5$. Verify that $m_{ij} = d(n - d)$, where d is the clockwise distance from i to j.

10. Two players match pennies and have between them a total of 5 pennies. If at any time one player has all of the pennies, to keep the game going, he gives one back to the other player and the game will continue. Show that this game can be formulated as an ergodic chain. Study this chain using the program **Ergodic Chain**.

11. Calculate the reverse transition matrix for the Land of Oz example. Is the chain reversible in this example?

12. Give an example of a three-state ergodic Markov chain that is not reversible.

13. Let **P** be the transition matrix of an ergodic Markov chain and **P*** the reverse transition matrix. Show that they have the same fixed probability vector **w**.

14. If **P** is a reversible Markov chain, is it necessarily true that the mean time to go from state i to state j is equal to the mean time to go from state j to state i? *Hint:* try the Land of Oz example.

15. Show that any ergodic Markov chain with a symmetric transition matrix (i.e., $p_{ij} = p_{ji}$), is reversible.

16. Prove that for an ergodic chain $(\mathbf{I} - \mathbf{P})\mathbf{Z} = \mathbf{I} - \mathbf{cw}$.

17. Let **P** be the transition matrix of a regular Markov chain and let $\mathbf{W} = \mathbf{cw}$.
    (a) Show that $(\mathbf{P} - \mathbf{W})^n = \mathbf{P}^n - \mathbf{W}$.
    (b) Show that, if we choose $\mathbf{b} = \mathbf{w}$ to define **Z** then

$$\mathbf{Z} = \mathbf{I} + (\mathbf{P} - \mathbf{W}) + (\mathbf{P}^2 - \mathbf{W}) \\ + (\mathbf{P}^3 - \mathbf{W}) + \cdots + (\mathbf{P}^n - \mathbf{W}) + \cdots.$$

Hint: You may use the fact that if **A** is a matrix such that $\mathbf{A}^n \to 0$, then

$$(\mathbf{I} - \mathbf{A})^{-1} \text{ exists and } (\mathbf{I} - \mathbf{A})^{-1} = \mathbf{I} + \mathbf{A} + \mathbf{A}^2 + \cdots.$$

18. (Crowell)[13] Let **P** be the transition matrix of an ergodic Markov chain and choose **b** with $\mathbf{bc} \neq 0$. Show that

$$(\mathbf{I} + \cdots + \mathbf{P}^{n-1})(\mathbf{I} - \mathbf{P} + \mathbf{cb}) = \mathbf{I} - \mathbf{P}^n + n\mathbf{cb},$$

and from this show that

$$\frac{\mathbf{I} + \mathbf{P} + \cdots + \mathbf{P}^{n-1}}{n} \to \mathbf{cw} \text{ as } n \to \infty.$$

19. An ergodic Markov chain is started in equilibrium (i.e., with initial probability vector **w**). The mean time until the next occurrence of state s_i is $\overline{m}_i = \sum_k w_k m_{ki} + w_i r_i$.

Show that if we choose $\mathbf{b} = \mathbf{w}$ to define **Z**, then $\mathbf{wZ} = \mathbf{w}$ and $\overline{m}_i = \dfrac{z_{ii}}{w_i}$.

20. A perpetual crap game goes on at Charley's. Jones comes into Charley's on an evening when there have already been 100 plays. He plans to play until the next time that snake eyes (a pair of ones) are rolled . Jones wonders how many times he will play. On the one hand he realizes that the average time between snake eyes is 36 so he should play about 18 times as he is equally likely to have come in on either side of the half-way point between occurrence of snake eyes. On the other hand, the dice have no memory, and so it would seem that he would have to play for 36 more times no matter what the previous outcomes have been. Which, if either, of Jones's arguments do you believe? Using the result of Exercise 19, calculate the expected time to reach snake eyes, in equilibrium, and see if this explains the apparent paradox. If you are still in doubt, simulate the experiment to decide which argument is correct (cf. the bus problem of Chapter 2, Section 2.2, Example 4).

[13]Private communication.

21. Let $\mathbf{P}$ be the transition matrix for an ergodic chain. Let $\mathbf{g}$ be any column vector such that $\mathbf{wg} \neq 0$, where $\mathbf{w}$ is the fixed vector for $\mathbf{P}$. Let $\mathbf{v}$ be any row vector such that $\mathbf{vc} \neq 0$, where $\mathbf{c}$ is the constant column vector of all ones. Show that $\mathbf{Z} = (\mathbf{I} - \mathbf{P} + \mathbf{gv})^{-1}$ exists. (Kemeny[14] has shown that this larger class of matrices can serve as fundamental matrices for an ergodic chain.)

22. Show that, for an ergodic Markov chain (see Theorems 18 and 19),

$$\sum_j m_{ij}w_j = \sum_j z_{jj} - k = k = \text{constant, independent of } i.$$

The constant k is called *Kemeny's constant*. A prize is offered for the first person to give an intuitively plausible reason for the above sum to be independent of i. Note that it does not depend upon the choice of $\mathbf{b}$. (See also Exercise 27.)

23. A matrix $\mathbf{X}$ is called a *generalized inverse* for $\mathbf{A}$ if $\mathbf{AXA} = \mathbf{A}$ and $\mathbf{XAX} = \mathbf{X}$.
    (a) Show that if $\mathbf{A}$ has an inverse then $\mathbf{X} = \mathbf{A}^{-1}$ is the unique generalized inverse for $\mathbf{A}$.
    (b) Let $\mathbf{P}$ be the transition matrix for an ergodic Markov chain. Show that any fundamental matrix $\mathbf{Z}$ is a generalized inverse of the matrix $\mathbf{I} - \mathbf{P}$.

24. A highly simplified game of "monopoly" is played on a board with four squares as indicated.

-5 B	20 C
-30 A	15 GO

You start at GO. You roll a die and move clockwise around the board a number of squares equal to the number that turns up on the die. You collect or pay an amount indicated on the square on which you land. You then roll the die again and move around the board in the same manner from your last position. Form a Markov chain to represent your position after n rolls. Show that your expected winning after n rolls can be represented by a column vector $\mathbf{g}_n$ with $\mathbf{g}_n = (\mathbf{I} + \mathbf{P} + \mathbf{P}^2 + \cdots + \mathbf{P}^n)\mathbf{f}$, where $\mathbf{f}$ is column vector whose entries are the amounts indicated on the squares. Show that as $n \to \infty$, $\mathbf{g}_n \to \mathbf{g}$ with $\mathbf{g} = \mathbf{Zf}$, where $\mathbf{Z} = (\mathbf{I} - \mathbf{P} + \mathbf{cw})^{-1}$.

25. Let $\mathbf{P}$ be the transition matrix of an ergodic Markov chain. Let T_i be the time to reach state i for the first time, T_E the time to enter the set E for the first time, and b_{0i}^E the probability that the chain, started at $0 \notin E$, enters E at the state $i \in E$. According to Gerber and Li,[15] we have

$$m_{0i} = E_0(T_i) = E_0(T_E) + E_0(T_i - T_E).$$

[14]J.G. Kemeny, "Generalization of a Fundamental Matrix," *Linear Algebra and its Applications*, vol. 38 (1981), pp. 193–206.

[15]H.U. Gerber and S-Y.R. Li, "The Occurrence of Sequence Patterns in Repeated Experiments and Hitting Times in a Markov Chain," *Stochastic, Processes and Their Applications*, vol. 11 (1981), pp. 101–108.

If E is entered at j, the expected value of $T_i - T_E$ is m_{ji}. Thus, conditioning on the point of entry of E, we have:

$$m_{0i} = E_0(T_E) + \sum_{j \in E} b_{0j}^E m_{ji}, \qquad i \in E.$$

If $E = \{1,2\}$ is a two-point set, this gives the two equations:

$$m_{01} = E_0(T_E) + b_{02}^E m_{21},$$

$$m_{02} = E_0(T_E) + b_{01}^E m_{12}.$$

Using the fact that $b_{01}^E + b_{02}^E = 1$, show that

$$b_{01}^E = \frac{m_{02} + m_{21} - m_{01}}{m_{12} + m_{21}},$$

$$b_{02}^E = \frac{m_{01} + m_{12} - m_{02}}{m_{12} + m_{21}},$$

and

$$E_0(T_E) = \frac{m_{01} m_{12} + m_{02} m_{21} - m_{12} m_{21}}{m_{12} + m_{21}}.$$

26. We consider next a game called *Penney-ante* by its inventor W. Penney.[16] There are two players; the first player picks a pattern of Hs and Ts of length k, and then the second player, knowing the choice of the first player, picks a different pattern of the same length. A coin is tossed a sequence of times, and the player whose pattern comes up first is the winner. To analyze the game, we need to find the probability that a particular pattern, say HTH, will occur before a second pattern, say HHH. To determine this probability, it is useful to associate with any two patterns A and B, of the same length, a number AB. The number AB is defined as follows: set AB initially equal to 0; then write the pattern B under the pattern A so that the first entries line up. If the length of the overlap between A and B is j and the patterns agree at *all* points of this overlap, add 2^j to AB. Then move B over one unit and again look at the overlap between A and B—now of length $j - 1$; if all the elements of the two strings agree in this overlap, add 2^{j-1} to AB. Continue this until there is no more overlap; the resulting sum is AB. Here is an example: assume that $A =$ HHHH and $B =$ HHHT. Then write:

$$A = \text{HHHH}$$

$$B = \text{HHHT} \qquad AB = 0$$

$$\text{HHHT} \qquad AB = 8$$

$$\text{HHHT} \qquad AB = 12$$

$$\text{HHHT} \qquad AB = 14$$

[16]W. Penney, "Problem: Penney-Ante," *Journal of Recreational Math.* vol. 2 (1969), p. 241.

We end up with $AB = 14$. In Exercises 26 and 27 of Section 11.2 of this chapter you were asked to show that, if T_A is the time to reach a pattern A for the first time,

$$E_0(T_A) = AA,$$

and, if B is a pattern that does not include A, then

$$E_B(T_A) = AA - BA.$$

(a) Show that the odds that the second player will win are given by Conway's formula:

$$\frac{AA - AB}{BB - BA}.$$

Hint: consider the outcomes of the tosses to be a Markov chain whose states are the last k outcomes, or if there have not been k outcomes, then the outcomes that have occurred. The resulting chain is not quite an ergodic chain but the argument in Exercise 25 applies to allow you to compute the ratio b_{02}^E/b_{01}^E, where 0 is the initial empty set and 1 and 2 are patterns of the two players.

(b) Show that, if $k = 2$, this is a fair game, but, if $k = 3$, the second player has an advantage no matter what choice the first player makes. (It has been shown that, for $k \geq 3$, if the first player chooses $a_1, a_2, \ldots, a_k$, then the optimal strategy for the second player is of the form $b, a_1, a_2, \ldots, a_{k-1}$ where b is the better of the two choices H or T.[17]

27. Peter Doyle[18] has suggested the following interpretation for *Kemeny's constant* (see Exercise 22). We are given an ergodic chain and do not know the starting state. However, we would like to start watching it at a time when it can be considered to be in equilibrium (i.e., as if we had started with the fixed vector **w** or as if we had waited a long time). However, we don't know the starting state and we don't want to wait a long time. Peter says to choose a state according to the fixed vector **w**. That is, choose state j with probability w_j using a spinner, for example. Then wait until the time T that this state occurs for the first time. We consider T as our starting time and observe the chain from this time on. Of course the probability that we start in state j is w_j, so we are starting in equilibrium. Kemeny's constant is the expected value of T, and it is independent of the way in which the chain was started. Should Peter be given the prize?

Historical Remarks

Markov chains were introduced by Andrei Andreevich Markov (1856–1922) and were named in his honor. He was a talented undergraduate who received a gold medal for his undergraduate thesis at St. Petersburg University. Besides being an active research mathematician and teacher, he was also active in politics and participated in the liberal

---

[17]See Guibas and Odlysko, "String Overlaps, Pattern Matching, and Non-transitive Games."
[18]Private communication.

movement in Russia at the beginning of the twentieth century. In 1913, when the government celebrated the 300th anniversary of the House of Romanov family, Markov organized a counter celebration of the 200th anniversary of Bernoulli's discovery of the law of large numbers.

Markov was led to develop Markov chains as a natural extension of sequences of independent random variables. In his first paper, in 1906, he proved that for a Markov chain with positive transition probabilities and numerical states the average of the outcomes converges to the expected value of the limiting distribution (the fixed vector). In a later paper he proved the central limit theorem for such chains. Writing about Markov, A. P. Youschkevitch remarks:

> Markov arrived at his chains starting from the internal needs of probability theory, and he never wrote about their applications to physical science. For him the only real examples of the chains were literary texts, where the two states denoted the vowels and consonants[19]

In a paper written in 1913,[20] Markov chose a sequence of 20,000 letters from Pushkin's *Eugene Onegin* to see if this sequence can be approximately considered as a simple chain. He obtained the Markov chain with transition matrix

	vowel	consonant
vowel	.128	.872
consonant	.663	.337

The fixed vector for this chain is (.432, .568) indicating that we should expect about 43.2 percent vowels and 56.8 percent consonants in the novel, which was borne out by the actual count.

Claude Shannon considered an interesting extension of this idea in his book *The Mathematical Theory of Communication*,[21] in which he developed the information-theoretic concept of entropy. Shannon considers a series of Markov chain approximations to English prose. He does this first by chains in which the states are letters and then by chains in which the states are words. For example, for the case of words he presents first a simulation where the words are chosen independently but with appropriate frequencies.

REPRESENTING AND SPEEDILY IS AN GOOD APT OR COME CAN DIFFERENT NATURAL HERE HE THE A IN CAME THE TO OF TO EXPERT GRAY COME TO FURNISHES THE LINE MESSAGE HAD BE THESE.

---

[19]See *Dictionary of Scientific Biography*, ed. C.C. Gillespie (New York: Scribner's Sons, 1970), pp. 124–130.

[20]A.A. Markov, "An Example of Statistical Analysis of the Text of Eugene Onegin Illustrating the Association of Trials into a Chain," *Bulletin de l'Acadamie Imperiale des Sciences de St. Petersbourg, Ser. 6*, vol. 7 (1913), pp. 153–162.

[21]See C.E. Shannon and W. Weaver, *The Mathematical Theory of Communication* (Urbana: Univ. of Illinois Press, 1964).

He then notes the increased resemblance to ordinary English text when the words are chosen as a Markov chain, in which case he obtains

THE HEAD AND IN FRONTAL ATTACK ON AN ENGLISH WRITER THAT THE CHARACTER OF THIS POINT IS THEREFORE ANOTHER METHOD FOR THE LETTERS THAT THE TIME OF WHO EVER TOLD THE PROBLEM FOR AN UN-EXPECTED.

A simulation like the last one is carried out by opening a book and choosing the first word, say it is *the*. Then the book is read until the word *the* appears again and the word after this is chosen as the second word, which turned out to be *head*. The book is then read until the word head appears again and the next word, *and*, is chosen, and so on.

Other early examples of the use of Markov chains occurred in Galton's study of the problem of survival of family names in 1889 and in the Markov chain introduced by P. and T. Ehrenfest in 1907 for diffusion (See Section 11.5). Poincare in 1912 discussed card shuffling in terms of an ergodic Markov chain defined on a permutation group. Brownian motion, a continuous time version of random walk, was introduced in 1900–1901 by L. Bachelier in his study of the stock market, and in 1905–1907 in works of A. Einstein and M. Smoluchowsky in their study of physical processes.

One of the first systematic studies of finite Markov chains was carried out by M. Frechet.[22] The treatment of Markov chains in terms of the two fundamental matrices that we have used was developed by Kemeny and Snell[23] to avoid the use of eigenvalues that one of these authors found too complex. The fundamental matrix N occurred also in the work of J. L. Doob and others in studying the connection between Markov processes and classical potential theory. The fundamental matrix Z for ergodic chains appeared first in the work of Frechet, who used it to find the limiting variance for the central limit theorem for Markov chains.

---

[22]M. Frechet, "Théorie des événements en chaine dans le cas d'un nombre fini d'états possible," in *Recherches théoriques Modernes sur le calcul des probabilités*, vol. 2 (Paris, 1938).

[23]Kemeny and Snell, *Finite Markov Chains*.

Appendix A

Normal distribution table

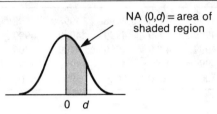

NA $(0,d)$ = area of shaded region

0 d

	.00	.01	.02	.03	.04	.05	.06	.07	.08	.09
0.0	.0000	.0040	.0080	.0120	.0160	.0199	.0239	.0279	.0319	.0359
0.1	.0398	.0438	.0478	.0517	.0557	.0596	.0636	.0675	.0714	.0753
0.2	.0793	.0832	.0871	.0910	.0948	.0987	.1026	.1064	.1103	.1141
0.3	.1179	.1217	.1255	.1293	.1331	.1368	.1406	.1443	.1480	.1517
0.4	.1554	.1591	.1628	.1664	.1700	.1736	.1772	.1808	.1844	.1879
0.5	.1915	.1950	.1985	.2019	.2054	.2088	.2123	.2157	.2190	.2224
0.6	.2257	.2291	.2324	.2357	.2389	.2422	.2454	.2486	.2517	.2549
0.7	.2580	.2611	.2642	.2673	.2704	.2734	.2764	.2794	.2823	.2852
0.8	.2881	.2910	.2939	.2967	.2995	.3023	.3051	.3078	.3106	.3133
0.9	.3159	.3186	.3212	.3238	.3264	.3289	.3315	.3340	.3365	.3389
1.0	.3413	.3438	.3461	.3485	.3508	.3531	.3554	.3577	.3599	.3621
1.1	.3643	.3665	.3686	.3708	.3729	.3749	.3770	.3790	.3810	.3830
1.2	.3849	.3869	.3888	.3907	.3925	.3944	.3962	.3980	.3997	.4015
1.3	.4032	.4049	.4066	.4082	.4099	.4115	.4131	.4147	.4162	.4177
1.4	.4192	.4207	.4222	.4236	.4251	.4265	.4279	.4292	.4306	.4319
1.5	.4332	.4345	.4357	.4370	.4382	.4394	.4406	.4418	.4429	.4441
1.6	.4452	.4463	.4474	.4484	.4495	.4505	.4515	.4525	.4535	.4545
1.7	.4554	.4564	.4573	.4582	.4591	.4599	.4608	.4616	.4625	.4633
1.8	.4641	.4649	.4656	.4664	.4671	.4678	.4686	.4693	.4699	.4706
1.9	.4713	.4719	.4726	.4732	.4738	.4744	.4750	.4756	.4761	.4767
2.0	.4772	.4778	.4783	.4788	.4793	.4798	.4803	.4808	.4812	.4817
2.1	.4821	.4826	.4830	.4834	.4838	.4842	.4846	.4850	.4854	.4857
2.2	.4861	.4864	.4868	.4871	.4875	.4878	.4881	.4884	.4887	.4890
2.3	.4893	.4896	.4898	.4901	.4904	.4906	.4909	.4911	.4913	.4916
2.4	.4918	.4920	.4922	.4925	.4927	.4929	.4931	.4932	.4934	.4936
2.5	.4938	.4940	.4941	.4943	.4945	.4946	.4948	.4949	.4951	.4952
2.6	.4953	.4955	.4956	.4957	.4959	.4960	.4961	.4962	.4963	.4964
2.7	.4965	.4966	.4967	.4968	.4969	.4970	.4971	.4972	.4973	.4974
2.8	.4974	.4975	.4976	.4977	.4977	.4978	.4979	.4979	.4980	.4981
2.9	.4981	.4982	.4982	.4983	.4984	.4984	.4985	.4985	.4986	.4986
3.0	.4987	.4987	.4987	.4988	.4988	.4989	.4989	.4989	.4990	.4990
3.1	.4990	.4991	.4991	.4991	.4992	.4992	.4992	.4992	.4993	.4993
3.2	.4993	.4993	.4994	.4994	.4994	.4994	.4994	.4995	.4995	.4995
3.3	.4995	.4995	.4995	.4996	.4996	.4996	.4996	.4996	.4996	.4997
3.4	.4997	.4997	.4997	.4997	.4997	.4997	.4997	.4997	.4997	.4998

Normal distribution table (*continued*)

	.00	.01	.02	.03	.04	.05	.06	.07	.08	.09
3.5	.4998	.4998	.4998	.4998	.4998	.4998	.4998	.4998	.4998	.4998
3.6	.4998	.4998	.4999	.4999	.4999	.4999	.4999	.4999	.4999	.4999
3.7	.4999	.4999	.4999	.4999	.4999	.4999	.4999	.4999	.4999	.4999
3.8	.4999	.4999	.4999	.4999	.4999	.4999	.4999	.4999	.4999	.4999
3.9	.5000	.5000	.5000	.5000	.5000	.5000	.5000	.5000	.5000	.5000

Appendix B

Number of adult children of various statures born of 205 mid-parents of various statures. (All female heights have been multiplied by 1.08).

Heights of the Mid-parents in inches.	Heights of the adult children.														Total number of		
	Below	62.2	63.2	64.2	65.2	66.2	67.2	68.2	69.2	70.2	71.2	72.2	73.2	Above	Adult children.	Mid-parents.	Medians
Above	..	..	..	..	..	..	..	..	..	..	..	1	3	..	4	5	..
72.5	..	..	..	..	..	..	..	1	2	1	2	7	2	4	19	6	72.2
71.5	..	..	..	..	1	3	4	3	5	10	4	9	2	2	43	11	69.9
70.5	1	..	1	..	1	1	3	12	18	14	7	4	3	3	68	22	69.5
69.5	..	..	1	16	4	17	27	20	33	25	20	11	4	5	183	41	68.9
68.5	1	..	7	11	16	25	31	34	48	21	18	4	3	..	219	49	68.2
67.5	..	3	5	14	15	36	38	28	38	19	11	4	..	..	211	33	67.6
66.5	..	3	3	5	2	17	17	14	13	4	..	..	..	..	78	20	67.2
65.5	..	1	9	5	7	11	11	7	7	5	2	1	..	..	66	12	66.7
64.5	2	..	4	4	1	5	5	..	2	..	..	..	..	..	23	5	65.8
Below	1	..	2	4	1	2	2	1	1	..	..	..	..	..	14	1	..
Totals	5	7	32	59	48	117	138	120	167	99	64	41	17	14	928	205	..
Medians	..	66.3	67.8	67.9	67.7	67.9	68.3	68.5	69.0	69.0	70.0	..	..	..	..	..	..

NOTE.—In calculating the Medians, the entries have been taken as referring to the middle of the squares in which they stand. The reason why the headings run 62.2, 63.2, 63.5, &c., instead of 62.5, 63.5, &c., is that the observations are unequally distributed between 62 and 63, 63 and 64, &c., there being a strong bias in favour of integral inches. After careful consideration, I concluded that the headings, as adopted, best satisfied the conditions. This inequality was not apparent in the case of the Mid-parents.

SOURCE: F. Galton. "Regression towards Mediocrity in Hereditary Stature." *Journal Antropological Inst.*, vol. 15 (1885), p. 248.

Appendix C

Life Table

Number of survivors at single years of age, out of 100,000 born alive, by sex: United States, 1981.

	All races			All races			All races	
Age	Male	Female	Age	Male	Female	Age	Male	Female
0	100000	100000	29	95796	97701	58	82004	90059
1	98684	98933	30	95616	97632	59	80724	89337
2	98593	98863	31	95438	97650	60	79391	88559
3	98523	98807	32	95260	97486	61	77948	87721
4	98468	98762	33	95081	97408	62	76411	86819
5	98421	98726	34	94897	97324	63	74775	85850
6	98380	98696	35	94706	97233	64	73033	84810
7	98342	98670	36	94505	97134	65	71182	83696
8	98307	98647	37	94293	97027	66	69222	82503
9	98277	98627	38	94068	96910	67	67155	81227
10	98251	98609	39	93829	96783	68	64980	79863
11	98229	98592	40	93574	96645	69	62696	78406
12	98207	98575	41	93300	96495	70	60305	76850
13	98179	98555	42	93004	96331	71	57812	75190
14	98135	98531	43	92681	96150	72	55223	73422
15	98070	98500	44	92327	95950	73	52551	71543
16	97980	98461	45	91936	95728	74	49812	69553
17	97868	98415	46	91506	95482	75	47020	67448
18	97736	98363	47	91033	95210	76	44187	65223
19	97589	98308	48	90514	94911	77	41324	62872
20	97432	98253	49	89945	94584	78	38440	60386
21	97265	98197	50	89323	94228	79	35546	57758
22	97088	98140	51	88644	93840	80	32653	54978
23	96904	98082	52	87905	93417	81	29755	52039
24	96718	98023	53	87102	92958	82	26929	48934
25	96531	97962	54	86232	92462	83	24134	45655
26	96345	97899	55	85290	91927	84	21411	42196
27	96160	97835	56	84274	91350	85	18785	38552
28	95977	97769	57	83180	90729			

SOURCE: *Vital Statistics of the United States, 1981*, vol II, Mortality, Part A, U.S. Dept. of Health and Human Services. National Center for Health Statistics, Maryland, 1986.

Appendix D

Using Library Procedures

The use of library procedures (subroutines and functions) is illustrated in the text in the listings of many programs (see the Directory of Library Procedures, Appendix E); here we give two very simple examples to illustrate the bare essentials. Once you know how to call library procedures, you can use any of the procedures listed in the Contents of Libraries (Appendix F) to create short, easy to read, yet powerful programs with attractive output.

Suppose that we have written the function **average** and have included it in the same file as a calling program:

```
declare function average

do
   input prompt "x,y =": x,y
   print "The average is"; average(x,y)
loop

end


function average(a,b)

   let average = (a+b)/2

end function
```

There are several things to note here:

(1) We must include the **declaration** declare function average in the calling program.

(2) The function *knows absolutely nothing* about any of the variables in the calling program, except the two values explicitly passed to it as parameters. Further, the function can return only a single value to the calling program, which it does by assigning the value to its own name.

(3) The *names* of these parameters in the function need bear no relation to the names in the calling program; here we called them *a* and *b*, but we could have just as well used *y* and *x*, for instance. The only restriction is that the parameters in the function listing must agree in *number* and *type* with those in the calling program; thus either

```
print average(x,y,z)
```

or

```
print average(x,y$)
```

would result in an error message.

The next step is to move **average** to a library, which we can do by creating the following file, and naming it, say, **Lib.Math**:

```
! Library of math procedures

External

function average(a,b)

   let average = (a+b)/2

end function
```

To save time in compiling programs, which call procedures in this library, we compile the library and save the compiled version as **Lib.Math***. We can now modify our calling program thus:

```
library "Lib.Math*"
declare function average

do
   input prompt "x,y =": x,y
   print "The average is"; average(x,y)
loop

end
```

Note that in addition to the function declaration, a **library** statement is necessary to tell the compiler where to find the function.

For a slightly less trivial example, suppose that we want to run a simulation and present the results in a histogram. A perusal of the contents of the libraries will quickly suggest that we use the subroutine **bargraph** (result(), trials, xmin, xmax, cells) which resides in **Lib.Prob**.

Perhaps in our program we have kept the results in an array named **data()**, and perhaps we haven't bothered to define any variables corresponding to *xmin,xmax*, and *cells*, but we want to know what portion of our results have fallen in each subinterval [7,8], [9,10], . . . , [11,12], of [7,12]. Here is a program which does exactly that (note

that here we do not have to declare the subroutine **bargraph**, since the **call** statement
does so implicitly):

```
library "Lib.Prob*"

dim data(1000)

set window 6,13,0,1/3

for trial = 1 to 1000
let data(trial) = 7 + 5*rnd
next trial

call bargraph(data,1000, 7, 12, 5)

end
```

Appendix E

Directory of Library Procedures

This contains only those procedures which are called by programs listed in the text. See Appendix F, Contents of Libraries, for a complete list.

Procedure	Library	Calling Programs	Section	Page
random_density	Lib.CLT	CLT General	9.2	347
random_integer	Lib.Prob	CLT General	9.2	347
sample_normal	Lib.Cont	Branching Simulation	10.1	389
sample_statistics	Lib.Prob	Bus Paradox	2.2	67
shuffle	Lib.Prob	Random Permutations	3.1	94
		Records	3.1	95
simulate_discrete_X	Lib.Prob	Branching Simulation	10.1	389
Sn_density_sum	Lib.CLT	CLT Ind Trials Global	9.2	345
standard_normal	Lib.Cont	CLT Bernoulli Plot	9.1	317
		CLT Bernoulli Local	9.1	319
		CLT Ind Trials Plot	9.2	340
variance_cont	Lib.Cont	Continuous Mean & Variance	6.1	261
variance_discrete	Lib.Prob	Branching Simulation	10.1	389
vector_labels	Lib.Markov	Bayes	4.1	145
		Absorbing Chain	11.2	428
		Ergodic Chain	11.5	466

Appendix F

Contents of Libraries

Here we merely list the various procedures with their parameters. A detailed
description is included with each procedure in its library.

Lib.Prob (Library of discrete probability procedures.)

bargraph(result(),trials,xmin,xmax,cells)	[sub]
binomial(n,p,k)	[function]
choose(n,k)	[function]
convolve(p(),q(), r())	[sub]
density_statistics(density(), mean,std)	[sub]
expectation_discrete(p())	[function]
factorial(n)	[function]
gen_function_discrete(p(),x)	[function]
next_diadic(list(), flag)	[sub]
next_permutation(list(), flag)	[sub]
poisson(m, k)	[function]
random_integer(a,b)	[function]
random_real(a,b)	[function]
sample_statistics(result(), trials, mean,std)	[sub]
shuffle(list())	[sub]
simulate_discrete_X(p())	[function]
variance_discrete(p)	[function]

Lib.Cont (Library of routines for continuous probability.)

beta(x,a,b)	[function]
chi-squared(x,n)	[function]
expectation_cont(a,b,n)	[function]
exponential(x,lambda)	[function]
gamma(x)	[function]
integral(a,b,n)	[function]
normal(x,mu,sigma)	[function]
normal_area(a,b)	[function]
sample_normal(mean,std)	[function]
standard_normal(x)	[function]
variance_cont(a,b,n)	[function]

Lib.CLT (Library of procedures relating to the Central Limit Theorem. The first ten are arranged in exact-approximation pairs, following the order in which they are introduced in the text.)

binomial(n,p,k)	[function]
local_Bernoulli_approx(n,p,k)	[function]
binomial_sum(n,p,k,m)	[function]
global_Bernoulli_approx(n,p,k,m,flag)	[function]
Sn_density(n,p(),k)	[function]
local_ind_trials_approx(n,p(),k)	[function]
Sn_density_sum(n,p(),k,m)	[function]
global_ind_trials_approx(n,p(),k,m,flag)	[function]
Bernoulli_statistics(n,p, mean,std)	[sub]
density_statistics(p(), mean,std)	[sub]
get_Sn_density(n,p(), density())	[sub]
ind_trials_statistics(n,p(), mean,std)	[sub]
pick_distinct(m,a,b, list())	[sub]
plot_standardized(p(), deviations)	[sub]
random_density(p())	[sub]

Lib.Markov (Library of procedures for Markov chains.)

absorb(Q(,), R(,), N(,), B(,), t())	[sub]
ergodic(P(,), w(), r(), M(,) Z(,))	[sub]
get_fixed_vector(P(,), w())	[sub]
matrix_labels(M(,),row_label$(),col_label$(),format$)	[sub]
vector_labels(vector(),label$(),format$)	[sub]

Lib.Labels (Procedures for providing attractive labels for graphs.)

format(string$, length, integer, decimal)	[sub]
nice_labels(y,z,n, w,m,format$)	[sub]
set_window(xmin, xmax, x$, ymin, ymax, y$)	[sub]
text_info(line, column)	[sub]
x_labels(xmin, xmax, x$, tick_step, label_step)	[sub]
y_labels(ymin, ymax, y$, tick_step, label_step)	[sub]

Appendix G

Programs by Chapter

A parenthetical page number indicates the first mention of an unlisted program.

Appendix H

Programs Alphabetically

A parenthetical page number indicates the first mention of an unlisted program.

Name in Text	Name on IBM	Section	Page
Law Continuous	LAWCONT	8.2	307
Lead	LEAD	5.1	175
Lead Plot	LEADPLOT	5.1	(175)
Limit Vector	LIMVECT	11.3	449
London Bombs	BOMBS	9.3	(335)
Matrix Powers	MATPOWER	11.1	413
Monte Carlo	MONTE	2.1	47
Normal Area	NORMAREA	9.3	321
Normal Distribution	NORMDIST	5.2	191
Power	POWER	3.2	(121)
Queue	QUEUE	5.2	203
Random	RANDOM	1.1	9
Random Permutations	RANDPERM	3.1	94
Records	RECORDS	3.1	95
Simulate Chain	SIMCHAIN	11.3	443
Stepping Stone	STEPSTON	11.1	(419)
Stirling	STIRLING	3.1	(91)
Stock System	STOCKS	6.1	(225)
Sum	SUM	7.1	270
Sum Plot	SUM PLOT	7.1	(270)
Tree	TREE	4.1	(140)
Two Arm	TWOARM	4.2	(163)
Win Plot	WINPLOT	5.1	(174)

Answers to Selected Exercises

Chapter 1 Section 1

1. Program. As n increases, the *proportion* of heads gets closer to $1/2$, but the *difference* between the number of heads and half the number of flips increases.

3. (a) Program.
   (b) Yes.

5. Program: smallest n should be about 150.

7. Program. The graph of winnings for betting on a color is much smoother (i.e., has smaller fluctuations) then that for betting on a number.

9. Program. You don't always stop before exhausting your stake.

For $n = 2$

maximum	probability
0	1/2
1	1/4
2	1/4

For $n = 4$

maximum	probability
0	6/16
1	4/16
2	4/16
3	1/16
4	1/16

The probability that the maximum $= 2j$ is equal to the probability that the total fortune $= 2j$.

15. About $1/2$ the time you win 2, $1/4$ of the time you win 4, $1/8$ of the time you win 8, etc. If you add up all these potential winnings you get infinity, so it would seem that you should be willing to pay quite a lot to play this game. Few are willing to pay more than $10.

17. In the case of having children until they have a boy, they should have about 200,000, and in the case that they have children until they have both a boy and a girl, they should have about 300,000 children, or 100,000 more.

Chapter 1 Section 2

1. $P\{a,b,c\} = 1$ $P\{a\} = 1/2$
   $P\{a,b\} = 5/6$ $P\{b\} = 1/3$
   $P\{b,c\} = 1/2$ $P\{c\} = 1/6$
   $P\{a,c\} = 2/3$ $P\{empty\ set\} = 0$

3. **(b), (c), (d)**

5. **(a)** $1/2$ **(b)** $1/4$ **(c)** $3/8$ **(d)** $7/8$

7. $11/12$

9. $3/4, 1$

11. 1:12, 1:3, 1:35

13. 11:4

15. 10 percent.
    An example: 10 lost eye, ear, hand, and leg; 15 eye, ear, and hand; 20 eye, ear, and leg; 25 eye, hand, and leg; 30 ear, hand, and leg.

19. $7/2^{12}$

25. 67/136

Chapter 2 Section 2

1. (a) $p(\omega) = \dfrac{1}{8}$ on $[2,10]$

$$p([a,b]) = \frac{b-a}{8}$$

(b) $p(x > 5) = \dfrac{5}{8}$

$$p(5 < x < 7) = \frac{1}{4}$$

$$p(x^2 - 12x + 35 > 0) = \frac{3}{4}$$

3. (a) $C = \dfrac{1}{\log(5)} = .621$

(b) $P([a,b]) = (.621)\log\dfrac{b}{a}$

(c) $P(x > 5) = \dfrac{\log(2)}{\log(5)} = .431$

$$P(x < 7) = \frac{\log(7/2)}{\log(5)} = .778$$

$$P(x^2 - 12x + 35 > 0) = \frac{\log(25/7)}{\log(5)} = .791$$

5. (a) $1 - \dfrac{1}{e^{.1}} = .632$

(b) $1 - \dfrac{1}{e^{.3}} = .950$

(c) $\dfrac{1}{e^{.3}} - \dfrac{1}{e^{.4}} = .031$

(d) $\dfrac{1}{e^{.4}} = .018$

7. (a) $^1/_3$ **(b)** $^1/_2$ **(c)** $^1/_2$ **(d)** $^1/_3$

13. $^1/_4$

15. yes

Chapter 3 Section 1

1. $4! = 24$

3. $10!/1,000,000 =$ approximately 3.63

5. P(of 40 people, 2 have same birthday) $= .89$; odds $= 89/11$. Yes; Jefferson, Adams, and Monroe (all signers of the Declaration of Independence) died on July 4.

9. Each subset represents a distinct marking of r, where each element is marked "in" or "out." There are $2 \cdot 2 \cdot 2 \cdot \cdots \cdot 2 = 2^n$ such markings.

11. $1/13$

13. (a) $30 \cdot 15 \cdot 9 = 4050$
   (b) $4050 \cdot (3 \cdot 2 \cdot 1) = 24300$
   (c) 148824

15. (a) $5 \cdot 4 \cdot 3 \cdot 2 \cdot 1 = 120$
   (b) 60

19. $1 - \dfrac{12 \cdot 11 \cdot \cdots \cdot (12 - n + 1)}{n^{12}}$ if $n \leq 12$,

   1 if $n > 12$

21. 36

23. They are the same

25. (a) $\dfrac{1}{n}, \dfrac{1}{n}$
   (b) She will get the best candidate if the second best candidate is in the first half and the best candidate is in the second half. The probability that this happens is greater than $1/4$.

Chapter 3 Section 1 Appendix

1. The theorem shows that $\dfrac{n(n+1)}{2} - (1 + 2 + \cdots + n) - > D_0$ where $0 \leq D_0 \leq 1/8$, but in fact we know that $D_0 = 0$.

Chapter 3 Section 2

1. (a) 20
   (b) $.0064$
   (c) 21
   (d) 1
   (e) $.0256$
   (f) 15
   (g) 10

3. $11/64$

7. $.998, .965, .729$

11. $11/64 = .172$

13. (a) $4/\binom{52}{5} = .0000015$
   (b) $36/\binom{52}{5} = .000014$

   (c) $624/(\binom{52}{5}) = .00024$
   (d) $3744/(\binom{52}{5}) = .0014$
   (e) $5108/(\binom{52}{5}) = .0020$
   (f) $10200/(\binom{52}{5}) = .0039$

19. Pr(no student gets 2 or less correct) $= b(340,7/128,0) = 4.96 \cdot 10^{-9}$; Pr(0 student gets all wrong) $= b(340,1/1024,0) = .717$. So Prosser is right to expect at least one student with 2 or less correct, but Crowell is wrong to expect at least one student with none correct.

21. (a) $(\binom{13}{6})/(\binom{52}{6}) = .000084$
   (b) $(\binom{4}{3})(\binom{4}{2})(\binom{4}{1})/(\binom{52}{6}) = .0000047$
   (c) $(\binom{4}{2})(\binom{13}{3})(\binom{13}{3})/(\binom{52}{6}) = .024$

23. $(\binom{8}{2}) = 28$

25. $(\binom{19}{10})/(\binom{29}{20}) = .009$

27. (a) pq, qp, p^2, q^2

29. $n = 114$, $m = 81$

31. (a) $p(.5) = .5$, $p(.6) = .71$, $p(.7) = .87$
   (b) Mets have a 95.2 percent chance of winning in a 67 game series.

33. If $u = 1$, you only need to be sure to send at least one to each side. If $u = 0$, it doesn't matter what you do. Let $v = 1 - u$ and $q = 1 - p$. If $0 < v < 1$, let x be the nearest integer to

$$\frac{n}{2} - \frac{1}{2} \frac{\log\left(\frac{p}{q}\right)}{\log(v)}$$

If $0 < x < n$, send x to the east side. If $x < 0$, send 0; and if $x > n$, send n to the east side.

Chapter 4 Section 1

1. $^1/_2$, $^1/_4$, $^1/_2$, 0, $^1/_2$

3. $^1/_2$, $^4/_{13}$, $^1/_{13}$

5. $^3/_{10}$

9. .0481

11. $^1/_8$

15. $P(D1|+) = {}^4/_9$
   $P(D2|+) = {}^1/_3$
   $P(D3|+) = {}^2/_9$

19. $^1/_2$

29. (a) pq **(b)** $1 - (1 - p)(1 - q)$ **(c)** .958

Chapter 4 Section 2

1. (a) $^2/_3$ **(b)** $^1/_3$ **(c)** $^1/_2$ **(d)** $^1/_2$

3. (a) .01

  (b) $e^{-.01T}$ where T is time from 20.

  (c) $e^{-.2} = .819$

  (d) $1 - e^{-.01} = .010$

5. (a) 1   **(b)** 1   **(c)** $^1/_2$ **(d)** $\dfrac{\pi}{8}$ **(e)** $^1/_2$

11. A new beta density with $\alpha = 6$ and $\beta = 9$. It will be successful next time with probability .4.

Chapter 5 Section 1

1. (a) -1 **(b)** 3   **(c)** -1 **(d)** -1

3. (a) 0   **(b)** 5   **(c)** 0   **(d)** -3

5. X_1 and X_2 have the same densities and in each case the range values are 1 to 10 and the probability for each value is 1/10. They are independent. If the first number is not replaced the two densities are the same but the random variables are not independent.

11. $p = 1/2$ $p_X = \begin{pmatrix} 0 & 1 \\ 1/2 & 1/2 \end{pmatrix}$ $p_Y = \begin{pmatrix} 3 & 4 & 5 \\ 1/4 & 3/8 & 3/8 \end{pmatrix}$ indep

     $p = 2/3$ $p_X = \begin{pmatrix} 0 & 1 \\ 17/81 & 64/81 \end{pmatrix}$ $p_Y = \begin{pmatrix} 3 & 4 & 5 \\ 1/3 & 10/27 & 8/27 \end{pmatrix}$ not indep

19. $P(X = i) = P(Y = i) = \dfrac{\dbinom{4}{i}\dbinom{5 - i}{48}}{\dbinom{52}{5}}$

$P(X = i, Y = j) = \dfrac{\dbinom{4}{i}\dbinom{4}{j}\dbinom{44}{5 - i - j}}{\dbinom{52}{5}}$ if $i \le 4, j \le 4$ and $i + j \le 5$

0 otherwise.

23. $p(X = 1)$ with replacement $= .396$

     $p(X = 1)$ without replacement $= .440$

Chapter 5 Section 2

1. (a) $F(x) = x - 2; f(x) = 1$ on $[0,1]$

   (b) $F(x) = x^{1/3}; f(x) = \dfrac{1}{3}x^{-2/3}$ on $[0,1]$

9. (a) $F(x) = x^2$ and $f(x) = 2x$ on $[0,1]$
   (b) $F(x) = 2x - x^2$ and $f(x) = 2 - 2x$ on $[0,1]$

11. (a) $^{1}/_{2}$ **(b)** 1 **(c)** .2

13. (a) $^{3}/_{4}$ **(b)** $\pi/16$

15. (a) $c = 6$ **(b)** $F(x) = 3x^2 - 2x^3$ **(c)** .156

17. $f_{aX+b}(x) = \dfrac{1}{a}f_X\!\left(\dfrac{x - b}{a}\right)$ (this answers all three parts)

19. (a) $\dfrac{1}{d - c}$ **(b)** $\dfrac{c}{c - d}$

21. median of uniform is $\dfrac{a + b}{2}$, of normal is μ, of exponential is $\dfrac{1}{\lambda}\log(2)$

23. mode of uniform is any number in $[0,1]$, normal is μ, exponential is 0.

25. 13.4% rejected. For 1% rejection rate, let $\sigma = .0012$

27. 2.4%

29. The car will last 4 years with probability $1/e = .368$

37. $\dfrac{1}{\sqrt{2\pi y}}\, e^{-\frac{\log^2(y)}{2}}$ for $y > 0$.

Chapter 6 Section 1

1. $-\,^{1}/_{9}$

3. 18.9

5. $-\,^{1}/_{19}$

9. $-.0141$

11. roller has expected winning $-.0141$; pass bettor has expected winning $-.0136$

13. 45

23. 3.5

Chapter 6 Section 2

1. $E(X) = 0$, $V(X) = {}^2/_3$, $D(X) = \sqrt{\dfrac{2}{3}}$

3. $E(X) = -{}^1/_{19}$, $E(Y) = -{}^1/_{19}$, $V(X) = 33.21$, $V(Y) = .99$

5. (a) $E(T) = 0$, $V(T) = 1.2$, $E(F) = 62$, $V(F) = 1.2$
 (b) $E(C) = 50/3$, $V(C) = 10/27$

7. $V(X) = {}^3/_4$, $D(X) = \dfrac{\sqrt{3}}{2}$

9. $V(X) = 20/9$, $D(X) = (2/3)\sqrt{5}$

15. ${}^7/_8$, ${}^7/_8$, ${}^7/_{64}$, ${}^{71}/_{64}$

21. $E(X_1)$; $V(X_2)/(V(X_1) + V(X_2))$

Chapter 6 Section 3

1. (a) $\mu = 0$, $\sigma^2 = {}^1/_3$
 (b) $\mu = 0$, $\sigma^2 = {}^1/_2$
 (c) $\mu = 0$, $\sigma^2 = {}^3/_5$
 (d) $\mu = 0$, $\sigma^2 = {}^3/_5$

3. (a) $\mu = 0$, $\sigma^2 = {}^1/_5$
 (b) $\mu = 0$, $\sigma^2 = \dfrac{\pi^2 - 8}{\pi^2}$
 (c) $\mu = {}^1/_3$, $\sigma^2 = {}^2/_9$
 (d) $\mu = {}^1/_2$, $\sigma^2 = {}^3/_{20}$

5. $\mu = 40$, $\sigma^2 = 800$

7. (d) $a = -{}^3/_2$, $b = 0$, $c = 1$
 (e) $a = \dfrac{45}{48}$, $b = 0$, $c = \dfrac{3}{16}$

11. (a) 3μ, $3\sigma^2$
 (b) $E(A) = \mu$, $V(A) = \sigma^2/3$
 (c) $E(S^2) = 3\sigma^2 + 9\mu^2$, $E(A^2) = \sigma^2/3 + \mu^2$

13. The mean $b = 50$. The median $b = \dfrac{100}{\sqrt{2}} = 70.71$

Chapter 7 Section 1

1. (a) .625
 (b) .5

3. $\begin{pmatrix} 0 & 1 & 2 & 3 & 4 \\ 1/64 & 3/32 & 12/64 & 3/8 & 1/4 \end{pmatrix}$

5. **(a)** $\begin{pmatrix} 3 & 4 & 5 & 6 \\ 1/12 & 4/12 & 4/12 & 3/12 \end{pmatrix}$

   (b) $\begin{pmatrix} 1 & 2 & 3 & 4 \\ 1/12 & 4/12 & 4/12 & 3/12 \end{pmatrix}$

Chapter 7 Section 2

1.
 (a) $f_Z(x) = \dfrac{x + 2}{4}$ on $[-2,0]$ and $\dfrac{2 - x}{4}$ on $[0,2]$

  (b) $f_Z(x) = \dfrac{x - 6}{4}$ on $[6,8]$ and $\dfrac{10 - x}{4}$ on $[8,10]$

  (c) $f_Z(x) = \dfrac{x - 2}{4}$ on $[2,4]$ and $\dfrac{6 - x}{4}$ on $[4,6]$

3. $F_W(x) = \dfrac{x^2}{2}$ on $[0,1]$

       $= \dfrac{-2x^2 + 6x - 3}{2}$ on $[1,2]$

       $= \dfrac{(x - 3)^2}{2}$ on $[2,3]$

5. f_Z has a normal density with mean $\mu = \mu_1 + \mu_2$ and variance $\sigma^2 = \sigma_1^2 + \sigma_2^2$

7. $f_{R^2} = \dfrac{\pi}{4}$ on $[0,1]$

       $= \dfrac{1}{2}\arcsin\left(\dfrac{2 - x}{x}\right)$ on $[1,2]$

   $f_R = \dfrac{\pi}{2}x$ on $[0,1]$

       $= x\arcsin\left(\dfrac{2 - x^2}{x^2}\right)$ on $[1,\sqrt{2}]$

Chapter 8 Section 1

1. $1/9$

5. 10

9. no

Chapter 8 Section 2

1.(a) 1
   (b) 1
   (c) 100/243
   (d) 1/12

3. $f(x) = 1 - \dfrac{x}{10}$ if $0 \leqslant x \leqslant 10$

   $ = 0$ otherwise

   $g(x) = \dfrac{100}{3x^2}$

5. (a) $1, \frac{1}{4}, \frac{1}{9}$
   (b) 1 vs .3173, .25 vs .0455, .11 vs .0027

7. (b) 1,1, 100/243, 1/12

9. (a) 0
   (b) 7/12
   (c) 11/12

11. (a) 0
   (b) 7/12

13. (a) $\frac{2}{3}$
   (b) $\frac{2}{3}$
   (c) $\frac{2}{3}$

Chapter 9 Section 1

Note: The answers in parentheses are the answers using the 1/2 correction.

1. (a) .159 (.184)   **(b)** .682 (.632)   **(c)** .005 (.0035)

3. p(June passes) is appr. .977 (.985)
   p(April passes) is appr. .042 (.056)

5. .116 (Not just bad luck)

7. .312 (.322)

9. (a) 0
   (b) 1 (Law of Large Numbers)
   (c) .977 (Central Limit Theorem)
   (d) 1 (Law of Large Numbers)

13. 13

15. (a) 64 to 96
(b) 6400

17. $n = 114, m = 81$

Chapter 9 Section 2

1. .7408, .2222, .037

5. 649741

9. $e^{-5} = .00674$

15.

number	observed	expected
0	229	227
1	211	211
2	93	99
3	35	31
4	7	9
5	1	1

17. .9084

19. $P(\text{win} \geq 3 \text{ times}) = .5071$, expected winning $= -2.703$

23. .168

Chapter 9 Section 3

1. (a) .4762   **(b)** .0477

2. (a) .5   **(b)** .9987

3. (a) .0757   **(b)** .0655   **(c)** .9236

7. (a) Expected value $= 200$, variance $= 2$
(b) .9973

11. Expected loss is 60 dollars; one standard deviation $= 20$

13. 1/1600

Chapter 9 Section 4

11. (a) .5   **(b)** .148   **(c)** .018

13. .0013

15. (20.53, 25.87)

Chapter 10 Section 1

In each case to get $g(t)$ just replace z by e^t in $h(z)$

1. (a) $h(z) = \dfrac{1}{2}(1 + z)$

(b) $h(z) = \dfrac{1}{6}\displaystyle\sum_{j=1}^{6} z^j$

(c) $h(z) = z^3$

(d) $h(z) = \dfrac{1}{k+1}z^n \displaystyle\sum_{j=1}^{k} z^j$

(e) $h(z) = z^n(pz + q)^k$

(f) $h(z) = \dfrac{2}{3 - z}$

3. $h(z) = \dfrac{1}{4} + \dfrac{1}{2}z + \dfrac{1}{4}z^2$

5. (a) $\mu_1(p) = \mu_2(p') = 3,\ \mu_2(p) = \mu_2(p') = 11$
$\mu_3(p) = 43,\ \mu_3(p') = 47$
$\mu_4(p) = 171,\ \mu_4(p') = 219$

(b) for p, $h(z) = \dfrac{1}{3}z + \dfrac{2}{3}z^4$

for p', $h(z) = \dfrac{2}{3}z^2 + \dfrac{1}{3}z^5$

7. (a) $g_{-x}(t) = g(-t)$
(b) $g_{x+1}(t) = e^t g(t)$
(c) $g_{3x}(t) = g(3t)$
(d) $g_{ax+b} = e^{bt}g(at)$

Chapter 10 Section 2

1. For **(a)–(d)** $d = 1$
   (e) $d = \frac{1}{2}$
   (f) $d = .203$

3. (a) 0
   (b) 276.26

Chapter 10 Section 3

1. (a) $g(t) = \dfrac{1}{2t}(e^{2t} - 1)$

(b) $g(t) = \dfrac{e^{2t}(2t - 1) + 1}{2t^2}$

(c) $g(t) = \dfrac{e^{2t} - 2t - 1}{2t^2}$

(d) $g(t) = \dfrac{e^{2t}(1 - t) + 2e^t - t - 1}{t^2}$

(e) $g(t) = \dfrac{3}{8} \left(\dfrac{e^{2t}(4t^2 - 4t + 2) - 2}{t^3} \right)$

3. (a) $g(t) = \dfrac{2}{2 - t}$

(b) $g(t) = \dfrac{4 - 3t}{2(1 - t)(2 - t)}$

(c) $g(t) = \dfrac{4}{(2 - t)^2}$

5. (a) $k(\tau) = \dfrac{1}{2i\tau}(e^{2i\tau} - 1)$

(b) $k(\tau) = \dfrac{e^{2i\tau}(2i\tau - 1) + 1}{-2\tau^2}$

(c) $k(\tau) = \dfrac{e^{2i\tau} - 2i\tau - 1}{-2\tau^2}$

(d) $k(\tau) = \dfrac{e^{2i\tau}(1 - i\tau) + 2e^{i\tau} - i\tau - 1}{-\tau^2}$

(e) $k(\tau) = \dfrac{3}{8} \left(\dfrac{e^{2i\tau}(-4\tau^2 - 4i\tau + 2) - 2}{-i\tau^3} \right)$

7. (a) $g(-t) = \dfrac{1 - e^{-t}}{t}$

(b) $e^t g(t) = \dfrac{e^{2t} - e^t}{t}$

(c) $g(3t) = \dfrac{e^{3t} - 1}{t}$

(d) $e^b g(at) = \dfrac{e^b(e^{at} - 1)}{t}$

9. (a) $g(t) = \dfrac{e^{2t^2} + 1}{2}$

(b) $g(t)^2$

(c) $g(t)^n$

(d) $g(t/n)^n$

(e) $e^{t^2}/2$

Chapter 11 Section 1

1. $w(1) = .5, .25, .25$
$w(2) = .4375, .1875, .375$
$w(3) = .40625, .203125, .390625$

3. All P

5. 1

7. (a) $p'' = p$

   (b) $p'' = p$ if n odd

9. $p^2 + q^2, q^2$

11. .375

15. For Example 7 the probabilities are .25,.5,.25 for being in the various states independent of the starting state, and for Example 8 they are 1, 0, 0.

Chapter 11 Section 2

1. $a = 0$ or $b = 0$

3. 8, 9

7.
$$N = \begin{pmatrix} 2.5 & 3 & 1.5 \\ 2 & 4 & 2 \\ 1.5 & 3 & 2.5 \end{pmatrix}$$

$$t = (7, 8, 7)$$

$$B = \begin{pmatrix} 5/8 & 3/8 \\ 1/2 & 1/2 \\ 3/8 & 5/8 \end{pmatrix}$$

9. 2.08

11.

	ABC	AC	BC	A	B	C	none
ABC	5/18	5/18	4/18	0	0	4/18	0
AC	0	5/12	0	5/12	0	1/12	1/12
BC	0	0	10/18	0	5/18	2/18	1/18
P = A	0	0	0	1	0	0	0
B	0	0	0	0	1	0	0
C	0	0	0	0	0	1	0
none	0	0	0	0	0	0	1

$$N = \begin{pmatrix} 1.385 & .659 & .692 \\ 0 & 1.714 & 0 \\ 0 & 0 & 2.250 \end{pmatrix}$$

$$t = 2.736 \quad 1.714 \quad 2.250$$

$$B = \begin{array}{c} \\ ABC \\ AC \\ BC \end{array} \begin{array}{cccc} A & B & C & \text{none} \\ \begin{pmatrix} .275 & .192 & .440 & .093 \\ .714 & 0 & .143 & .143 \\ 0 & .625 & .25 & .125 \end{pmatrix} \end{array}$$

13. It is the same.

15.

$$\begin{array}{c} \\ G,GG \\ g,GG \\ G,Gg \\ g,Gg \\ G,gg \\ g,gg \end{array} \begin{array}{cccccc} G,GG & g,GG & G,Gg & g,Gb & G,gg & g,gg \\ \begin{pmatrix} 1 & 0 & 0 & 0 & 0 & 0 \\ 0 & 0 & 1 & 0 & 0 & 0 \\ .25 & .25 & .25 & .25 & 0 & 0 \\ 0 & 0 & .25 & .25 & .25 & .25 \\ 0 & 0 & 0 & 1 & 0 & 0 \\ 0 & 0 & 0 & 0 & 0 & 1 \end{pmatrix} \end{array}$$

$$N = \begin{pmatrix} 1.667 & 2.667 & 1.333 & .333 \\ .667 & 2.667 & 1.333 & .333 \\ .333 & 1.333 & 2.667 & .667 \\ .333 & 1.333 & 2.667 & 1.667 \end{pmatrix}$$

$$t = (6 \quad 5 \quad 5 \quad 6)$$

$$B = \begin{pmatrix} .667 & .333 \\ .667 & .333 \\ .333 & .667 \\ .333 & .667 \end{pmatrix}$$

17. (a)

$$p = \begin{array}{c} \\ 1 \\ 2 \\ 3 \\ F \\ G \end{array} \begin{array}{ccccc} 1 & 2 & 3 & F & G \\ \begin{pmatrix} r & p & 0 & q & 0 \\ 0 & r & p & q & 0 \\ 0 & 0 & r & q & p \\ \hline 0 & 0 & 0 & 1 & 0 \\ 0 & 0 & 0 & 0 & 1 \end{pmatrix} \end{array}$$

(b) Expected time in second year = 1.09
Expected time in med school = 3.3 years

(c) Probability of an incoming student graduating = .67

19. $\dfrac{10^9 - 1}{9}$, which is about 111 million. There are several other nine-length runs in the first 100 million digits of pi, as might be expected in a random sequence.

Chapter 11 Section 3

1. (a),(b),(f)

3. (a) $a = 0$ or $b = 0$
(b) $a = b = 1$

   (c) $0 < a < 1$ and $0 < b < 1$
      $a = 1$ and $0 < b < 1$
      $0 < a < b$ and $b = 1$

5. (a) $(^2/_3, ^1/_3)$
  (b) $(^1/_2, ^1/_2)$
  (c) $(^2/_7, ^3/_7, ^2/_7)$

7. Fixed vector is $(1,0)$ and the entries are not strictly positive, as required for the fixed vector of an ergodic chain.

11. The chain is ergodic but not regular.

13. The fixed vector is the common row of P.
The chain is regular if and only if the entries of this vector are strictly positive.

15. P^2 is strictly positive. The fixed vector is $\mathbf{w} = (^1/_4, ^1/_2, ^1/_4)$.

17. $2^r + 1$ (by this power there must have been a repetition of the pattern of positive numbers in the matrix so nothing new can occur). $N(3) = 5$. See Exercise 18.

23. $p = ^1/_8$ makes the fixed vector $\mathbf{w} = (^1/_5, ^4/_5)$

Chapter 11 Section 4

1. The column vector with each component $^1/_3$.

3. For regular chain only the constant vectors are fixed column vectors.

Chapter 11 Section 5

1. With $b = (1,1)$

$$Z = \begin{pmatrix} 5/6 & -1/3 \\ -1/2 & 1 \end{pmatrix}$$

and with $b = w = (^1/_3, ^2/_3)$ it is

$$Z = \begin{pmatrix} 11/9 & -2/9 \\ -1/9 & 10/9 \end{pmatrix}$$

In either case you get

$$M = \begin{pmatrix} 0 & 2 \\ 4 & 0 \end{pmatrix}$$

3. 2

7. (a)

$$
\begin{array}{c c c c c c c}
 & 1 & 2 & 3 & 4 & 5 & 6 \\
1 & 0 & 0 & 1 & 0 & 0 & 0 \\
2 & 0 & 0 & 1 & 0 & 0 & 0 \\
3 & 1/4 & 1/4 & 0 & 1/4 & 1/4 & 0 \\
4 & 0 & 0 & 1/2 & 0 & 0 & 1/2 \\
5 & 0 & 0 & 1/2 & 0 & 0 & 1/2 \\
6 & 0 & 0 & 0 & 1/2 & 1/2 & 0
\end{array}
$$

(b) The rat alternates between the sets $\{1, 2, 4, 5\}$ and $\{3, 6\}$.

(c) $\mathbf{w} = (1/12, 1/12, 4/12, 2/12, 2/12, 2/12)$

(d) $n_{1,5} = 7$

11. Yes the reverse transition matrix is the same matrix.

27. He got it!

Index